Annotated Teacher's Edition
Laboratory Manual

Biology
MILLER • LEVINE

 Prentice Hall
Englewood Cliffs, New Jersey
Needham, Massachusetts

CONTENTS

Biology
Miller • Levine

Laboratory Manual
Annotated Teacher's Edition

©1991 by Prentice-Hall, Inc., Englewood Cliffs, New Jersey 07632.
All rights reserved. No part of this book may be reproduced in any form
or by any means without permission in writing from the publisher.
Printed in the United States of America.

ISBN 0-13-081431-8

10 9 8 7 6 5 4

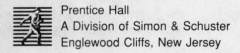

Prentice Hall
A Division of Simon & Schuster
Englewood Cliffs, New Jersey

Introduction to the Teacher

Biology is an exciting area of study for the high school student. And many recent developments that have been extensively reported in the news media—the Alaskan oil spill, AIDS epidemic, and genetic fingerprinting, to name a few—have made biology perhaps even more exciting and relevant during this final decade of the twentieth century than ever before.

The *Biology Laboratory Manual* is designed to capture the excitement of biology through a variety of interesting and informative activities. In addition to reinforcing key concepts and scientific terms, these activities help students understand and appreciate the processes involved in scientific experimentation.

The *Laboratory Manual* contains 99 Laboratory Investigations directly related to the information presented in *Biology* by Miller and Levine. It also contains 8 Laboratory Skills activities that give students an opportunity to practice and master specific laboratory skills, which include making metric measurements, applying the scientific method, using a microscope, and using graphing skills.

This Annotated Teacher's Edition provides the information you will need to perform the investigations and activities with your students. It includes answers to all investigations and activities, guidelines for laboratory safety and the use of animals in the classroom, comprehensive lists of laboratory equipment and materials, notes on the care and maintenance of live organisms, instructions on the preparation of specific chemical solutions, and a number of essays and annotations that will help you organize and stock your biology laboratory and facilitate your teaching.

Laboratory Investigation Format

The investigations and activities in the *Laboratory Manual* are designed to strengthen students' laboratory, critical thinking, and creative thinking skills and to provide a practical application of material presented in the student textbook. The easy-to-follow format of each Laboratory Investigation allows students to complete the investigations on their own, perhaps after an overview and brief explanation from you. This gives you an opportunity to provide the necessary help to those individuals or groups of students who require teacher assistance.

Each Laboratory Investigation has the following format:

Title A brief title presents the topic explored in the investigation. To the right of the title are teacher annotations regarding the time required for the investigation and the textbook pages in *Biology* by Miller and Levine that correspond to the laboratory investigation.

Pre-Lab Discussion The Pre-Lab Discussion provides background information that the student will need to complete the investigation, develops relevant concepts, or relates the Laboratory Investigation to specific concepts discussed in the student textbook. In a few cases, this section may also provide new concepts and terms specific to the investigation.

Problem Each Laboratory Investigation challenges the student by introducing a problem in the form of a question or series of questions. Students should be able to solve the problem(s) upon successful completion of the Laboratory Investigation.

Materials This section lists all materials required to conduct the investigation. The quantity of material for each investigation is indicated for individual students, pairs of students, or groups of students. Teacher annotations on how to prepare materials specific to the investigation are found in or near the Materials section. The necessary equipment and materials for all of the Laboratory Investigations are listed alphabetically and by category on pages T 8 to T 17.

Safety If a Laboratory Investigation requires specific safety precautions, students are alerted to that fact in the special Safety section as well as in the Procedure. The Safety section is intended to make students aware of potential hazards before the investigation is begun, thereby decreasing the risk of accidents.

Procedure This section provides a detailed step-by-step outline of the Laboratory Investigation procedure. Diagrams are included where necessary to further explain a technique or illustrate an experimental setup.

The Procedure contains a number of symbols and instructions that guide students as the lab is performed. Safety symbols, which appear next to certain steps in the Procedure, signal students to begin following specific safety precautions for an indicated step in the procedure and all following steps. **CAUTION** statements within the steps of the Procedure warn students of possible hazards and indicate how accidents can be avoided. **Notes** in the Procedure direct students' attention to special directions or techniques. At the end of some steps in the Procedure, students may be instructed to record data or answer questions in Observations.

Observations In keeping with the traditional scientific method, observations are asked for after the Procedure in each investigation. Observations often include filling in data tables, graphing data, labeling diagrams, and drawing observed structures, as well as answering general questions.

In the Annotated Teacher's Edition, annotations to the questions in Observations, Analysis and Conclusions, and Critical Thinking and Application are printed in red on the pages corresponding to the student pages. These annotations include answers to objective questions, sample drawings and diagrams, and anticipated student data when these can be predicted. In some cases, data tables and questions are marked by the statement "Answers will vary." In such cases, the teacher should look for a logical response based on the observations and data collected by the students during the investigation.

Analysis and Conclusions Questions in this section are designed to assist students in answering the investigation's Problem, relating the investigation to concepts learned in the textbook, and drawing conclusions about the results of their investigation. Using data gathered during the investigation and knowledge gained from the textbook and Pre-Lab Discussion, students are asked to analyze and interpret their experimental results.

Critical Thinking and Application This section challenges students to use critical-thinking skills to answer a variety of questions based on the Laboratory Investigation and their textbook reading. Many questions emphasize possible applications of the experiment and allow students to relate the investigation to real-life situations.

Going Further Each Laboratory Investigation concludes with a section entitled Going Further. This section suggests additional activities that may be used to enrich or supplement the investigation. The Going Further activities may also be used as alternatives to the Laboratory Investigation. Complete instructions are included so that individual students can perform the Going Further activities without additional teacher help.

For a Shorter Laboratory Period

School schedules often do not permit extended laboratory periods. The *Laboratory Manual* provides a number of options to help you circumvent the difficulties associated with having limited laboratory time. First, most investigations require only 30 to 40 minutes and thus can be completed within a single class period. Second, the investigations are often divided into two or more parts. This provides flexibility by allowing you to select the parts of the investigation that best suit your needs, objectives, and laboratory situation. In addition, you can often schedule the parts of an investigation to be performed during different class periods, as your schedule permits. Finally, a number of the investigations have annotations that suggest specific ways in which the investigation may be modified for a shorter laboratory period.

Correlation Between Textbook Chapters and Laboratory Investigations

The *Laboratory Manual* is designed to accompany *Biology* by Miller and Levine in the presentation of a comprehensive biology program for high school students. When used in conjunction with the textbook, the *Laboratory Manual* reinforces, expands, and enhances the student's experiences of reading the textbook and participating in classroom discussions. The following chart shows the correlation between textbook chapters and investigations. Although the investigations correspond to chapters in *Biology*, they can be used with any high school biology program.

Chapter	Investigations	Chapter	Investigations	Chapter	Investigations	Chapter	Investigations
1	1, 2	14	26, 27	27	54, 55	40	78, 79
2	3, 4	15	28, 29	28	56, 57	41	80, 81
3	5, 6	16	30	29	58	42	82
4	7, 8	17	31, 32	30	59, 60	43	83, 84, 85
5	9, 10	18	33, 34	31	61, 62	44	86, 87
6	11, 12	19	35, 36	32	63, 64	45	88, 89
7	13, 14	20	37, 38	33	65	46	90, 91
8	15, 16	21	39, 40	34	66, 67	47	92, 93
9	17, 18	22	41, 42	35	68, 69	48	94, 95, 96
10	19, 20	23	43, 44, 45	36	70	49	97, 98, 99
11	21, 22	24	46, 47, 48	37	71, 72		
12	23	25	49, 50, 51	38	73, 74, 75		
13	24, 25	26	52, 53	39	76, 77		

Guidelines for Laboratory Safety

Safety should be an integral part of the planning, preparation, and implementation of a laboratory program. Both the biology teacher and the student are responsible for creating and maintaining an enjoyable, instructional, and safe environment in the biology laboratory.

A number of general safety concerns are discussed. You should also refer to pages 9 through 12 in the student edition of the *Biology Laboratory Manual* for a detailed discussion of safety rules and procedures. You may want to expand or modify the safety guidelines, procedures, and rules suggested here according to local and state government regulations and policies, as well as school regulations and policies. The school administration should be able to provide you with specifics on local safety requirements.

General Safety Considerations

Emphasis on proper safety precautions for each laboratory investigation is an essential part of any pre-laboratory discussion. Prior to each investigation, demonstrate the proper use of the required equipment. Demonstrate any potentially hazardous procedure used in that investigation. Always wear the required safety protective devices during the demonstrations and the investigations. If students are required to wear safety goggles, you and any visitors to the class must also wear them.

During an investigation, move about the laboratory to keep a constant watch for potentially dangerous situations. Behavior that is inappropriate to a laboratory situation should be curtailed immediately. Wild play and practical jokes are forbidden in the laboratory. Once students realize that the practice of safety is a required part of the course, they will accept a serious approach to laboratory work.

Any laboratory investigation a student performs should have your prior approval. Students should never work in the laboratory without adult supervision. At the conclusion of the lab investigation, cleanup should follow authorized guidelines for waste disposal. The laboratory should be restored to a safe condition for the next class.

Classroom Organization

Furniture and equipment in the laboratory should be arranged to minimize accidents. Assign students to laboratory stations. Each station should be equipped with a flat-topped table and laboratory bench. Do not use desks with slanted tops. Provide several locations where students can obtain needed supplies. Control traffic flow in the room to prevent collisions between students who are carrying or handling equipment. Tell students to leave their personal property in a designated location, away from the laboratory stations. Do not use the floor and benches for storage areas. Stress that good housekeeping is important in maintaining safe laboratory conditions. Students should keep all laboratory work areas clean. Unnecessary papers, books, and equipment should be removed from working areas.

Be sure that water faucets, hot plates, gas outlets, and alcohol or Bunsen burners are turned off when not in use.

Safety Equipment

Any classroom where laboratory investigations are done should contain at least one each of the following pieces of safety equipment: (1) fire extinguisher, (2) fire blanket, (3) fire alarm, (4) phone or intercom to the office, (5) eyewash station, (6) safety shower, (7) safety hood, and (8) first-aid kit. If any of these basic pieces of safety equipment are not available, you may need to modify your laboratory program until the situation is remedied.

Make sure students know the location and proper use of all safety equipment. Where appropriate and practical, have students handle or operate the equipment so that they become familiar with it. Make sure all safety equipment is in good working order. All malfunctions should be promptly reported in writing to the proper school or district administrator.

Fire equipment At the beginning of the school year, you may wish to give each student the opportunity to actually operate a fire extinguisher, as the sound and action of a CO_2 fire extinguisher can be quite alarming to those who have never used one. You may also want to have students practice smothering imaginary flames on one another with the fire blanket.

Eyewash station The eyewash station should be used if chemicals are splashed onto the face or eyes. The exposed area should be left in the running water for five to ten minutes.

Safety shower The shower is used when chemicals have been spilled on a student's body or clothing. The student should stand under the shower until the chemical is completely diluted. Have a bathrobe or some other type of replacement clothing handy in case the student's clothing is so badly contaminated that it must be removed.

You may want to set up one or two spill kits in your laboratory. The contents of a spill kit are used to neutralize chemicals such as acids and bases so that they can be cleaned up more easily. Baking soda (sodium bicarbonate) can be used to neutralize acids. Vinegar (acetic acid) can be used to neutralize bases. Commercial spill kits for acids, bases, and a number of other chemicals are available from supply houses.

Safety hood Use a safety hood whenever students are working with volatile or noxious chemicals. Make sure that the room is well-ventilated when students are using any kind of chemicals or are working with preserved specimens. Warn students of the flammability and toxicity of various chemicals.

First-aid kit A typical first-aid kit contains an assortment of antiseptics, bandages, gauze pads, and scissors. Most also contain simple instructions for use. Be sure to read the instructions if you are not familiar with basic first-aid procedures. A first-aid kit should be taken on all field trips. For field trips, you may wish to add such items as a bee-sting kit, meat tenderizer, tweezers, and calamine lotion. Do not dispense medication (including aspirin).

Cleanup

Before beginning an investigation, instruct students in the proper cleanup procedures. Mark certain containers for the disposal of wastes and the collection of soiled glassware and equipment. Have students dispose of broken glassware in a separate trash container. Before the end of the laboratory period, have students unplug microscopes and other pieces of equipment and put them away in their proper location. Have students wash glassware, wipe up spills, and do whatever else is necessary to clean up their work area. At the conclusion of the laboratory investigation, the room should be restored to a clean and safe condition for the next class. You may wish to institute a policy of not dismissing the class until the laboratory area meets with your approval.

Preparations and the Storage Room

Reagents stored in the biology stockroom should be clearly labeled and stored safely. Take inventory of reagents frequently and keep up-to-date records of their use. Check local and state regulations for maximum permissible amounts of reagents allowed in school. In case of fire or vandalism, inform the authorities of possible hazards to the community. Keep all chemicals in a locked storage area that is accessible only to you or individuals under your direct supervision.

Some chemicals are incompatible and should be stored separately. For suggested shelf storage patterns, refer to *School Science Laboratories: A Guide to Some Hazardous Substances*, U.S. Product Safety Commission, Washington, DC, 1984. This publication may be obtained from your state science supervisor or the U.S. Consumer Product Safety Commission, Room 412—EX-O, Washington, DC, 20207. Check local and state laws for regulations on storage of flammable liquids. The National Fire Protection Association recommends that flammable liquids be stored in vented, flame-resistant cabinets. Store large containers near floor level. Make sure that storage shelves have a raised lip at the front to prevent containers from sliding forward.

Hazardous Materials

Some reagents can be explosive and should not be on the premises. If found they should be removed by trained fire or police bomb squads or by other qualified officials.

Known carcinogens and probable carcinogens have frequently been found in biology stockrooms and should be removed by health authorities or a licensed commercial company. If you have doubts about the hazards of any reagent in the stockroom, contact an appropriate agency (NIOSH or a local health agency).

Known carcinogens commonly found in school science laboratories include the following:

arsenic powder	formaldehyde
arsenic trichloride	lead arsenate
arsenic pentoxide	benzene
arsenic trioxide	chromium powder
asbestos	sodium arsenate
benzidine	

Probable carcinogens include the following:

acrylonitrile	cadmium powder
cadmium chloride	cadmium sulfate
carbon tetrachloride	chloroform
ethylene oxide	nickel powder

Exercise great care in using refrigerators. Never store flammable liquids in a refrigerator unless it is explosion-proof. Do not store food where microbial cultures are stored. Clean refrigerators frequently and safely discard old material.

Laboratory Glassware

Probably the most common school laboratory accidents involve cuts from chipped or broken glassware and burns from hot glassware. Discard any glassware that has a crack or chip. Use only borosilicate glassware. Fire-polish the ends of glass tubing. Allow hot glassware to cool on a hot pad for several minutes before picking it up. If an accident should happen, first aid for minor cuts and burns is immersion in cool running water. For cuts that are bleeding heavily, apply pressure with folded toweling or gauze. Call a health professional immediately.

To insert glass tubing into a stopper, lubricate the stopper hole and the tubing. Wrap the tubing in several layers of toweling and gently work the tubing into the stopper, using a twisting motion and keeping the hands as close together as possible. Wear heavy gloves. Remove the tubing in the same manner as soon as possible. Tubing that is stuck is nearly impossible to remove without cutting the stopper.

To avoid unwanted cultures, clean glassware frequently by using laboratory detergent. Most deposits can be removed with dilute hydrochloric acid or sodium hydroxide solution. Do not permit students to eat or drink from laboratory glassware.

Measuring small amounts of liquids with pipettes is common in investigations. But never pipette by mouth. Use rubber suction bulbs designed for use with pipettes or pipette fillers.

Safety Procedures with Microbial Cultures

Never culture pathogenic bacteria. However, treat all bacterial cultures as if they are pathogenic. Firmly seal with clear tape any bacterial plates that are used for student inspection. For sterilization, use a high-temperature gas flame rather than an alcohol burner or candle flame.

Cultures should be killed before disposal. Autoclave all cultures and contaminated glassware at 15 pounds pressure per square inch (103.4 Pa) for 20 minutes. Disposable plates should be incinerated.

Safety Procedures with Microscopes

Never use direct sunlight as a light source for the microscope. The lenses may concentrate the light and cause permanent retinal damage. With a soft cloth dipped in isopropyl alcohol, clean the eyepiece of each microscope between viewers. Make sure any electrical cords are out of the main traffic pattern of the classroom.

Safety Procedures with Dissections

Handle sharp and pointed instruments with care.

Make sure the specimen is firmly secured on a dissection tray or cutting board. Caution students never to dissect a hand-held specimen. Make sure that the scalpels and scissors are sharp and adequate for the job. If razor blades are used for cutting tissues for slide mounts, use only single-edge noninjectable blades. Dissecting instruments should not be removed from the laboratory and should be stored in a locked cabinet.

Formaldehyde has been identified as a carcinogen and mutagen. Any formaldehyde-preserved specimens in the stockroom or classroom should be removed from the school site by qualified health authorities or a licensed commercial company. Specimens are now sold in alternate preservatives. Follow the instructions on the package for preparing specimens for dissection. Most should be rinsed in running water before use. Some may need to be soaked in water overnight if the preservative is particularly strong-smelling. Specimens that have not been preserved should be used sparingly and only for a short time. Use only healthy specimens. Instruct students to wear masks and gloves to guard against infection. After dissection, specimens should be discarded in separate containers that can be transported to an incineration site.

Field Studies

Before taking the students on a field study, examine the area for possible safety hazards. Look for terrain or water hazards and poisonous plants and animals. Obtain the necessary written permission from parents and school authorities. Instruct students on proper dress and behavior. Make sure that students are thoroughly familiar with the investigations they are to conduct. If students are to form small groups, decide in advance when and where they will reassemble. Do not allow any student to travel alone.

Identify any students who have special health problems, especially allergies. Alert these students to potential hazards. Be sure they are adequately prepared to deal with emergencies.

Laboratory Skills Materials and Equipment

Note: Safety equipment has not been listed. It is recommended that a laboratory apron, safety goggles, and heat-resistant gloves be worn when required.

Item	Quantity per Group	Laboratory Investigation
Balance, triple-beam	1	2, 3, 7
Beaker		
50-mL	1	3
100-mL	2	7
250-mL	1	2
	2	6
Bunsen burner	1	2, 6
Cloth, soft	1	5
Coin	1	3
Coverslip	1	2, 5
Dissecting needle	1	5
Dissecting pins	1 box per class	2
Dissecting scissors	1	2
Dissecting tray	1	2
Filter paper	1	7
Flint striker (or matches)	1	6
Food coloring, red	10 mL	7
Forceps	1	2
Funnel	1	2, 7
Graduated cylinder		
10-mL	1	7
100-mL	1	2, 3, 6, 7
Hand lens	1	2
Iron ring	1	6, 7
Knife	1	4
Lens paper	1 package per class	5
Medicine dripper	1	2, 5
Meterstick	1	3
Metric ruler	1	2, 3, 6
Microscope	1	2, 5
Newspaper	1 page per class	5
Paper towels	2	4
Petri dish	1	2
Pipette	1	2
Plastic bags with twist ties	2	4
Potato, medium	1	4
Probe	1	2
Ring stand	1	6, 7
Rubber stopper	1	3
Safety equipment	See laboratory skill.	1
Scalpel	1	5
Scissors	1	5
Scoop	1	7
Slide		
glass	1	2, 5
prepared	1	5
Sodium chloride	5 g	7
Test tube	1	2, 3
Test tube rack	1	2
Thermometer, Celsius	1	2
Tongs	1	6
Weighing paper (filter paper or a piece or paper towel)	1	7
Wire gauze	1	6

Laboratory Investigations Materials and Equipment

Note: Safety equipment has not been listed. It is recommended that a laboratory apron, safety goggles, and heat-resistant gloves be worn when required.

Item	Quantity per Group	Laboratory Investigation
Acids		
acetic, 10%	10 mL	81
hydrochloric, 1M	10 mL	6
hydrochloric, 1%	1 mL	30
hydrochloric, 5%	30 mL	76
hydrochloric, 20%	100 mL	73
hydrochloric, 10%	10 mL	54
Agar-phenolphthalein blocks (1 cm, 2 cm, and 3 cm on a side)	1 of each	15
Agar, sterile nutrient plates	1	88
	2	32
Agaricus campestris	1	35
Alcohol		
ethyl, 95%	150 mL	12
	70 mL	40, 43
isopropyl, 70%	1 bottle per class	11, 89
Alga, brown (*Fucus*)	1	39
Algae, green, culture	2 cultures per class	38
Alligator clips	2	71
Aluminum foil	1 large sheet	6, 12, 91
Ammonia solution, 4%	65 mL	79
Amoeba proteus culture	1 culture per class	34
Animal cage (or cardboard box)	1	68
Animal maze	1	68
Anole		
live	1	63
preserved	1	63
Antacid	1 tablet	6
Antibiotic disks: aureomycin, chloromycetin, penicillin, streptomycin, tetracycline, terramycin	any 3	32
Apple	1	50
Apple juice, unsweetened	250 mL	8
Aquarium	1	62, 63
Aquarium water	200 mL	61
Bacillus subtilis culture	1 culture per class	31
Bacteriophage culture	1 culture per class	88
Balance, triple-beam	1 per class	2
	1 per pair of students	5
	1	1, 73, 76, 77
Balloons, round	2	78
Barium chloride solution, 0.2M	1 dropper bottle	80
Beaker		
50-mL	3	91
100-mL	1	89
150-mL	1	32, 43, 47
	2	11, 26, 71
	2 per class	2
250-mL	1	7, 12, 15, 61, 73, 98
	1 per class	2
400-mL	1	81
600-mL	1	8, 23
1000-mL	1	12
Bean seeds	4	48
	10	98
Beans, white kidney	1	50
	10	27
Benedict's solution	1 dropper bottle	8, 81
Biuret reagent	1 dropper bottle	8
Blindfold	1	72
Bones	See investigation.	70
Bones		
chicken leg	1	64, 74
uncooked pork	2	73
Bottle		
2-L soft-drink	1	51
with screw-on cap	1	67

Item	Quantity per Group	Laboratory Investigation
Bowl, large, shallow	1	39
Box, large, cardboard	1	48
Bracken ferns		
sporophyte	1	40
with sori	1	40
Bracket fungus	1	35
Brassica rapa seeds	10	51
Bread (variety of different types and brands)	1/4 slice of each	36
Bristles (3 of various thickness)	1 of each	72
Bromthymol blue	200 mL	3, 79, 92
Bunsen burner	1	8, 23, 31, 32, 81, 86, 88
Butter, melted	20 mL	8
Calculator	1	45, 87
Candle	1	6
Carmine solution	1 dropper bottle	33, 54
Carrot	1	43
Chicken egg, unfertilized	1	85
Chicken wing, whole	1	75
Chlamydomonas culture	1 culture per class	37
Chlorine bleach solution		
concentrated	1 dropper bottle	52
10%	50 mL	23
Cigarettes, filterless	10	91
Clam		
live, freshwater	1	54
fresh or preserved	1	54
shell	1 valve	54
Clay, modeling	1 stick	6, 48
Clock (or watch with second hand)	1	48, 61, 62, 65, 67, 68, 69, 79, 90
Clothing (winter article such as heavy sock, mitten, hat, or scarf)	1	93
Coins, penny or dime	1	11
	2	22, 89
Comb	1	67
Congo red solution	1 dropper bottle	33
Conifer leaf	1	44
Containers		
250-mL with lids	3	93
750–1000-mL with lids	3	93
Cookie sheet (or cooking tray)	1 large	73
Cork stopper (base diameter of at least 4 cm)	1	77
Corn oil	20 mL	8
Corn seeds	1	50
	4	48
Cotton	1 small package	91
Cotton balls	1	33
	3	38
Cotton swabs		
nonsterile	2	46
sterile	1	88
	2	32
	3	86
Coverslips	1 per student	10
	1	18, 19, 30, 33, 38, 39, 41, 52, 61
	2	3, 34, 35, 40, 45, 49
	3	96
	4	37
Culture tubes (with tops, 20 mm x 200 mm)	4	92
DC millivolt meter	1	71
Dialysis membrane	1	71
Diatoms (mixed culture)	1 culture per class	34
Disinfectants: chlorine bleach, household cleaner, household disinfectant, lye, phenol	any 3	32
Disks, small plastic or cardboard	4	17
sterile filter paper	4	32
Dissecting needle	1	39, 49, 62
Dissecting pins	1 box	55, 62
Dissecting tray	1	39, 40, 43, 49, 50, 54, 55, 56, 58, 60, 61, 62, 63, 74, 75, 76
Duckweed culture	1 culture per class	23

Item	Quantity per Group	Laboratory Investigation
Earthworm, preserved	1	55
Egg		
white, boiled	1/2	76
white, liquid	3	8
Elodea		
plant	4 sprigs	92
leaf	1 per student	10
Erlenmeyer flasks		
250-mL	1	91
	3	38
500-mL	2	79
Escherichia coli culture	1 culture per class	31, 32, 88
Ethanol	25 mL	91
Euglena gracilis culture	1 culture per class	34
Faucet aspirator	1	91
Feathers		
contour	1	64
down	1	64
pin	1	64
Filter paper circle	1	51
	2	47
	3	91
rectangle (larger than 12 cm x 7 cm)	2	11
Fireproof pad	1	73, 77
Fish net	1	61
Flower pots, large	4	46
Flowers		
fresh	See investigation.	49
dicot with leaves	2	42
monocot with leaves	2	42
Foam rubber (21 cm x 28 cm x 2.5 cm)	1	93
Food samples (See investigation.)	4	77
Forceps	1 per pair of students	10
	1	12, 18, 32, 35, 36, 39, 40, 41, 43, 45, 49, 51, 55, 61, 62, 75, 85, 89, 91, 94, 98, 99
Frog		
live	1	62
preserved	1	62
Funnel	1	47
Garbage	See investigation.	99
Gelatin solution, 1%	6 mL	8
	20 mL	30
Gibberellic acid solution	1 dropper bottle	46
Glass plates	2	11
Gloves		
heat-resistant	1	73, 77
thick, leather	1	68
Glue	1 small container	20
Goldfish, live	1	61
Graduated cylinder		
10-mL	1	1, 6, 7, 30, 38, 76, 81
	2	18
50-mL	1	3, 26, 89
100-mL	1	1, 38, 73, 77, 79, 91, 93
	2 per class	2
250-mL	1	91
Gram stain	1 set of dropper bottles	31
Grantia, preserved whole specimen	1	52
Grasshopper		
live	1	56
preserved	1	56
Gum arabic solution, 1%	4 mL	30
Hand lens	1	23, 35, 39, 44, 49, 50, 51, 52, 55, 56, 57, 58, 60, 61, 62, 64, 75, 85
Honey	20 mL	8
Hose (30–40 cm long)	3 pieces	3
Hot plate	1	12, 81
Ice	10 cubes per class	2

Item	Quantity per Group	Laboratory Investigation
Identification charts for plants and weeds	1	94
Incubator	1	34
Index cards		
red, blue, yellow, orange	1 package of each per class	13
white	1 package	34
Inoculating loop	1	23, 31, 86, 88
Invertebrate specimens, unidentified and preserved	See investigation.	60
Iodine solution	1 dropper bottle	8, 12, 26
Iron ring	1	23
Jacket or sweater	1	67
Jar, large glass	1	62, 96
Lead nitrate solution, 0.2M	1 dropper bottle	80
Leaves	1	41
Coleus	1	11
dicot	1	44
maple	10	27
monocot	1	44
pine	1	44
spinach	1	11
Lens paper	2 packages per class	4, 9
Lettuce		
macerated	20 mL	8
crisp	1 leaf	45, 56
wilted	1 leaf	45
Lichen	1	35
Light		
fluorescent	1	51
fluorescent with timer	1	23
Litmus paper		
blue	1 vial per class	7
red	1 vial per class	7
Lugol's solution	1 mL	18
Magnesium ribbon (2 cm long)	1	6
Magnet, bar	1 per pair of students	5
Masking tape	1 large roll per class	8, 17, 46, 48, 57, 67, 72, 73, 89, 90, 92, 93, 99
Matches (or flint striker)	1 book	6, 31, 32, 77, 86, 91
Medicine droppers	1 per pair of students	10
	1	12, 19, 26, 33, 34, 35, 36, 38, 40, 41, 45, 49, 56, 61, 62, 76, 79, 96, 98, 99
	2	3, 30
	3	18, 97
	4	37
Metersticks	1	78, 82
	2 per class	2
Methyl cellulose	1 dropper bottle	33, 34
Methylene blue stain	1 dropper bottle	10, 19, 43
Metric ruler	1 per class	2
	1	1, 11, 15, 27, 32, 46, 48, 51, 63, 66, 72, 77, 78, 84, 85, 91, 94, 98, 99
transparent	1	4, 45
Microscope		
compound light	1	3, 4, 9, 18, 19, 30, 31, 33, 34, 35, 37, 38, 39, 40, 41, 42, 43, 44, 45, 49, 52, 53, 59, 74, 75, 83, 96, 97
dissecting	1	39, 40, 43, 56, 61
Molasses	1 bottle per class	3
Mortar and pestle	1	18, 47
Moss, *Polytrichum*	1 small clump	39
Mustard seeds	150	91
Nails, large	4	94
Natural materials (leaves, dry grass, sawdust or shredded paper)	See investigation.	93
Needle, sewing	1	67
Newspaper	1 per class	99
Notepad	1	95
Olive oil	1 mL	76
Orange	1	50

Item	Quantity per Group	Laboratory Investigation
Oven	1 per class	73
Pancreatin solution, 1%	10 mL	76
Paper		
bibulous	8 sheets	31
brown	1 large sheet per class	8
construction: black, brown, green, red, white, yellow	1 sheet of each	12, 57, 63
notebook	3 sheets	94
translucent tissue	1 sheet	38
white		
unlined	1 sheet	46, 49
lined	1 sheet per pair of students	65
Paper clips	1	12, 77
	2	89
Paper cups	1	17
	2	48, 57
Paper towels	2 large rolls per class	2, 8, 10, 15, 18, 19, 23, 48, 54, 55, 56, 57, 61, 62, 63, 73, 75
Paramecium caudatum culture	1 culture per class	33
Pea seeds		
Alaska	16	46
Little Marvel	16	46
smooth	6	18
wrinkled	6	18
Peach	1	50
Pebble	1 per class	2
Pen, felt-tip-marking	1	73
Pencils		
graphite	1	11, 17, 23, 24, 51, 57, 65, 66, 72, 87, 90, 95
glass-marking	1	3, 18, 19, 23, 26, 31, 32, 36, 38, 47, 48, 76, 81, 86, 88, 89, 91, 96, 97, 98, 99
colored	2	51, 74, 82, 84
	3	84
blue	1	14
orange	1	14
red	1	46
black	1	46
Pepsin solution, 1%	10 mL	76
Perch, preserved	1	61
Petri dishes	3	12
bottoms only	4	47, 98
with covers	1	18, 36, 48, 51, 57, 85
	4	86, 91, 97, 99
Petroleum jelly	1 jar per class	97
pH paper	1 vial per class	7, 30, 76, 96, 97, 98
Physarum polycephalum culture	1 culture per class	35
prepared slide	1	35
Pill bugs	6	57
Pistil from dissected flower	1	49
Plant		
Geranium	1	12
Mimosa pudica	1	48
seedling	1	98
Plant growth medium	50 mL	23
Plastic bags with twist ties	1	55, 62
	4	46
Plastic spoon	1	15
Plastic wrap	1 roll per class	47
Pollutant solution, 1%	150 mL	38
Pond water	150 mL	38, 92, 96
Pot, clay flower (10 cm high)	1	68
Potassium chloride solution	75 mL	71
Potato, macerated	20 mL	8
Prepared slides		
Aristolochia, mature stem, l.s.	1	41
bacteria (coccus, bacillus, spirillum)	1 of each	4, 31
blood cells, human	1	4
cardiac muscle	1	75
cat ovary	1	83
Coleus stem tip, l.s.	1	41

Item	Quantity per Group	Laboratory Investigation
compact bone with Haversian system	1	73
diatoms	1	4
dicot stem, c.s.	1	42
earthworm (*Lumbricus*) c.s.	1	59
eukaryotic (animal, plant, protist, fungus) cells	1 of each	9
flatworm (*Duglesia*), c.s.	1	59
Grantia, l.s.	1	52
Helianthus root, c.s.	1	43
Helianthus stem, c.s.	1	43
hyaline cartilage, c.s	1	74
Hydra, c.s.	1	59
monocot stem, c.s.	1	42
mitosis, animal (whitefish blastula)	1	16
mitosis, plant (onion root tip)	1	16
moss antheridia and archegonia	1	39
moss protonema	1	39
pollen grains	1	4
privet leaf, c.s.	1	44
prokaryotic (moneran) cells	2	9
protist	1	4
rat epididymis	1	83
rat testis	1	83
roundworm (*Ascaris*)	1	59
skeletal muscle	1	75
smooth muscle	1	75
sycamore stem, l.s	1	41
Taenia	1	53
Trichinella	1	53
Turbatrix aceti	1	53
yeast	1	4
Zea root	1	43
Zea stem	1	43
Probe	1	35, 45, 55, 56, 61, 62, 72, 75
Protractor	1	48, 66
Radish seedling, 2-week-old	1	43
Rain solution (See investigation.)	100 mL	98
Razor blade, single-edged	1	50
Reference books	See investigation.	44
Ring stand	1	23, 77
Rodent	1	68
Rubber band	1	71
Rubber stoppers		
to fit medium test tube	1	30
one-hole, with glass tube inserts to fit large test tubes	3	3
two-hole	1	91
Salt, table	1 container per class	6
Sand	1 bag per class	46, 54
Scale, bathroom	1 per class	78
Scalpel	1	15, 39, 40, 43, 49, 50, 52, 54, 55, 56, 62, 64, 74, 75, 76
Scissors	1	11, 12, 17, 20, 28, 34, 39, 46, 48, 49, 55, 57, 62, 71, 75, 91, 93, 99
Scoop	1	6
Screwdriver	1	71
Sea water	250 mL	39
Shoe box	1 per pair of students	5
Silver nitrate solution		
0.1M	1 dropper bottle	6
0.2M	1 dropper bottle	80
Slides, glass	1 per student	4
	1	10, 18, 19, 30, 33, 38, 39, 41, 43, 52, 56, 61
	2	3, 34, 35, 40, 45, 49
	3	96
	4	37, 97
Snails	2	92
Soap, 5% (or bile salt solution)	3 mL	76
Sodium chloride solution	75 mL	71
Sodium hydroxide solution. 0.4%	100 mL	15

Item	Quantity per Group	Laboratory Investigation
Sodium iodide solution, 0.2M	1 dropper bottle	80
Soil, garden	1 large bag per class	48, 93, 99
Stakes, wooden	20	46
Stamens from dissected flower	3	49
Stapler	1	11
Starch solution	7 mL	26
Starfish, preserved	1	58
Stentor coeruleus culture	1 culture per class	34
Stirring rod, glass	1	7, 30, 54, 79, 97
	2	71
Stones, small	1 bag per class	46
Strainer	1	47
Straw, drinking	1	3, 26
	8	79
String	1 large ball per class	13, 71, 94
Sudan III stain	1 dropper bottle	8
Tape, transparent	1 roll per class	32
Test liquids (See investigation.)	10 mL of each	7
Test tubes	1	30, 77
	3	3, 6, 97
	4	3
	6	76
	10	7, 8, 26
	12	81
with stoppers	3	97
sterile and containing nutrient broth	6	88
Test tube clamp	1	77
Test tube holder	1	8, 81
Test tube rack	1	3, 6, 7, 8, 26, 31, 32, 76, 81, 88, 92
Thermometer, Celsius	1	1, 6, 77
	1 per class	2
	3	93
Thread, sewing	1 spool per class	67
Thumbtacks	2	89
Tomatoes (2 different varieties)	1 of each	47
Tongs	1	23, 73
Tongue depressors	1 box per class	97
Toothpicks	1 per student	10
	1	18, 19, 33, 34, 48
	9	72
	25	46
colored	(100 each of 5 different colors, including green)	95
Trowel	1	99
Tubing glass		
20 cm	1 piece	91
30 cm	1 piece	91
narrow rubber, 5-mm bore, 55 cm long	1 piece	91
wide rubber, 8-mm bore, 6 cm long	1 piece	91
Ulothrix culture	1 culture per class	37
Ulva culture	1 culture per class	37
"Urine" samples (See investigation.)		
known	100 mL	81
unknown	50 mL	81
Volvox culture	1 culture per class	37
Watch glass	1	23
Water samples (See investigation.)	3	97
Wire		
nickel-chromium alloy, 15 cm	2 pieces	71
copper, 40 cm	2 pieces	71
Wire gauze	1	23
Yeast	1 package per class	33, 86
	2 packages per class	3

Materials Inventory

Equipment

Alligator clips
Animal cage
Animal maze
Aquarium
Balance, triple-beam
Blindfold
Bowl, large and shallow
Bottle, 2-L-soft-drink with
    screw-on cap
Bowl, large and shallow
Bunsen burner
Calculator
Coins
Containers
    25-mL with lids
    750–1000 mL with lids
Cookie sheet
Cork stopper with a
    base diameter of
    at least 4 cm
Coverslips
Culture tubes with tops,
    20 mm x 200 mm
DC millivolt meter
Dissecting needle
Dissecting pins
Dissecting tray
Faucet aspirator
Fireproof pad
Forceps
Funnel
Gloves
    heat-resistant
    thick, leather
Hand lens (or dissecting
    microscope)
Hose, 30–40 cm long
Hot plate
Identification charts for
    plants and weeds
Incubator
Inoculating loop
Iron ring
Magnet, bar
Medicine droppers
Meterstick
Metric ruler
Microscope
    compound light
    dissecting
Mortar and pestle
Oven
Petri dishes with covers
Probe
Protractor
Razor blades, single-edged
Reference books
Ring stand
Rubber stoppers
    to fit medium test tube
    one-hole with glass
        tube inserts to fit
        large test tubes
    two-hole
Scalpel
Scissors
Scoop
Screwdriver
Stakes, wooden
Stapler

Strainer
Test tube clamp
Test tube holder
Test tube rack
Tongs
Trowel (or scoop)
Tubing, rubber
    5-mm bore
    8-mm bore
Wire gauze

Glassware

Beakers
    50-mL
    100-mL
    150-mL
    250-mL
    400-mL
    600-mL
    1000-mL
Erlenmeyer flask
    250-mL
    500-mL
Glass plates
Graduated cylinder
    10-mL
    50-mL
    100-mL
    250-mL
Jar, large
Petri dishes
Slides, glass
Stirring rod
Test tubes
    small, medium, large
    with stoppers
    sterile
Tubing, glass
    20-cm
    30-cm
Watch glass

Living Organisms

Alga, brown *(Fucus)*
Algae, green culture
Amoeba proteus culture
Anole
Bacillus subtilis culture
Bacteriophage culture
Bracken ferns
    sporophyte
    frond with sori
Bracket fungus
Brassica rapa seeds
Chlamydomonas culture
Clam, freshwater
Clam shell
Diatoms
Duckweed culture
Elodea
Escherichia coli culture
Euglena gracilis culture
Frog
Goldfish
Grasshopper
Moss *(Polytrichum)*
Mustard seeds
Paramecium caudatum
    culture

Pea seeds
    Alaska
    Little Marvel
Physarum polycephalum
    culture
Pill bugs
Plant
    geranium
    Mimosa pudica
    seedling
Radish seedling,
    two-week-old
Rodent
Snails
Stentor coeruleus culture
Ulothrix culture
Ulva culture
Volvox culture

Prepared Slides

Aristolochia, mature
    stem, l.s.
Bacteria (coccus, bacillus,
    spirillum)
Blood cells, human
Cardiac muscle
Cat ovary
Coleus stem tip, l.s.
Compact bone with
    Haversian system
Diatoms
Dicot stem, c.s.
Earthworm
    (Lumbricus), c.s.
Eukaryotic (animal, plant,
    protist, fungus) cells
Flatworm *(Duglesia),* c.s.
Grantia, l.s
Helianthus root, c.s.
Helianthus stem, c.s.
Hyaline cartilage, c.s.
Hydra, c.s.
Mitosis, animal (whitefish
    blastula)
Mitosis, plant (onion
    root tip)
Monocot stem, c.s.
Moss antheridia
    and archegonia
Moss protonema
Pollen grains
Privet leaf, c.s.
Prokaryotic (moneran)
    cells
Protist
Rat epididymis
Rat testis
Roundworm *(Ascaris)*
Skeletal muscle
Smooth muscle
Sycamore stem, l.s.
Taenia
Trichinella
Turbatrix aceti
Yeast
Zea root
Zea Stem

Preserved Specimens

Anole
Clam

Earthworm
Frog
Grantia
Grasshopper
Invertebrate specimens,
     unidentified
Perch
Starfish

Other Biological Supplies

Agar, glucose
Agar-phenolphthalein blocks
Agar, sterile nutrient plates
Aquarium water
Dialysis membrane
Natural materials (leaves,
     dry grass, sawdust, or
     shredded paper)
Pond water
Sea water

Chemical Supplies

Acid
     acetic, 10%
     hydrochloric, 1 M
     hydrochloric, 1%
     hydrochloric, 5%
     hydrochloric, 10%
     hydrochloric, 20%
Alcohol
     70% isopropyl
     95% ethyl
Ammonia solution
Antibiotic disks
     (See investigation.)
Barium chloride solution,
     0.2 M
Benedict's solution
Biuret reagent
Bleach solution, 10%
Bromthymol blue
Carmine solution
Congo red solution
Ethanol
Gibberellic acid solution
Gram stain
Gum arabic solution, 1%
Iodine solution
Lead nitrate solution, 0.2M
Lugol's solution
Methylene blue stain
Methyl cellulose
Pancreatin solution, 1%
Pepsin solution, 1%
Plant growth medium
Pollutant solution, 1%
     (See investigation.)
Potassium chloride solution
Rain solution (See
     investigation.)
Silver nitrate solution
     0.1M
     0.2M
Sodium chloride solution
Sodium hydroxide solution,
     0.4%
Sodium iodide solution, 0.2M
Sudan III stain

Consumables

Agaricus campestris
Aluminum foil
Antacid

Apple
Apple juice
Balloons, round
Bean seeds
Beans, white kidney
Bones (See investigation.)
Bones, uncooked pork
Box, large cardboard
Bread (variety of different
     types and brands)
Bristles of various
     thickness
Butter, melted
Candle
Carrot
Chicken egg, unfertilized
Chicken leg bone
Chicken wing, whole
Chlorine bleach solution
Cigarettes, filterless
Clay, modeling
Clock (or watch with
     second hand)
Clothing (winter article)
Coleus leaf
Comb
Conifer leaf
Corn oil
Corn seed
Cotton balls
Cotton swabs
Dicot leaf
Dicot flower with leaves
Disinfectants (See
     investigation.)
Disks (small plastic or
     cardboard)
Disks, filter paper
Egg white
     liquid
     solid
Elodea leaf
Feather
     contour
     down
     pin
Filter paper
Fish net
Flower pots, large
Foam rubber, 2.5 cm x
     21 cm x 28 cm
Food samples (See
     investigation.)
Fresh flowers
Garbage
     (See investigation.)
Gelatin solution
Glue
Honey solution
Index cards
Jacket or sweater
Kidney bean seeds
Leaves (See investigation.)
Lens paper
Lettuce
     crisp
     wilted
Light, fluorescent with
     timer
Litmus paper, red and
     blue
Magnesium ribbon
Maple leaves
Masking tape
Matches (or flint striker)

Molasses
Monocot flowers with
     leaves
Monocot leaf
Nails
Needle, sewing
Newspaper
Notepad
Nutrient agar
Olive oil
Orange
Paper
     bibulous
     brown
     construction: black,
          yellow, brown, red,
          green, and white
     notebook
     translucent tissue
     white, unlined and lined
Paper clips
Paper cups
Paper towels
Peach
Peas
     smooth
     wrinkled
Pebble
Pen
Pencils
     glass-marking
     colored: blue, orange,
          red, and black
Pennies
Petroleum jelly
pH paper
Pistils from flower
Plastic bag with twist ties
Plastic spoon
Plastic wrap
Pot, clay flower
Potato
Rubber band
Salt, table
Sand
Scale, bathroom
Shoe box
Soap
Soil garden
Spinach leaf
Stamens from flower
Starch solution
Stones, small
Straw, drinking
String
Tape, transparent
Test liquid
     (See investigation.)
Thread, sewing
Thumbtacks
Tomatoes (two different
     varieties)
Tongue depressors
Toothpicks
"Urine" samples
     (See investigation.)
Water samples
     (See investigation.)
Wire
     nickel-chromium
          alloy 15–cm
     copper 40–cm
Yeast

Laboratory Procedures

The purpose of this section is to provide some general information about preparing solutions and media, making substitutions for pH indicators, and culturing live materials. For more specific information regarding the preparation and use of solutions, media, and organisms in a particular Laboratory Investigation, consult the on-page annotations.

Solutions

General guidelines for preparing solutions and media include the following:

1. Prepare necessary solutions well in advance of the investigations in which they will be used. Each solution should be clearly labeled with its name, concentration, date of preparation, and any appropriate warnings such as toxic or flammable.
2. Always use clean glassware that has been washed with a low-sudsing laboratory soap. All glassware should be rinsed thoroughly in distilled water before use.
3. Mix each solution in a beaker or flask that holds 100 to 300 mL more than the amount of solution being prepared.
4. Use distilled water to make all preparations. Tap water may contain chemicals that alter the properties of solutions.
5. Pour concentrated acids and bases into water, stirring constantly. Never pour water into concentrated acids or bases.
6. Add solvents to solutes. Stir until solute is completely dissolved.
7. Store stains in dropper bottles.

Percentage solutions: volume/volume To prepare a solution of a given percentage, dissolve the number of milliliters of solute equal to the percentage in enough solvent to make 100 mL of solution. For example, a 10% solution of hydrochloric acid (HCl) can be made by adding 10 mL of concentrated HCl to enough distilled water to bring the volume to 100 mL.

Percentage solutions: mass/volume To prepare a solution of a given percentage, dissolve the number of grams of solute equal to the percentage in enough solvent to make 100 mL of the solution. For example, a 3% solution of sodium chloride (NaCl) can be made by adding 3 g NaCl to a graduated cylinder and then adding enough distilled water to bring the volume to 100 mL.

Reducing the concentration of a solution To reduce the concentration of an existing solution, pour the number of milliliters of the existing solution that is equal to the percentage of the new concentration into a graduated cylinder. Add enough distilled water to bring the volume in milliliters to an amount equal to the percentage of the original solution. For example, to reduce an 80% glucose solution to 20%, pour 20 mL of 80% glucose solution into a graduated cylinder. Add enough distilled water to bring the volume to 80 mL of 20% glucose.

Indicator Substitutions

In the biology laboratory, the pH indicators that are suggested for use can often be replaced by others that are equally effective. The following table lists some common indicators, the pH values at which they undergo a color change, and the expected color change.

Indicator	pH Value at Which Color Change Occurs	Color Change
thymol blue (acid)	1.5–2.5	red to yellow
bromphenol blue	3.0–4.5	yellow to blue
Congo red	3.0–5.0	blue to red
methyl orange	3.0–4.5	orange-red to yellow
litmus	4.5–8.5	red to blue
alizarin red	5.0–7.0	yellow to red
bromcresol purple	5.5–7.0	yellow to purple
bromthymol blue	6.0–7.5	yellow to blue
phenol red	6.5–8.0	yellow to red
neutral red	7.0–8.0	red to yellow
cresol red	7.0–9.0	yellow to red
thymol blue (alkaline)	8.0–10.0	yellow to blue
phenolphthalein	8.0–10.0	colorless to red
alizarin yellow	10.0–12.0	colorless to yellow

Live Organisms

The live organisms used in the *Biology Laboratory Manual* are readily available and can be cultured and maintained in a classroom or laboratory environment. Organisms are available from biological supply houses and often from pet stores or supermarkets. Some organisms can be collected locally from ponds, streams, fields, and forests.

In many schools, circumstances require that laboratory supplies, including live organisms, be ordered a year in advance. If this situation exists at your school, you may need to maintain cultures of organisms for long periods of time. The following directions on how to care for and maintain live organisms can be easily followed by you or a student laboratory assistant.

Careful attention to directions and the use of proper equipment and materials is important in caring for live organisms. Be especially careful when using glassware. Be sure that all glassware is clean and free of any soap residue.

Ideally, glassware used to culture organisms should be new and untouched by chemicals, including soap. Laboratory glassware often retains traces of the chemicals it has contacted even after it has been cleaned—and even the faintest traces of some chemicals can have a serious impact on live organisms. Because the organisms used in the Laboratory Investigations are quite hardy, they can be cultured under less than ideal conditions. However, you may want to set aside some glassware to use exclusively for culturing organisms and preparing media. This glassware should not come in contact with chemicals harsher than laboratory soap.

You should refer to pages T 29–T 31and 9–12 for guidelines for using live animals and safety rules regarding animals, respectively.

Algae Order specific species of algae such as the brown alga *Fucus* and the green algae *Ulothrix, Ulva,* and *Volvox* from a biological supply company. Follow the instructions provided by the supplier to maintain the algae cultures.

Many types of algae can be collected locally from ponds, streams, and fish hatcheries. Thoroughly rinse locally collected algae to remove debris and small organisms that may be tangled in the algae, using tap water that has been standing at room temperature at least 24 hours. Loosely place algae in jars containing tap water that has been allowed to stand at room temperature at least 24 hours and a 0.1% solution of commercial 1–10–5 fertilizer. Store the uncovered jars in a cool room beneath fluorescent lights.

Anoles Anoles and other small lizards may be raised in a terrarium constructed from a fine mesh cage or from a glass aquarium. If an aquarium is used, the top of the lizards' living quarters should be made of screen for good ventilation. The living quarters should contain some twigs on which the lizards can climb. Spray the plants in the terrarium daily to supply water for the lizards; they will lick up droplets of moisture from leaves but will seldom, if ever, drink water from a dish. The lizards subsist mainly on live insects. You may feed the lizards by offering them small mealworms held with forceps. Alternatively, you may place live insects such as crickets and fruit flies in the terrarium. If you do the latter, take precautions to ensure that the insects cannot escape from the terrarium. You may wish to cover the top of the terrarium with a few layers of cheesecloth.

Bacteria Pure cultures of *Escherichia coli, Bacillus subtilis,* and other types of bacteria can be obtained from a biological supply company. Make sure that you are familiar with bacteriological techniques and have all necessary equipment and supplies—autoclaves, incubators, media, plates, slants, etc.—before using any bacteria in the biology laboratory. Never use pathogenic bacteria, but always treat all bacteria cultures as if they were pathogenic.

Bacteria are easily cultured in tubes of nutrient broth. To prepare the nutrient broth, bring 350 mL distilled water to a boil in a 500-mL beaker. Slowly add 3 g dehydrated nutrient broth, stirring constantly. Pour the broth into small test tubes and insert a cotton plug into each tube. Sterilize the tubes of broth for 15 minutes at 15 pounds pressure in an autoclave or pressure cooker. The sterilized tubes can be stored in a refrigerator until they are used. Transfer bacteria to the tubes of sterile nutrient broth using an inoculating loop and following sterile technique. Store inoculated tubes at room temperature for two to three days to allow the bacteria to grow. Tubes of bacteria can also be incubated at 37°C for 24 hours and then be used immediately. Subcultures and dilutions of the cultures can be made at two-week intervals. Cultures remain viable stored in a refrigerator for several weeks.

Bacteria may also be cultured on agar plates or slants. Biological supply companies often provide bacterial cultures on slants. Make subcultures of bacteria as soon as possible after receiving the original cultures. You can extend the life of slant cultures by covering the slants with a thin layer of sterile mineral oil and storing them in a refrigerator. These oil-covered slants will usually survive for several months.

Clams Clams and other bivalves can be maintained for a few days in an aquarium. Marine clams can also be stored for short periods of time in large beakers filled with a 4% solution of sodium chloride.

Elodea *Elodea* is a common freshwater aquarium plant and is generally available from pet stores. *Elodea* can also be collected throughout most of the year from ponds and slow-moving streams. To maintain *Elodea* in the classroom, fill an aquarium or large (4 L) glass jar with pond or spring water. If pond or spring water is not available, fill the container with tap water and set it aside for at least 24 hours before introducing the *Elodea*. Float *Elodea* sprigs loosely on the surface of the water. Overcrowding of the *Elodea* will cause the plants to deteriorate. Replenish water as necessary due to water loss from evaporation. Nutrients for *Elodea* can be provided by adding six to eight guppies or a mature duckweed culture to the aquarium. Do not add snails to the *Elodea*: they will quickly eat and destroy the plants. Nutrients also can be provided by adding dilute (1%) commercial fertilizer (5–10–5) to the water. Provide a minimum of 15 hours of fluorescent light each day.

Ferns Ferns may be grown in clay pots or terraria. The soil should be kept moist but not wet. Most ferns prefer medium light and relatively cool temperatures. Certain ferns, such as the bracken fern, should not be placed in direct or strong sunlight. Fern gametophytes take at least six weeks to grow from spores. The spores from crushed sori may be cultured in flowerpots, on the surface of an inverted flowerpot, or in sterile agar medium.

Frogs Live adult frogs can be maintained for short periods of time in plastic containers approximately 35 x 25 x 11 cm. Add enough tap water to half cover the frogs. At one end, insert an upside down glass dish on which the frogs can rest out of the water. Provide hiding places by including broken pieces of clay pots. Cover the container to prevent escape. Clean the water every two to three days. Feed the frogs live insects or worms daily.

Eggs of *Xenopus* and *Rana pipiens* are recommended for hatching in the classroom. Use only tap water that has been allowed to stand at least 24 hours at room temperature to hatch the eggs and raise the tadpoles. Separate the eggs into clumps of about 10. Place the eggs in shallow containers of water. Maintain the eggs at room temperature and near a window where they can receive direct sunlight at least part of the day. Ten immature tadpoles can be maintained in a liter of water. Begin feeding tadpoles when strands of fecal matter appear in the water. Twice a week, feed tadpoles dry yeast or dry pea-soup powder. Clean the water as necessary. Larger tadpoles should be kept one each in a liter of water.

Goldfish The hardiest and least expensive type of goldfish are the wild-type fishes that are generally sold in pet stores as food for exotic fishes. Goldfish may also be obtained from biological supply companies.

Goldfish can be maintained in an aquarium or large glass container. Use tap water that has stood at room temperature at least 24 hours. If possible use an aquarium with a corner or under-gravel filter to clean the water. Feed the goldfish daily, using commercial food, crushed dog or cat food, or dry high-protein baby cereal. Approximately one-half teaspoon of food is adequate for five fish. Keep the water clean to avoid contamination by bacteria and fungi.

Grasshoppers Collect live grasshoppers from nearby fields. Maintain live grasshoppers in glass jars or aquariums with mesh or screen coverings. Provide twigs on which the grasshoppers can crawl and perch, water, and food such as leaves of lettuce and spinach.

Lichens Lichens may be obtained from biological supply companies. Alternatively, you may collect lichens from the surfaces of rocks, buildings, and dead trees. Spraying the attached lichens with water softens them and loosens their hold. Use a sharp knife to gently remove the lichens and place them in a cardboard box. The lichens can be stored in loosely covered cardboard boxes in a cool dry location. Spraying the lichens with water before they are used in the investigation softens them somewhat and reduces their brittleness.

Mosses Mosses may be obtained from biological supply companies or collected in woodland areas. A moist, covered terrarium in medium light provides the best growing conditions for mosses. If molds start to grow in the terrarium, remove the cover and reduce the amount of water until the molds disappear. Sprinkling a small amount of powdered sulfur in the terrarium may also discourage molds.

Pill bugs Terrestrial isopods such as pill bugs, wood lice, and sow bugs can be raised in a terrarium that contains damp, rich humus with small rocks under which the isopods can hide. These isopods will eat small pieces of apples, raw potatoes, and lettuce.

Plants Terrestrial plants such as *Coleus,* geraniums, and *Mimosa pudica* can be obtained from biological supply companies. Follow the supplier's directions regarding frequency of watering, exposure to light, and fertilizing. *Coleus* can be easily propagated from stem cuttings.

Protists Protists such as *Euglena, Amoeba, Stentor,* and *Paramecium* can be cultured in the classroom. Protists are easily cultured in stackable containers, such as finger bowls, Syracuse dishes, watch glasses, and petri dishes. The successful culturing of protists requires clean glassware. If possible, sterilize all glassware in an autoclave or pressure cooker. If sterilization is not possible, thoroughly wash all glassware in a solution of 10% nitric acid. Take care to avoid burns when working with nitric acid. Rinse the glassware several times with distilled water. Chemical and soap residues are harmful to protists and may prevent their successful culturing.

Pure stock cultures of protists can be purchased from a biological supply company. Mixed species of protists can be collected from ponds and slow-moving streams.

Cultures of protists can be successfully grown in pond water. Before using pond water, filter it through several layers of muslin or cheesecloth to remove debris. Protists can also be cultured in pasteurized spring water with a pH near 7. To pasteurize spring water, place 12 to 16 L spring water in a large enamel container. Heat the water to 65°C for 15 minutes. Pasteurized spring water can be stored up to two weeks in covered plastic containers. Longer storage requires repasteurization at two-week intervals to control the growth of hydrogen sulfide bacteria. Pond or pasteurized spring water should be used in the preparation of growth media. The following recipe for wheat medium is a good all-purpose growth medium for most protists.

- Wheat Medium: Collect wheat seeds that have not been sprayed with pesticides; obtain the seeds from farmers or order them from a biological supply company. Dried split peas or rice (not the quick-cooking variety) can be substituted for wheat seeds. Place 50 to 75 wheat seeds in a glass jar, seal the jar, and place it in an 82°C (180°F) oven for four hours. Or place 50 to 75 wheat seeds in a screw-top test tube filled with spring water. In an autoclave or pressure cooker, heat the test tubes for 15 minutes at 15 pounds pressure. In a culture dish, add three to five wheat seeds to pasteurized spring water. Add 3 to 4 mL stock protist culture to the dish. Loosely cover the culture dish and set it aside in a dimly lit area of the laboratory. Replenish evaporated water with distilled, pond, pasteurized spring, or tap water that has been allowed to stand at room temperature for at least 24 hours.

Amoeba Amebas are easily grown in a special salt solution called Chalkley's solution mixed with rice or a population of small ciliates such as *Chilomonas.*

- Chalkley's Solution: To prepare 1 L of stock solution, mix 1 g sodium chloride (NaCl), 0.04 g potassium chloride (KCl), and 0.06 g calcium chloride ($CaCl_2$) to 1 L distilled water. Stir until completely dissolved. The salts in the solution closely resemble those found in pond water. To use Chalkley's solution, add 100 mL of the prepared stock solution to 900

mL distilled water. This diluted solution is called the working solution.

- Chalkley's Solution–Rice Medium: Place about 250 mL Chalkley's working solution into several finger bowls or similar containers. To each container, add four or five grains of polished rice (not the quick-cooking variety). Place 50 to 100 *Amoeba* in each dish. Stack the dishes and cover the top dish with a loosely fitting lid. Place the cultures in a dark location at room temperature for two to four weeks. Once the cultures are established, occasionally add a few rice grains or several drops of *Chilomonas* culture to replenish the food supply.

Amoeba will need to be subcultured about once every four to five weeks. To subculture *Amoeba*, drain off about half the liquid. Divide the remaining liquid containing the *Amoeba* into two new culture dishes containing Chalkley's solution–rice medium. Set the cultures aside in a dark location for two to four weeks until the cultures become clearly established.

Chlamydomonas *Chlamydomonas* does well in Chalkley's solution–rice medium and in wheat-grain medium. Like *Euglena* and other photosynthetic protists, *Chlamydomonas* requires light.

Diatoms Although commercial media for diatoms are available, diatoms usually do not survive for long in the classroom.

Euglena *Euglena* cultures thrive in water that contains relatively large amounts of organic matter. *Euglena* can be grown successfully in three different media.

- Manure-Wheat Medium: Bring to a boil 250 mL spring water containing three wheat grains and six rabbit or sheep pellets (or equivalent mass of fresh or dried horse or cow manure). Boil for 15 minutes. Pour the mixture into a deep container such as a mayonnaise jar or large beaker. Set the container aside at room temperature for two days. Add *Euglena* from a pure culture. Cover the culture and place it near a window with diffuse light. In about two weeks, a large population of *Euglena* will be present, indicated by a greenish tinge to the water.

- Wheat-Rice-Milk Medium: For five minutes, boil a mixture of 20 wheat grains, 15 rice grains (not the quick-cooking variety), 5 mL nonfat milk, and 500 mL pasteurized spring water. Set the mixture aside overnight before adding *Euglena* from a pure culture. Store the culture in dim light near a window for about two weeks or until the *Euglena* culture becomes established.

- Rice Medium: Boil seven or eight grains of rice (not the quick-cooking variety) in 475 mL distilled water or old aquarium water for about one minute. Pour the mixture into a shallow dish. Allow the dish to stand at room temperature until a bacterial scum forms on the surface, about one week. Add *Euglena* from a pure culture and cover. Place the infusion in dim light near a window for six to eight weeks to allow the *Euglena* culture to develop and grow. Replenish water as necessary, using distilled or old aquarium water.

Euglena cultures can be maintained up to a year before subculturing becomes necessary.

Paramecium Paramecia can be successfully cultured in an infusion of dried lettuce leaves. To prepare the infusion, remove several large outer leaves from a head of lettuce. Placed the leaves in an oven at low temperature for several hours to dry. Remove the lettuce leaves when they have become crisp and brown. Discard any blackened or charred leaves. Grind the dried leaves with a mortar and pestle. The ground leaves can be stored almost indefinitely in a tightly sealed glass container. In an Erlenmeyer flask, add 1.5 g powered lettuce leaves to 1 L boiling distilled water. Boil for five minutes. Filter the infusion into smaller Erlenmeyer flasks. Seal the flasks with cotton plugs. Sterilize the flasks for 15 minutes at 15 pounds pressure in an autoclave or pressure cooker. Allow the infusion to stand overnight. Using sterile pipettes and flasks, add two parts of the lettuce infusion to one part distilled water. Add several drops of pure concentrated *Paramecium* culture to each flask. Stopper the flasks with cotton plugs. Set the cultures in dim light at room temperature for one to two weeks.

Paramecia need to be subcultured every month. Place several drops of the existing culture into flasks of dilute lettuce infusion.

Physarum polycephalum Slime molds, such as *Physarum polycephalum*, can be cultured on filter paper and oatmeal. Wrap a small glass bowl with a piece of filter paper or a paper towel so that the mouth of the bowl is covered by a smooth flat paper surface. Place the covered bowl in a large container such as a battery jar so that the mouth of the bowl and the flat paper surface face upward. Partially fill the battery jar with water so that the water level is about three-quarters of the way up the sides of the bowl. Place the slime mold on the filter paper. Sprinkle about 0.2 g oatmeal or pulverized rolled oats into the paper. Feed the slime mold with oatmeal every one to two days. The slime mold can be stored in a dormant state by drying the filter paper at room temperature and placing it in sealed containers in a refrigerator. The slime mold will survive for a year or two under these conditions.

Stentor The easiest way to grow *Stentor* is in a medium made of Chalkley's solution, wheat, and *Chilomonas*.

- Chalkley's Solution–Wheat–*Chilomonas* Medium: Boil five to six wheat grains in distilled water for about one minute. Add the boiled wheat grains and 5 mL dense *Chilomonas* culture to 100 mL working Chalkley's solution. (See directions for the preparation of Chalkley's solution under *Amoeba*). Allow the medium to stand at room temperature for two days. Add 10 to 20 *Stentor* to the medium. Cover the culture and place it in a cool, even-temperature room for two to three weeks. Replenish evaporated water with distilled water or pasteurized spring water as necessary.

The *Stentor* culture should last about six months without subculturing. Add one additional boiled wheat grain per month to the culture to maintain the food supply.

Radish seedlings Plant radish seeds in a light and porous mixture of soil and vermiculite. Plant seeds about 1 cm below the soil surface and about 2 to 3 cm apart. Keep soil evenly moist before and after seedlings emerge. Before seedlings emerge, the container in which they are planted can be covered with plastic wrap. The plastic wrap forms a mini-greenhouse, conserving heat and moisture. Remove the plastic once the seedlings emerge.

Rodents Small rodents such as hamsters, gerbils, mice, and rats may be housed in cages that are available commercially or in glass aquaria with a screen top. If you choose to raise mice, make sure that the classroom is well-ventilated, as mice have an offensive odor. Separate males and females to avoid unwanted litters. Clean the rodents' habitat daily (except for the first two days after the birth of a litter). The rodents should be provided with an exercise wheel and chewing sticks; some may require a salt lick. Make sure that a supply of fresh water is available at all times. Use a glass or plastic water fountain rather than a water bowl; open bowls become fouled easily. Rodents can be fed commercial food pellets supplemented with pieces of fresh vegetables such as carrots.

Snails Freshwater snails will flourish in an established aquarium with *Elodea* provided for food. Remove dead snails immediately to prevent fouling of the water. Snails can help keep the glass in a freshwater aquarium relatively free of algae. Place two medium-sized snails in the aquarium for each gallon of water.

The following notes deal with organisms that

are not used in the Laboratory Investigations. You may wish to culture these organisms for enrichment activities, independent student projects, or teacher demonstrations.

Bread mold Spores of the black bread mold, *Rhizopus stolonifer,* can be ordered from a biological supply company. Spores of bread mold also are commonly found on dry onions from a supermarket. Sprinkle purchased spores over the surface of a piece of wet bread in a dish. Or rub a moist cotton swab over the surface of an onion to collect spores and then rub the swab across the bread surface to transfer the spores. Seal the dish tightly and set it aside at room temperature. Mold should appear in about three days. After all investigations requiring mold are complete, allow the covered dish of mold to dry out. This procedure provides spores for the following year.

Brine shrimp The brine shrimp *Artemia* is a good source of food for hydras, fish, and other aquatic animals. It is also rather interesting to observe in its own right, as it exhibits a strong positive response to light.

Brine shrimp eggs are available from pet stores, tropical fish stores, and biological supply companies. Hatch brine shrimp eggs in a shallow glass dish containing a dilute (4%) solution of sodium chloride. Sprinkle 0.5 mL brine shrimp eggs on the surface of the water. Larvae will hatch in 18 to 72 hours, depending on the temperature of the water. At a constant temperature of 21°C, brine shrimp eggs usually hatch within 48 hours. Aerating the water with an airstone increases the hatching success rate.

Brine shrimp will grow to maturity in about 20 days if they are cultured in a well-aerated aquarium at temperatures below 25°C. They can be fed a yeast suspension supplemented with scrapings of algae from the sides of aquaria.

To capture brine shrimp for observation or for feeding to other organisms, shine a light at one side of the container. Siphon off the brine shrimp with a piece of plastic tubing or a kitchen bulb baster. Before being fed to hydras or other freshwater organisms, brine shrimp must first be washed with distilled water to remove any traces of salt. To wash the brine shrimp, pour them through a filter or fine mesh net. Rinse them thoroughly with a gentle stream of tap or distilled water. Brine shrimp can survive only a few hours in fresh water, so remove and wash only as many as are needed.

Crickets Crickets are quite easy to raise, and they provide a good source of food for other animals in the classroom. You may collect crickets in fields and other grassy areas or obtain them from a biological supply company. Crickets can be kept in a glass aquarium that has a secure screen top. Put about a centimeter of cat pan filler or clean sand on the bottom of the aquarium. Provide the crickets with small rocks and branches for hiding and climbing. Place a small container filled with wet cotton on the bottom of the aquarium to help maintain the humidity in the crickets' habitat and provide a source of water. Keep the cotton wet at all times. The crickets may be fed on dry dog food and bits of fresh fruits and vegetables. Avoid overcrowding. Crickets tend to be cannibalistic, especially at high population densities.

Daphnia *Daphnia* are available from a biological supply company. To culture *Daphnia,* nearly fill a 4-L jar with pasteurized spring water or tap water that has been allowed to stand at room temperature at least 24 hours. To the water add green unicellular algae or 100 mL of an established *Euglena* culture. Add several *Daphnia* to the jar and place the jar near a light source. Replenish the water and *Euglena* culture as necessary. Subculture the *Daphnia* about every three weeks.

Drosophila Fruit flies can be collected from fruit and vegetable markets or purchased from biological supply companies. Fruit flies with the specific traits required in the investigations must be ordered from a biological supply company far enough in advance to allow for the desired increase in the population size of the flies. Store flies in clear plastic or glass vials or jars with stoppers that allow for air exchange. Stoppers must be escape proof. Include in each vial a small piece of paper towel on which the flies can perch. Store the vials in a warm (18°–20°C) area away from bright light.

Fruit flies can be cultured on a few slices of overripe banana that have been sprinkled with a few grains of yeast. They can also be cultured on one of a large number of commercial or "homemade" media. The recipe for one particularly effective home-made medium is as follows.

- Banana-Agar Medium: Bring 625 mL water to a boil. Add 20 g agar powder and boil until thoroughly dissolved, stirring constantly. Add 25 mL white corn syrup and 250 mL mashed very ripe bananas. Add 20 g dried brewer's yeast. Bring this mixture to a boil. If desired, add 20 g of a commercial mold inhibitor at this point. Stir mixture until all ingredients are thoroughly mixed. Pour into sterile culture vials as needed.

Fill a culture bottle with about 1 to 2 cm of medium. Insert a piece of crumpled paper toweling into the medium before it hardens. This provides a surface for egg-laying and pupation. Bottles may be stoppered with pieces of foam rubber or cotton wrapped in cheesecloth.

The life cycle of *Drosophila* takes about two weeks and varies with temperature. At 20°C, the life cycle usually takes 15 days. A magnifying glass is useful in sexing adult fruit flies. Males, which are slightly smaller than females, have a wide pigmented band that covers the posterior third of their rounded abdomen. Females have 5 to 8 thin bands on their slightly pointed abdomen.

Because female *Drosophila* store sperm within their body for some time after mating, virgin females must be obtained for genetic crosses. One way of ensuring that the females in a culture are virgin is to remove all the adult flies in a culture as pupae begin to form. The emerging female flies will be virgin for the first 10 hours.

Fruit flies must be anesthetized so that they can be examined. Traditionally, ether has been used; however, there are a number of commercial anesthetics available that are much less volatile. You can obtain anesthetizers from biological supply companies or construct them yourself.

To construct an anesthetizer, you will need a bottle whose mouth is the same size as that of the culture bottles, a cork stopper that fits the bottle, a nail about 3 cm long, cotton or gauze, and thread. Push the nail into the cork stopper so that the head of the nail is flush with the top of the stopper and the point of the nail protrudes from the bottom side of the stopper. Cover the nail with cotton; secure the cotton with thread. When ready to use the anesthetizer, put a few drops of anesthetic on the cotton.

To transfer flies from the culture bottle to the anesthetizer, tap the side of the culture bottle so that the flies fall to the bottom of the bottle. Quickly place the mouth of the anesthetizer over the mouth of the culture bottle. Invert the culture bottle and tap it so the flies (but not the medium or larvae) fall into the anesthetizer. Then quickly separate and stopper the bottles.

When the flies stop moving, spill them onto a sheet of white paper. Have on hand a petri dish cover that has a piece of filter paper taped to the inside. If the flies begin reviving too soon, put a drop or two of anesthetic on the filter paper and then cover the flies for a few seconds until they are reanesthetized.

Manipulate the flies using a small paintbrush. Transfer dead or unwanted flies to the "morgue"— a container of mineral oil. When transferring flies into a culture bottle, make sure that they fall on the paper toweling. If they fall on the medium, they will get stuck and die.

Duckweed Duckweed can be purchased from a biological supply company or collected from ponds and slow-moving streams in spring and early summer. A manure medium for duckweed can be prepared by adding 10 mL fresh or dried cow manure to 2 L tap water that has been allowed to stand at least 24 hours. Boil this mixture for 15 minutes and then allow it to cool. Pour the manure medium into several large jars. Add about 50 duckweed clusters to each jar. Duckweed can also be maintained on the surface of an established aquarium that contains snails and fish.

Earthworms Earthworms are readily collected when they come to the surface at night or after a heavy rain. They can also be obtained from a biological supply company. Food and habitats for worms are available commercially. You can also house worms in wooden containers such as cigar boxes. Fill the container with 5 to 15 centimeters of moist soil or peat moss. Keep the container covered and store it at a temperature of about 15°C. Make sure the soil remains moist. Twice a week, bury some lettuce and bits of bread soaked in milk in the soil.

Hydra Hydras are easily grown in a culture dish containing a 5-cm sprig of *Elodea* and pasteurized spring water (pH 7). (See the section on *Amoeba* for directions on the preparation of pasteurized spring water.) Place 20 to 30 hydras in the culture dish. Place the dish near a fluorescent light where it will receive 16 hours of light per day. Hydras are active carnivorous feeders that will eat only live food. Providing an adequate food supply is the most difficult aspect of maintaining hydras in the classroom. Feed hydras the washed larvae of brine shrimp, *Daphnia,* or chopped *Tubifex* worms every other day. Hydras require clean water. About 30 minutes after each feeding, remove uneaten brine shrimp and other debris from the bottom of the dish with a medicine dropper. Remove half the water from the dish and replace it with pasteurized spring water. Replace the sprig of *Elodea* as it deteriorates. When the population reaches 50 hydras, begin a new culture with half of the individuals from the existing culture.

Mealworms These larvae of *Tenebrio* beetles may be obtained from pet stores or from biological supply companies. they can be cultured in jars half-filled with slightly moist bran, oatmeal, or cornflakes. The jars should be covered with cheesecloth or a fine wire mesh so that adult beetles cannot fly away. Adult beetles may be fed bits of raw carrots or potatoes.

Planarians Planarians such as *Dugesia* can be collected from the underside of logs and stones in bodies of cold, clear fresh water. They can also be obtained from biological supply companies. Planarians should be kept in black or opaque containers such as enameled pans at a temperature of about 18°C. The water should be changed frequently. Feed the planarians bits of raw liver, *Tubifex* worms, or egg yolk. Remove excess food with a medicine dropper or pipette after several hours to avoid fouling the water.

Vinegar eels Order *Anguilla aceti* or *Turbatrix aceti* from a biological supply company. These roundworms are harmless and nonparasitic, and are commonly found in bulk cider vinegar. Vinegar eels can also be obtained from local cider mills or vinegar manufacturers. Ask for pure bulk vinegar that contains "mother of vinegar." To culture vinegar eels, place about 200 mL unadulterated cider vinegar (from a grocery store) and 2 tablespoons of commercial vinegar eel medium into finger bowls or similar containers. A 2-cm cube of peeled raw apple can be substituted for commercial vinegar eel medium. Add vinegar eels. Cover containers loosely and place them in a dimly lit location. No further care is necessary. Subculture every three months if required.

Yeast   To prepare an actively growing culture of yeast, dissolve 0.1 g dry yeast and 5 g sucrose in 75 mL distilled water. Mix thoroughly. The yeast culture should be used within two to four days. This culture should provide enough yeast for three classes of 30 students each.

Suppliers of Laboratory Materials and Equipment

Accent Science
P.O. Box 1444
Saginaw, MI 48605

Analytical Scientific
11049 Bandera Road
San Antonio, TX 78250

Andor Chemical Corporation
P.O. Box K
Rochester, NY 14623

Ann Arbor Biologicals
6780 Jackson Road
Ann Arbor, MI 48103

Apple Computer, Inc.
20525 Mariani Avenue
Cupertino, CA 95014

Aquarium and Science Supply
    Company
P.O. Box 41
Dresher, PA 19025

Arbor Scientific
P.O. Box 2750
924 North Main Street
Ann Arbor, MI 48106

Bausch & Lomb
Scientific Optical Products Division
P.O. Box 450
1400 North Goodman Street
Rochester, NY 14692-0450

California Corporation of
    Biochemical Research
3625 Medford Street
Los Angeles, CA 90063

Carolina Biological Supply Company
2700 York Road
Burlington, NC 27215

Central Scientific Company (CENCO)
11222 Melrose Avenue
Franklin Park, IL 60131

Chem Scientific, Inc.
67 Chapel Street
Newton, MA 02158

College Biological Supply Company
8857 Mount Israel Road
Escondido, CA 92025

Connecticut Valley Biological Supply
    Company, Inc.
P.O. Box 326
82 Valley Road
Southampton, MA 01073

Damon/Instructional Systems
    Division
80 Wilson Way
Westwood, MA 02090

Delta Biologicals
P.O. Box 26666
Tucson, AZ 85726-6666

Edmund Scientific Company
101 East Gloucester Pike
Barrington, NJ 08007-1380

Fisher Scientific Company
Educational Materials Division
4901 West LeMoyne Street
Chicago, IL 60651

Flinn Scientific, Inc.
P.O. Box 219
131 Flinn Street
Batavia, IL 60510

Forestry Suppliers, Inc.
P.O. Box 8397
205 West Rankin Street
Jackson, MS 39204

Frey Scientific Company
905 Hickory Lane
Mansfield. OH 44905

General Supply Corporation
P.O. Box 9347
Jackson, MS 39206

Grau-Hall Scientific Corporation
6501 Elvas Avenue
Sacramento, CA 95819

H & H Research, Inc.
P.O. Box 5156, Station One
Wilmington, NC 28403

Hach Company
P.O. Box 389
Loveland, CO 80539

Harvard Apparatus Company
Dover, MA 02118

Hubbard Scientific Company
P.O. Box 104
1946 Raymond Drive
Northbrook, IL 60062

Ideal School Supply Company
11000 South Lavergne Avenue
Oak Lawn, IL 60453

Kons Scientific Company, Inc.
P.O. Box 3
Germantown, WI 53022-0003

La Pine Scientific Company
6001 Knox Avenue
Chicago, IL 60018

Lab-Aids, Inc.
249 Trade Zone Drive
Ronkonkoma, NY 11779

Learning Alternatives
P.O. Box 219
Vienna, OH 44473

Learning Spectrum
1390 Westridge Drive
Portola Valley, CA 94025

Learning Things, Inc.
P.O. Box 436
68A Broadway
Arlington, MA 02174

William A. Lemberger Company
2500 Waukau Avenue
Oshkosh, WI 54903

McKilligan Supply Corporation
435 Main Street
Johnson City, NY 13790

Ben Meadows Company
3589 Broad Street
Chamblee, GA 30341

Merrell Scientific Division
Educational Modules, Incorporated
1665 Buffalo Road
Rochester, NY 14624

Nasco
901 Janesville Avenue
Fort Atkinson, WI 53538

Nasco West, Inc.
P.O. Box 3837
Modesto, CA 95352

National Teaching Aids, Inc.
1845 Highland Avenue
New Hyde Park, NY 11040

Niles Biological
P.O. Box 191543
Sacramento, CA 95819

Norris Science Labs & Kits
P.O. Box 61281
Las Vegas, NV 89160

Nutritional Biochemicals
    Corporation
26201 Miles Road
Cleveland, OH 44128

Parco Scientific Company
P.O. Box 189
316 Youngstown-Kingsville Road
Vienna, OH 44473

Phipps and Bird, Inc.
P.O. Box 189
Richmond, VA 23261

Prentice-Hall Equipment Division
10 Oriskany Drive
Tonawanda, NY 14150

Redco Science, Inc.
11 Robinson Lane
Oxford, CT 06483

Sargent-Welch Scientific Company
7300 North Linder Avenue
Skokie, IL 60077

Scavengers Scientific Supply
    Company
P.O. Box 211328
Auke Bay, WI 99821

Schoolmasters Science
P.O. Box 1941
745 State Circle
Ann Arbor, MI 48106

Schwarz BioResearch, Inc.
Mountain View Avenue
Orangeburg, NY 10962

Science Kit and Boreal Labs
777 East Park Drive
Tonawanda, NY 14150

The Science Man Company
A Division of TSM Marketing, Inc.
4738 North Harlem Avenue
Harwood Heights, IL 60656

Scientific Glass Apparatus Company
737 Broad Street
Bloomfield, NJ 07003

Southern Precision Instrument
    Company
3419 East Commerce Street
San Antonio, TX 78820

Southwestern Biological Supply
    Company
P.O. Box 4084
Dallas, TX 75208

Spectrum Educational Supplies
    Limited
125 Mary Street
Aurora, Ontario, Canada

Swift Instruments, Inc.
P.O. Box 562
San Jose, CA 95106

Triarch, Inc.
P.O. Box 98
Ripon, WI 59471

Turtox, Inc.
P.O. Box 266
Palos Heights, IL 60463-0266

Ward's Natural Science
    Establishment Inc.
P.O. Box 92912
5100 West Henrietta Road
Rochester, NY 14692-9012

Wildlife Supply Company
301 Cass Street
Saginaw, MI 48602

Wilkens-Anderson Company
4525 West Division Street
Chicago, IL 60651

Bibliography

Allen, Dorothea. *Biology Teacher's Desk Book*. West Nyack, NY: Parker Publishing Co., Inc., 1979.

Behringer, Marjorie P. *Techniques and Materials in Biology*. Huntington, NY: Krieger Publishing Co., 1981.

Biesengerz, P.C. and D. G. Olstad. "The Use of Laboratory Instruction in High School Biology." *American Biology Teacher,* March 1980.

Biology Teacher's Handbook. New York: John Wiley & Sons, Inc., 1978.

Claflin, William E. *Collecting, Culturing, and Caring for Living Materials: A Guide for the Teacher, Student, and Hobbyist*. Saratoga, CA: Century Twenty One, 1981.

Cothron J.H., R.N. Giese, and R.J. Rezba. "Designing Students: Helping Students Learn to Create Experiments." *Science Scope*, January 1990.

Cothron, J.H., R.N. Giese, and R. J. Rezba. "Simple Principles of Data Analysis." *The American Biology Teacher,* October 1989.

Cronin, L.C. "Creativity in the Science Classroom." *The Science Teacher,* February 1989.

Cross, B. "A Passion Within Reason: The Human Side of Process." *Science and Children*, January 1990.

DeDecker, P.F. "Teaching Bioethical Decision Making in High School." *The American Biology Teacher,* October 1987.

Harper, C. and B. Bartlett. "Putting in a Plug for Classroom Safety." *The Science Teacher,* December 1989.

Kizer, Franklin D., ed. *Safety in the Secondary Science Classroom*. Washington, DC: National Science Teacher's Association, 1983.

Livingston, J.B. "Reading into the Subject of Science." *The Science Teacher,* February 1989.

Lunetta, V., A. Hofsyein, and G. Giddings. "Evaluating Science Laboratory Skills." *The Science Teacher,* January 1981.

McCormack, A.J. and R.E. Yager. "A New Taxonomy of Science Education." *The Science Teacher,* February 1989.

Morholt, Evelyn and P. Brandwein. *A Sourcebook for the Biological Sciences*. Orlando, FL: Harcourt Brace Jovanovich, 1986.

Parakh, J.S. and I.L. Slesnick. "Difficult Decisions: Animal Rights." *The Science Teacher,* April 1989.

Pizzini, E.L., S.K. Abell, and D.S. Shepardson, "Rethinking Thinking in the Science Classroom." *The Science Teacher,* December 1988.

Powell, R. "Research Projects in High School Biology." *The American Biology Teacher,* April 1987.

Sarinsky, G.B. and C.A. Biermann, "Learning How to Observe." *The American Biology Teacher,* September 1989.

Shapin, S. "The Invisible Technician." *American Scientist,* November-December 1989.

Guidelines for the Use and Care of Animals

Animals are an essential part of a biology curriculum. Few things are as interesting and motivating to students as animals. The judicious use of live or preserved animals can help students realize that the study of biology is relevant, fascinating, rewarding, and not merely another dull textbook exercise.

Although there are many advantages to providing biology students with opportunities to study real animals, it is important to be aware of and sensitive to ethical and practical concerns. The purpose of this section is to discuss some realistic guidelines for using animals in a secondary classroom. The final decision regarding the use of animals in your classroom should take into consideration these recommendations, the safety rules on page 12 of the *Laboratory Manual*, local and school guidelines, your personal views, and your assessment of your students' needs, interests, maturity, and ability to behave responsibly.

1. Whenever possible, live animals should be observed in their natural habitats or in zoos, parks, and aquaria.
2. Check the state and federal codes regarding animal welfare that apply in your area. You may also wish to refer to guidelines published by the National Science Teachers' Association, the National Association of Biology Teachers, and the International Science Fair. Make students aware of all safety rules and regulations regarding animals.
3. Before bringing a live animal into the classroom, determine whether a proper habitat can be maintained in the classroom situation. Such a habitat includes temperature, space, and type of food. Students should have a clear understanding of the appropriate care needed by the live animals brought in the classroom. Do not allow students to tap on animal enclosures or otherwise disturb the animals.
4. No wild vertebrate animals should be brought into the classroom. Purchase animals from a reputable dealer only.
5. Live animals should be nonpoisonous and healthy. Any mammals used in the classroom should be vaccinated against rabies unless the animals were purchased recently from a reliable scientific supply company. Quarantine any animal to make sure it is disease-free before bringing it into the classroom.
6. Make sure that the living quarters of classroom animals are clean, located away from stressful situations, appropriately spacious, and secure enough to confine the animal. You may wish to lock cages to prevent the accidental release of animals; the small padlocks used on luggage are good for this purpose.
7. Remove wastes from animal living quarters daily. Thoroughly clean animal living quarters periodically to ensure that they are odor- and germ-free. Provide a daily supply of fresh water and any other need specific to the particular animal.
8. Provide for the care of animals during weekends and school vacations. Inform the custodial staff of the presence of animals and warn them of any special requirements. For example, turning off the aquarium pump to save electricity or spraying the classroom for insects can be fatal to animal collections.
9. Students should be instructed as to how to handle each species brought into the classroom. For example, students can receive painful wounds from the improper handling of some fishes, mollusks, and sea urchins.
10. Animals should be handled only if necessary. If an animal is frightened or excited, pregnant, feeding, or with its young, special handling is required.
11. Students should thoroughly clean their hands after handling animals or the cage containing animals.
12. Animals should be returned to their natural habitat after an observation period of not longer than 14 days. However, laboratory-bred animals or species that are not indigenous to an area should not be released into the environment.
13. If an animal must be euthanized, do not allow students to watch. Do the sacrificing humanely. Contact the local humane society for advice.
14. Before performing any experiment involving live animals, check local and state regulations. In some states, certification is required before a teacher is permitted to experiment with animals.
15. No animal studies involving anesthetic drugs, pathogenic organisms, toxicological products, carcinogens, or radiation should be performed.
16. Any experiment requiring live animals should have a clearly defined objective relating to the teaching/learning of some scientific principle.
17. No experimental procedures that will cause pain, discomfort, or harm to mammals, birds, reptiles, fishes, and amphibians should be done in the classroom or at home.
18. Surgical procedures should not be performed on live vertebrate animals.

19. If fertilized bird eggs are opened, the embryo should be destroyed humanely two days before it would have hatched, at the latest.
20. Whenever possible, substitute plants or invertebrate animals for vertebrates.
21. When working with preserved animals, make sure that students maintain a serious and respectful attitude toward the specimens.

Handling Ethical Issues

There is much controversy regarding the use of animals in science research. This controversy extends to preserved animals in dissections as well as live animals in experiments. Although the battle over what uses of animals are appropriate in a biology classroom can be frustrating and emotionally charged, it can also provide an opportunity for students to closely examine a current issue. You may wish to have students read current literature on the subject and contact groups and individuals with varying points of view.

Stress that it is important to make a rational, informed decision before taking a stand on any issue. Point out that it is vital to know and understand the arguments on both sides of an issue. Help students analyze the sources they find in terms of slant, bias, and the reliability and objectivity of the author(s). Teach them to learn to distinguish between fact and opinion. Encourage them to question what they read and hear. Challenge them to discover the hidden assumptions and implications of different points of view.

If dissections are a part of your curriculum and a student chooses to avoid dissections because of ethical concerns, you should respect that student's opinion. Point out, however, that no simulation or videotape can replace hands-on, first-hand experience.

NABT Guidelines for the Use of Live Animals

> **The National Association of Biology Teachers (NABT) has developed the following set of guidelines to be used when working with live animals.**

Living things are the subject of biology, and their direct study is an appropriate and necessary part of biology teaching. Textbook instruction alone cannot provide students with a basic understanding of life and life processes. We further recognize the importance of research to understanding life processes and providing information on health, disease, medical care, and agriculture.

The abuse of any living organism for experimentation or any other purpose is intolerable in any segment of society. Because biology deals specifically with living things, professional biological educators must be especially cognizant of their responsibility to prevent inhumane treatment to living organisms in the name of science and research. This responsibility should extend beyond the confines of the teacher's classroom to the rest of the school and community.

The National Association of Biology Teachers, in speaking to the dilemma of providing a sound biological education, while addressing the problem of humane experimentation, presents the following guidelines on the use of live animals.

A. Biological experimentation should lead to and be consistent with a respect for life and all living things. Humane treatment and care of animals should be an integral part of any lesson that includes living animals.

B. All aspects of exercises and/or experiments dealing with living things must be within the comprehension and capabilities of the students involved. It is recognized that these parameters are necessarily vague, but it is expected that competent teachers of biology can recognize these limitations.

C. Lower orders of life such as bacteria, fungi, protozoans, and invertebrates can reveal much basic biological information and are preferable as subjects for invasive studies wherever and whenever possible.

D. Vertebrate animals may be used as experimental organisms in the following situations:
1. Observations of normal living patterns of wild animals in the free living state or in zoological parks, gardens, or aquaria.
2. Observations of normal living patterns of pets, fish, or domestic animals.
3. Observations of biological phenomena, i.e., including ovulation in frogs through hormone injections that do not cause discomfort or adverse effects to the animals.

E. Animals should be properly cared for as described in the following guidelines:
1. Appropriate quarters for the animals being used should be provided in a place free from undue stresses. If housed in the classroom itself, animals should not be constantly subjected to disturbances that might be caused by students in the classroom or other upsetting activities.
2. All animals used in teaching or research programs must receive proper care. Quarters should provide for sanitation, protection from the elements, and have sufficient space for normal behavioral and postural requirements of the species. Quarters shall be easily cleaned, ventilated, and lighted. Proper temperature regulation shall be provided.
3. Proper food and clean drinking water for those animals requiring water shall be available at all times in suitable containers.

4. Animals' care shall be supervised by a science teacher experienced in proper animal care.

5. If euthanasia is necessary, animals shall be sacrificed in an approved, humane manner by an adult experienced in the use of such procedures. Laboratory animals should not be released in the environment if they were not originally a part of the native fauna. The introduction of nonnative species which may become feral must be avoided.

6. The procurement and use of wild or domestic animals must comply with existing local, state, or federal rules regarding same.

F. Animal studies should be carried out under the provisions of the following guidelines:

1. All animal studies should be carried out under the direct supervision of a competent science teacher. It is the responsibility of that teacher to ensure that the student has the necessary comprehension for the study being done.

2. Students should not be allowed to take animals home to carry out experimental studies. These studies should be done in a suitable area in the school.

3. Students doing projects with vertebrate animals should adhere to the following:

   a. No experimental procedures should be attempted that would subject vertebrate animals to pain or distinct discomfort, or interfere with their health in any way. Pithing of live frogs should be carried out by a teacher experienced in such procedures and should not be part of the general class activity.

   b. Students should not perform surgery on living vertebrate animals except under the direct supervision of a qualified biomedical scientist.

4. Experimental procedures should not involve the use of microorganisms pathogenic to humans or other animals, ionizing radiation, carcinogens, drugs, or chemicals at toxic levels, drugs known to produce adverse or teratogenic effects, pain causing drugs, alcohol in any form, electric shock, exercise until exhaustion, or other distressing stimuli.

5. Behavioral studies should use only positive reinforcement in training studies.

6. Egg embryos subjected to experimental manipulation must be destroyed humanely at least two days prior to hatching. Normal egg embryos allowed to hatch must be treated humanely within these guidelines.

7. The administration of anesthetics should be carried out by a qualified science teacher competent in such procedures. (The legal ramifications of student use of anesthetics are complex and such use should be avoided.)

G. The use of living animals for science fair projects and displays shall be in accordance with these guidelines. In addition, no living vertebrate animals shall be used in displays for science fair exhibitions.

H. It is recognized that an exceptionally talented student may wish to conduct original research in the biological or medical sciences. In those cases where the research value of a specific project is obvious by its potential contribution to science, but its execution would be otherwise prohibited by the guidelines governing the selection of an appropriate experimental animal or procedure, exceptions can be obtained if:

1. the project is approved by and carried out under the direct supervision of a qualified biomedical scientist or a designated adult supervisor in the field of the investigation; and

2. the project is carried out in an appropriate research facility; and

3. the project is carried out with the utmost regard for the humane care and treatment of the animals involved in the project; and

4. a research plan is developed and approved by the qualified biomedical scientist prior to the start of any research.

Laboratory Manual

Biology
MILLER · LEVINE

Prentice Hall
Englewood Cliffs, New Jersey
Needham, Massachusetts

BIOLOGY
Miller • Levine

Laboratory Manual

Designed and produced by
Function Thru Form Inc.

Other Components of the Program

Student Text with Annotated Teacher's Edition
Teacher's Resource Book
Study Guide with Annotated Teacher's Edition
Test Bank with Software and DIAL-A-TEST™ Service
Biology Posters
Biology Transparencies
Biotechnology Workbook with Solutions Manual
Biology Coursework
Biology Videos

1992 Printing
©1991 by Prentice-Hall, Inc., Englewood Cliffs, New Jersey 07632.
Printed in the United States of America

ISBN 0-13-081423-7

10 9 8 7 6 5

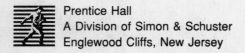

Prentice Hall
A Division of Simon & Schuster
Englewood Cliffs, New Jersey

Contents

Safety in the Biology Laboratory

Working in the biology laboratory can be interesting, exciting, and rewarding. But it can also be quite dangerous if you are not serious and alert and if proper safety precautions are not taken at all times. You are responsible for maintaining an enjoyable, instructional, and safe environment in the biology laboratory. Unsafe practices endanger not only you but the people around you as well.

Read the following information about safety in the biology laboratory carefully. Review applicable safety information before you begin each Laboratory Investigation. If you have any questions about safety or laboratory procedures, be sure to ask your teacher.

SAFETY SYMBOL GUIDE

All the investigations in this laboratory manual have been designed with safety in mind. If you follow the instructions, you should have a safe and interesting year in the laboratory. Before beginning any investigation, make sure you read the safety rules on pages 10–12 of the *Laboratory Manual*.

The eight safety symbols shown on page 10 are used throughout the *Laboratory Manual*. They appear first next to the Safety section of an investigation and then next to certain steps in an investigation where specific safety precautions are required. The symbols alert you to the need for special safety precautions. The description of each symbol indicates the precaution(s) you should take whenever you see the symbol in an investigation.

Glassware Safety

1. Whenever you see this symbol, you will know that you are working with glassware that can be easily broken. Take particular care to handle such glassware safely. And never use broken glassware.

2. Never heat glassware that is not thoroughly dry. Never pick up any glassware unless you are sure it is not hot. If it is hot, use heat-resistant gloves.

3. Always clean glassware thoroughly before putting it away.

Fire Safety

1. Whenever you see this symbol, you will know that you are working with fire. Never use any source of fire without wearing safety goggles.

2. Never heat anything—particularly chemicals—unless instructed to do so.

3. Never heat anything in a closed container.

4. Never reach across a flame.

5. Always use a clamp, tongs, or heat-resistant gloves to handle hot objects.

6. Always maintain a clean working area, particularly when using a flame.

Heat Safety

Whenever you see this symbol, you will know that you should put on heat-resistant gloves to avoid burning your hands.

Chemical Safety

1. Whenever you see this symbol, you will know that you are working with chemicals that could be hazardous.

2. Never smell any chemical directly from its container. Always use your hand to waft some of the odors from the top of the container toward your nose—and only when instructed to do so.

3. Never mix chemicals unless instructed to do so.

4. Never touch or taste any chemical unless instructed to do so.

5. Keep all lids closed when chemicals are not in use. Dispose of all chemicals as instructed by your teacher.

6. Immediately rinse with water any chemicals, particularly acids, off your skin and clothes. Then notify your teacher.

Eye and Face Safety

1. Whenever you see this symbol, you will know that you are performing an investigation in which you must take precautions to protect your eyes and face by wearing safety goggles.

2. Always point a test tube or bottle that is being heated away from you and others. Chemicals can splash or boil out of the heated test tube.

Sharp Instrument Safety

1. Whenever you see this symbol, you will know that you are working with a sharp instrument.

2. Always use single-edged razors; double-edged razors are too dangerous for use.

3. Handle any sharp instrument with extreme care. Never cut any material toward you; always cut away from you.

4. Notify your teacher immediately if you cut yourself or receive a cut.

Electrical Safety

1. Whenever you see this symbol, you will know that you are using electricity in the laboratory.

2. Never use long extension cords to plug in any electrical device. Do not plug too many different appliances into one socket or you may overload the socket and cause a fire.

3. Never touch an electrical appliance or outlet with wet hands.

Animal Safety

1. Whenever you see this symbol, you will know that you are working with live animals.

2. Do not cause pain, discomfort, or injury to any animal.

3. Follow your teacher's directions when handling animals. Wash your hands thoroughly after handling animals or their cages.

SCIENCE SAFETY RULES

One of the first things a scientist learns is that working in the laboratory can be an exciting experience. But the laboratory can also be quite dangerous if proper safety rules are not followed at all times. To prepare yourself for a safe year in the laboratory, read over the following safety rules. Then read them a second time. Make sure you understand each rule. If you do not, ask your teacher to explain any rules you are unsure of.

DRESS CODE

1. Many materials in the laboratory can cause eye injury. To protect yourself from possible injury, wear safety goggles whenever you are working with chemicals, burners, or any substance that might get into your eyes. Never wear contact lenses in the laboratory.

2. Wear a laboratory apron or coat whenever you are working with chemicals or heated substances.

3. Tie back long hair to keep your hair away from any chemicals, burners and candles, or other laboratory equipment.

4. Remove or tie back any article of clothing or jewelry that can hang down and touch chemicals and flames. Do not wear sandals or open-toed shoes in the laboratory. Never walk around the laboratory barefoot or in stocking feet.

GENERAL SAFETY RULES

5. Be serious and alert when working in the laboratory. Never "horse around" in the laboratory.

6. Be prepared to work when you arrive in the laboratory. Be sure that you understand the procedure to be employed in any laboratory investigation and the possible hazards associated with it.

7. Read all directions for an investigation several times. Follow the directions exactly as they are written. If you are in doubt about any part of the investigation, ask your teacher for assistance.

8. Never perform activities that are not authorized by your teacher. Obtain permission before "experimenting" on your own.

9. Never handle any equipment unless you have specific permission.

10. Take extreme care not to spill any material in the laboratory. If spills occur, ask your teacher immediately about the proper cleanup procedure. Never simply pour chemicals or other substances into the sink or trash container.

11. Never eat or taste anything in the laboratory unless directed to do so. This includes food, drinks, candy, and gum, as well as chemicals. Wash your hands before and after performing every investigation.

12. Know the location and proper use of safety equipment such as the fire extinguisher, fire blanket, first-aid kit, safety shower, and eye-wash station.

13. Notify your teacher of any medical problems you may have, such as allergies or asthma.

14. Keep your laboratory area clean and free of unnecessary books, papers, and equipment.

FIRST AID

15. Report all accidents, no matter how minor, to your teacher immediately.

16. Learn what to do in case of specific accidents such as getting acid in your eyes or on your skin. (Rinse acids off your body with lots of water.)

17. Become aware of the location of the first-aid kit. But remember that your teacher should administer any required first aid due to injury. Or your teacher may send you to the school nurse or call a physician.

18. Know where and how to report an accident or fire. Find out the location of the fire extinguisher, phone, and fire alarm. Keep a list of important phone numbers such as the fire department and school nurse near the phone. Report any fires to your teacher at once.

HEATING AND FIRE SAFETY

19. Never use a heat source such as a candle or burner without wearing safety goggles.

20. Never heat a chemical you are not instructed to heat. A chemical that is harmless when cool can be dangerous when heated.

21. Maintain a clean work area and keep all materials away from flames.

22. Never reach across a flame.

23. Make sure you know how to light a Bunsen burner. (Your teacher will demonstrate the proper procedure for lighting a burner.) If the flame leaps out of a burner toward you, turn the gas off immediately. Do not touch the burner. It may be hot. And never leave a lighted burner unattended.

24. Point a test tube or bottle that is being heated away from you and others. Chemicals can splash or boil out of a heated test tube.

25. Never heat a liquid in a closed container. The expanding gases produced may blow the container apart, injuring you or others.

26. Never pick up a container that has been heated without first holding the back of your hand near it. If you can feel the heat on the back of your hand, the container may be too hot to handle. Use a clamp, tongs, or heat-resistant gloves when handling hot containers.

USING CHEMICALS SAFELY

27. Never mix chemicals for the "fun of it." You might produce a dangerous, possibly explosive, substance.
28. Never touch, taste, or smell a chemical that you do not know for a fact is harmless. Many chemicals are poisonous. If you are instructed to note the fumes in an investigation, gently wave your hand over the opening of a container and direct the fumes toward your nose. Do not inhale the fumes directly from the container.
29. Use only those chemicals needed in the investigation. Keep all lids closed when a chemical is not being used. Notify your teacher whenever chemicals are spilled.
30. Dispose of all chemicals as instructed by your teacher. To avoid contamination, never return chemicals to their original containers.
31. Be extra careful when working with acids or bases. Pour such chemicals over the sink, not over your work bench.
32. When diluting an acid, pour the acid into water. Never pour water into the acid.
33. Rinse any acids off your skin or clothing with water. Immediately notify your teacher of any acid spill.

USING GLASSWARE SAFELY

34. Never force glass tubing into a rubber stopper. A turning motion and lubricant will be helpful when inserting glass tubing into rubber stoppers or rubber tubing. Your teacher will demonstrate the proper way to insert glass tubing.
35. Never heat glassware that is not thoroughly dry. Use a wire screen to protect glassware from any flame.
36. Keep in mind that hot glassware will not appear hot. Never pick up glassware without first checking to see if it is hot.
37. If you are instructed to cut glass tubing, fire polish the ends immediately to remove sharp edges.
38. Never use broken or chipped glassware. If glassware breaks, notify your teacher and dispose of the glassware in the proper trash container.

39. Never eat or drink from laboratory glassware. Clean glassware thoroughly before putting it away.

USING SHARP INSTRUMENTS

40. Handle scalpels or razor blades with extreme care. Never cut material toward you; cut away from you.
41. Be careful when handling sharp, pointed objects such as scissors, pins, and dissecting probes.
42. Notify your teacher immediately if you cut yourself or receive a cut.

HANDLING LIVING ORGANISMS

43. No investigations that will cause pain, discomfort, or harm to mammals, birds, reptiles, fishes, and amphibians should be done in the classroom or at home.
44. Treat all living things with care and respect. Do not touch any organism in the classroom or laboratory unless given permission to do so. Many plants are poisonous or have thorns, and even tame animals may bite or scratch if alarmed.
45. Animals should be handled only if necessary. If an animal is excited or frightened, pregnant, feeding, or with its young, special handling is required.
46. Your teacher will instruct you as to how to handle each species that may be brought into the classroom.
47. Treat all microorganisms as if they were harmful. Use antiseptic procedure, as directed by your teacher, when working with microbes. Dispose of microbes as your teacher directs.
48. Clean your hands thoroughly after handling animals or the cage containing animals.
49. Wear gloves when handling small mammals. Report animal bites or stings to your teacher at once.

END-OF-INVESTIGATION RULES

50. When an investigation is completed, clean up your work area and return all equipment to its proper place.
51. Wash your hands after every investigation.
52. Turn off all burners before leaving the laboratory. Check that the gas line leading to the burner is off as well.

SAFETY CONTRACT

Once you have read all the safety information on pages 10–12 in the *Laboratory Manual* and are sure you understand all the rules, fill out the safety contract that follows. Signing this contract tells your teacher that you are aware of the rules of the laboratory. Return your signed contract to your teacher. You will not be allowed to work in the laboratory until you have returned your signed contract.

Safety Contract

I, _____ , have read the

Safety in the Biology Laboratory section on pages 9–12 in the *Biology*

Laboratory Manual. I understand its contents completely, and agree to follow

all the safety rules and guidelines that have been established in each of the

following areas:

(please check)

_____ Dress Code

_____ General Safety Rules

_____ First Aid

_____ Heating and Fire Safety

_____ Using Chemicals Safely

_____ Using Glassware Safely

_____ Using Sharp Instruments

_____ Handling Living Organisms

_____ End-of-Investigation Rules

Signature _____ Date _____

How to Use the Laboratory Manual

This is probably the most exciting time in history to be studying biology. The science of biology is progressing at a rapid rate; scientists are learning more about the nature of life and the living world than they ever have before. Biology is directly related to many of the most important news stories reported on television and radio and in the newspapers and magazines. The Alaskan oil spill; the AIDS epidemic; animal rights; genetic finger-printing; acid rain; the war against drugs; and efforts to save whales, elephants, pandas, and other endangered species are but a few of the current events and issues that can be better understood and evaluated by a person familiar with the principles of biology.

In order to gain a working knowledge of biological principles, you need to understand some of the processes that biologists and other scientists use to study and find answers to problems. The Laboratory Investigations and activities in the *Biology Laboratory Manual* provide an opportunity to learn about and practice processes and techniques used by scientists in their quest to increase human knowledge.

In each Laboratory Investigation, your objective is to solve a problem or problems using organized common sense, which is formally known as the scientific method. Each Laboratory Investigation follows a standard outline that will help you tackle the problem or problems in a systematic and organized manner.

Pre-Lab Discussion The Pre-Lab Discussion provides background information you will need to complete the investigation and ties the Laboratory Investigation to specific concepts discussed in the textbook. The Pre-Lab Discussion corresponds to an initial step in any scientific endeavor—gathering information about the topic you wish to study so that you can develop a hypothesis.

Problem This section presents a problem in the form of a question or series of questions. Your job during the Laboratory Investigation is to solve the problem based on your observations.

Materials A list of all materials required to conduct the investigation appears at the beginning of the investigation. The quantity of material for each investigation is indicated for individual students, pairs of students, or groups of students.

Safety The Safety section warns you of potential hazards before the investigation is begun and tells you about precautions you should take to decrease the risk of accidents. The safety symbols that are relevant to the Laboratory Investigation appear next to the title of the Safety section. They also appear next to certain steps of the Procedure.

Procedure This section provides a detailed step-by-step outline of the Laboratory Investigation procedure. Diagrams are included where necessary to further explain a technique or illustrate an experimental setup. The Procedure corresponds to the step of the scientific method known as testing the hypothesis.

Make sure you read the entire procedure carefully before you begin the investigation. Look for safety symbols and special instructions. If safety symbols appear next to a certain step in the Procedure, you should begin to follow the corresponding safety precaution(s) for that step and all following steps. **CAUTION** statements within the steps of the Procedure warn of possible hazards and indicate how accidents can be avoided. **Notes** in the Procedure provide special directions or explain techniques.

Observations In keeping with the traditional scientific method, you are asked to record your data in Observations in each investigation. Observations often include filling in data tables, graphing data, labeling diagrams, and drawing observed structures, as well as answering general questions related to the investigation.

Analysis and Conclusions Two steps of the traditional scientific method—analyzing data and forming a conclusion—are represented in this section. Using data gathered during the investigation and knowledge gained from the textbook and Pre-Lab Discussion, you are to analyze and interpret your experimental results.

Critical Thinking and Application This section challenges you to use critical-thinking skills to answer a variety of questions based on the Laboratory Investigation and your textbook reading.

Going Further Each Laboratory Investigation concludes with a section entitled Going Further. This section suggests additional activities for you to pursue on your own. Some of these are brief extensions of the Laboratory Investigation. Others involve library research. Still others suggest experimental research that you might perform with your teacher's permission.

Presenting Data

To seek answers to problems or questions they have about the world, scientists typically perform many experiments in the laboratory. In doing so, they observe physical characteristics and processes, select areas for study, and review the scientific literature to gain background information about the topic they are investigating. They then form hypotheses, test these hypotheses through controlled experiments, record and analyze data, and develop a conclusion about the correctness of the hypotheses. Finally, they report their findings in detail, giving enough information about their experimental procedure so that other scientists are able to replicate the experiments and verify the results.

The Laboratory Investigations in the *Biology Laboratory Manual* provide an opportunity for you to investigate scientific problems in the same manner as that of a typical scientist. As you perform these investigations, you will employ many of the techniques and steps of the scientific method a working scientist does. Some of the most important skills you will acquire are associated with the step of the scientific method known as recording and analyzing data. Three of these skills are creating and filling in data tables, making drawings, and finding averages. Another set of skills useful in presenting data is examined in the Laboratory Skills activity titled Using Graphing Skills.

It is important to record data precisely—even if the results of an investigation appear to be wrong. And it is extremely important to keep in mind that developing laboratory skills and data analysis skills is actually more valuable than simply arriving at the correct answers. If you analyze your data correctly—even if the data are not perfect—you will be learning to think as a scientist thinks. And that is the purpose of this laboratory manual and your experience in the biology laboratory.

DATA TABLES

When scientists conduct various experiments and do research, they collect vast amounts of information: for example, measurements, descriptions, and other observations. To communicate and interpret this information, they must record it in an organized fashion. Scientists use data tables for this purpose.

You will be responsible for completing data tables for many of the Laboratory Investigations. Each column in a data table has a heading. The column headings explain where particular data are to be placed. The completed data tables will help you interpret the information you collected and answer the questions found at the end of each Laboratory Investigation.

EXERCISE 1

Given the following information, complete Data Table 1. Then interpret the data and answer the five questions that follow.

Information: The following hair colors were found among three classes of students:

Class 1: brown—20
          black—1
          blond—4

Class 2: brown—18
          black—0
          blond—6

Class 3: brown—15
          black—4
          blond—5

Data Table 1

Hair Color	Class 1	Class 2	Class 3	Total
Brown	20	18	15	53
Black	1	0	4	5
Blond	4	6	15	25

1. What type of information is being gathered? Hair color among three classes of students.

2. Which hair color occurs most often? Brown.

3. From the information in the Data Table, can you give the number of boys with black hair? No. What information can you give about the number of students with black hair? Total of 5.

4. Which class has the most blond students? Class 2.

5. How many students made up the entire student population? 83.

EXERCISE 2

Given the following information, organize the data into a table. Use the blank table provided in Figure 1 to draw in the necessary columns and rows. Then interpret the data and answer the questions that follow.

Information: On an expedition around the world, several scientists collected the venom of various snakes. One of the tests that the scientists conducted determined the toxicity of the venom of each snake. Other data obtained by the scientists included the mortality percentage, or relative death rate, from the bites of various snakes.

The snakes observed were the (1) southern United States copperhead, (2) western diamondback rattlesnake, (3) eastern coral snake, (4) king cobra, (5) Indian krait, (6) European viper, (7) bushmaster, (8) fer-de-lance, (9) black-necked cobra, and (10) puff adder.

The mortality percentage of people bitten by the snakes varied from 100% to less than 1%. The scientists noted the mortality percentage for each of the snakes was (1) less than 1%, (2) 5–15%, (3) 5–20%, (4) greater than 40%, (5) 77%, (6) 1–5%, (7) usually 100%, (8) 10–20%, (9) 11–40%, and (10) 11–40%.

Answers will vary, but will probably resemble the following:

Snakes Observed	Mortality Percentage
Copperhead	less than 1%
Rattlesnake	5–15%
Coral snake	5–20%
King cobra	greater than 40%
Indian krait	77%
European viper	1–5%
Bushmaster	usually 100%
Fer-de-lance	10–20%
Black-necked cobra	11–40%
Puff adder	11–40%

Figure 1

1. Which snake's venom has the highest mortality rate. Bushmaster.

2. Which snake's venom has the lowest mortality rate? Southern United States copperhead.

3. From the information recorded, can you determine the snake whose venom works the most rapidly? The least rapidly? No. No.

4. Which two snakes' venom have the same mortality rate? Black-necked cobra and the puff adder.

5. How many snakes were observed? 10.

DRAWINGS

Laboratory drawings can be made using several methods, depending on a particular Laboratory Investigation. Some drawings are made in circles that represent the viewing field of a microscope or another type of magnifier. When completing these drawings, be sure to include the magnification at which you viewed the object. Other laboratory drawings are representative of entire organisms or parts of organisms. These drawings show the relative size, shape, and location of anatomical structures. When completing representative drawings, make the structures as clear and as accurate as possible.

Most laboratory drawings are labeled. Use the following guidelines to help make your laboratory drawings clear and legible.

- Use a ruler to draw label lines.
- Label lines should point to the center of the structure being labeled.
- Do not write on the label lines.
- Print all labels horizontally.
- Label the right-hand side of the drawing, if possible.
- Do not cross label lines.

EXERCISE 3

The following laboratory drawing was completed without using the guidelines for laboratory drawings. Circle those parts of the drawing that do not follow the guidelines. Then, on the lines provided, explain how these parts of the drawing should be done properly.

Figure 2   Onion Cells

Magnification should be inserted. Nucleus label should be printed. Cell wall label should appear at the end of the label line. Nuclear membrane label should be printed horizontally. Label lines should not cross.

AVERAGES

Occasionally you will be required to find the average of data gathered from an investigation. To find an average, add the items in the group together and then divide the total by the number of items. For example, if there were five students of different ages—12, 13, 14, 17, and 19—how would you find the average age of the group? Add the five ages together and divide the total by 5, which is the number of items (students) in the group. What is the average age of this group of students? Your answer should be 15 years old.

EXERCISE 4

In a garden the heights of six sunflowers are 135 cm, 162.5 cm, 180 cm, 235 cm, 185 cm, and 167.5 cm. What is the average height of the sunflowers?
177.5 cm.

EXERCISE 5

Find the average for the following group of data. Then use the results to answer the questions that follow.

   In an experiment on plant growth and overcrowding, plants of the following heights are in three equal-sized containers.

Flowerpot 1: 20 cm and 18 cm
Flowerpot 2: 12 cm, 10.8 cm, 11.2 cm, and 12.4 cm
Flowerpot 3: 7.5 cm, 8 cm, 6 cm, 6.2 cm, 5.8 cm, and 7.3 cm

1. What is the average height of the plants in each flowerpot? <u>Flowerpot 1: 19 cm;</u>
   <u>Flowerpot 2: 11.6 cm; Flowerpot 3: 6.8 cm.</u>

2. In which flowerpot did the plants grow the tallest? Explain. <u>The plants in Flowerpot 1 grew the</u>
   <u>tallest because they had more room to grow. Also the competition for food and water was less in Flowerpot</u>
   <u>1 than in the other flowerpots.</u>

EXERCISE 6

Find the averages for the following group of data. Express your answers to the nearest tenth.

   In a sample group of students, the number of breaths per minute was taken at rest and after exercise. The results were as follows:

At rest
Males: 10.1, 13, 12.5, 10.2, 13.1, 11.8
Females: 10.4, 13.0, 12.1, 11.9, 10.5, 12.8

After exercise
Males: 18.9, 23.7, 22.6, 21.3, 19.2, 20.6
Females: 25, 26.7, 29, 35.3, 33.1, 31.7

1. What is the average number of breaths per minute for males at rest? <u>11.8.</u>
   Females at rest? <u>11.8.</u>

2. What is the average number of breaths per minute for males after exercise? <u>21.1.</u>
   Females after exercise? <u>30.1.</u>

3. How many students make up the sample group? <u>12.</u>

4. What is the average number of breaths per minute for the entire group at rest? <u>11.8.</u>
   After exercise? <u>25.6.</u>

5. Do males or females take more breaths per minute at rest? <u>Neither, the results are the same.</u>
   After exercise? <u>Females.</u>

LABORATORY SKILLS 1

Recognizing Laboratory Safety

Pre-Lab Discussion

An important part of your study of biology will be working in a laboratory. In the laboratory, you and your classmates will learn biology by actively conducting and observing experiments. Working directly with living things will provide opportunities for you to better understand the principles of biology discussed in your textbook or talked about in class.

Most of the laboratory work you will do is quite safe. However, some laboratory equipment, chemicals, and specimens can be dangerous if handled improperly. Laboratory accidents do not just happen. They are caused by carelessness, improper handling of equipment and specimens, or inappropriate behavior.

In this investigation, you will learn how to prevent accidents and thus work safely in a laboratory. You will review some safety guidelines and become acquainted with the location and proper use of safety equipment in your classroom laboratory.

Problem

What are the proper practices for working safely in a biology laboratory?

Materials *(per group)*

Biology textbook
Laboratory safety equipment (for demonstration)

Procedure
Part A. Reviewing Laboratory Safety Rules and Symbols

1. Carefully read the list of laboratory safety rules listed on page 19 of your textbook.

2. Special symbols are used throughout this laboratory manual to call attention to investigations that require extra caution. Use page 19 in your textbook as a reference to describe what each symbol means by completing numbers 1 through 8 of Observations.

Part B. Location of Safety Equipment in Your Biology Laboratory

1. Your teacher will point out the location of the safety equipment in your classroom laboratory. Pay special attention to instructions for using such equipment as fire extinguishers, eyewash fountains, fire blankets, safety showers, and items in first-aid kits. Use the space provided under Observations to list the location of all safety equipment in your laboratory.

Be sure to show the location of all safety equipment in your laboratory. Also give instructions on its proper use. Guidelines pertaining to the use of special equipment, fire drill procedures, or penalties for misbehavior in lab might also be discussed at this time.

Observations
Part A. Reviewing Laboratory Safety Rules and Symbols

1. Student is working with glassware that can easily be broken.

2. Student is working with fire source.

3. Student should put on heat-resistant gloves to avoid burning his or her hands.

4. Student is working with chemicals that could be hazardous.

5. Student is performing an experiment in which the eyes and face should be protected by safety goggles.

6. Student is working with a sharp instrument.

7. Student is using electricity in the laboratory.

8. Student is working with live animals.

Part B. Location of Safety Equipment in Your Biology Laboratory

Student responses will depend on the specific safety features of your classroom laboratory.

_____

_____

_____

_____

_____

Analysis and Conclusions

Look at each of the following drawings and explain why the laboratory activities pictured are unsafe.

1. Safety goggles should always be worn whenever a person is working with chemicals, alcohol or Bunsen burners, or any substance that might get into the eyes.

_____

2. When heating a test tube, always point its open end away from yourself or others. Wear heat-resistant gloves when holding a heated object.

_____

_____

3. Never heat a liquid in a closed container. The expanding gases produced may blow the container apart.

_____

_____

4. Never eat or drink from laboratory glassware. The last material in the glassware may have been poisonous and traces of it may still remain in the glassware.

_____

Critical Thinking and Application

In each of the following situations, write "yes" if the proper safety procedures are being followed and "no" if they are not. Then give a reason for your answer.

1. Kathy cannot find matches to light her Bunsen burner. The student next to her picks up a lighted burner and says, "Here, you can use my flame to light your burner."

   No. A lighted Bunsen burner or alcohol burner should not be picked up or moved.

2. Jim notices that the electrical cord on his microscope is frayed near the plug. He takes the microscope to his teacher and asks for permission to use another one.

   Yes. Electrical appliances with frayed cords or broken insulation may present a hazard and should not be used.

3. The printed directions in the laboratory manual tell a student to pour a small amount of hydrochloric acid into a beaker. Alan puts on safety goggles before pouring the acid into the beaker. Yes. Safety goggles should always be worn when working with dangerous chemicals.

4. It is rather warm in the biology laboratory during a late spring day. Joanne slips off her shoes and walks barefoot to the sink to clean her glassware. No. Shoes should always be kept on while working in the laboratory.

5. While washing glassware, Mike splashes some water on Tim. To get even, Tim splashes him back. No. Horseplay or rough behavior is never acceptable in a laboratory.

Going Further

Many houseplants and some plants found in biology laboratories are poisonous. Use appropriate library resources to do research on several common poisonous plants. You might like to share your research with your classmates. You may prepare a booklet describing common poisonous plants. Use drawings or photographs to illustrate your booklet.

LABORATORY SKILLS 2

Time required: 40 minutes.

Identifying Laboratory Equipment

Pre-Lab Discussion

Scientists use a variety of tools to explore the world around them. Tools are very important in the advancement of science. The type of tools scientists use depends on the problems they are trying to solve. A scientist may use something as simple as a metric ruler to measure the length of a leaf. At another time, the same scientist may use a complex computer to analyze large amounts of data concerning hundreds of leaves.

In this investigation, you will identify pieces of laboratory equipment likely to be found in a biology laboratory. You will also learn the function of each piece of laboratory equipment.

Problem

What are the names and functions of some of the pieces of laboratory equipment found in a typical biology laboratory?

Materials *(per group)*

Equipment shown in this activity (for inspection and demonstration) Equipment should be set up for display before students begin the lab.

Safety 🔺 ▨

Handle all glassware carefully. Be careful when handling sharp instruments. Always handle the microscope with extreme care. You are responsible for its proper care and use. Use caution when handling glass slides as they can break easily and cut you. Note all safety alert symbols next to the steps in the Procedure and review the meanings of each symbol by referring to the symbol guide on page 10.

Procedure
Part A. Identifying Laboratory Equipment

1. Look at the drawings of the laboratory equipment. In Observations, write the letter of the drawing next to the name that correctly identifies it.

Part B. Identifying the Function of Certain Types of Laboratory Equipment

🔺 1. Carefully inspect the different types of laboratory equipment that have been set out by your
▨   teacher.

2. In Observations, identify the function of each piece of laboratory equipment.

Figure 1

Observations

Part A. Identifying Laboratory Equipment

__L__ **1.** beaker

__N__ **2.** Bunsen burner

__S__ **3.** coverslip

__C__ **4.** dissecting pins

__E__ **5.** dissecting scissors

__B__ **6.** dissecting tray

__O__ **7.** medicine dropper

__D__ **8.** forceps

__V__ **9.** funnel

__J__ **10.** graduated cylinder

__A__ **11.** hand lens

__Q__ **12.** microscope

__R__ **13.** glass slide

__T__ **14.** petri dish

__P__ **15.** pipette

__F__ **16.** probe

__W__ **17.** metric ruler

__H__ **18.** safety goggles

__G__ **19.** scalpel

__K__ **20.** test tube

__M__ **21.** test tube rack

__U__ **22.** thermometer

__I__ **23.** triple-beam balance

Part B. Identifying the Function of Certain Types of Laboratory Equipment

1. beaker Holds and measures liquids.

2. Bunsen burner Source of heat.

3. coverslip Covers material on a glass slide.

4. dissecting pins Hold specimen on dissecting tray.

5. dissecting scissors Cut specimen to be studied.

6. dissecting tray Holds a specimen for dissection.

7. medicine dropper Measures out drops of a liquid.

8. forceps Grasps small objects.

9. funnel Transfers liquid from one place to another; filters liquid using filter paper.

10. graduated cylinder Measures liquids.

11. hand lens Magnifies small objects.

12. microscope Makes an enlarged image of a very small object.

13. glass slide Provides a mounting surface for examination by microscope.

14. petri dish Shallow dish used for bacterial cultures.

15. pipette Draws fluid by suction.

16. probe Pointed object used to examine specimens.

17. metric ruler Measures length.

18. safety goggles _Protects eyes when using heat and chemicals._

19. scalpel _Small, sharp knife used to dissect specimens._

20. test tube _Holds liquids._

21. test tube rack _Holds test tubes._

22. thermometer _Measures temperature._

23. triple-beam balance _Measures mass._

Analysis and Conclusions

1. Which laboratory tools can be used to magnify small objects so they can be seen more easily?

   Microscope and hand lens.

2. Which laboratory tools are useful when looking at the internal organs of an earthworm?

   Dissecting tray, dissecting pins, dissecting scissors, forceps, probe, scalpel, and hand lens.

Critical Thinking and Application

1. What tool or tools would you use to make each of the following measurements?

   a. amount of milk in a small glass _Graduated cylinder._

   b. length of a sheet of paper _Metric ruler._

   c. temperature of a swimming pool _Thermometer._

   d. mass of a baseball _Triple-beam balance._

2. How do laboratory tools improve the observations made by a scientist?

   Certain laboratory tools can be used to extend the range and accuracy of the scientist's senses.

Going Further

Examine other types of laboratory equipment that you will be using in the biology laboratory. Try to determine the function of each piece of equipment.

You may wish to include items such as a hot plate, inoculating loop, Erlenmeyer or Florence flask, test tube holder, beaker tongs, depression slide, and stereomicroscope.

Name _____ Class _____ Date _____

Time required: 50 minutes.

Making Metric Measurements

Pre-Lab Discussion

In many biology investigations, precise measurements must be made before observations can be interpreted. For everyday measuring, we still use English units such as the inch, quart, and pound. For scientific work, and for everyday measuring in most countries, the International System of Units (SI) is used. Eventually our country will use SI units for everyday measuring too.

Like our money system, SI is a metric system. All units are based on the number 10. In the SI system it is easy to change one unit to another because all units are related to one another by a power of 10.

In this investigation, you will review SI units for measuring length, liquid volume, and mass. You will also learn how to use some common laboratory equipment used for measuring.

Problem

How are metric units of measurement used in the laboratory?

Materials *(per group)*

Meterstick	Coin
Metric ruler	Triple-beam balance
Small test tube	50-mL beaker
Rubber stopper	100-mL graduated cylinder

Safety ⚠

Handle all glassware carefully. Note all safety alert symbols next to the steps in the Procedure and review the meanings of each symbol by referring to the symbol guide on page 10.

Procedure
Part A. Measuring Length

1. Use the meterstick to measure the length, width, and height of your laboratory table or desk in meters. Record your measurements to the nearest centimeter in Data Table 1.

2. Convert the measurements from meters to centimeters and then to millimeters. Record these measurements in Data Table 1.

3. Use a metric ruler to measure the length of a small test tube and the diameter of its mouth in centimeters. Record your measurements to the nearest millimeter in Data Table 2.

4. Convert the measurements from centimeters to millimeters. Record these measurements in Data Table 2.

Part B. Measuring the Volume of a Liquid

1. Fill the test tube to the top with water. Pour the water into the graduated cylinder.

2. If the graduated cylinder is made of glass, the surface of the liquid will be slightly curved. This curved surface is called a *meniscus*. To measure the volume accurately, your eye must be at the same level as the bottom of the meniscus. This is the mark on the graduated cylinder you must read. See Figure 1. Record the volume of the water from the test tube to the nearest milliliter in Data Table 3.

Figure 1

Part C. Measuring Mass

Before beginning this part of the investigation, be sure that the riders on the triple-beam balance are moved all the way to the left and that the pointer rests on zero. See Figure 2.

1. Place the 50-mL beaker on the pan of the balance.

2. Move the rider on the middle beam one notch at a time until the pointer drops below zero. Move the rider back one notch.

Figure 2

3. Move the rider on the back beam one notch at a time until the pointer again drops below zero. Move the rider back one notch.

4. Slide the rider along the front beam until the pointer stops at zero. The mass of the object is equal to the sum of the readings on the three beams.

5. Record the mass of the beaker to the nearest tenth of a gram in Data Table 4.

6. Remove the beaker and repeat steps 2 through 5 using the rubber stopper and then the coin.

7. Use the graduated cylinder to place exactly 40 mL of water in the beaker. Determine the combined mass of the beaker and water. Record this mass to the nearest tenth of a gram in Data Table 4.

Observations

Data Table 1

Lab Table Measurements			
Dimension	m	cm	mm
Length			
Width		Answers will vary.	
Height			

Data Table 2

Test Tube Measurements		
Dimension	cm	mm
Length	Answers will vary.	
Diameter of mouth		

Data Table 3

Measurement of Volume	
Object	mL
Water in test tube	Answers will vary.

Data Table 4

Measurement of Mass	
Object	g
50-mL beaker	
Rubber stopper	Answers will vary.
Coin	
50-mL beaker plus 40 mL of water	

Analysis and Conclusions

1. How do you convert meters to centimeters? Centimeters to millimeters?

To convert meters to centimeters, multiply by 100. To convert centimeters to millimeters, multiply by 10.

2. What is the largest volume of a liquid your graduated cylinder can measure?

100 mL.

3. What is the smallest volume of a liquid your graduated cylinder can measure?

1 mL.

4. What is the largest mass of an object your balance can measure? 610 g.

5. What is the smallest mass of an object your balance can measure? 0.1 g.

6. What is the mass of 40 mL of water? 40 g.

Critical Thinking and Application

1. Why is it easier to convert meters to centimeters or millimeters than it is to convert miles to yards or feet? All conversions in the metric system are based on multiples of 10. In the English system, there is no uniform relationship between units. For example, a yard is equal to 3 feet or 36 inches.

2. How would you find the mass of a certain amount of water that you poured into a paper cup? First find the mass of the paper cup. Then pour the water into the paper cup and find their combined mass. Subtract the mass of the paper cup from the combined mass.

3. In this investigation you found the mass of 40 mL of water. Based on your observations, what is the mass of 1 mL of water? 1 mL of water has a mass of 1 g.

Going Further

If other types of laboratory balances are available, such as an electronic balance or a double-pan balance, use them to find the masses of several different objects. Compare the accuracy of the different balances.

LABORATORY SKILLS 4

Applying the Scientific Method

Time required: 30 minutes and a
15-minute observation period
after one week.

Pre-Lab Discussion

The scientific method is a procedure used to gather information and test ideas. Scientists use the scientific method to answer questions about life and living organisms. Experimentation is an important part of the scientific method. In order to ensure that the results of an experiment are due to the variable being tested, a scientist must have both an experimental setup and a control setup. The experimental setup contains the variable that is being tested. The control setup is exactly like the experimental setup except it does not contain the variable being tested.

In this investigation, you will form a hypothesis, test it, and draw a conclusion based on your observations.

Problem

Is light necessary for the sprouting of a potato?

Materials *(per group)*

1 medium-sized potato
2 plastic bags with twist ties
Knife
2 paper towels

Have students wash the potato with a brush because some potatoes have a wax coating that can inhibit sprout growth.

Safety ▨

Put on a laboratory apron if one is available. Be careful when handling sharp instruments. Note all safety alert symbols next to the steps in the Procedure and review the meanings of each symbol by referring to the symbol guide on page 10.

Procedure

1. With the members of your group, discuss whether or not the potato needs light to sprout. Based on your discussion, record your hypothesis in Observations.

▨ 2. Carefully cut the potato in half lengthwise. Count the number of eyes on the potato half to be put in the dark and the half to be put in the light. Record this in Data Table 1.

3. Fold each paper towel repeatedly until you have a rectangle about the same size as your potato halves. Moisten the towels with water. Place a folded paper towel in each plastic bag.

4. Place a potato half in each plastic bag with the cut surface on the paper towel. Tie each bag with a twist tie. See Figure 1.

Figure 1

5. Place one of the plastic bags in a place that receives light. Place the other plastic bag in a dark place. Be sure that the potato halves remain on top of the paper towels and that both potato halves are kept at the same temperature.

6. After one week, open each plastic bag and count the number of sprouts. Record this information in Data Table 2.

7. To calculate the percentage of eyes sprouting, divide the number of sprouts by the number of eyes and multiply the result by 100. Record your answers in Data Table 3.

8. Have one person from your group go to the chalkboard to record your group's data in the table that has been drawn by your teacher.

Observations

Hypothesis Hypotheses will vary. _____

Data Table 1

Number of Eyes	
Potato in dark	Answers will vary.
Potato in light	

Data Table 2

Number of Sprouts	
Potato in dark	Answers will vary.
Potato in light	

Data Table 3

Percentage of Eyes Sprouting	
Potato in dark	Answers will vary.
Potato in light	

Analysis and Conclusions

1. Did the most sprouts grow in the light or in the dark? Potato halves in the dark should show a greater percentage of sprouts.

2. What was the control setup in this investigation? The potato halves in the dark because potatoes normally grow under ground in the absence of light.

3. What was the experimental setup in this investigation? The potato halves exposed to the light.

4. What conclusion can you draw from this investigation? Light inhibits sprouting in potatoes.

5. How does your hypothesis compare with your results after completing the investigation?
Answers will vary depending on the student's original hypothesis.

Critical Thinking and Application

1. Why was it important to keep both the control setup and the experimental setup at the same temperature throughout the experiment? By keeping the temperature constant, you can be sure that the results of the experimental setup were due only to the absence or presence of light and not to differences in temperature.

2. Why were the plastic bags sealed? To ensure that no other factors would influence the results of the experiment.

3. Why was it necessary to keep the potato halves on moist paper towels?
Water is necessary for plant growth.

Going Further

Devise an experiment to see if another variable, such as temperature or water, affects the number of sprouts a potato produces.

LABORATORY SKILLS 5

Time required: 50 minutes.

Using a Compound Light Microscope

Pre-Lab Discussion

Many objects are too small to be seen by the eye alone. They can be seen, however, with the use of an instrument that magnifies, or visually enlarges, the object. One such instrument, which is of great importance to biologists and other scientists, is the compound light microscope. A compound light microscope consists of a light source or mirror that illuminates the object to be observed, an objective lens that magnifies the image of the object, and an eyepiece (ocular lens) that further magnifies the image of the object and projects it into the viewer's eye.

Objects, or specimens, to be observed under a microscope are generally prepared in one of two ways. Prepared or permanent slides are made to last a long time. They are usually purchased from biological supply houses. Temporary or wet mount slides are made to last only a short time—usually one laboratory period.

The microscope is an expensive precision instrument that requires special care and handling. In this investigation, you will learn the parts of a compound light microscope, the functions of those parts, and the proper use and care of the microscope. You will also learn the technique of preparing wet-mount slides.

Problem

What is the proper use of a compound light microscope?

Materials *(per group)*

Compound light microscope
Prepared glass slide
Lens paper
Soft cloth (or cheesecloth)
Newspaper

Glass slide
Coverslip
Dissecting needle
Medicine dropper
Scissors

Before class, make sure all microscopes are in correct storage position with a cover on, with the lowest-power objective in place, and with the lowest-power objective as near to the stage as possible.

Safety ⚠ ▨ ◀▮▸

Put on a laboratory apron if one is available. Always handle the microscope with extreme care. You are responsible for its proper care and use. Use caution when handling glass slides as they can break easily and cut you. Never use direct sunlight as a light source for a compound light microscope. The sunlight reflecting off the mirror up through the microscope could damage your eye. Be careful when handling sharp instruments. Observe proper laboratory procedures when using electrical equipment. Note all safety alert symbols next to the steps in the Procedure and review the meanings of each symbol by referring to the symbol guide on page 10.

Procedure
Part A. Care of the Compound Light Microscope; Parts of the Compound Light Microscope

1. Figure 1 shows the proper way to carry a microscope. Always carry the microscope with both hands. Grasp the arm of the microscope with one hand and place your other hand under the base. Always hold the microscope in an upright position so that the eyepiece cannot fall out. Take a microscope and place it on your worktable or desk at least 10 cm from the edge. Position the microscope with the arm facing you.

Figure 1

2. Study the labeled drawings of the microscopes in Figure 2. Identify the following parts on your microscope: eyepiece, arm, coarse adjustment, fine adjustment, revolving nosepiece, low-power objective, high-power objective, stage, stage clips, stage opening, diaphragm, light source (mirror or lamp), and base. Review the function of each part of the microscope in Figure 2. Do not proceed with this investigation until you can identify all the parts of your microscope and describe the function of each part. **Note:** *Tell your teacher at once if you find any parts of the microscope missing or damaged.*

Figure 2

3. Notice the numbers etched on the objectives and on the eyepiece. Each number is followed by an "X" that means "times." For example, the low-power objective may have the number "10X" on its side, as shown in Figure 3. That objective magnifies an object 10 times its normal size. Record the magnifications of your microscope in the Data Table. The total magnification of a microscope is calculated by multiplying the magnification of the objective by the magnification of the eyepiece. For example:

$$\begin{array}{ccc} \text{magnification} & \text{magnification} & \text{total} \\ \text{of low-power} \quad \text{x} & \text{of eyepiece} \quad = & \text{magnification} \\ \text{objective} & & \end{array}$$

$$10X \quad\quad \text{x} \quad\quad 10X \quad\quad = \quad\quad 100X$$

Use the above formula to complete the Data Table.

Figure 3

4. Before you use the microscope, clean the lenses of the objectives and eyepiece with lens paper. **Note:** *To avoid scratching the lenses, never clean or wipe them with anything other than lens paper. Use a new piece of lens paper on each lens you clean. Never touch a lens with your finger. The oils on your skin may attract dust or lint that could scratch the lens.*

5. Use a soft cloth or a piece of cheesecloth to wipe the stage and the mirror or light.

Part B. Use of a Compound Light Microscope

1. Look at the microscope from the side as shown in Figure 4. Locate the coarse adjustment knob which moves the objectives up and down. Practice moving the coarse adjustment knob to see how it moves its objectives with each turn.

2. Turn the coarse adjustment so that the low-power objective is positioned about 3 cm from the stage. Locate the revolving nosepiece. Turn the nosepiece until you hear the high-power objective click into position. See Figure 5. When an objective clicks into position, it is in the proper alignment for light to pass from the light source through the objective into the viewer's eye. Now turn the nosepiece until the low-power objective clicks back into position. **Note:** *Always look at the microscope from the side when moving an objective so that the microscope does not hit or damage the slide.*

Figure 4

Figure 5

3. If your microscope has an electric light source, plug in the cord and turn on the light. If your microscope has a mirror, turn the mirror toward a light source such as a desk lamp or window. **CAUTION:** *Never use the sun as a direct source of light.* Look through the eyepiece. Adjust the diaphragm to permit sufficient light to enter the microscope. The white circle of light you see is the field of view. If your microscope has a mirror, move the mirror until the field of view is evenly illuminated.

4. Place a prepared slide on the stage so that it is centered over the stage opening. Use the stage clips to hold the slide in position. Turn the low-power objective into place. Look at the microscope from the side and turn the coarse adjustment so that the low-power objective is as close as possible to the stage without touching it.

5. Look through the eyepiece and turn the coarse adjustment to move the low-power objective away from the stage until the object comes into focus. To avoid eyestrain, keep both eyes open while looking through a microscope. **CAUTION:** *To avoid moving the objective into the slide, never lower the objective toward the stage while looking through the eyepiece.*

6. Turn the fine adjustment to bring the object into sharp focus. You may wish to move the diaphragm to adjust the amount of light so that you can see the object more clearly. In the appropriate place in Observations, draw what you see through the microscope. Note the magnification.

7. Look at the microscope from the side and rotate the nosepiece until the high-power objective clicks into position. Look through the eyepiece. Turn the fine adjustment to bring the object on the slide into focus. **CAUTION:** *Never use the coarse adjustment when focusing the high-power objective lens. This could break your slide or damage the lens.* In the appropriate place in Observations, draw what you see through the microscope. Note the magnification.

8. Remove the slide. Move the low-power objective into position.

Part C. Preparing a Wet Mount

1. Use a pair of scissors to cut a letter "e" from a piece of newspaper. Cut out the smallest letter "e" you can find. Position the "e" on the center of a clean glass slide.

2. Use a medicine dropper to place one drop of water on the cut piece of newspaper. See Figure 6.

Figure 6

3. Hold a clean coverslip in your fingers as shown in Figure 6. Make sure the bottom edge of the coverslip is in the drop of water. Use a dissecting needle to slowly lower the coverslip onto the wet newspaper. Slowly lowering the coverslip prevents air bubbles from being trapped between the slide and the coverslip. The type of slide you have just made is called a wet mount. Practice the technique of making a wet mount until you can do so without trapping air bubbles on the slide.

4. Center the wet mount of the letter "e" on the stage with the "e" in its normal upright position. **Note:** *Make sure the bottom of the slide is dry before you place it on the stage.* Turn the low-power objective into position and bring the letter "e" into focus. In the appropriate place in Observations, draw the letter "e" as seen through the microscope. Note the magnification.

5. Turn the high-power objective into position and bring the letter "e" into focus. In the appropriate place in Observations, draw the letter "e" as seen through the microscope. Note the magnification.

6. Rotate the nosepiece until the low-power objective clicks back into position and bring the letter "e" into focus. While looking through the eyepiece, move the slide to the left. Notice the way the letter seems to move. Now move the slide to the right. Again notice the way the letter seems to move. Move the slide up and observe the direction the letter moves. Move the slide down and observe the direction the letter moves.

7. Take apart the wet mount. Clean the slide and coverslip with soap and water. Carefully dry the slide and coverslip with paper towels and return them to their boxes.

8. Rotate the low-power objective into position and use the coarse adjustment to place it as close to the stage as possible without touching. Carefully pick up the microscope and return it to its storage area. A student's inability to bring an object into focus may have one or more causes: dirty lenses on ocular or objectives, dirty slide, slide not centered over stage opening, incorrect amount of light, mirror improperly positioned, objective not properly aligned, objective raised too high, or objective not raised high enough.

Observations

1. Label the parts of the microscope shown below.

Coarse adjustment

Fine adjustment

Stage clip

Base

Revolving nosepiece

Mirror

2. Fill in the magnification of each objective and the eyepiece of your microscope. To determine the total magnification, multiply the magnification of each objective by the magnification of the eyepiece.

Data Table

Objective	Magnification of Objective	Magnification of Eyepiece	Total Magnification
Low power	10X	10X	100X
High power	43X	10X	430X
Other		Answers will vary.	

3. Make a detailed drawing of the object on your prepared slide as seen under low power and high power.

Low-power
magnification

_____

High-power
magnification

_____

4. Make a detailed drawing of the letter "e" as seen under low power and high power.

Low-power
magnification

_____

High-power
magnification

_____

Analysis and Conclusions

1. Why do you place one hand under the base of the microscope as you carry it?

To support the weight of the microscope and to prevent dropping it.

_____

_____

2. What kind of light source do you have on your microscope? Answers will vary with the type of

microscope used.

_____

3. How is the image of an object seen through the high-power objective different from the image

seen through the low-power objective? The high-power objective will have a narrower field of view,

but the image seen through it will be larger and contain more detail than an image seen through the low-

power objective.

_____

4. How does the letter "e" as seen through the microscope differ from the way an "e" normally

appears? The letter "e" is upside down and backward. _____

_____

_____

5. When you move the slide to the left, in what direction does the image appear to move?

The image appears to move to the right. _____

_____

6. When you move the slide up, in what direction does the image appear to move?

The image appears to move down. _____

_____

Critical Thinking and Application

1. Explain why a specimen to be viewed under the microscope must be thin.

Light must be able to pass through the specimen in order for you to see microscopic detail. The light is

reflected from the mirror below the stage, through the specimen, the objective lens, the body of the

microscope, and the eyepiece to your eye.

2. Why should a glass slide and a coverslip be held by their edges?

To prevent fingerprints and smudges from getting on them, thus interfering with the view of the object under

the microscope.

3. Why should you use a piece of lens paper only once? Lens paper that has been used may collect

dust that could scratch the next lens on which it is used.

_____

4. Why is it a good idea to place your microscope at least 10 cm from the edge of the table?

To keep from knocking the microscope off the table.

5. Suppose you were observing an organism through the microscope and noticed that it moved toward the bottom of the slide and then it moved to the right. What does this tell you about the actual movement of the organism? Specimens viewed through the microscope appear to move in a direction exactly opposite to that of their actual movement on the slide. In this case, the organism actually moved toward the top of the slide and then to the left.

Going Further

1. Obtain some common objects, such as a piece of cotton, a piece of nylon, a small piece of a color photograph from a magazine, and so on. View each object under the low-power and high-power objectives of the microscope. Make a drawing for each object. Describe the appearance of the objects when viewed under a microscope. How did each object differ from the way you see it with the unaided eye?

2. Use an appropriate resource to investigate the development of the microscope and the advancements that have been made in microscope technology. Write a report or make an oral presentation as directed by your teacher.

LABORATORY SKILLS 6

Using the Bunsen Burner

Pre-Lab Discussion

Sometimes a biologist needs to heat materials. In the laboratory, one of the most efficient ways to do this is to use a Bunsen burner. Bunsen burners are made in a variety of designs. In every one, however, a mixture of air and gas is burned. In most Bunsen burners, the amounts of air and gas can be controlled. In some laboratories, electric hot plates or portable liquid-petroleum burners are used instead of Bunsen burners.

In this investigation, you will learn the parts of the Bunsen burner and their functions. You will also learn how to use the Bunsen burner safely in the laboratory.

Problem

How can the Bunsen burner be safely used to heat materials in the laboratory?

Materials *(per group)*

Bunsen burner
Ring stand
2 250-mL beakers
Wire gauze
Metric ruler
Heat-resistant gloves

Beaker tongs
Iron ring
100-mL graduated cylinder
Flint striker or matches
Clock with second hand

Safety 　🔥 🥽 🧤 👁

Put on a laboratory apron if one is available. Put on safety goggles. Handle all glassware carefully. Tie back loose hair and clothing when using the Bunsen burner. Use extreme care when working with heated equipment or materials to avoid burns. Note all safety alert symbols next to the steps in the Procedure and review the meanings of each symbol by referring to the symbol guide on page 10.

Procedure

1. Examine your burner when it is *not* connected to the gas outlet. If your burner is the type that can easily be taken apart, unscrew the barrel from the base and locate the parts shown in Figure 1. As you examine the parts, think about their functions.

   - The *barrel* is the area where the air and gas mix.

   - The *collar* can be turned to adjust the intake of air. If you turn the collar so that the holes are larger, more air will be drawn into the barrel.

- The *air intake openings* are the holes in the collar through which air is drawn in.
- The *base* supports the burner so that it does not tip over.
- The *gas intake tube* brings the supply of gas from the outlet to the burner.
- The *spud* is the small opening through which the gas flows. The small opening causes the gas to enter with great speed.

Figure 1

2. Reassemble the Bunsen burner if necessary and connect the gas intake tube to the gas outlet. **CAUTION:** *Put on safety goggles.* Make sure that the burner is placed away from flammable materials.

3. Adjust the collar so that the air intake openings are half open. If you use a match to light the burner, light the match and hold it about 2 cm above and just to the right of the barrel. Hold the match in this position while you open the gas outlet valve slowly until it is fully open. **CAUTION:** *To avoid burns on your hands, always use extreme care when handling lighted matches.* The burner can also be turned off by using the valve. Do not lean over the burner when lighting it.

4. If you use a flint striker to light the burner, hold the striker in the same position you would hold a lighted match. To light the burner with a striker, you must produce a spark at the same time you open the gas valve.

5. Practice lighting the burner several times. Every member of your group should be given the opportunity to light the burner.

6. The most efficient and hottest flame is blue in color and has distinct regions as shown in Figure 2. Adjust the collar so that the flame is blue and a pale blue inner cone is visible.

Figure 2

7. Adjust the flow of gas until the flame is about 6 cm high. Some burners have a valve in the base to regulate the flow of gas, but the flow of gas can always be adjusted at the gas outlet valve. After adjusting the flow of gas, shut off the burner. Leave your safety goggles on for the remainder of the investigation.

🔺 8. Arrange the apparatus as pictured in Figure 3.

Figure 3

9. Adjust the iron ring so that the bottom of the beaker is about 2 cm above the mouth of the burner barrel. Measure 100 mL of water in the graduated cylinder and pour it into one of the beakers.

10. Light the burner and heat the beaker of water. The bottom of the beaker should just be touching the top of the inner cone of the flame. In the Data Table, record the time it takes for the water to start boiling rapidly. Using the beaker tongs, carefully remove the beaker and pour out the water.

🖐 11. Repeat the procedure with the other beaker at a height of about 8 cm above the mouth of the barrel. **CAUTION:** *Be very careful when raising the iron ring. If it is too warm to touch, use heat-resistant gloves.* In the Data Table, record the time it takes for the water to start boiling rapidly at this height. **Note:** *Be sure that the starting temperature of the water is the same in each trial.*

In steps 10 and 11, caution students to ignore the appearance of *small* bubbles and wait until rapid boiling begins.

Observations

Data Table

Height Above Burner (cm)	Time to Boil (min)
2	Answers will vary.
8	Answers will vary.

Analysis and Conclusions

1. What would happen if the air intake openings were made very small? The gas would not burn as

well. The flame would become yellow. The flame would not be as hot.

2. If the burner does not light after the gas outlet valve is opened, what might be wrong?

The spud or gas intake tube might be clogged.

3. Where is the hottest part of the flame of a Bunsen burner? At a point just above the inner blue

cone.

4. At what height, 2 cm or 8 cm, did the water come to a rapid boil faster?

The water should come to a rapid boil faster at a height of 2 cm.

5. Why is it important to make sure that the volume of water and the starting temperature are

the same in each trial? The amount of heat given off by the flame must be the only variable in the

experiment.

Critical Thinking and Application

1. Why is it important to wear safety goggles when using a Bunsen burner?

To protect the eyes from an injury that might occur as a substance or object reacts to the heat being

applied to it.

2. Why is it important to tie back loose hair and clothing when using a Bunsen burner?

To prevent hair and clothing from catching on fire as they brush past a flame.

3. In addition to the items mentioned in questions 1 and 2, what other safety precautions should

be followed before lighting a Bunsen burner? Students should know the locations of fire extinguishers,

fire blankets, emergency showers, and emergency shutoff valves, and how to use them. Students should

also know the locations of fire alarms and emergency exits.

4. State two reasons why a blue flame is preferred over a yellow flame in a Bunsen burner.

A blue flame burns hotter and cleaner than a yellow flame.

Going Further

Test the ability of different kinds of laboratory burners, such as a hot plate, to heat water to boiling. Determine if there is a difference in the efficiency with which different burners are able to heat objects.

LABORATORY SKILLS 7

Time required: 40 minutes.

Preparing Laboratory Solutions

Pre-Lab Discussion

A *solution* is a type of mixture in which one substance dissolves in another. In a solution, the substance that is dissolved is called the *solute*. The substance that does the dissolving is called the *solvent*. The most common solvent is water. Most solutions cannot easily be separated by simple physical means such as filtering.

Solutions in which water is the solvent, or *aqueous solutions,* are important to all types of living organisms. Marine microorganisms spend their entire lives in the ocean, an aqueous solution of water, salt, and other substances. Most of the nutrients needed by plants are in aqueous solution in moist soil. Plasma, the liquid part of the blood, is an aqueous solution containing dissolved nutrients and gases.

In this investigation, you will learn some of the techniques used to prepare laboratory solutions. You will also learn some of the proper uses of a triple-beam balance and a filtering apparatus.

Problem

What are some of the different ways in which laboratory solutions can be prepared?

Materials *(per group)*

Sodium chloride	Weighing paper	Filter paper or a piece of paper towel can be used as weighing paper.
10 mL of red food coloring	Triple-beam balance	
100-mL graduated cylinder	Scoop	
Filter paper	10-mL graduated cylinder	
Funnel	Ring stand	
2 100-mL beakers	Iron ring	

Safety 🔺 📷 👁 🥽

Put on a laboratory apron if one is available. Put on safety goggles. Handle all glassware carefully. Always use special caution when working with laboratory chemicals, as they may irritate the skin or cause staining of the skin or clothing. Never touch or taste any chemical unless instructed to do so. Note all safety alert symbols next to the steps in the Procedure and review the meanings of each symbol by referring to the symbol guide on page 10.

Procedure

Part A. Preparing the Weight/Volume Solution

To prepare a solution of a given percentage, dissolve the number of grams of solid solute equal to the percentage in enough water to make 100 mL of the solution. Use the following steps to prepare a 5% sodium chloride solution.

1. Place a piece of weighing paper on the pan of the triple-beam balance and find its mass.

2. Add exactly 5 g to the value of the mass of the weighing paper and move the riders of the balance to this number.

3. Using the scoop, add a small amount of sodium chloride at a time to the paper on the balance until the pointer rests on zero.

 4. Add the 5 grams of sodium chloride to the 100-mL graduated cylinder.

5. Add enough water to bring the volume of the solution to 100 mL. Answer question 1 in Observations.

6. Dispose of this solution according to your teacher's instructions.

Part B. Preparing a Volume/Volume Solution

To prepare a solution of a given percentage, dissolve the number of milliliters of liquid solute equal to the percentage in enough solvent to make 100 mL of the solution. Use the following steps to prepare a 10% colored water solution.

 1. Measure 10 mL of red food coloring in the small graduated cylinder and pour it into the large graduated cylinder. **CAUTION:** *Use special caution when working with red food coloring to avoid staining your hands or clothing.*

2. Add enough water to the large graduated cylinder to bring the volume to 100 mL. Answer question 2 in Observations.

3. Keep this solution for use in Part C of this investigation.

Part C. Reducing the Concentration of a Solution

To reduce the concentration of an existing solution, pour the number of milliliters of the existing solution that is equal to the percentage of the new concentration into a graduated cylinder. Add enough solvent to bring the volume in milliliters to an amount equal to the percentage of the original solution. Use the following steps to reduce a 10% colored water solution to a 1% solution.

 1. Pour the 10% colored water solution you prepared in Part B into a 100-mL beaker.

2. Measure 1 mL of the 10% solution in the small graduated cylinder.

3. Add enough water to the graduated cylinder to bring the volume to 10 mL. Answer question 3 in Observations.

4. Dispose of the 1% solution in the graduated cylinder according to your teacher's instructions. Keep the 10% solution in the beaker for use in Part D of this investigation.

Part D. Filtering

1. Prepare filter paper as shown in Figure 1. Fold a circle of filter paper across the middle. Fold the resulting half-circle to form a quarter-circle. Open the folded paper into a cone, leaving a triple layer on one side and a single layer on the other.

 2. Support a funnel as shown in Figure 2. Place the cone of the filter paper in the funnel and wet the paper so that it adheres smoothly to the walls of the funnel. Set a clean beaker beneath the funnel in such a way that the stem of the funnel touches the side of the beaker.

 3. Pour the 10% colored water solution prepared in Part B slowly into the funnel. Do not let the mixture overflow the filter paper. As the mixture filters through the filter paper, record your observations in the Data Table.

Figure 1   **Figure 2**

4. After all of the solution has passed through the filter paper into the beaker, observe the appearance of the filter paper. Record your observations in the Data Table.

5. Carefully remove the filter paper from the funnel and dispose of it and the colored water solution according to your teacher's instructions.

Observations

Data Table

Appearance of Liquid Before Filtering	Appearance of Liquid After Filtering	Appearance of Filter Paper After Filtering
Red	Red	No materials collected.

1. What happens to the sodium chloride crystals as water is mixed with them?

The sodium chloride crystals dissolve and disappear as the water is mixed with them.

2. What happens to the red food coloring as water is mixed with it? The red food coloring is diluted

by the water and its color changes to a lighter red.   .

3. What differences do you observe between the 10% and 1% solutions of colored water?

The 10% solution of colored water appears darker in color than the 1% solution.

Analysis and Conclusions

1. Why is a chemical placed on a piece of weighing paper instead of directly on the pan of the

balance when its mass is being measured? If a chemical were placed directly on the pan of a triple-

beam balance, it could react with the metal pan or become contaminated by another substance that had

previously been placed on the pan.

2. Relate the colors of the 10% and 1% colored water solutions to the number of solute molecules each solution contains. The darker 10% solution contains a greater number of solute molecules per unit of volume than the lighter 1% solution.

3. Was the filter paper successful in separating the two parts of the red food coloring solution? Use your observations to support your answer. No. The solution remained red after filtering, indicating that both the red food color molecules and water molecules went through the filter paper.

Critical Thinking and Application

1. Describe the procedure needed to prepare a 30% sugar solution. Use a triple-beam balance to measure 30 g of sugar. Add the 30 g of sugar to a graduated cylinder. Add water to the 100-mL mark of the graduated cylinder.

2. Describe the procedure needed to produce a 20% liquid bleach solution. Add 20 mL liquid bleach to a graduated cylinder. Add water to the 100-mL mark of the graduated cylinder.

3. Describe the procedure needed to reduce an 80% starch solution to a 20% solution. Pour 20 mL of 80% starch solution into a graduated cylinder. Add enough water to bring the volume to 80 mL of 20% starch solution.

Going Further

Solution concentrations can be expressed in a number of different ways, including molarity (the number of moles of solute per liter of solution) and molality (the number of moles of solute per kilogram of solvent). Using a chemistry reference text, describe the procedures used to prepare 1 molar and 1 molal concentrations.

LABORATORY SKILLS 8

Time required: 30 minutes.

Using Graphing Skills

Pre-Lab Discussion

Recorded data can be plotted on a graph. A graph is a pictorial representation of information recorded in a data table. It is used to show a relationship between two or more different factors. Two common types of graphs are line graphs and bar graphs.

In this investigation, you will interpret and construct a bar graph and a line graph.

Problem

How do you correctly interpret and construct a line graph and a bar graph?

Materials

No special materials needed

Procedure
Part A. Interpreting Graphs

1. The type of graph that best shows the relationship between two variables is the line graph. A line graph has one or more lines connecting a series of points. See Figure 1. Along the horizontal axis, or x–axis, you will find the most consistent variable in the experiment. Along the vertical axis, or y-axis, you will find the other variable.

Line Graph

Numerical scale

Numerical scale

Figure 1

2. Use the line graph in Figure 2 to answer questions 1 through 6 in Observations.

Figure 2

3. A bar graph is another way of showing relationships between variables. A bar graph also contains an x-axis and a y-axis. But instead of points, a bar graph uses a series of columns to display data. See Figure 3. On some bar graphs, the x-axis has labels rather than a numerical scale. This type of bar graph is used only to show comparisons.

Figure 3

4. Use the bar graph in Figure 4 to answer questions 7 through 11 in Observations.

Figure 4

Part B. Constructing Graphs

1. When plotting data on a graph, you must decide which variable to place along the x-axis and which variable to place along the y-axis. Label the axes of your graph accordingly. Then you must decide on the scale of each axis; that is, how much each unit along the axis represents. Scales should be chosen to make the graph as large as possible within the limits of the paper and still include the largest item of data. If the scale unit is too large, your graph will be cramped into a small area and will be hard to read and interpret. If the scale unit is too small, the graph will run off the paper. Scale units should also be selected for ease of locating points on the graph. Multiples of 1, 2, 5, or 10 are easiest to work with.

2. Use the information recorded in Data Table 1 to construct a line graph on the grid provided in number 12 of Observations. You should label each axis, mark an appropriate scale on each axis, plot the data, connect the points, and give your graph a title.

3. Use the information recorded in Data Table 2 to construct a bar graph on the grid provided in number 13 of Observations. You should label each axis, mark an appropriate scale on each axis, plot the data, darken the columns of the graph, and give your graph a title.

Observations

Part A. Interpreting Graphs

Use the line graph in Figure 2 to answer questions 1 through 6.

1. Which plant grew the tallest? <u>Plant 2.</u>

2. How many plants grew to be at least 6 cm tall? <u>All the plants.</u>

3. Which plant grew the fastest in the first five days? <u>Plant 3.</u>

4. Which line represents plant 2? <u>The dotted line.</u>

5. After 10 days, how much had plant 3 grown? <u>6 cm.</u>

6. How long did it take for plant 1 to grow 6 cm? <u>15 days.</u>

Use the bar graph in Figure 4 to answer questions 7 through 11.

7. At birth, what is the average number of red blood cells per mm³ of blood?

    5.7 million.

8. What appears to happen to the number of red blood cells between birth and 2 months?

    It decreases.

9. What happens to the number of red blood cells between the ages of 6 and 8 years?

    It stays the same.

10. Between what ages is a human likely to have 4.6 million red blood cells?

    Between 6 months to 12 months.

11. After 14 years of age, do males or females have a higher red blood cell count?

    Males.

Part B. Constructing Graphs

Data Table 1   Breathing Rate of the Freshwater Sunfish

Temperature (°C)	Breathing Rate (per minute)
10	15
15	25
18	30
20	38
23	60
25	57
27	25

12. Use the grid below to construct a line graph for the information shown in Data Table 1.

Breathing Rate of the Freshwater Sunfish

Data Table 2   Average Rainfall in Willamette Valley

Month	Jan.	Feb.	Mar.	April	May	June	July	Aug.	Sept.	Oct.	Nov.	Dec.
Rainfall (mL)	15	21	28	24	16	8	2	1	2	3	5	10

13. Use the grid below to construct a bar graph for the information shown in Data Table 2.

Average Rainfall in Willamette Valley

Analysis and Conclusions

1. How is a graph similar to a data table? A graph is a pictorial representation of the information found in a data table.

2. How is a line graph different from a bar graph? A line graph contains a series of points connected together. A bar graph uses a series of columns to display data.

3. Does a steep curve on a line graph indicate a rapid or a slow rate of change?
   A rapid rate of change.

Critical Thinking and Application

1. You are conducting an experiment to measure the gain in mass of a young mouse over a ten-week period. In constructing a graph to represent your data, which variable should you place along the x-axis and which variable should you place along the y-axis? Explain your answer.

   Because the most consistent variable should be placed along the x-axis, the time period should be plotted there. The more unpredictable or inconsistent variable, the gain in mass of the mouse, should be placed along the y-axis.

2. What is an advantage of using multiple lines on a line graph? (See Figure 2.)
   The use of multiple lines on a line graph allows for the comparison of several different experiments with similar data.

3. Why is it important to have all parts of a graph clearly labeled and drawn?
   Graphs that are clearly labeled and drawn are much less likely to be misread or misinterpreted.

Going Further

A circle graph (sometimes called a "pie chart") is a convenient way to show the relative sizes of the parts that together form a whole body of data. Look through magazines and newspapers to find examples of circle graphs. Construct a chart listing the similarities and differences between circle graphs, line graphs, and bar graphs.

A Metric Scavenger Hunt

You may want to refer students to pages 11–13 in the textbook for a discussion of the metric system.

Time required: 45 minutes.

Pre-Lab Discussion

In many biology investigations, precise measurements must be made before conclusions can be formed. For everyday measuring we still use English units such as the inch, quart, and pound. But for scientific work, the metric system, or International System of Units (SI), is used. The universal language of science, the metric system allows scientists everywhere to share information.

In this investigation, you will have to "think metric" as you select objects that will correctly match the descriptions on your "metric scavenger hunt."

Problem

How closely can you estimate the metric measurements of everyday items?

A variety of objects should be on display throughout the room so that students will have to select the object they feel best meets the description.

Materials (per group)

Metric ruler
10-mL graduated cylinder
100-mL graduated cylinder
Triple-beam balance
Celsius thermometer

The sample range of measurement in each description is for the following items:

a. Large test tube
b. Test tube clamp
c. Quarter or nickel
d. Piece of paper
e. 3-L soda bottle
f. Human body

g. Ballpoint pen
h. Biology textbook
i. Lab table
j. Air at room temperature
k. Human body

Safety 🔺

The range of measurement for each description has been left blank to allow you to select items available in your classroom.

Handle all glassware carefully. Note all safety alert symbols next to the steps in the Procedure and review the meanings of each symbol by referring to the symbol guide on page 10.

Procedure

1. Carefully read the description of each object you are to find in the "metric scavenger hunt."

METRIC SCAVENGER HUNT

   a. An object that when filled to the top with water has a volume between __30__ and __35__ milliliters.

   b. A metallic object that has a mass less than __18__ grams.

   c. A coin that has a diameter (the distance from one side of a circle through the center to the other side) between __20__ and __25__ millimeters.

d. An object with a length between __27__ and __30__ centimeters.

e. An item that when half filled with water has a volume between __1__ and __2__ liters.

f. An object with a normal temperature of 37°C. (*Hint:* You brought this object to class!)

g. An object that has a mass between __400__ and __700__ centigrams.

h. An object that has a volume between __2100__ and __2400__ cubic centimeters.

i. An object with a length between __13__ and __15__ decimeters. (You may not be able to take this object to your lab station.)

j. A substance with a temperature between __18__ °C and __24__ °C.

k. A person with a mass between __45__ and __68__ kilograms.

2. Complete Data Table 1 by listing several objects that you think might fit each description. (*Hint:* Look around the room, check your purse and pockets, and do not forget items you have brought to class.)

3. From your list of possible objects, select the one item that you feel will best fit each description. Take the selected item to your lab station.

4. Using the proper measuring tool, make the appropriate measurement and record your answer in Data Table 2. Remember to indicate the correct units.

Observations

Data Table 1

Description	Possible Objects
a	
b	
c	
d	
e	Answers will vary depending upon objects you have on display.
f	
g	
h	
i	
j	
k	

Data Table 2

Description	Object	Measurement	Was Object Within Given Range?
a			
b			
c			
d		Answers will vary.	
e			
f		Not required	
g			
h			
i			
j			
k			

Analysis and Conclusions

1. Which objects were easiest to find? Hardest? Why? Answers will vary, but students may respond that object e was easiest because of their familiarity with soft-drink containers.

2. Was it easy to "think metric"? Why? Answers will vary but should reflect the number of "Yes" answers in Data Table 2.

3. Would students in other parts of the world have difficulty "thinking metric"? Why? No. Other countries use the metric system for everyday measuring.

4. Why is it important that all scientific measurements be made using metric units? So that scientists worldwide can share information and verify each other's work.

Critical Thinking and Application

1. The metric system is based on the number 10 and is a decimal system of measurement. What United States system is based on the number 10? <u>Monetary system.</u>

2. The United States is one of the few countries in the world that does not use the metric system for everyday measuring. Do you think Congress should pass a law requiring the use of the metric system throughout the country? Explain your answer. <u>Answers will vary.</u>

3. If the United States did convert to the metric system, how would you implement this change?
<u>Answers will vary.</u>

Going Further

1. In the laboratory investigation, you have worked with SI units for measuring length, mass, temperature, and volume. Other SI base units include the second, ampere, kelvin, mole, and candela. Find out what these SI base units are used to measure and report your findings to your classmates.

2. Conduct a survey to determine the familiarity of different age groups with the metric system. Questions might include the base units for different types of measurements and the prefixes used for making smaller and larger measurements.

2

Observing the Uncertainty of Measurements

You may want to refer students to pages 11–13 in the textbook for a discussion of the nature of measurements.

Time required: 40 minutes.

Pre-Lab Discussion

Biologists use a wide variety of laboratory tools to make scientific measurements. Some basic tools of measurement are the meterstick, triple-beam balance, graduated cylinder, and Celsius thermometer.

The accuracy of a scientific measurement depends on three things: the smallest unit on the measuring scale, the ability of the observer to read the scale properly, and the degree of precision of the measuring instrument and scale.

In this investigation, you will learn about the uncertainty of measurement and how accurately matter can be measured using common laboratory instruments.

Problem

How accurately can matter be measured?

Materials (per station)

Station 1: meterstick
Station 2: meterstick
Station 3: metric ruler
           regular object
Station 4: 100-mL graduated cylinder
           150-mL beaker of colored liquid
Station 5: triple-beam balance
           small pebble

Station 6: 100-mL graduated cylinder
           150-mL beaker of water
           irregular object
Station 7: Celsius thermometer
           250-mL beaker of ice and water
           paper towel
Use any food coloring or ink to prepare colored water.

Safety 🔬

Put on a laboratory apron if one is available. Handle all glassware carefully. Note all safety alert symbols next to the steps in the Procedure and review the meanings of each symbol by referring to the symbol guide on page 10.

Procedure

Assign each group of students a starting station. After the groups have completed one station, they should proceed to the next station. Allow about 5 minutes per station.

1. Station 1: Use the meterstick to measure the length and width of your science classroom. If the room has an irregular shape, measure the longest width and the longest length. Express your measurements in meters and record them in the Data Table.

2. Station 2: Use the meterstick to measure the length and width of your desk or lab table. If the table has an irregular shape, measure the longest width and the longest length. Express your measurements in centimeters and record them in the Data Table.

3. Station 3: Use the metric ruler to find the volume of the regular object. Volume is found by multiplying the length times the width times the height of the object. Express the volume in cubic centimeters and record it in the Data Table.

4. Station 4: Use the graduated cylinder to find the volume of the colored liquid in the beaker. Remember to always read a graduated cylinder at the bottom curve of the meniscus. Pour the liquid back into the beaker. Express your measurement in milliliters and record it in the Data Table.

5. Station 5: Make certain that the riders on the triple-beam balance are moved all the way to the left and that the pointer rests on zero. Place the pebble on the pan on the triple-beam balance. Move the riders until the pointer is at zero. Express your measurement in grams and record it in the Data Table. Remove the pebble and return all riders to the far left of the balance.

6. Station 6: Fill the graduated cylinder half full with water from the beaker. Find the volume of the irregular object. Express the volume of the object in cubic centimeters and record it in the Data Table. Carefully remove the object from the graduated cylinder. Pour the water back into the beaker.

7. Station 7: Use the Celsius thermometer to find the temperature of the ice water. Express the temperature in degrees Celsius and record it in the Data Table. Remove the thermometer and carefully dry it with a paper towel.

8. Your teacher will construct a large class data table on the chalkboard. Have one member from your group record your data on the class data table. Before class begins, prepare a class data table so that each group of students can record the data for each workstation.

Observations

Data Table

Station	Measurement
1	
2	
3	Answers will vary.
4	
5	
6	
7	

1. What is the smallest unit shown on the meterstick? 1 mm

2. What is the smallest unit shown on the metric ruler? 1 mm

3. What is the smallest unit shown on the graduated cylinder? 1 mL (Note: Some graduated cylinders may have different graduations.)

4. What is the smallest unit on the triple-beam balance? 0.1 g _____

5. What is the smallest unit on the Celsius thermometer? 1°C (Note: Some thermometers may have

different graduations.) _____

Analysis and Conclusions

1. Study the class data table. Do each group's measurements have the exact same value for each

   station? It is unlikely that each group's data for each station will be exactly the same. _____

   _____

2. Which stations had measurements that were most nearly alike? Explain why these

   measurements were so similar. Answers will vary. In most cases, Stations 3, 4, and 5 will have the

   closest data. This is because the object being measured was very exact and the groups are more likely to

   arrive at very similar figures. _____

   _____

3. Which stations had measurements that were most varied? Explain why these measurements

   were so varied. Answers will vary. In most cases, Stations 1, 2, 6, and 7 will have the most dissimilar

   data. In particular, Station 7, in which students measure the temperature of ice water, will likely have quite

   different measurements because the ice may melt during the class period. _____

   _____

Critical Thinking and Application

1. Why is it important for the riders on a triple-beam balance to always start at the far left of the

   balance? The riders should be to the far left so you can tell if the balance is evenly balanced at 0 grams.

   _____

   _____

2. Of the following graduated cylinders—100 mL, 25 mL, or 10 mL—which would you use to
   most accurately measure 8 mL of a liquid? Explain your answer.

   It is best to use a 10-mL graduated cylinder because it has finer graduations and thus provides for a more

   accurate measurement. _____

   _____

3. Which is more accurate for measuring liquid volume, a beaker or a graduated cylinder? Explain your answer. The graduated cylinder is more accurate because it is marked off in smaller units.

4. Describe two variables that might affect the accuracy of your measurement of volume when using a metric ruler to measure the dimensions of an object. The metric ruler may be used incorrectly or inaccurately. The multiplication of the length, width, and height may be incorrect. The end of the ruler may be cracked or worn away.

Going Further

1. Calculate the average (mean) of the measurements at each station. To do this, add each measurement to find a total and then divide by the number of measurements. An average of several measurements is usually more precise than a single measurement.

2. Repeat the investigation, this time aiming for the best precision and accuracy possible. Record the measurements as you did before and calculate a class average for each station. Compare the measurements and averages for the two trials. Discuss factors that led to more precise measurements.

3

Characteristics of Life

You may want to refer students to pages 27–31 in the textbook for a discussion of the characteristics of life.

Time required:
Part A–10 minutes
Part B–30 minutes
Part C–15 minutes

Pre-Lab Discussion

Dogs, cats, people, and trees are living things. Rocks, water, and air are nonliving things. Distinguishing between living and nonliving things seems simple, yet the differences have been a source of argument among scientists for many years. But scientists agree that all living things are made up of one or more cells, reproduce, grow and develop, obtain and use energy, and respond to the environment.

To help you observe some of the characteristics of life, you will work with bromthymol blue, an indicator that is used to determine the presence of carbon dioxide. Carbon dioxide is produced when many living organisms burn their food to produce the energy that allows them to carry out the processes of life.

In this investigation, you will observe characteristics that indicate yeast are living organisms. To demonstrate the difficulties involved in determining whether an object is a living thing, you might want to do the following demonstration and have your students answer the question: "Is it alive?"

Problem Mix in a beaker 40 mL of liquid detergent, 20 mL of water, several drops of green food coloring, and a 10-cm cube of dry ice. This chemical "slime mold" will exhibit many characteristics of life.

What characteristics of life can you observe that indicate yeast are living organisms?

1500 mL of the following solutions are needed for a class of 30 students.

Materials *(per group)*

Bromthymol blue in dropper bottle
Straw
4 large test tubes
3 small test tubes
3 one-hole rubber stoppers
   with glass tube inserts
   to fit large test tubes
Glass-marking pencil
3 pieces of plastic hose, 30–40 cm long

Test tube rack
Graduated cylinder
2 glass slides
2 coverslips
2 medicine droppers
Microscope
Yeast and molasses mixture
Yeast and water mixture
Water and molasses mixture

Yeast-Molasses: Dissolve 1 package of active dry yeast and 10 mL of molasses in 1 L of lukewarm tap water. Stir. Let stand at least 24 hours. Stir occasionally.

Yeast-Water: Dissolve 1 package of active dry yeast in 1 L of lukewarm tap water. Stir. Let stand 24 hours. Stir occasionally.

Water-Molasses: Dissolve 10 mL of molasses in 1 L lukewarm tap water. Stir.

Safety ⚗ 🧤 👁

Put on a laboratory apron if one is available. Put on safety goggles. Handle all glassware carefully. Always use special caution when working with chemicals, as they may irritate the skin or cause staining of the skin or clothing. Never touch or taste any chemical unless instructed to do so. Bromthymol blue is a dye that can stain your clothing and your skin. Note all safety alert symbols next to the steps in the Procedure and review the meanings of each symbol by referring to the symbol guide on page 10.

Procedure
Part A

1. Add 30 drops of bromthymol blue to a test tube. **CAUTION:** *Bromthymol blue is a dye. Use care to prevent spills.*

2. Place a straw in the test tube, making sure that the straw extends into the bromthymol blue.

3. Gently blow bubbles through the straw into the bromthymol blue. **CAUTION:** *Do not inhale through the straw.* See Figure 1. Record your observations.

Figure 1

Part B

1. Using a glass-marking pencil, label three large test tubes A, B, and C.

2. Put 5 mL of bromthymol blue in each small test tube and place the test tubes in the test tube rack. **CAUTION:** *Bromthymol blue is a dye. Use care to prevent spills.*

3. Put 30 mL of the yeast and molasses mixture in test tube A.

4. Place a rubber stopper with a glass tube insert firmly into the mouth of test tube A.

5. Attach a plastic hose to the glass tube in the stopper. Place test tube A in the test tube rack next to one of the small test tubes containing bromthymol blue.

6. Put 30 mL of the yeast and water mixture in test tube B.

7. Place a rubber stopper with a glass tube insert firmly into the mouth of test tube B.

8. Attach a plastic hose to the glass tube in the stopper. Place test tube B in the test tube rack next to one of the small test tubes containing bromthymol blue.

9. Put 30 mL of the water and molasses mixture in test tube C.

10. Place a rubber stopper with a glass tube insert firmly in the mouth of test tube C.

11. Attach a plastic hose to the glass tube in the stopper. Place test tube C in the test tube rack next to the third small test tube containing bromthymol blue.

12. Place the free end of the plastic hose attached to test tube A in the small test tube containing bromthymol blue, making sure it almost touches the bottom. Do the same thing for test tube B and its small test tube and again for test tube C and its small test tube. See Figure 2.

Figure 2

13. Record your initial observations in the Data Table.

14. After 30 minutes, again record your observations in the Data Table.

Part C

1. With a glass-marking pencil, label one glass slide A and a second glass slide B.

2. Using a clean medicine dropper, make a wet mount of the yeast and molasses mixture.

3. Using a clean medicine dropper, make a wet mount of the yeast and water mixture.

4. Examine each slide under the high-power objective of a microscope. You may need to adjust the diaphragm to see the yeast clearly. Be sure to note the presence of any *buds*—small yeast cells still attached to larger yeast cells. Record your observations.

Observations
Part A

1. What color was the bromthymol blue before you exhaled into the test tube?

Blue.

2. What color was the bromthymol blue after you exhaled into the test tube?

Yellow-green.

Part B

Data Table

	Initial Observations			After 30 Minutes		
	Color	**Presence of bubbles**	**Presence of CO$_2$**	**Color**	**Presence of bubbles**	**Presence of CO$_2$**
Setup A yeast and molasses	brown	yes		brown	yes	yes
bromthymol blue	blue	no		yellow-green	yes	yes
Setup B yeast and water	tan	yes		tan	yes	yes
bromthymol blue	blue	no		blue or yellow	yes	yes
Setup C water and molasses	brown	no		brown	no	no
bromthymol blue	blue	no		blue	no	no

In which test tube(s) did you observe a chemical reaction in which carbon dioxide was produced? How did you know a chemical reaction was occurring?

A and B. Bromthymol blue turned colors, indicating the presence of CO$_2$.

Part C

1. In the spaces below, draw what you observed on slides A and B under the microscope.

Magnification _____

Magnification _____

Answers will vary.

2. In which mixture were more buds present? Yeast-molasses.

Analysis and Conclusions
Part A

Why did the bromthymol blue change color when you exhaled into the test tube?

CO_2 is a waste product we exhale. We take in O_2 to carry out life processes (respiration) and give off CO_2 as a waste product.

Part B

1. What does the production of carbon dioxide gas indicate about yeast?

They are alive.

2. How do you know that the carbon dioxide gas was produced by the yeast?

The bromthymol blue changed color only in test tubes where yeast was present. The H_2O and molasses mixture did not produce a color change in the bromthymol blue.

Part C

1. What does the presence of buds indicate about the yeast? Yeast are reproducing.

2. Why were more buds present in one of the mixtures? The molasses served as a food source for the yeast. Reproduction occurred in the most suitable environment.

3. What have you observed in this laboratory investigation (all three parts) that allows you to classify yeast as living organisms? 1. Reproduction.

2. Production of CO_2 due to burning of food source for energy.

Critical Thinking and Application

The baking industry uses yeast as an ingredient in bread dough to make the dough "rise." Using the recipe below, answer the questions that follow.

Biscuits

5 cups flour
$\frac{1}{4}$ cup sugar
3 teaspoons baking powder
1 teaspoon baking soda
2 cups buttermilk

1 cup shortening
1 package yeast
2 tablespoons water
1 teaspoon salt

Dissolve yeast in 2 tablespoons of warm, not hot, water. Let yeast and water mixture stand for 5 minutes or until bubbly. Mix dry ingredients. Cut in shortening. Add buttermilk and yeast mixture to the dry ingredients. Stir and then knead a few times. Roll out to $\frac{1}{2}$ inch thickness. Cut with a biscuit cutter. Bake at 400° for 12 to 15 minutes.

1. How does yeast make biscuit dough rise? The bubbles of CO_2 produced by the yeast create air pockets in the dough that cause it to expand or rise.

2. The recipe instructs the cook to dissolve the yeast in "warm, not hot" water. Why?
Water that was too hot might kill the yeast.

3. Why does the recipe instruct the cook to let the yeast and water "stand for 5 minutes or until bubbly"? The yeast needs time to begin the reaction that produces the bubbles of CO_2, which make the dough rise.

Going Further

1. Design an experiment that would test the effect of different temperatures on the rate of carbon dioxide production by yeast.

2. Write a report on how the alcohol industry uses yeast.

4

Measuring with a Microscope

You may want to refer students to pages 34–37 and Appendix C in the textbook for a discussion of microscopes.

Time required: 40 minutes.

Pre-Lab Discussion

The microscope, developed more than three hundred years ago, is the basic tool of the biologist. The microscope enables biologists to investigate living things and objects that are too small to be seen with the unaided eye. The microscope is able to magnify these tiny specimens by means of lenses located in the eyepiece and objectives. The light microscope is also capable of revealing fine detail. This ability to reveal fine detail is known as resolving power. The type of microscope that you will be using throughout your study of biology is the compound light microscope.

Although it is interesting and informative to observe specimens under the microscope, it is often difficult to know the actual size of the object being observed. Magnification causes us to lose the idea of actual size. You cannot hold up a ruler to a paramecium or a plant cell while it is under the microscope. Therefore size must be measured indirectly—that is, it must be compared with the size of something you already know. The diameter of the microscope field seen through the eyepiece is a convenient standard to use. To measure objects under the microscope, a unit called the micrometer (μm) is used. One micrometer equals 0.001 millimeter.

In this investigation, you will develop skill in using the compound light microscope. You will also learn how to estimate the sizes of objects under the microscope.

Problem

How is the compound microscope used to make measurements of microscopic specimens?

Materials *(per group)*

Microscope	Transparent metric ruler
Lens paper	Prepared slides Use any of the following: bacteria, pollen grains, yeast, protists, human red blood cells, diatoms, and others.

Safety ⚗

Always handle the microscope with extreme care. You are responsible for its proper care and use. Use caution when handling glass slides as they can break easily and cut you. Note all safety alert symbols next to the steps in the Procedure and review the meanings of each symbol by referring to the symbol guide on page 10.

Procedure

1. Take a microscope from the storage area and place it about 10 centimeters from the edge of the laboratory table.

2. Carefully clean the eyepiece and objective lenses with lens paper.

3. Examine the markings on a metric ruler. Decide which marks indicate millimeter lengths. Place the ruler on the stage so that it covers half of the stage opening, as shown in Figure 1.

Figure 1

4. Prepare your microscope for low-power observation of the ruler.

5. Look through the eyepiece. Focus on the edge of the ruler using the coarse adjustment. Adjust the position of the ruler so that the view in the low-power field is similar to Figure 2.

6. Place the center of one mark at the left side of the field of view. Make sure that the edge of the ruler is exactly across the center of the field. If the ruler sticks to your fingers, use the eraser end of a pencil to arrange it.

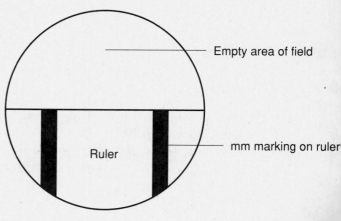

Figure 2

7. Note that 1 millimeter is the distance from the middle of one mark to the middle of the next mark. The diameter of the low-power field measures 1 millimeter plus a fraction of another. In Observations, record the measurement of the low-power field diameter in millimeters, expressing the length to the nearest tenth of a millimeter.

8. In Observations, record the measurement of the low-power field diameter in micrometers.

9. You cannot measure the diameter of the high-power field using the process you have just completed. Viewing a ruler under high power presents problems with light and focusing. Also, the high-power field diameter is less than 1 millimeter. But you can obtain the high-power field diameter indirectly. You know the low-power field diameter and the magnifying power of both objectives. Since the magnification of the objectives is inversely proportional to the field size, you can use this formula:

$$\text{high-power field diameter} = \frac{\text{low-power field diameter} \times \text{low-power magnification}}{\text{high-power magnification}}$$

In Observations, record the high-power field diameter in micrometers. Show your calculations.

10. Now that you know the diameter of your field size under both low and high power, you can estimate the sizes of the objects you view under the microscope by comparing them with the diameter of the field of vision. For example, if a tiny organism takes up approximately one-half of a field of view that is 1000 micrometers in diameter, then its size is about one-half of 1000 micrometers, or 500 micrometers.

74

11. Obtain prepared slides of various organisms and practice estimating their lengths. Write the name of the organism or part you examine and its estimated size in micrometers in the Data Table.

12. When you have finished examining the organisms in step 11, return your microscope to the storage area.

Observations

1. Measurement of the low-power field diameter = <u>Answers will vary. Usually 1.3–1.6 millimeters.</u>

2. Measurement of the low-power field diameter = <u>1300–1600</u> micrometers.

3. Low-power magnification = <u>Usually 100X, but this varies with the microscope.</u>

4. High-power magnification = <u>Usually 430X, but this varies with the microscope.</u>

5. Use the formula shown in step 9 of Procedure to calculate the high-power field diameter. Show your calculations.

Assuming low-power field diameter = 1500 μm, low-power magnification = 100X, and high-power magnification = 430X:

high-power field diameter = 1500 μm x 100 / 430 = 348.8 (349) μm

Data Table

Name of Object	Measurement of Object (μm)
Answers will vary.	

Analysis and Conclusions

1. How many micrometers are in 1 millimeter? <u>1000</u>

2. How many micrometers are in 1 meter? <u>1,000,000</u>

3. What happens to the field of view when you change from low-power magnification to high-power magnification? <u>As the magnification increases, the field of view decreases.</u>

_____

_____

4. How many times is the magnification increased when you change from low-power to high-power magnification? Answers will vary with the type of microscope used but should correspond to the magnification of the high-power objective divided by the magnification of the low-power objective.

5. How many times is the diameter of a field decreased when you change from low-power to high-power magnification? Answers will vary with the type of microscope used but should be the same as in Question 4.

Critical Thinking and Application

1. Approximately 500 of a certain type of bacteria can fit across your low-power field of vision. What is the approximate size of 1 bacterium? Answers will vary. 1500 µm / 500 = 3 µm

2. Approximately 7 of a certain type of protist can fit across your high-power field of vision. What is the approximate size of 1 protist? Answers will vary. 349 µm / 7 = 49.9 µm

3. If a microscope has a low-power magnification of 100X, a high-power magnification of 600X, and a low-power field diameter of 1800 micrometers, what is the high-power field diameter in micrometers? High-power field diameter = 1800 x 100 / 600 = 300 µm

4. If 20 objects fit across a low-power field of view whose field diameter is 3000 micrometers, what is the approximate size of each object? 3000 µm / 20 = 150 µm

Going Further

Make a temporary wet-mount slide of a culture of mixed protists. Choose one protist and observe it under low and high power. Estimate its length in micrometers.

5

Making Predictions Using Indirect Evidence

You may want to refer students to pages 47–49 in their textbook for a discussion of atomic structure.

Time required: 25 minutes.

Pre-Lab Discussion

How do scientists know what the inside of an atom looks like? After all, it is impossible to see inside an atom. Scientists have used observations of how atoms behave to develop a model of atomic structure. These observations are one type of indirect evidence for the structure of an atom.

Another type of indirect evidence comes from making predictions. Based on the model they have developed, scientists predict how atoms will behave in certain circumstances. They design experiments to test these predictions. If the predictions are shown to be accurate, they are taken as additional indirect evidence that the model is correct.

In this investigation, you will use indirect evidence to determine the properties of objects you cannot see.

Problem

How can you determine the characteristics of something you cannot observe directly?

Materials *(per pair of students)*

Shoe box, wrapped or with cover, that contains small objects
Triple-beam balance
Bar magnet

Pencils, pieces of chalk, marbles, rubber stoppers, coins, magnets, wood cubes, or wood beads are some examples of items that may be placed in the boxes. Boxes should contain no more than 5 items and should be filled and sealed before lab begins. You may wish to make the contents of each box different or to make all boxes identical. Boxes may be wrapped with craft or wrapping paper to discourage "peeking." Make a list of the contents of each box.

Procedure

1. Obtain a sealed shoe box from your teacher.

2. Without opening the box, perform several tests on the box to determine the characteristics of the contents. Tests might include tipping it, shaking it, sliding it, checking for magnetic attraction, and finding its mass. In each case, record your observations in the Data Table. Observations might include sound or the way the contents behave (roll, slide, etc.). You might also wish to find the mass of an identical box and lid that is empty. The difference in mass would be the mass of the object or objects inside.

3. On the basis of your observations, sketch and label the box and its contents in Figure 1 in Analysis and Conclusions.

Observations

Describe some of the ways in which you tested the unknown objects to determine their characteristics. Record your descriptions in the Data Table.

Data Table

Test	Observations
	Answers will vary.

Analysis and Conclusions

Drawings will vary.

Figure 1

1. What senses did you use to determine a model of the object or objects inside the box?

   Answers will vary but might include hearing and touch.

2. How does this investigation compare with the way in which scientists have learned about the atom? In both situations, indirect observations are made to determine characteristics.

3. Do you think that all the boxes used in this investigation contain the same number and types of objects? What evidence would you use to support your answer? Answers will vary depending on the contents of the boxes. Students might use similarities or differences in masses or sounds to support their answers.

Critical Thinking and Application

1. In what ways could you test the accuracy of your model of the contents of the box without opening the box? Put objects like those that you think are in the shoe box in another shoe box and see if that box behaves in the same way. Determine the mass of the identical box and contents and see if it matches that of the shoe box.

2. What kinds of special instruments could also be used to make indirect observations of the contents of the box? An X-ray machine or an instrument that uses ultrasonic waves to produce pictures (sonograms) could be used.

3. If you used some of these special instruments and found that the results did not agree with what you originally thought to be contained within the box, what would you need to do? Redo the original experiment, making careful observations. From these observations, make new, but logical, predictions.

4. If your teacher allows you to do so, open the box and directly observe the object(s) inside or look at a list of the objects contained within the box. How accurate is your indirect determination? Answers will vary.

What does this tell you about the current model of the atom? The current atomic model represents

scientists' best attempts to predict atomic structure on the basis of careful experimentation and observation.

However, it is a model subject to change should new information be gathered and shown to be correct.

If you wish to keep the contents of the boxes unknown until all classes have finished this investigation, Question 4 may be omitted for the lab write-up and covered during the post-lab discussion.

Going Further

1. Glue an object inside a shoe box. Trade boxes with another student who has done the same. Using knitting needles, determine the location and shape of the object by sticking the needles through the box.

2. How would you determine what kind of liquid was inside of a completely filled, closed, opaque bottle? How would it be helpful if you had an identical empty bottle?

6

Physical and Chemical Changes

You may want to refer students to pages 45–56 in the textbook for a discussion of physical and chemical changes.

Time required: 45 minutes.

Pre-Lab Discussion

Matter is constantly changing. The two kinds of changes that occur in matter are physical and chemical changes. In a physical change, no new substances are formed. However, physical properties such as size, shape, color, or phase may change. Dissolving, melting, evaporating, and grinding are physical changes.

As a result of a chemical change, one or more new substances with new and different properties are formed. The new substances are different from the original substance. Chemical changes, which are often called chemical reactions, are taking place around you and even inside you all the time. Respiration and digestion are chemical changes you could not live without. Photosynthesis, or the food-making process in green plants, is a chemical change. Burning, the rusting of iron, and the changing colors of leaves in autumn are other examples of chemical changes.

In this investigation, you will observe physical and chemical changes and learn to recognize each type of change when it occurs.

Problem

What are the differences between physical and chemical changes?

Materials *(per group)*

Birthday candle
Aluminum foil (10 cm x 10 cm)
Modeling clay
Test tube rack
3 test tubes
Matches
Scoop

Celsius thermometer
10-mL graduated cylinder
Antacid tablet
Magnesium ribbon (2 cm long)
10 mL 1 M hydrochloric acid   To prepare: Add 86 mL 12 M HCl to 914 mL distilled water.
Table salt
Dropper bottle of 0.1 M   AgNO₃ may be purchased at this
    silver nitrate   concentration or may be prepared by
    adding 8.5 g AgNO₃ to 500 mL distilled
    water. Store it in brown dropper bottles.

Safety 🔥 🥽 📷 👁

Put on a laboratory apron if one is available. Put on safety goggles. Handle all glassware carefully. Always use special caution when working with laboratory chemicals, as they may irritate the skin or cause staining of the skin or clothing. Never touch or taste any chemical unless instructed to do so. Note all safety alert symbols next to the steps in the Procedure and review the meanings of each symbol by referring to the symbol guide on page 10.

Procedure

1. Take a small piece of modeling clay and place it on the square of aluminum foil. Firmly place a candle in the clay so that it is well supported. Light the candle and allow it to burn while you continue the rest of the investigation. Record your observations of the burning candle.

2. Add a small scoop of table salt to a test tube that has been half-filled with tap water. Place your thumb over the top of the test tube and shake to dissolve the salt. Record your observations. Using the dropper, add 5 drops of silver nitrate to the salt water. Record your observations.

3. Place 10 mL of hydrochloric acid in a test tube. Place the thermometer in the solution and record the temperature. Cut off a small piece of magnesium ribbon and place it in the test tube. Record your observations of the reaction. Record the temperature of the hydrochloric acid at the end of the reaction.

4. Place 10 mL of water in a test tube. Place the thermometer in the water and record the temperature. Break the antacid tablet into small pieces and add them to the test tube of water. Record your observations of the reaction. Record the temperature of the water at the end of the reaction.

Observations

1. What did you observe as the candle burned? Smoke was given off; wick turned black; candle got smaller; wax melted and dripped.

What was left after the candle burned? Melted wax.

2. What did you observe when you added the salt to the water in the test tube and shook it?
The salt "disappeared."

What did you observe when the silver nitrate was added to the salt water?
A white, cloudy substance formed.

3. Original temperature of the hydrochloric acid = _____ Answers will vary. Students should observe a rise in temperature after magnesium is added.

Temperature of the hydrochloric acid after
magnesium is added   = _____

What did you observe when the magnesium was added to the hydrochloric acid?
The acid started bubbling; magnesium disappeared; test tube became warm.

4. Original temperature of the water = _____   Answers will vary. Students should
observe a drop in temperature after
Temperature of the water after   antacid tablet is added to the water.
  antacid is added   = _____

What did you observe when the antacid tablet was added to the water?

The water started bubbling; antacid disappeared; test tube became cooler.

_____

_____

Analysis and Conclusions

1. Identify each of the following as either a physical change or a chemical change. Give a reason for your answer.

a. Melting candle wax   Physical. Wax goes through a phase change only.

_____

b. Burning a candle   Chemical. Candle changes to other substances such as smoke.

_____

c. Dissolving salt in water   Physical. Salt is still present in water; it has been separated into much

smaller particles.

d. Adding silver nitrate to salt water   Chemical. New substances are formed.

_____

e. Cutting a piece of magnesium ribbon   Physical. Ribbon is only separated into smaller pieces.

_____

f. Adding magnesium metal to hydrochloric acid   Chemical. New substances are produced. Energy

change occurs (heat is given off).

g. Breaking an antacid tablet into small pieces   Physical. Tablet is only separated into smaller pieces.

_____

h. Adding an antacid tablet to water   Chemical. New substances are produced. Energy change occurs

(heat is absorbed).

2. What happened to the temperature of the hydrochloric acid when you added the magnesium

to it?   Temperature rose.

_____

_____

3. What happened to the temperature of the water when you added the antacid tablet to it?

Temperature dropped.

4. Describe two observations you might make when a physical change occurs.

The original substances stay the same. No energy changes occur.

5. Describe two observations you might make when a chemical change occurs.

New substances are produced. Gas is released in the reaction. Energy, usually in the form of heat, is given

off or taken in.

Critical Thinking and Application

1. How could you prove that dissolving the salt in water resulted in only a physical change?

The water could be evaporated, leaving the salt.

2. How could you prove that adding magnesium to hydrochloric acid resulted in a chemical change? After the reaction stops, you could evaporate the liquid. Magnesium will not be left because it has

changed as a result of the chemical reaction.

3. The following changes often indicate that a chemical change has occurred. But they can also indicate the occurrence of a physical change. Explain how each change might result from a physical, not a chemical, change.

   a. Change of color Object may be dyed.

   b. Loss of mass Evaporation may reduce the mass (but it is only a phase change).

   c. The substance seems to "disappear." Substance may dissolve but does not change to a new

   substance and may be reclaimed after the liquid is evaporated.

Going Further

Write out a recipe that involves cooking or baking. Identify each step in the recipe as resulting in either a physical change or a chemical change in the ingredients.

7

Using Acid-Base Indicators to Test Unknown Substances

You may want to refer students to pages 65–66 in the textbook for a discussion of acids and bases.

Time required: 45 minutes.

Pre-Lab Discussion

The science laboratory is not the only place where acids and bases are found. Many items commonly found at home are acids or bases. For example, many of the foods you eat contain acids. Many commonly used cleaning products owe their effectiveness to the fact that they are alkaline, or contain bases.

Indicators are special chemicals that can show whether a given substance is an acid, a base, or neither. Indicators usually react with an acid or a base to form a slightly different chemical with a different color. Two examples of indicators are litmus paper (blue and red) and pH paper. Blue litmus paper turns red in an acid and stays blue in a base. Red litmus paper turns blue in a base and stays red in an acid. One type of pH paper turns a different color at each of several pH values ranging from 2 to 10.

In this investigation, you will test a number of substances using litmus paper and pH paper.

Problem

How can you determine whether a substance is an acid or a base?

Materials *(per group)*

10 mL of each test liquid
10 small test tubes
Test tube rack
10-mL graduated cylinder
Glass stirring rod
Vials of red and blue litmus paper
Vial of pH paper
Distilled water

Use liquids such as vinegar, tomato juice, ammonia, soft drinks, soapy water, milk of magnesia, cleaning products, fruit juices, milk, baking soda solution, shampoo, and aspirin dissolved in water.

Safety ⚗ 🔥 👁

Put on a laboratory apron if one is available. Put on safety goggles. Handle all glassware carefully. Always use special caution when working with laboratory chemicals, as they may irritate the skin or cause staining of the skin or clothing. Never touch or taste any chemical unless instructed to do so. Note all safety alert symbols next to the steps in the Procedure and review the meanings of each symbol by referring to the symbol guide on page 10.

Procedure

1. Use the graduated cylinder to measure 10 mL of distilled water into one of the test tubes.

2. Dip the glass stirring rod into the test tube containing the distilled water and then touch it to a piece of red litmus paper. Get a bit more on the stirring rod and touch it to a piece of blue litmus paper. Get a bit more on the rod and touch it to a piece of pH paper. Record your observations in the Data Table.

3. Based on the color change you observe in the pH paper, approximate the pH of the distilled water. Record this value in the Data Table.

4. Taking care to rinse and dry the stirring rod and graduated cylinder thoroughly, repeat steps 1 through 3 with the other substances provided by your teacher. Be sure to write the names of the substances in the Data Table. Write the names of the other substances you want students to test on the chalkboard and have students copy these names onto the Data Table.

Observations

Data Table

Substance	Color of Indicator			Approximate pH of Substance
	Blue Litmus	Red Litmus	pH Paper	
Distilled Water	blue	red	(depends on type of pH paper used)	7
		Answers will vary.		

Analysis and Conclusions

1. Which substances are acids? Answers will vary depending on substances used.

_____

2. Which substances are bases? Answers will vary depending on substances used.

_____

3. Which substances are neutral? Answers will vary depending on substances used.

_____

4. Which substance is probably the strongest acid? Explain your conclusion.

Students should choose the substance with the lowest pH.

_____

_____

5. Which substance is probably the strongest base? Explain your conclusion.

Students should choose the substance with the highest pH.

_____

_____

6. Is litmus paper useful in determining the exact pH of a substance? Explain your answer.

No. Blue litmus, for example, will turn red in a weak acid as well as in a strong acid. This type of indicator is

not helpful in distinguishing the relative strength or weakness of an acid or base.

_____

Critical Thinking and Application

1. Describe three situations in which acid-base indicators might be useful in everyday life.

Answers will vary. Possible answers include testing products such as shampoo for the proper acidity; testing

soil for acidity; testing swimming-pool water; testing rain water to see if it is acid rain; testing lakes or rivers

for possible acid-rain contamination.

2. Suppose you are manufacturing a certain type of cosmetic. You know that it can be slightly acidic, but it should not be strongly acidic. Which of the indicators you have just studied will help you determine the degree of acidity? Explain your answer.

pH paper turns a variety of colors corresponding to the strength of the acid or base and would, therefore, be

helpful. Litmus paper can be used only to determine if a substance is an acid or a base. It cannot be used

to determine a substance's relative strength.

3. You may have found that the results you obtained were different from those of other groups. What variables might have affected your results? Not completely rinsing and drying the stirring rod and/or graduated cylinder after testing each substance; using unclean test tubes; having different interpretations of pH paper color scale.

4. Design an experiment in which you could investigate which of two antacids is more effective in neutralizing stomach acid. Answers will vary. Students might suggest filling two test tubes with equal amounts of a particular acid. Equal masses of two different antacids could then be added to the test tubes and the pH of each tube could be tested. The tube with a pH closest to 7 (neutral) might be judged to contain the more effective antacid.

Going Further

1. Test the pH of the substances used in this investigation with different indicators: phenolphthalein, phenol red, methyl orange, bromthymol blue, red cabbage juice, and grape juice, for example.

2. Using indicators, test the acidity of various soils near your home or school. Find out which kinds of plants grow well in acidic soil.

8

Identifying Organic Compounds

You may want to refer students to pages 68–77 of the textbook for a discussion of organic compounds.

Time required: 60 minutes.

Pre-Lab Discussion

The most common organic compounds found in living organisms are lipids, carbohydrates, proteins, and nucleic acids. Common foods, which often consist of plant materials or substances derived from animals, are also combinations of these organic compounds. Simple chemical tests with substances called indicators can be conducted to determine the presence of organic compounds. A color change of an indicator is usually a positive test for the presence of an organic compound.

In this investigation, you will use several indicators to test for the presence of lipids, carbohydrates, and proteins in particular foods.

Problem

How are indicators used to test for the presence of organic compounds?

Materials *(per group)*

10 test tubes
Test tube rack
Test tube holder
Masking tape
Bunsen burner or hot plate
Iodine solution   Dissolve 5 g potassium iodide and 1.5 g iodine crystals in 500 mL distilled water.
20 mL honey solution   Dissolve 20 mL honey in 500 mL distilled water.
20 mL egg white and water mixture   Mix egg whites from 3 eggs with 500 mL distilled water.
20 mL corn oil
20 mL lettuce and water mixture   Mix 20 mL macerated lettuce with 500 mL distilled water.
20 mL gelatin and water solution   Dissolve 3.5 g gelatin in 346.5 mL distilled water. Refrigerate until
20 mL melted butter   needed.
20 mL potato and water mixture   Mix 20 mL macerated potato with 500 mL distilled water.
20 mL apple juice and water mixture   Mix 250 mL unsweetened apple juice with 250 mL distilled
20 mL distilled water   water.
20 mL unknown substance   You might use clear meat broth (without flour or cornstarch), crackers and
Paper towels   distilled water, oats and distilled water, olive oil, melted lard, orange juice,
600-mL beaker   cream cheese and distilled water, and peanut butter and distilled water.
Brown paper   Soak solid foods overnight to soften them. Then, mash softened food and
Sudan III stain   mix with distilled water.
Biuret reagent   Indicators are available from chemical supply houses and should be put in dropper bottles.
Benedict's solution

Put on a laboratory apron if one is available. Put on safety goggles. Handle all glassware carefully. Always use special caution when using any laboratory chemicals, as they may irritate the skin or cause staining of the skin or clothing. Never touch or taste any chemical unless instructed to do so. Use extreme care when working with heated equipment or materials to avoid burns. Note all safety alert symbols next to the steps in the Procedure and review the meanings of each symbol by referring to the symbol guide on page 10.

Procedure   For suggestions for a shorter lab period, see the Note at the end of Going Further.

Part A. Testing for Lipids

1. Obtain 9 test tubes and place them in a test tube rack. Use masking tape to make labels for each test tube. As shown in Figure 1, write the name of a different food sample (listed in Materials) on each masking-tape label. Label the ninth test tube "distilled water."

2. Fill each test tube with 5 mL of the substance indicated on the masking-tape label. Add 5 drops of Sudan III stain to each test tube. Sudan III stain will turn red in the presence of lipids.

3. Gently shake the contents of each test tube. **CAUTION:** *Use extreme care when handling Sudan III to avoid staining hands or clothing.* In the Data Table record any color changes and place a check mark next to those substances testing positively for lipids.

4. Wash the test tubes thoroughly.

5. For another test for lipids, divide a piece of brown paper into 9 equal sections. In each section, write the name of one test substance. See Figure 2.

Figure 1

Honey	Egg white	Corn oil	Lettuce	Gelatin
Butter	Potato	Apple juice	Distilled water	

Figure 2   Empty square can be used later to test unknown substance.

6. In each section, rub a small amount of the identified food onto the brown paper. Rub the food until a "wet" spot appears on the paper. With a paper towel, rub off any excess pieces of food that may stick to the paper. Set the paper aside until the spots appear dry—about 10 to 15 minutes.

7. Hold the piece of brown paper up to a bright light or window. You will notice that some foods leave a translucent spot on the brown paper. The translucent spot indicates the presence of lipids.

Part B. Testing for Carbohydrates

1. Sugars and starches are two common types of carbohydrates. To test for starch, refill each cleaned test tube with 5 mL of the substance indicated on the masking-tape label. Add 5 drops of iodine solution to each test tube. Iodine will change color from yellow-brown to blue-black in the presence of starch.

2. Gently shake the contents of each test tube. **CAUTION:** *Use extreme caution when using iodine as it is poisonous and can also stain hands and clothing.* In the Data Table, record any color changes and place a check mark next to those substances testing positive for starch.

3. Wash the test tubes thoroughly.

4. For a sugar test, set up a hot-water bath as shown in Figure 3. Half fill the beaker with tap water. Heat the water to a gentle boil. **CAUTION:** *Use extreme care when working with hot water. Do not let the water splash onto your hands.*

5. While the water bath is heating, fill each cleaned test tube with 5 mL of the substance indicated on the masking-tape label. Add 10 drops of Benedict's solution to each test tube. When heated, Benedict's solution will change color from blue to green, yellow, orange, or red in the presence of a single sugar, or monosaccharide.

6. Gently shake the contents of each test tube. **CAUTION:** *Use extreme caution when using Benedict's solution to avoid staining hands or clothing.*

Figure 3

7. Place the test tubes in the hot-water bath. Heat the test tubes for 3 to 5 minutes. With the test tube holder, remove the test tubes from the hot-water bath and place them back in the test tube rack. **CAUTION:** *Never touch hot test tubes with your bare hands. Always use a test tube holder to handle hot test tubes.* In the Data Table, record any color changes and place a check mark next to any substances that test positive for a single sugar.   Benedict's solution will not react with sucrose. Avoid materials that contain sucrose.

8. After they have cooled, wash the test tubes thoroughly.

As an alternate test for proteins, have students add 10 drops of nitric acid to each
Part C. Testing for Proteins material. A yellow-brown color indicates the presence of protein. Warn students to
be careful with nitric acid as it is very caustic and can burn the skin.

1. Put 5 mL of the appropriate substance in each labeled test tube. Add 5 drops of Biuret reagent to each test tube. **CAUTION:** *Biuret reagent contains sodium hydroxide, a strong base. If you splash any reagent on yourself, wash it off immediately with water. Call your teacher for assistance.*

2. Gently shake the contents of each test tube. Biuret reagent changes color from yellow to blue-violet in the presence of protein. In the Data Table, record any changes in color and place a check mark next to any substances that test positively for protein.

3. Wash test tubes thoroughly.

Part D. Testing an Unknown Substance for Organic Compounds

1. Obtain a sample of an unknown substance from your teacher and pour it into the remaining test tube. Repeat the tests described in Parts A, B, and C of the Procedure to determine the main organic compounds in your sample. Record your results in the Data Table.

2. Wash the test tube thoroughly.

Observations

Data Table

Substance	Lipid Test		Carbohydrate Test				Protein Test	
	Sudan color	Lipids Present (✓)	Iodine color	Starches present (✓)	Benedict color	Sugar present (✓)	Biuret color	Proteins present (✓)
Honey					Orange	√		
Egg white							Blue-violet	√
Corn oil	Red	√						
Lettuce								
Gelatin							Blue-violet	√
Butter	Red	√						
Potato			Black	√				
Apple juice					Orange	√		
Distilled water								
Unkown			Answers will vary depending on unknown.					

Analysis and Conclusions

1. Which test substances contain lipids? Corn oil and butter (possibly the unknown).

2. Which test substances contain starch? Potato (possibly the unknown).

3. Which test substances contain single sugar? Honey and apple juice (possibly the unknown).

4. Which test substances contain protein? Egg white and gelatin (possibly the unknown).

5. Which test substances did not test positive for any of the organic compounds?
Lettuce (possibly the unknown).

6. What is the purpose of using distilled water as one of your test substances?

Distilled water acts as a control and is used as a standard in color comparisons.

7. What do all of the indicators you have used have in common? The indicators change color in the presence of certain organic compounds and are therefore useful in identifying these compounds.

Critical Thinking and Application

1. Your brown lunch bag has a large, translucent spot on the bottom. What explanation could you give for this occurrence? Some food item in the lunch bag contains lipids. (Students might say that the bag accidentally rested on a substance containing lipids.)

2. What conclusion could you make if a positive test for any of the organic compounds occurred in the test tube containing only distilled water? The test tube, distilled water, or indicators may have been contaminated. The tests should be conducted again to achieve accurate results.

3. A very thin slice is removed from a peanut and treated with Sudan III stain. Then a drop of Biuret reagent is added to the peanut slice. When you examine the peanut slice under a microscope, patches of red and blue-violet are visible. What conclusions can you draw from your examination? Peanuts contain lipids and proteins.

Going Further

1. Test each food from a school lunch for the presence of lipids, starch, single sugars, and proteins. Construct a data table to summarize your findings.

2. Make three-dimensional models of the molecules of the organic compounds described in this investigation. Use polystyrene spheres, gum drops, or pieces of clay to represent the atoms of each molecule. Each type of atom should have its own distinct color. Use toothpicks to represent the bonds between atoms.

A Shorter Lab Period:

If you wish to shorten this investigation, you may want to have your students omit Part D of the Procedure (testing of an unknown substance). It is also possible to have students test fewer than the eight listed food substances. If you wish to have students complete the entire investigation but do not feel that the time within one class period is adequate, schedule Parts A, B, and C for one class period and Part D for part of another class period.

9

Characteristics of Prokaryotic and Eukaryotic Cells

You may want to refer students to pages 87–99 in the textbook for a discussion of prokaryotic and eukaryotic cells.

Time required: 50 minutes.

Pre-Lab Discussion

Cells are the basic units of structure and function of all living things. There are two major divisions into which all cells fall—prokaryotic and eukaryotic.

Prokaryotic cells are cells that lack a nucleus and membrane-bound organelles. Bacteria and related microorganisms are prokaryotes. *Eukaryotic cells* are cells that contain a nucleus and membrane-bound organelles. Organisms such as animals, plants, fungi, and protists are all eukaryotes.

In this investigation, you will observe several prepared slides to examine the differences between prokaryotic and eukaryotic cells. You will also use these differences to classify an unknown specimen.

Problem

What are the differences between prokaryotic and eukaryotic cells?

Materials *(per group)*

Microscope
Lens paper
Prepared slides of prokaryotic and eukaryotic cells

Prepared slides could include:
Animal cells (eukaryotic): human and/or frog blood cells, skeletal and cardiac muscle cells, epithelial cells, and nerve cells
Plant cells (eukaryotic): cross sections of leaves, stems, and roots
Fungal cells (eukaryotic): *Lycogala, Rhizopus,* and mushroom cross sections
Protist cells (eukaryotic): paramecia, diatoms, amebas, and *Nostoc*
Moneran cells (prokaryotic): bacteria types and cyanobacteria, such as *Anabaena*

Safety ⚗

Always handle the microscope with extreme care. You are responsible for its proper care and use. Use caution when handling glass slides as they can break easily and cut you. Note all safety alert symbols next to the steps in the Procedure and review the meanings of each symbol by referring to the symbol guide on page 10.

Procedure   For suggestions for a shorter lab period, see the Note at the end of Going Further.

1. Take a microscope from the storage area and place it about 10 centimeters from the edge of the laboratory table.

2. Carefully clean the eyepiece and objective lens with lens paper.

⚗ 3. Place your first prepared slide on the microscope stage so that it is centered over the stage opening. Hold the slide in position with the stage clips.

4. Using the low-power objective lens, locate the cell(s) under the microscope. Turn the coarse adjustment knob until the cell comes into focus.

5. In the Data Table, write the name of the type of cell that you examined. Describe the general shape of the cell in the space provided. Estimate the length of the cell and record this figure. Refer to Laboratory Investigation 4 if you need to review how to estimate the size of objects under the microscope. Put a check mark next to the cell structures you are able to observe under low power.

6. Switch to the high-power objective lens. **CAUTION:** *When turning to the high-power objective lens, you should always look at the objective from the side of your microscope so that the objective lens does not hit or damage the slide.* Look for cell structures unobservable under low power. Put a check mark next to these structures in the Data Table. Based on your observations, decide if the cell is prokaryotic or eukaryotic and record this in the Data Table.

7. In the appropriate place in Observations, draw and label what you see using the high-power objective lens. Record the magnification of the microscope.

8. Repeat steps 1 through 7 using other prepared slides provided by your teacher.

9. Repeat steps 1 through 7 using an unidentified prepared slide provided by your teacher.

10. When you have finished examining all of the prepared slides, return the microscope to the storage area.

Observations
Data Table

| Cell Type | Shape | Size (µm) | Cell Structures | | | | | | | Prokaryotic or Eukaryotic |
			Cell wall	Cell membrane	Nucleus	Nuclear envelope	Cytoplasm	Vacuoles	Plastids	
		Answers will vary depending on slides available.								
Unknown										

Students may need to use their textbooks to complete the Data Table.

Prepared Slide 1 High-power objective

Magnification _____

Prepared Slide 2 High-power objective

Magnification _____

Prepared Slide 3 High-power objective

Magnification _____

Drawings will vary
depending on slides
available.

_____

Prepared Slide 4 High-power objective

Magnification _____

_____

Prepared Slide 5 High-power objective

Magnification _____

Unknown

_____

Analysis and Conclusions

1. Based on your observations, do all cells have the same shape? Support your answer.

   No. Students should find that cells have different shapes. Students should use their findings to support this
   fact.

2. Based on your observations, do all cells have the same size? Support your answer.

   No. Students should find that cells vary greatly in size. Students should use their findings to support this
   fact.

3. What cell structures are common to all cells? A cell membrane and cytoplasm.

_____

4. What cell structures are found only in eukaryotic cells? Nucleus, nuclear envelope, vacuoles, and plastids.

5. Are the nuclei always found in the same place within different types of cells? Support your answer. No. Students should find that the nuclei can be found in many different locations within a cell.

Critical Thinking and Application

1. Skin cells seem to fit together like pieces of a jigsaw puzzle. How is this arrangement of cells helpful to an organism? Skin cells act as protection for an organism. Interlocking or overlapping of cells helps provide a better protective layer.

2. Why do cells have different shapes and sizes? Cells with different shapes and sizes have different jobs. Cell shape and size is related to cell function.

3. What cell structure might you be able to compare to the main (principal's) office in your school? Explain your answer. The nucleus acts similarly to the main office of a school. The main office directs the activities of the school and the nucleus directs the activities of a living cell.

Going Further

1. Observe characteristics of living cells by making wet-mount slides of plant and animal tissues or protist cultures. Construct a data table to record the shapes and sizes of the cells and the structures they contain.

2. Think about the cell structures that you were unable to see with a compound light microscope. Use resources from your library to locate electron micrographs of these structures.

3. Research the use of some of the stains used in the preparation of wet-mount slides. Some of the stains that might be included in your report are methylene blue, neutral red, acetocarmine, Congo red, Janus green B, and Sudan III. What cell structures do each of these stains make more visible?

A Shorter Lab Period:

To shorten this investigation, you may wish to have students look at fewer prepared slides than suggested in the Procedure. You may also wish to omit the observation and identification of the unknown slide.

10

Comparing Plant and Animal Cells

You may want to refer students to pages 87–99 of the textbook for a discussion of plant and animal cells.

Time required: 40 minutes.

Pre-Lab Discussion

Ever since the first microscope was used, biologists have been interested in studying the cellular organization of all living things. After hundreds of years of observations by many biologists, the cell theory was developed. The cell theory states that the cell is the structural and functional unit of living things. Cells contain structures called organelles that carry out life processes. Cells can be classified by the types of organelles they contain. In plant and animal cells, similarities and differences exist because of varied life functions.

In this investigation, you will compare the structures of a typical plant cell *(Elodea)* and a typical animal cell (human).

Problem

How are plant and animal cells alike? How are they different?

Materials *(per group)*

Forceps
Medicine dropper
Elodea leaf   Can be purchased from a supply house or aquarium (pet) store.
Water
Microscope
Glass slide   This investigation is set up for 2 or more students to share a microscope,
Coverslip   but each student should make up his or her own slides.
Toothpicks
Methylene blue stain   Available from a chemical supply house.
Paper towel
Lens paper

Safety 🧪 🥽 ⊡ ▨

Put on a laboratory apron if one is available. Put on safety goggles. Always handle the microscope with extreme care. You are responsible for its proper care and use. Use caution when handling glass slides as they can break easily and cut you. Always use special caution when working with laboratory chemicals, as they may irritate the skin or cause staining of the skin or clothing. Never touch or taste any chemical unless instructed to do so. Note all safety alert symbols next to the steps in the Procedure and review the meanings of each symbol by referring to the symbol guide on page 10.

Procedure

Part A. Examining Plant Cells

1. Take a microscope from the storage area and place it about 10 centimeters from the edge of the laboratory table.

2. Carefully clean the eyepiece and objective lenses with lens paper.

3. Place a drop of water in the center of a clean glass slide.

4. With the forceps, remove a leaf from the *Elodea* plant and place it on the drop of water on the slide. Make sure that the leaf is flat. If it is folded, straighten it with the forceps.

5. Carefully place a coverslip over the drop of water and *Elodea* leaf.

6. Place the slide on the stage of the microscope with the leaf directly over the opening in the stage.

7. Using the low-power objective lens, locate the leaf under the microscope. Turn the coarse adjustment knob until the leaf comes into focus.

8. Switch to the high-power objective lens. **CAUTION:** *When turning to the high-power objective lens, you should always look at the objective from the side of your microscope so that the objective lens does not hit or damage the slide.*

9. Observe the cells of the *Elodea* leaf. Draw and label what you see in the appropriate place in Observations. Record the magnification of the microscope.

10. Carefully clean and dry your slide and coverslip.

Part B. Examining Animal Cells

1. Place a drop of water in the center of a clean glass slide.

2. Using the flat end of a toothpick, gently scrape the inside of your cheek. See Figure 1. **CAUTION:** *Do not use force when scraping the inside of your cheek. Only a few cells are needed.* The end of the toothpick will have several cheek cells stuck to it even though you may see nothing but a drop of saliva.

3. Stir the water on the slide with the end of the toothpick to mix the cheek cells with the water. See Figure 2. Dispose of the toothpick as instructed by your teacher.

   Because each student is responsible for making his or her own slides, emphasize the importance of using a clean, unused toothpick for this part of the investigation.

Figure 1

Toothpick
cheek cell

Drop of water

Figure 2

4. Put one drop of methylene blue stain on top of the drop of water containing the cheek cells. **CAUTION:** *Use care when working with methylene blue to avoid staining hands and clothing.*

5. Wait one minute, then carefully place a coverslip over the stained cheek cells.

6. To remove the stain from under the coverslip and replace it with clear water, place a piece of paper towel at the edge of one side of the coverslip. Then place a drop of water at the edge of the coverslip on the opposite side. See Figure 3. The stained water under the coverslip will be absorbed by the paper towel. As the stain is removed, the clear water next to the coverslip on the opposite side will be drawn under the coverslip. Discard the paper towel after it has absorbed the stained water.

Top view   **Side view**

Figure 3

7. Place the slide on the stage of the microscope with the center of the coverslip directly over the opening in the stage.

8. Using the low-power objective lens, locate a few cheek cells under the microscope. **Note:** *You will need to reduce the amount of light coming through the slide in order to see the cells more clearly. Adjust the diaphragm as necessary.*

9. Switch to the high-power objective lens. **CAUTION:** *When turning to the high-power objective lens, you should always look at the objective from the side of your microscope so that the objective lens does not hit or damage the slide.*

10. Observe some cheek cells. Draw and label what you see in the appropriate place in Observations. Record the magnification of the microscope.

11. Carefully clean and dry your slide and coverslip.

12. Return your microscope to the storage area.

Magnification _____   Magnification _____

Elodea Cells   **Cheek Cells**
(Plant cells)   (Animal cells)

Observations

1. **What is the shape of an *Elodea* cell?** *Elodea* cells are rectangular and are stacked on top of one another like bricks in a building.

2. **What is the general location of the nucleus in an *Elodea* cell?** The nucleus is found at the outside edge of an *Elodea* cell.

3. **What is the shape of the cheek cell?** Cheek cells have an elongated, irregular shape.

4. **What is the general location of the nucleus in a cheek cell?** The nucleus is found in the middle of the cheek cell.

Analysis and Conclusions

1. **How are plant and animal cells similar in structure?** Both plant and animal cells have a cell membrane, cytoplasm, and nucleus.

2. **How are plant and animal cells different in structure?** Plant cells have a cell wall and chloroplasts; animal cells lack these structures.

3. Why are stains such as methylene blue used when observing cells under the microscope?

Stains are used so that it is easier to observe under the microscope certain cell structures that are normally

transparent.

Critical Thinking and Application

1. What is an advantage of using a wet-mount preparation instead of a dry-mount preparation in the study of living cells? Students might say that if water were not used, the living material would tend to

dry out. Also, the use of water allows stains to be added and removed with relative ease. Water also tends

to flatten out a specimen for better viewing with the microscope.

2. Explain why you could not use an oak leaf in this investigation. An entire oak leaf is not only too

large to fit under the microscope, it is also too thick to allow light to pass through. As a result, no cells can

be seen.

3. Why is it possible to easily collect cells by gently scraping the inside of your cheek?

Cheek cells, which are types of epithelial cells, provide covering and protection for the organism. They are

always sloughing off and being replaced by new cells, making them easy to collect.

4. In general, the surface of a tree has a harder "feel" than does the surface of a dog. What cell characteristic of each organism can be used to explain this difference?

Plants such as trees have cellulose cell walls that result in their rigidity. Animal cells do not have cell walls

and, therefore, have a softer "feel" than plant tissues.

5. If you were given a slide containing living cells of an unknown organism, how would you

identify the cells as either plant or animal? Plant cells have cell walls and chloroplasts, whereas

animal cells do not. You would look for the presence or absence of these structures to identify the cells.

Going Further

1. Remove the skin from fruits and vegetables such as tomatoes, onions, and leeks. Prepare wet-mount slides for each skin and observe the cells under the low-power and high-power objectives of your microscope. Sketch and label what you see. What cell structures do these cells have in common? How do these cells compare with animal cells?

2. Make a wet-mount slide of an *Elodea* leaf using a 10% salt solution (10 g of table salt dissolved in 100 mL of water) instead of water. Examine the leaf under low power and high power. Describe any differences in characteristics between these *Elodea* cells and the cells observed in water.

11

Plant Pigments

You may want to refer students to pages 113–129 in the textbook for a discussion of photosynthesis and respiration.

Time required: 40 minutes.

Pre-Lab Discussion

Photosynthesis begins when light is absorbed by pigments in the plant cell. One technique for separating and identifying these pigments is paper chromatography. In paper chromatography, solvent moves up the paper carrying with it dissolved substances—in this case plant pigments. The pigments are carried along at different rates because they are not equally soluble in the solvent and are attracted in different degrees to the paper.

Many green leaves contain pigment colors that are not seen until autumn because they are hidden by the chlorophyll. A few plants have leaves that are red, orange, or yellow all year long.

In this investigation, you will use paper chromatography to determine what differences exist in the plant pigments of various colors of leaves. You will also determine which leaves or which parts of leaves contain the chlorophyll necessary to carry out photosynthesis.

Problem

What plant pigments can be found in different colored leaves?

Materials *(per group)*

Pretest your filter paper for speed of solvent movement. Purchase "fast" filter paper if ordering.

2 pieces of filter paper   Each piece should be larger than 12 cm x 7 cm.
2 150-mL beakers
2 glass plates (covers for beakers)   Any suitably sized cover will work.
Coin   A penny or a dime works best.
70% isopropyl alcohol (rubbing alcohol)   Available at supermarkets.
Fresh spinach leaf   Available at supermarkets; other green leaves will also work.
Red leaf such as a *Coleus* leaf
Scissors
Stapler
Metric ruler
Pencil

Safety 🔥 ▭ 🖻 ▰

Put on a laboratory apron if one is available. Put on safety goggles. Handle all glassware carefully. Alcohol is flammable. Do not expose it to heat or flames. Do this laboratory investigation in a well-ventilated room. Be careful when handling sharp instruments. Note all safety alert symbols next to the steps in the Procedure and review the meanings of each symbol by referring to the symbol guide on page 10.

Procedure

1. Make two filter-paper rectangles that are each approximately 12 cm by 7 cm. Using a pencil, draw a base line 1.5 cm from the bottom of the long side of each rectangle. See Figure 1.

7 cm

Base line
1.5 cm

12 cm

Figure 1

2. Place a spinach leaf over the pencil line on one of the rectangles. Roll the coin over the leaf so that a horizontal green line is transferred to the pencil line. Repeat this step with the red leaf and the second filter-paper rectangle. See Figure 2.

Figure 2

Coin

3. Add just enough isopropyl alcohol to each of the two beakers to cover the bottom. Do not add more than 1 cm to ensure that the pigment line will not be submerged when the paper is lowered into the beaker. **CAUTION:** *Avoid inhaling the alcohol.*

4. Make a cylinder of each piece of filter paper by stapling it end to end. Lower each paper cylinder into a beaker containing alcohol. See Figure 3. The solvent will begin to move up the paper and cause the pigments to move as well.

Staple

Base line

Alcohol

Figure 3

5. Cover each beaker with a glass plate. Do not disturb the beakers for approximately 15 minutes, or until the solvent is about 1 cm from the top of the paper.

6. When the solvent is about 1 cm from the top of the paper, remove the paper and mark the farthest point of the solvent's progress (front line) with your pencil before this line evaporates.

7. Allow the filter-paper cylinders to dry, and then make a sketch of the chromatogram. Some possible colors and the pigments they represent are: faint yellow–carotenes; yellow–xanthophyll; bright green–chlorophyll *a;* yellow–green–chlorophyll *b;* red–anthocyanin *
   These are listed in order of appearance with anthocyanin nearest the base line.

Observations

Data Table   Answers will vary. Data given represent possible results.

	Line	Color Observed	Probable Pigment
S p i n a c h	1 (base line)	none	
	2	yellow-green	chlorophyll *b*
	3	bright green	chlorophyll *a*
	4	yellow	xanthophyll
	5 (front line)	faint yellow	carotenes
R e d L e a f	1 (base line)	red	anthocyanin
	2	yellow-green	chlorophyll *b*
	3	bright green	chlorophyll *a*
	4	yellow	xanthophyll
	5 (front line)	faint yellow	carotenes

Analysis and Conclusions

1. How many pigments were separated in each type of leaf? Spinach–4 pigments. Red leaf–5 pigments.

   _____

   _____

2. How did the pigments in the spinach leaf compare with the pigments in the red leaf?

   The red leaf had one more pigment (anthocyanin) than the spinach leaf. This pigment masked the other

   pigments.

* The anthocyanin is a form of stored sugar and provides color to attract insects. All other pigments are involved in photosynthesis.

3. Which of these leaves can carry on photosynthesis? Explain your answer.

They both can do photosynthesis. They both contain chlorophyll.

Critical Thinking and Application

1. Photosynthesis requires the green pigment chlorophyll. Explain how a Japanese maple tree, having only red leaves, can carry on photosynthesis. The green chlorophyll is present in the red leaf, but it is hidden by the red pigment.

2. Many trees have leaves that are green in the summer and red, yellow, or orange in autumn. Where were these colors during the summer? How can they suddenly appear in autumn?

The colors other than green are in the leaves all summer, but they are hidden by the chlorophyll. When the chlorophyll breaks down in autumn, the other colors are exposed.

3. In addition to separating plant pigments, what are some other possible applications for paper chromatography? Paper chromatography could separate the components of any mixture of molecules that have different solubilities in a solvent. It is used in many areas of chemical, medical, and biological research.

Going Further

Perform a similar experiment to compare the light pink portion of the *Coleus* leaf to the dark purple portion, or to compare leaves from plants grown in the dark to leaves from plants grown in the light.

12

What Plants Do With Sunlight

You may want to refer students to pages 113–123 in the textbook for a discussion of photosynthesis.

Time required:
    Day 1–15 minutes
    Day 2–45 minutes

Pre-Lab Discussion

The energy used by living things ultimately comes from the sun. Plants produce food by changing radiant energy to chemical energy. Plants do this in a process called photosynthesis. Photosynthesis captures light energy and stores it in glucose molecules. The glucose molecules are then almost immediately bound together into chainlike molecules of starch. You can test for the presence of starch by using iodine solution, which turns blue or blue-black in the presence of starch.

In this investigation, you will observe what plants do with sunlight. You will use the starch test to compare the contents of the leaves of plants that have grown with and without the presence of light. The covered leaves will be the experimental leaves and the uncovered one the control leaf.

Problem

What do plants do with sunlight?

Materials *(per group)*

Geranium or other green plant
    that has been in the dark for
    2 days
Aluminum foil
Dark construction paper
Scissors
1000-mL beaker   You may substitute
250-mL beaker   other heat-proof
    containers of a
    similar size.

150 mL 95% ethyl alcohol
200 mL tap water
Hot plate
Medicine dropper
Forceps
Iodine solution
Paper clips
3 petri dishes

At the beginning of the investigation, set up a water bath to heat water and alcohol as shown in Figure 2.

You may purchase Lugol's iodine solution from a chemical supply house or dissolve 10 g of potassium iodide and 5 g of iodine in 1 L of distilled water. Stir until completely dissolved.

You may substitute other containers large enough to hold one leaf each.

Safety ⚗ 🥽 🔥 👁

Put on a laboratory apron if one is available. Put on safety goggles. Alcohol is flammable. Do not expose it to heat or flames. Do this laboratory investigation in a well-ventilated room. Always use special caution when working with chemicals, as they may irritate the skin or cause staining of the skin or clothing. Never touch or taste any chemical unless instructed to do so. Note all safety alert symbols next to the steps in the Procedure and review the meanings of each symbol by referring to the symbol guide on page 10.

Procedure

Part A. Preparing the Plant

1. Completely cover one of the leaves on the plant with aluminum foil. You may need to secure the foil with a paper clip. On a second leaf, paper clip a piece of construction paper that has been cut in the shape of the letter X. See Figure 1. You might wish to have precut pieces of construction paper in the shape of your school mascot.

2. Identify each leaf you are using with a masking-tape label that gives your group number or name and your class period. Wrap the masking tape loosely around the petiole of the leaf. See Figure 1.

3. Place the plant in bright light for 2 to 3 days.

Figure 1

Part B. Testing the Leaves

1. After 2 to 3 days, remove 3 leaves from the plant: the 2 experimental leaves (1 covered with aluminum foil and 1 with paper shape attached) and 1 control leaf (leaf that has had no treatment). Remove the masking-tape labels, but in order to identify the leaves, cut their petioles different lengths according to the following:

   no petiole—control leaf (no treatment)
   half petiole—leaf with paper shape attached
   full petiole—leaf covered with aluminum foil

2. Your teacher has set up a water bath in which the alcohol is heating. Remove the aluminum foil and the paper shape from the 2 leaves. Then drop all 3 leaves into the boiling water in the larger beaker of the water bath. Allow the leaves to remain in the boiling water for 1 minute. **CAUTION:** *Do not remove the beaker containing alcohol from the water while you use the water around it.* See Figure 2.

3. Remove the leaves from the boiling water with forceps and drop them into the hot alcohol in the inner beaker. Keep them in the hot alcohol until they have lost most of their color.

4. When the leaves have lost most of their color, remove them from the alcohol with forceps and dip them into the hot water again for a few seconds. This will keep the leaves from getting brittle.

5. Place the leaves into three different petri dishes.

6. Use the medicine dropper to cover each of the leaves with iodine solution. After one minute, pour off the excess iodine solution and record your observations in the Data Table.

Figure 2

110

Observations

Data Table

Leaf	Treatment	Effect of Iodine
1	covered with aluminum foil	no color change; iodine remained brown
2	covered with paper shape	blue outside of shape; no color change within shape
3	no covering—full light	entire leaf blue

Analysis and Conclusions

1. What does a positive iodine test (blue or blue-black) indicate is present in the leaf?
   Starch is present in the leaf.

2. Which leaves showed a positive iodine test? Leaves 2 and 3 showed a positive iodine test.

3. What environmental factor is necessary in order to get a positive iodine test?
   Light is necessary for a positive test.

4. Can a plant store energy in its leaves in the absence of light? No. Light is necessary for energy to
   be stored as starch.

5. In those leaves in which you observed a negative iodine test, what can you say about the

   process of photosynthesis? Photosynthesis was not occurring.

6. What do plants do with sunlight? Plants use sunlight to store energy in their leaves in the form of starch. Plants need sunlight for the process of photosynthesis.

Critical Thinking and Application

1. Photosynthesis produces glucose. What is the relationship between glucose and starch?

Starch is a chain of glucose molecules. In a plant, glucose is quickly stored as starch.

2. Explain the importance of plants to the survival of animals. All energy for the survival of living things ultimately comes from the sun. Plants alone can change the radiant energy of the sun into the chemical energy that animals can utilize.

3. Does photosynthesis occur at night? Explain. No. Light is necessary for photosynthesis.

4. Some paleontologists hypothesize that dinosaurs became extinct after the impact of a huge meteorite darkened the atmosphere of the Earth with dust. Using knowledge gained in this laboratory investigation, explain how this darkening could affect animals.

Enough sunlight may have been blocked out to cause plants to die. Primary consumers would soon have starved to death, and higher-order consumers would have soon followed.

Going Further

Investigate starch production in plants by varying the color or intensity of the light used on the plants, rather than the presence or absence of light.

13

Assembling a Protein Molecule

You may want to refer students to pages 148–153 in the textbook for a discussion of protein synthesis.

Time required: 45 minutes. (Time required indicates the synthesizing of proteins 1 and 2. Additional proteins are practice only.)

Pre-Lab Discussion

DNA and RNA, the two types of nucleic acids found in cells, determine which protein molecules a cell makes, or synthesizes. Protein molecules, formed by sequencing twenty different amino acids in various combinations, are important to living things because they control biological pathways, direct the synthesis of organic molecules, and are responsible for cell structure and movement. DNA carries the information for the synthesis of all the proteins in code form. The three different types of RNA carry out the DNA instructions to synthesize proteins.

During *transcription,* the DNA code is transcribed by mRNA into the language of protein synthesis. Three base *codons* of mRNA carry this information to the ribosomes, where *translation* occurs. During translation, mRNA codons are translated into a protein molecule when tRNA *anticodons* bring the correct amino acids to the ribosome. The amino acids brought side-by-side by tRNA form *peptide bonds* and become protein molecules.

In this investigation you will model the process of protein synthesis carried out by the cells of your body.

Problem

How can you and your classmates carry out the different processes of protein synthesis and assemble a protein molecule?

Prepare the index cards in advance by using the Data Table to determine the cards needed for each protein. Use different color index cards or markers to identify each role. For example, cards needed to synthesize Protein 1:

Materials *(per class)*

Large index cards
String, 70 cm long

Red (amino acids)–Proline, Glutamic Acid, Alanine
Blue (DNA)–GGC, CTT, CGT, CCG,* GAA,* GCA*
Yellow (mRNA)–CCG, GAA, GCA
Orange (tRNA)–GGC, CUU, CGU

Add additional cards to each category to give every student a role as well as to serve as detractors.

Procedure

You may want to do step 1 the day before doing this investigation so that students can review their role in protein synthesis.

1. Obtain a large index card from your teacher. On this card, you will find your assignment for this investigation. You may have the role of an amino acid, a DNA triplet, an mRNA codon, or a tRNA anticodon. Put the card around your neck and make sure you understand your role in protein synthesis.

2. Report to the area of the cell where you will carry out your role. Designate certain parts of the classroom as the ribosome and the nucleus (you can also use string or rope to make a nuclear membrane with pores).

* These DNA triplets represent the other side of the DNA molecule coding for the given amino acid. Do not forget to make these cards to match each DNA triplet given in the Data Table.

3. When your teacher identifies the amino acids that make up the protein to be synthesized, use Figure 1 to determine the DNA triplets that code for that protein. Complete the Data Table for the protein to be synthesized.

4. The DNA nucleotides should form a double stranded DNA molecule in which the DNA triplets will code for the announced protein. Students can place hands on shoulders and/or hold hands to represent bond formation.

5. The DNA molecule unzips to allow the mRNA codons to form. Once the mRNA codons form and leave the nucleus, the DNA molecule reforms.

6. The mRNA codons move to the ribosomes and line up in the correct sequence.

7. On the ribosome, tRNA anticodons with the proper amino acids pair up with the correct mRNA codons.

8. As the mRNA moves along the ribosome, peptide bonds form between the amino acids. When the protein molecule has been made, mRNA, tRNA, and the protein leave the ribosome and return to the cytoplasm.

9. Repeat steps 1 through 8 to form another protein.

Amino Acid	DNA Triplet
Alanine	CGT
Glutamine	GTT
Glutamic Acid	CTT
Leucine	GAT
Lysine	TTT
Phenylalanine	AAA
Proline	GGC
Serine	AGC
Tyrosine	ATG
Valine	CAA

Figure 1

Observations

1. Using Figure 1, complete the Data Table for each protein molecule.

Data Table

Protein	Amino Acids	DNA Triplet	mRNA Codon	tRNA Anticodon
1	Proline Glutamic Acid Alanine	GGC CTT CGT	CCG GAA GCA	GGC CUU CGU
2	Lysine Glutamine Valine	TTT GTT CAA	AAA CAA GUU	UUU GUU CAA
3	Leucine Proline Tyrosine	GAT GGC ATG	CUA CCG UAC	GAU GGC AUG
4	Phenylalanine Glutamine Proline	AAA GTT GGC	UUU CAA CCG	AAA GUU GGC
5	Lysine Serine Leucine	TTT AGC GAT	AAA UCG CUA	UUU AGC GAU

2. In what ways do DNA and RNA molecules differ? DNA is a double-stranded molecule containing the

sugar deoxyribose and the base thymine. RNA is a single-stranded molecule containing ribose and the base

uracil (instead of thymine).

3. How was mRNA formed? Free mRNA nucleotides pair with their complementary bases along an

"unzipped" DNA molecule.

4. How do mRNA and tRNA differ? tRNA is found only in the cytoplasm and has a special affinity for

amino acids.

5. Where in the cell are protein molecules formed? In the ribosomes.

Analysis and Conclusions

1. What is the role of DNA in protein synthesis? DNA provides the instructions for the formation of

proteins that a cell may need.

2. What is the role of mRNA in protein synthesis? mRNA copies and carries out the instructions of the

genetic code.

3. Which step in the procedure represents transcription? Explain your answer.

Step 5—mRNA transcribes the genetic code into the language of protein synthesis.

4. Which step in the procedure represents translation? Explain your answer.

Step 7—tRNA anticodons translate the mRNA instructions into a protein molecule by bringing the proper

amino acids together.

5. What would happen to Protein 1 if the first DNA triplet was TTT instead of GGC?

A different protein would have formed. The protein would begin with the amino acid lysine instead of proline.

Critical Thinking and Application

1. How do the processes of transcription and translation differ? Transcription—instructions for protein are copied by mRNA. Translation—mRNA instructions are carried out by tRNA.

2. How do DNA replication and DNA transcription differ? DNA replication produces an exact copy of the cell's DNA. In transcription, mRNA makes a copy of the genetic code in a form that can be carried out by the mRNA to produce a protein molecule.

3. If an incorrect nucleotide is in a DNA molecule due to a mutation, will protein synthesis be affected? Explain your answer. Yes. mRNA will transcribe the mutation as part of the instructions for a protein molecule, and during translation the mutation will code for an incorrect amino acid.

Going Further

Design a system of communication using four different colors to represent each letter of the alphabet. (*Hint:* Use the genetic triplet code as a model.)

14

Simulating Protein Synthesis

You may want to refer students to pages 148–152 in the textbook for a discussion of transcription and translation.

Time required: 45 minutes.

Pre-Lab Discussion

Genes are the units that determine inherited characteristics, such as hair color and blood type. Genes are lengths of DNA molecules that determine the structure of polypeptides (the building blocks of proteins) that our cells make. The sequence of nucleotides in DNA determines the sequence of amino acids in polypeptides, and thus the structure of proteins.

In a process called *transcription,* which takes place in the nucleus of the cell, messenger RNA (mRNA) reads and copies the DNA's nucleotide sequences in the form of a complementary RNA molecule. Then the mRNA carries this information in the form of a code to the ribosomes, where protein synthesis takes place. The code, in DNA or mRNA, specifies the order in which the amino acids are joined together to form a polypeptide. The code words in mRNA, however, are not directly recognized by the corresponding amino acids. Another type of RNA called transfer RNA (tRNA) is needed to bring the mRNA and amino acids together. As the code carried by mRNA is "read" on a ribosome, the proper tRNAs arrive in turn and give up the amino acids they carry to the growing polypeptide chain. The process by which the information from DNA is transferred into the language of proteins is known as *translation.*

In this investigation, you will simulate the mechanism of protein synthesis and thereby determine the traits inherited by fictitious organisms called CHNOPS. CHNOPS, whose cells contain only one chromosome, are members of the kingdom Animalia. A CHNOPS chromosome is made up of six genes (A, B, C, D, E, and F), each of which is responsible for a certain trait.

Problem

How can the traits on a particular chromosome be determined? How can these traits determine the characteristics of an organism?

Materials *(per student)*

Blue pencil
Orange pencil

Procedure

1. To determine the trait for Gene A of your CHNOPS, fill in the information in the box labeled Gene A in the Data Table. Notice the sequence of nucleotides in DNA. On the line provided, write the sequence of nucleotides of mRNA that are complementary to DNA. Then, on the line provided, write the sequence of nucleotides of tRNA that are complementary to mRNA.

2. In order to determine the sequence of amino acids, match each tRNA triplet with the specific amino acid in Figure 1. Using a - (hyphen) to separate each amino acid number, record this information in the appropriate place in the Data Table.

3. Using Figure 2, find the trait that matches the amino acid sequence. Record this information in the appropriate place in the Data Table.

4. Repeat steps 1 through 3 for the remaining genes (B through F).

5. Using all the inherited traits, sketch your CHNOPS in the space provided.

tRNA Triplet	Amino Acid Number
ACC	20
AGC	16
CGA	2
AAC	4
CGC	3
GGG	5
AGG	7
AAA	8
UUU	9
GGU	12
UAU	13
CCC	1
AUC	6
CUA	10
GGA	11

Figure 1

Amino Acid Sequence	Trait
20-11-13	hairless
20-12-13	hairy
20-21-21	plump
13-14-15	skinny
16-2	four-legged
12-7-8-1	long nose
5-7-8-1	short nose
9-8	no freckles
9-4	freckles
11-3-2	blue skin
11-3-3	orange skin
6-6-10	male
6-6-14	female

Figure 2

Observations

Data Table

Gene A		
DNA	ACC GGT TAT	
mRNA	UGG CCA AUA	
tRNA	ACC GGU UAU	
Amino acid sequence	20-12-13	
Trait	hairy	

Gene B		
DNA	AGC CGA	
mRNA	UCG GCU	
tRNA	AGC CGA	
Amino acid sequence	16-2	
Trait	four-legged	

Gene C		
DNA	TTT AAC	
mRNA	AAA UUG	
tRNA	UUU AAC	
Amino acid sequence	9-4	
Trait	freckles	

Gene D		
DNA	GGA CGC CGA	
mRNA	CCU GCG GCU	
tRNA	GGA CGC CGA	
Amino acid sequence	11-3-2	
Trait	blue skin	

Gene E		
DNA	GGG AGG AAA CCC	
mRNA	CCC UCC UUU GGG	
tRNA	GGG AGG AAA CCC	
Amino acid sequence	5-7-8-1	
Trait	short nose	

Gene F		
DNA	ATC ATC CTA	
mRNA	UAG UAG GAU	
tRNA	AUC AUC CUA	
Amino acid sequence	6-6-10	
Trait	male	

118

Check student drawing.

Analysis and Conclusions

1. Distinguish between translation and transcription. Translation is the process by which information in a strand of mRNA directs the sequence of amino acids during protein synthesis. Transcription is the process where information in one strand of DNA specifies a complementary sequence of bases in RNA.

2. What is the specific site for transcription and translation in the cell?
   Transcription usually occurs in the area of the nucleus. Translation occurs at the ribosomes (in the cell's cytoplasm) where proteins are synthesized.

3. How many tRNA nucleotides form an anticodon that will attach to the mRNA codon?
   3.

Critical Thinking and Application

1. Suppose you knew the makeup of specific proteins in a cell. How would you determine the particular DNA code that coded for them? _Reverse the process of protein synthesis by first decoding_ each amino acid in the protein.

2. How could one change in a DNA nucleotide alter the formation of the translated protein? (An example would be the difference between normal and sickle-cell hemoglobin.)

   One change of a nucleotide in the DNA strand would alter the nucleotide triplet code and ultimately cause the wrong amino acid to be bonded into the protein being made.

Going Further

Create two additional traits for your CHNOPS and give their initial DNA sequence, mRNA codon, and tRNA anticodon. Include the resulting amino acid sequence.

15

Investigating the Limits of Cell Growth

You may want to refer students to pages 159–161 in the textbook for a discussion of the limits of cell growth.

Time required: 40 minutes.

Pre-Lab Discussion

In multicellular organisms, growth is accomplished by the production of more cells by cell division. Cell division will occur only when the cells have reached a size large enough to ensure that the resulting daughter cells will have all of the necessary materials and structures for survival.

The rate of exchange of materials entering (food, oxygen, and water) and leaving (waste products) the cell through the cell membrane is determined by the cell's surface area. And the rate at which these materials are used within the cell depends upon the cell's volume, or the amount of space within the cell. A number of factors, such as the reduction of food and changes in temperature, can cause cells to stop growing and dividing.

In this investigation, you will observe one factor that limits cell growth.

Problem

What is one factor that limits cell growth?

Materials *(per group)*

Plastic spoon
3 agar-phenolphthalein blocks   Annotations for preparation of agar-phenolphthalein blocks are found
   (1 cm, 2 cm, and 3 cm)   at the end of Going Further.
250-mL beaker
100 mL of 0.4% sodium hydroxide solution   To prepare the 0.4% sodium hydroxide solution, add 4 g
Paper towel   sodium hydroxide to 1000 mL water.
Scalpel
Metric ruler

Safety ⚗ 📷 👁 ▭

Put on a laboratory apron if one is available. Put on safety goggles. Handle all glassware carefully. Always use special caution when working with laboratory chemicals, as they may irritate the skin or cause staining of the skin or clothing. Never touch or taste any chemical unless instructed to do so. Be careful when handling sharp instruments. Note all safety alert symbols next to the steps in the Procedure and review the meanings of each symbol by referring to the symbol guide on page 10.

Procedure

1. Using the plastic spoon, place the 3 agar-phenolphthalein blocks in the beaker. Pour 100 mL of the 0.4% sodium hydroxide solution over the blocks. **CAUTION:** *Use extreme care when working with chemicals. Do not allow them to come into contact with the skin or clothing.* Allow the blocks to remain in the solution undisturbed for 10 minutes.

2. While the blocks are soaking, use the formulas given below to determine the surface area, volume, and surface-area-to-volume ratio for each block. Record this information in Data Table 1.

surface area = number of surfaces x length x width

volume = length x width x height

surface-area-to-volume ratio = $\dfrac{\text{surface area}}{\text{volume}}$

3. After 10 minutes, remove the blocks with the plastic spoon. Place them on the paper towel and blot them dry.

4. Cut each block in half with the scalpel. **CAUTION:** *Be careful when handling sharp instruments.* Using the metric ruler, measure the distance in millimeters that the pink color has diffused into each block. Then measure the distance from the end of the pink color to the center of the cube. Record these measurements in the appropriate places in Data Table 2.

Observations

Data Table 1

Cube Size	Surface Area (cm²)	Volume (cm³)	Surface-Area-to-Volume Ratio
3 cm	54 cm²	27 cm³	$\dfrac{54}{27} = \dfrac{2}{1}$
2 cm	24 cm²	8 cm³	$\dfrac{24}{8} = \dfrac{3}{1}$
1 cm	6 cm²	1 cm³	$\dfrac{6}{1}$

Data Table 2

Cube Size	Distance Pink Color Has Diffused into Block (mm)	Distance from End of Pink Color to Block's Center (mm)
3 cm		
2 cm	Although answers will vary, the smaller sized blocks will show more diffusion of the pink color.	
1 cm		

Analysis and Conclusions

1. Which block has the greatest surface area? The largest block—3 cm on a side.

   _____

2. Which block has the greatest surface-area-to-volume ratio? The smallest block—1 cm on a side.

   _____

3. In which block did the pink color diffuse the most? Explain your answer.

   The smallest block had the most extensive diffusion of pink color. The smaller the surface area is, the

   greater the diffusion will be.

   _____

4. If the blocks were actual cells, which would be the most efficient in terms of permitting

   materials to enter and leave the cell? The most efficient "cell" would be the smallest "cell" because it

   would allow more materials to enter and leave the cell.

   _____

   _____

   _____

5. Based on this investigation, what one factor may limit the growth of an individual cell?

   The ratio of surface area to volume. This ratio must be large enough so that materials can enter and leave

   the cell more efficiently.

   _____

   _____

Critical Thinking and Application

1. What happens to the surface-area-to-volume ratio of a cell as it grows?

   The ratio decreases.

   _____

2. Propose a hypothesis that explains why the growth of a cell decreases as its size increases.

As the cell increases in size, the ability to take in adequate food and oxygen decreases. As a result, the

cell's growth decreases.

Going Further

Calculate the surface-area-to-volume ratios for cells that are 0.1 cm and 0.01 cm on a side. Which has the greater surface area in proportion to its volume?

Add 30 g agar (agar-agar) to each 1000 mL of water and while stirring bring to a boil. Allow the mixture to cool, but before it hardens add 1 g phenolphthalein for each 1000 mL water used. If the mixture turns pink, add enough acid (HCl) so that the mixture becomes colorless again. Pour the mixture into cake pans to a depth of about 3 cm. Make sure that each group will get a block that is 3 cm x 3 cm x 6 cm, which they can then cut into the sizes needed.

16

Determining the Time Needed for Mitosis

You may want to refer students to pages 164–171 in the textbook for a discussion of the phases of mitosis.

Time required: 45 minutes.

Pre-Lab Discussion

Mitosis is the process by which the cell nucleus is divided into two nuclei. Mitosis takes place in four phases: prophase, metaphase, anaphase, and telophase. The period between one mitosis and the next is called interphase. Chromosome replication occurs during interphase.

Organisms such as the common intestinal bacteria *E. coli* can complete mitosis in 30 minutes. Other cells require days. In some cells, such as human muscle cells, mitosis never occurs.

In this investigation, you will determine the time required for plant and animal cells to go through each phase of mitosis.

Problem

How can the time needed for each phase of mitosis be determined in a plant and an animal cell?

Materials (per group)

Textbook
Prepared slide of plant mitosis (onion root tip)
Prepared slide of animal mitosis (whitefish blastula)
Microscope

Safety 🔺

Handle all glassware carefully. Always handle the microscope with extreme care. You are responsible for its proper care and use. Use caution when handling glass slides as they can break easily and cut you. Note all safety alert symbols next to the steps in the Procedure and review the meanings of each symbol by referring to the symbol guide on page 10.

Procedure

1. Review the phases of plant and animal cell mitosis by studying the illustrations and photographs on pages 164 through 171 in your textbook.

2. Place the prepared onion root tip slide on the stage of the microscope. Using the low-power objective, focus on the cells just above the tip of the root. Switch to high power and count the total number of cells in the field of view. Record this information in the appropriate place in Data Table 1.

3. Without changing the field of view, count the number of cells in each phase of mitosis: prophase, metaphase, anaphase, and telophase. Record this information in the appropriate place in Data Table 1.

4. To determine the approximate proportion of time a cell spends in each phase of mitosis, divide the number of cells in each phase by the total number of cells in the field of view. To convert each decimal to a percent, multiply by 100. Record this information in the appropriate place in Data Table 1.

5. Repeat steps 2 through 4 using the prepared animal mitosis slide. Record all of the information in the appropriate places in Data Table 2.

Observations

Data Table 1

Phase	Plant Cell Mitosis		
	Number of Cells in Phase	Number of Cells in Phase / Total Number of Cells	Percentage of Time Spent in Phase
Prophase			
Metaphase		Answers will vary.	
Anaphase			
Telophase			
Total number of cells in field of view			

Data Table 2

Phase	Animal Cell Mitosis		
	Number of Cells in Phase	Number of Cells in Phase / Total Number of Cells	Percentage of Time Spent in Phase
Prophase			
Metaphase		Answers will vary.	
Anaphase			
Telophase			
Total number of cells in field of view			

Analysis and Conclusions

1. In which phase of plant cell mitosis is the most time spent? In which phase of animal cell mitosis? Prophase, the first phase of mitosis, is frequently the longest phase, taking 50 to 60 percent of the total time required to complete mitosis.

2. In which phase of plant cell mitosis is the least time spent? In which phase of animal cell mitosis? In general, metaphase requires the least amount of time.

3. Based on this investigation, what is the total percentage of time the plant and animal cells spend undergoing mitosis? Plant and animal cells actually spend little time undergoing mitosis. Student data should reflect this.

4. What percentage of the time are the plant and animal cells not undergoing mitosis?
   To get the answer, students should subtract the total percentage of time the cells spend undergoing mitosis from 100 percent.

5. What are the plant and animal cells doing when they are not undergoing mitosis?
   The cells are in interphase.

Critical Thinking and Application

1. Determine the percentages of time spent in each phase of mitosis for the onion root tip using the total number of cells undergoing mitosis instead of the total number of cells in the field of view.

$$\text{percentage} = \frac{\text{Number of cells in phase}}{\text{Number of cells undergoing mitosis}}$$

prophase _____

metaphase _____   Answers will vary.

anaphase _____

telophase _____

2. In the Pre-Lab Discussion you were told that *E. coli* is capable of undergoing mitosis in 30 minutes. Using the information from the previous problem, determine how long *E.coli* spends in each phase of mitosis.

prophase _____

metaphase _____   Answers will vary.

anaphase _____

telophase _____

Going Further

Using reference sources, investigate the relationship between mitosis and cancer. What phases of mitosis might you expect to observe most frequently?

17

The Principles of Genetics

You may want to refer students to pages 181–189 in the textbook for a discussion of the principles of genetics.

Time required: 40 minutes.

Pre-Lab Discussion

Through his careful and detailed studies with garden pea plants, the Austrian monk and scientist Gregor Mendel determined that heredity is controlled by factors that are passed from generation to generation with predictable results. Mendel's experiments and conclusions led to the formulation of several basic genetic principles.

The principle of *dominance* states that some factors (alleles) are dominant, whereas others are recessive. The effects of a dominant allele are seen even if it is present with a contrasting recessive allele. The principle of *segregation* states that during gamete (sperm and egg) formation, the alleles for a trait separate, so that each gamete has only one of the alleles for that trait. The principle of *independent assortment* states that as gametes form, the genes for various traits separate independently of one another.

In this investigation, you will construct Punnett squares to observe the principles of genetics that were based on Mendel's work. You will also simulate a two-factor cross to learn the important role probability plays in the study of genetics.

Problem

How can the characteristics of offspring be predicted?

Materials *(per group)*

Textbook
Pencil
Masking tape
Scissors
4 disks   Small plastic or cardboard disks such as those used for bingo or tiddly-winks can be obtained
Paper cup   from a toy or hobby store. Although you may substitute coins for disks, coins will generate
             more noise than disks when tossed.

Safety ▨

Be careful when handling sharp instruments. Note all safety alert symbols next to the steps in the Procedure and review the meanings of each symbol by referring to the symbol guide on page 10.

Procedure   You may wish to have students perform Part A individually instead of in a group.

Part A. Constructing Punnett Squares for One-Factor and Two-Factor Crosses

1. Examine Figure 1. The capital letter T is used to represent the dominant allele for tallness in the stem length for pea plants. The lowercase letter t is used to represent the recessive allele for shortness in pea plants.

2. Notice the genotypes, or gene combinations, that result from the parental (P₁) generation cross between a female purebred tall (TT) pea plant and a male recessive short (tt) pea plant. All of the offspring that make up the first filial (F₁) generation are tall (Tt). Their phenotypes, or visible characteristics, are all tall.

3. Figure 2 shows the results of a one-factor cross between the offspring from the F₁ generation. Observe the genotypic and phenotypic ratios for the second filial (F₂) generation. When writing such ratios, the number(s) for the dominant genotype(s) or phenotype(s) comes first. In this example, 1/4 of the offspring are TT, 1/2 (or 2/4) are Tt, and 1/4 are tt. The genotypic ratio is therefore 1/4:2/4:1/4, or 1:2:1. Three fourths of the offspring have tall stems and 1/4 have short stems. The phenotypic ratio is therefore 3/4:1/4 or 3:1.

4. In soybeans, purple flower color is dominant and white flower color is recessive. Let P represent the dominant allele (purple), and p the recessive allele (white).

5. Predict the probable genotypes of the first filial (F₁) generation of offspring by completing the Punnett square in Data Table 1. Indicate the genotypic and phenotypic ratios of the F₁ generation.

Figure 1

Figure 2

6. In Data Table 2, cross two plants from the F₁ generation. Write the appropriate genotypes for this cross on the lines provided. Predict the probable genotypes of this cross by completing the Punnett square in Data Table 2.

7. Indicate the genotypic and phenotypic ratio of the F₂ generation in Data Table 2.

8. In corn plants, rough seed shape (R) is dominant over smooth seed shape (r) and yellow seeds (Y) are dominant over white seeds (y). Determine the probable seed shape and color of the F₁ generation of offspring whose parents are heterozygous for the traits by completing the Punnett square in Data Table 3.

9. After you have completed the Punnett square in Data Table 3, fill in Data Table 4.

Part B. Simulating a Two-Factor Cross

1. To simulate the two-factor cross discussed in step 8 of Part A, cut 8 pieces of masking tape just large enough to fit on the disks. Place the tape on both sides of all 4 disks. On one side of 2 of the disks write R. On the other side of these disks, write r. On one side of the remaining 2 disks write Y. On the other side of these disks, write y. Each labeled disk represents the alleles in the heterozygous plant. The tossing together of the labeled disks represents the crossing of the heterozygous plants. Explain to students that the purpose of tossing the disks is to simulate segregation during gamete formation and recombination during fertilization.

2. Place the 4 labeled disks into the paper cup. Holding one hand over the mouth of the cup, shake it so that the disks are tossed. Then empty the cup onto your desk or laboratory table. Record the results of each toss by making a tally mark in the appropriate place in Data Table 5.

3. Toss the 4 disks a total of 48 times, recording the results of each toss in Data Table 5. Count the tally marks for each phenotypic combination and record these totals in the appropriate place in Data Table 5. Check students' disk markings in Part B. If incorrectly marked, data will not be close to expected values.

Observations

Data Table 1   **Purebred purple female x White male**

P$_1$ generation   PP   x   pp

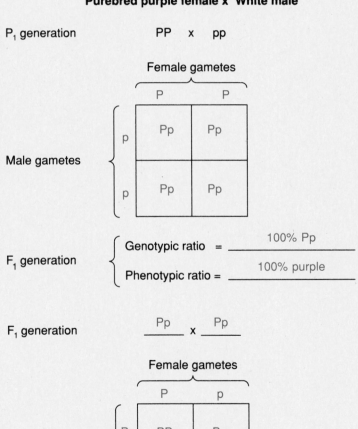

F$_1$ generation   Genotypic ratio = ___100% Pp___

Phenotypic ratio = ___100% purple___

Data Table 2

F$_1$ generation   ___Pp___ x ___Pp___

F$_2$ generation   Genotypic ratio = ___1:2:1___

Phenotypic ratio = ___3:1___

Data Table 3

P₁ generation   RrYy   x   RrYy

Female gametes

	RY	Ry	rY	ry
RY	RRYY	RRYy	RrYY	RrYy
Ry	RRYy	RRyy	RrYy	Rryy
rY	RrYY	RrYy	rrYY	rrYy
ry	RrYy	Rryy	rrYy	rryy

Male gametes

Data Table 4

Genotype	Genotypic Ratio	Phenotype	Phenotypic Ratio
RRYY	1:16	rough, yellow seed	9:16
RrYy	4:16	rough, yellow seed	
RrYY	2:16	rough, yellow seed	
RRYy	2:16	rough, yellow seed	
RRyy	1:16	rough, white seed	3:16
Rryy	2:16	rough, white seed	
rrYY	1:16	smooth, yellow seed	3:16
rrYy	2:16	smooth, yellow seed	
rryy	1:16	smooth, white seed	1:16

Data Table 5

Phenotypes	Genotypes	Number Expected for 16 Offspring	Number Expected for 48 Offspring	Toss Results	Total Number Observed
Rough, yellow seeds	RRYY RrYy RRYy RrYY	9	27	~~THL~~ ~~THL~~ ~~THL~~ ~~THL~~ ~~THL~~ ~~THL~~ I	31
Rough, white seeds	RRyy Rryy	3	9	~~THL~~ III	8
Smooth, yellow seeds	rrYY rrYy	3	9	~~THL~~ II	7
Smooth, white seeds	rryy	1	3	II	2

Actual results will vary.

Analysis and Conclusions

1. When two homozygous plants with contrasting traits are crossed, what are the expected genotypes for the offspring? All plants will be hybrids (heterozygous).

_____

2. What is the expected genotypic ratio for a one-factor cross of two hybrid organisms?
   1:2:1
   _____

3. What is the expected phenotypic ratio for a one-factor cross of two hybrid organisms?
   3:1
   _____

4. In your simulated two-factor cross, why might your actual experimental values have been different from the values you expected? Expected values are based on what probably will happen; experimental values are based on what actually happens.

_____

5. Why is it helpful to conduct a large number of trials when simulating genetic crosses? According to the laws of probability, the larger the number of trials, the closer you get to the expected values.

_____

Critical Thinking and Application

1. How is an understanding of genetics useful to an animal or plant breeder?

An understanding of genetics can help an animal or plant breeder choose more desirable traits so that they can be passed on to future generations.

2. Is it possible for two organisms to have different phenotypes but the same genotype? Explain your answer. No. If two animals have different physical characteristics (phenotypes), they must also have different genetic makeups (genotypes).

3. Is it possible for two organisms to have different genotypes but the same phenotype? Explain your answer. Yes. If one organism has a homozygous dominant genotype and another organism has a heterozygous dominant genotype, both organisms will display the dominant trait.

4. How could a guinea pig breeder determine whether a rough-coated guinea pig is homozygous or heterozygous for this trait? The breeder could cross the guinea pig with another guinea pig showing the recessive trait. If any of the resulting offspring have a smooth coat, the breeder will know that the rough-coated parent was hybrid (heterozygous) for the trait.

5. In dogs, wire hair is due to a dominant gene W. Two wire-hair dogs were mated and produced a puppy with smooth hair. What were the genotypes of the two parent dogs?
Ww and Ww

Going Further

Repeat Part B of this investigation using a cross between genotypes RrYy and Rryy. Construct a Punnett square to represent your expected results and calculate expected genotypic and phenotypic ratios. Tally the results of your 48 tosses and compare your experimental values with the expected values.

Biochemical Genetics

You may want to refer students to pages 181–189 in the textbook for a discussion of the work of Gregor Mendel.

Time required: 45 minutes.

Pre-Lab Discussion

Modern genetics is concerned with the role of genes and their control over enzyme action. *Enzymes* regulate metabolism and control biochemical reactions that may alter the phenotype, or the physical appearance, of an organism. Put another way, the phenotype of an individual is a reflection of its biochemical composition.

In green plants, glucose manufactured by the process of photosynthesis is converted to starch by the enzyme phosphorylase. By investigating this conversion reaction, differences in biochemical activity between smooth and wrinkled peas can be determined.

In this investigation, you will demonstrate the biochemical difference between smooth and wrinkled peas in their ability to convert glucose to starch.

Problem

How can biochemical genetics be studied?

Materials *(per group)*

Water-soaked smooth pea [1]	Paper towels	[1] Peas should be soaked for 24 hours prior to the beginning of the lab.
Water-soaked wrinkled pea	Glass slide	
5 dry smooth peas [2]	Coverslip	[2] Smooth and wrinkled peas are available from biological supply houses.
5 dry wrinkled peas [2]	Forceps	
Microscope	Toothpicks	[3] Place 5 g iodine and 10 g potassium iodide into a graduated cylinder. Add distilled water to the 100-mL mark. Stir until completely dissolved.
2 10-mL graduated cylinders	3 medicine droppers	
Mortar and pestle	Lugol solution [3]	
Glass-marking pencil	Petri dish with glucose agar [4]	

[4] Mix 5 g glucose or dextrose agar powder with 1 L water. Bring mixture to a boil and pour into petri dishes. Cool petri dishes of agar to room temperature. Refrigerate at least 1 hour before use.

Safety 🔺 🥽 🧤 👁

Put on a laboratory apron if one is available. Put on safety goggles. Always use special caution when working with laboratory chemicals, as they may irritate the skin or cause staining of the skin or clothing. Never touch or taste any chemical unless instructed to do so. Always handle the microscope with extreme care. You are responsible for its proper care and use. Use caution when handling glass slides as they can break easily and cut you. Note all safety alert symbols next to the steps in the Procedure and review the meanings of each symbol by referring to the symbol guide on page 10.

Procedure

Part A. Microscopic Differences Between Smooth and Wrinkled Peas

1. With a glass-marking pencil, divide a clean glass slide in half. Label the slide as shown in Figure 1.

2. Obtain a water-soaked smooth pea from your teacher.

3. With forceps, remove the seed coat from the smooth pea. This action exposes the cotyledon.

4. Using a clean toothpick, scrape a small amount of the cotyledon onto the half of the glass slide marked S.

5. Using a medicine dropper, place one drop of Lugol solution on the cotyledon. **CAUTION:** *Lugol solution is a chemical that can stain the skin and clothing.* With a toothpick, mix the Lugol solution and cotyledon scraping together. Discard the toothpick.

6. Repeat steps 3 through 5 using a water-soaked wrinkled pea. Be sure to use a clean toothpick to scrape the cotyledon.

7. Place a coverslip over each cotyledon scraping. Examine the cotyledon scraping from the smooth and wrinkled peas under the low-power objective of the microscope. The Lugol solution stains the starch in the cotyledon scrapings dark blue or black. Sketch what you see in the appropriate place in Observations. Record the magnification of the microscrope.

8. Switch to the high-power objective. **CAUTION:** *When switching to the high-power objective, always look at the objective from the side of your microscope so that the objective does not hit or damage the slide.* Sketch what you see in the appropriate place in Observations. Record the magnification of the microscope.

Part B. Biochemical Differences Between Smooth and Wrinkled Peas

1. With a glass-marking pencil, mark one 10-mL graduated cylinder S for smooth peas. Mark the other 10-mL graduated cylinder W for wrinkled peas.

2. Place 5 dry smooth peas into the mortar. Grind the peas into a fine powder with the pestle.

3. Place 1 mL of powdered smooth peas into the 10-mL graduated cylinder marked S. Add 3 mL of water. Set the mixture aside for 5 minutes or until the solids settle to the bottom of the graduated cylinder. **Note:** *Use a centrifuge if available to separate the powdered peas and the water.*

4. Repeat steps 2 and 3 using the 5 dry wrinkled peas.

5. With a glass-marking pencil, divide the bottom of the petri dish containing glucose agar in half. As shown in Figure 2, mark one half S for smooth peas and the other half W for wrinkled peas.

6. With another medicine dropper, place two drops of the clear liquid from the graduated cylinder marked S on the side of the glucose agar marked S.

7. Using the remaining medicine dropper, place two drops of the clear liquid from the graduated cylinder marked W on the side of the glucose agar marked W.

8. Set the petri dish aside for about 20 minutes to allow the pea extracts to work on the glucose in the agar. You may wish to begin cleaning your laboratory station while you are waiting.

Figure 1

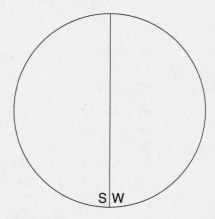

Figure 2

9. After 20 minutes, use a paper towel to carefully blot any excess extract from either side of the agar. Add a drop of Lugol solution to each half of the petri dish. **CAUTION:** *Lugol solution is a chemical that can stain the skin and clothing.* Look for a dark blue or black color, which indicates the presence of starch. The presence of starch indicates the conversion of glucose to starch by the enzyme phosphorylase. Record your observations in the Data Table.

Observations

Low-power objective

Magnification _____   Magnification _____

Smooth Pea   **Wrinkled Pea**

High-power objective

Magnification _____   Magnification _____

Smooth Pea   **Wrinkled Pea**

Data Table

Type of Pea	Starch Present?
Smooth	No
Wrinkled	Yes

Analysis and Conclusions

1. How does the shape of the starch grains from the smooth peas compare with those from the wrinkled peas? Smooth peas should have oval-shaped starch grains. Wrinkled peas should have round starch grains.

2. Which type of pea contains the enzyme phosphorylase? The wrinkled pea.

_____

3. Which type of pea does not contain the enzyme phosphorylase? The smooth pea.

_____

Critical Thinking and Application

1. All of the differences observed in this investigation are believed to be caused by a single gene. What characteristics are produced by each allele of this gene? The dominant allele is responsible for smooth seed coat, oval starch grains, and lack of phosphorylase. The recessive allele is responsible for wrinkled seed coat, round starch grains, and the presence of phosphorylase.

_____

2. Humans vary in their levels of various enzymes. If you were a geneticist who wanted to determine the normal level of a particular enzyme in the human digestive system, what kinds of people should your sample include? How large should your sample be? The sample should include people of different size, weight, sex, age, and race. The sample size should be as large as possible to better determine a normal measurement.

_____

3. The enzyme papain, found in the papaya fruit, breaks down large protein molecules and is used as a meat tenderizer. How might papain make meat tender? When placed on meat, papain speeds up the normal decomposition of the meat fibers, making the meat more tender.

_____

4. Cancer treatments such as chemotherapy or radiation therapy may cure one person of a certain type of cancer but leave another person with the same type of cancer unaffected. What is the most likely explanation of this difference in response? Different people have variations in their biochemical structures. This variation in biochemical reactions may cause people's bodies to respond differently to the same type of treatment or medication.

_____

Going Further

1. Repeat this investigation using other examples such as yellow and green peas or peas of different varieties.

2. Design experiments to determine the effects of light and/or heat on enzyme activity in seeds.

19

Human Sex Chromosomes

You may want to refer students to pages 209–211 in the textbook for a discussion of sex chromosomes.

Time required: 40 minutes.

Pre-Lab Discussion

The body cells of humans contain 23 pairs of chromosomes. Twenty-two pairs of these chromosomes are the same in both males and females and are called *autosomes,* or body chromosomes. The other pair of chromosomes, called *sex chromosomes,* is not the same in males and females. Human females have two matching sex chromosomes called *X chromosomes.* Human males have two dissimilar sex chromosomes—one X chromosome and one *Y chromosome.* The sex chromosomes are responsible for determining the sex and other traits in human offspring.

In 1960, the Canadian physician Murray Barr noticed darkly staining bodies of chromatin in some of the nuclei of the cells of female mammals. These bodies are absent from the nuclei of cells of males. Although females have two X chromosomes, one of them is condensed into a *Barr body,* as these chromatin bodies have come to be called. Many biologists believe that the formation of a Barr body deactivates parts of the second X chromosome in a female. This deactivation prevents the chromosome segments from producing double the necessary amount of enzymes and proteins, which would cause a chemical imbalance in the female.

In this investigation, you will examine human epithelial cells from the inside of the cheek for the presence or absence of Barr bodies.

Problem

How do male and female epithelial cells differ?

This investigation is set up for 2 or more students to share a microscope, but each student should make up his or her own slides.

Materials *(per group)*

Microscope
Glass slide
Coverslip
Toothpicks

Medicine dropper
Paper towels
Methylene blue   Available from a biological supply house.
Glass-marking pencil

Safety 🔬 ⬚ ▭

Put on a laboratory apron if one is available. Put on safety goggles. Always handle the microscope with extreme care. You are responsible for its proper care and use. Use caution when handling glass slides as they can break easily and cut you. Always use special care when working with laboratory chemicals, as they may irritate the skin or cause staining of the skin or clothing. Never touch or taste any chemical unless instructed to do so. Note all safety alert symbols next to the steps in the Procedure and review the meanings of each symbol by referring to the symbol guide on page 10.

Procedure   Teachers and students should use caution when working with human body fluids.

1. On the edge of a clean glass slide, use the glass-marking pencil to write an F if you are a female and an M if your are a male. Then place a drop of water in the center of the slide.

2. Using the flat end of the toothpick, gently scrape the inside of your cheek. **CAUTION:** *Do not use force when scraping the inside of your cheek. Only a few cells are needed.* The end of the toothpick will have several cheek cells stuck to it even though you may see nothing but a drop of saliva.   Because each student is responsible for making his or her own slides, emphasize the importance of using a clean, unused toothpick for this part of the activity.

3. Stir the water on the slide with the end of the toothpick in order to mix the cheek cells with the water. Immediately discard the toothpick in a place provided by your teacher.

4. Place one drop of methylene blue on top of the drop of water containing the cheek cells. **CAUTION:** *Use care when working with methylene blue as it may stain the skin and clothing.*

5. Wait one minute, then carefully place a coverslip over the cheek cells.

6. After waiting another minute, place a piece of paper towel at the edge of one side of the coverslip.

7. Place a drop of water at the edge of the coverslip on the side opposite the paper towel. See Figure 1. As methylene blue and water are absorbed by the paper towel, the drop of water on the opposite side of the coverslip will be drawn under the coverslip. This action will help to remove most of the methylene blue stain. Discard the paper towel.

Top view   **Side view**

Figure 1

8. Place the slide on the microscope stage and use the low-power objective to locate a few cheek cells. **Note:** *In order to see the cells more clearly, you will need to adjust the diaphragm to reduce the amount of light entering the microscope.*

9. Switch to the high-power objective. **CAUTION:** *When switching to the high-power objective, always look at the objective from the side of the microscope so that the objective does not hit or damage the slide.* Observe your cheek cells under high power. In cheek cells, the Barr body will appear as a darkly staining body inside the nuclear membrane. Females will have one Barr body in many of the cells, whereas males have no Barr bodies.

10. Using the appropriate place in Observations, sketch and label what you see under the microscope. Label the following cell parts: cell membrane, nucleus, and Barr body (if present). Record the magnification of the microscope.

11. Exchange slides with a student of the opposite sex. Repeat steps 8 through 10.

12. Return slides to the appropriate class members. Carefully clean and dry your own slide and coverslip.

Name _____ Class _____ Date _____

Observations

High-power objective

Magnification _____

Magnification _____

Drawings will vary, but students should find that female cheek cells contain Barr bodies and male cheek cells do not.

Female Cheek Cell

Male Cheek Cell

Analysis and Conclusions

1. What was the purpose of using methylene blue in this investigation?

Methylene blue was used to add color to cell structures that are normally transparent and difficult to see under the microscope.

2. How are male and female cheek cells similar in structure? The cells are similar in both shape and size. With the exception of Barr bodies, the cells also contain the same organelles.

3. How are male and female cheek cells different in structure? Female cheek cells contain Barr bodies; male cheek cells do not.

Critical Thinking and Application

1. Which parent is responsible for determining the sex of the offspring? Explain your answer.

The mother can contribute only an X chromosome to the offspring. Because the father can contribute either an X or a Y chromosome, it is his gamete that is responsible for determining the sex of the offspring.

2. A certain couple has three daughters. The mother is expecting a fourth child. What are the chances that the child will be a boy? Explain your answer. According to the rules of probability, previous events do not affect the probability of later occurrences of the same event. The couple still should have a 50 percent chance of having a male child.

3. A physician examines a small amount of amniotic fluid from an expectant mother and finds the presence of Barr bodies. What can the physician tell the mother? Due to the presence of Barr bodies, the physician would know that the expected child is a girl.

4. Much of genetic research is aimed at understanding human genetics. Instead of performing genetic experiments on humans, researchers commonly use fruit flies. Explain why. Research on fruit flies is less complicated, less expensive, and less controversial. Also, many generations of fruit flies can be studied in a short period of time.

Going Further

Interview an obstetrician about the advantages and disadvantages of amniocentesis, which is the procedure that involves the removal of some amniotic fluid from a pregnant woman for examination and analysis.

20

Karyotypes

You may want to refer students to pages 205–214 in the textbook for a discussion of genes, chromosomes, and mutations.

Time required: 40 minutes.

Pre-Lab Discussion

Several human genetic disorders are caused by additional, missing, or damaged chromosomes. One way of studying genetic disorders is to observe the chromosomes themselves. In order to do this, cells from a person are grown in a laboratory. After the cells have reproduced a few times, they are treated with a chemical that stops cell division at the metaphase stage. During metaphase, the chromosomes are at the best length for identification.

The cells are treated further, stained, and then placed on glass slides. The chromosomes are observed under the microscope, where they are counted, checked for abnormalities, and photographed. The photograph is then enlarged, and the chromosomes are individually cut out. The chromosomes are identified and arranged in *homologous* pairs. Homologous chromosomes are identical, or matching, chromosomes. The arrangement of homologous pairs is called a *karyotype.*

In this investigation, you will use a sketch of chromosomes to make a karyotype. You will also examine the karyotype to determine the presence of any genetic defects.

Problem

How can chromosomes be observed?

Materials *(per student)*

Scissors
Glue or transparent tape

Safety ▨

Be careful when handling sharp instruments. Note all safety alert symbols next to the steps in the Procedure and review the meanings of each symbol by referring to the symbol guide on page 10.

Procedure
Part A. Analyzing a Karyotype

1. Observe the karyotype in Figure 1. Notice that the two sex chromosomes, pair number 23, do not look alike. They are different because this karyotype is of a male, and a male has an X and a Y chromosome.

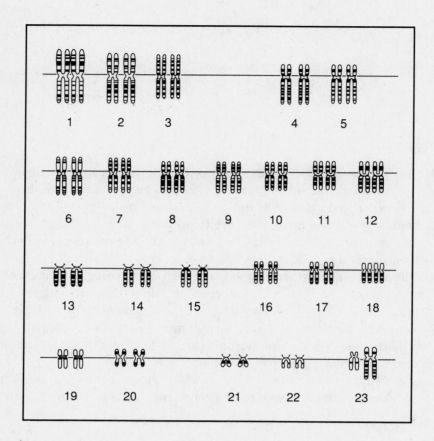

Figure 1

2. Identify the centromere in each pair of chromosomes. The centromere is the area where each chromosome narrows.

Part B. Using a Karyotype to Identify a Genetic Disorder

1. Study the human karyotype in Figure 2. Notice that 23 chromosomes are numbered 1 through 23.

2. To match the homologous chromosomes, look carefully at the unnumbered chromosomes. Note their overall size, the position of the centromere, and the pattern of the light and dark bands. Next to the unnumbered chromosome that is most similar to chromosome 1, write 1.

3. Repeat step 2 for chromosomes 2 through 23. **Note:** *Many genetic disorders involve missing or extra chromosomes.*

Figure 2

4. After all the chromosomes have been identified, use scissors to cut them out. Arrange the chromosomes in their appropriate place in Figure 3. Note the presence of any genetic defects.

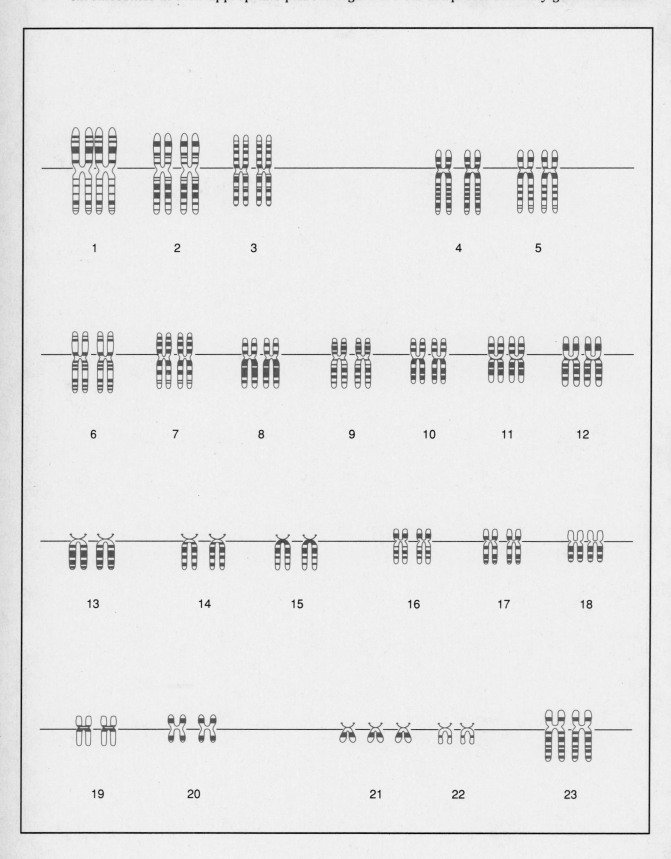

Figure 3

5. Observe the karyotypes in Figures 4 and 5. Note the presence of any genetic defects.

Figure 4

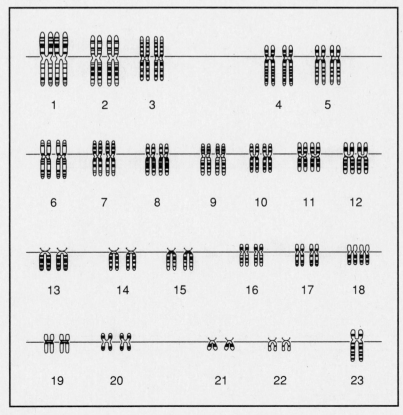

Figure 5

Observations

1. How many autosomes are present in your karyotype? 45.

2. How many sex chromosomes are present in your karyotype? 2.

3. Are there any abnormalities? If so, where? Yes. Extra chromosome in pair 21.

Analysis and Conclusions

1. Is your karyotype that of a normal person or a person with a genetic disorder? If it is the latter, identify the disorder. Karyotype is of a person with Down syndrome, or trisomy 21.

2. Is your karyotype that of a male or a female? Explain. Female. The two sex chromosomes (pair 23) that are present are similar. Therefore, they are two X chromosomes.

3. How does the karyotype in Figure 4 differ from the karyotype in Figure 1? The karyotype in Figure 4 has an extra sex chromosome (X chromosome) on pair 23.

4. How does the karyotype in Figure 5 differ from the karyotype in Figure 1? The karyotype in Figure 5 has only one chromosome (X chromosome) where there should be two chromosomes on pair 23.

5. Do the karyotypes in Figures 4 and 5 exhibit any genetic disorder? If so, identify the disorder. Yes. Figure 4 exhibits Klinefelter syndrome (47XXY) because the karyotype contains an extra X chromosome. Figure 5 exhibits Turner syndrome (45X) because the karyotype shows the absence of a second sex chromosome.

Critical Thinking and Application

1. What happens during meiosis that ultimately results in a defect characterized by the addition of chromosomes? By the deletion of chromosomes? During the phase of meiosis when paired chromatids are supposed to separate, the pair remains together. One gamete will receive the pair (addition) while the other gamete will not receive any (deletion).

2. The human male determines the sex of his offspring. Explain this statement.
Unlike females, males contain two different sex chromosomes—an X chromosome and a Y chromosome. During fertilization, the sex of the offspring is determined by whether an egg is fertilized by an X-carrying sperm or a Y-carrying sperm.

Going Further

Using reference material, research the following human genetic disorders: Patau syndrome and Edwards syndrome. For each disorder find the cause, type of mutation, and characteristics. Construct a karyotype of each.

21

Constructing a Human Pedigree

You may want to refer students to pages 227–239 in the textbook for a discussion of the inheritance of human traits.

Time required: 40 minutes (plus overnight to collect data).

Pre-Lab Discussion

Human traits are often difficult to study for several reasons. Unlike some organisms, which produce large numbers of offspring very quickly, humans reproduce slowly and produce few offspring at one time. Thus human traits must be studied through population sampling and pedigree analysis. A *pedigree* is a diagram that shows the phenotype of a particular genetic trait in a family from one generation to the next. Genotypes for individuals in a pedigree often can be determined with an understanding of inheritance and probability.

   In this investigation, you will use both population sampling and pedigree analysis to observe human traits.

Problem

How can pedigree analysis help in the study of human traits?

Materials *(per student)*

No special materials are needed.

Procedure
Part A. Interpreting a Pedigree Chart

You may want to review Punnett squares and one-factor crosses before beginning this investigation.

   1. Figure 1 is a pedigree, or a diagram of a family's pattern of inheritance for a specific trait.

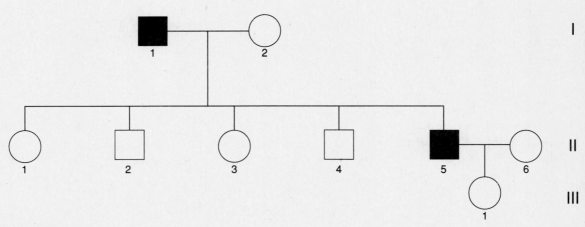

Figure 1

2. Notice that in a pedigree, each person is represented by an Arabic number and each generation is represented by a Roman numeral. In this way, each person can be identified by a generation numeral and an individual number. Males are represented by squares and females by circles. Unshaded symbols (squares or circles) indicate people who are homozygous or heterozygous for the dominant trait. Shaded symbols indicate people who are homozygous for the recessive trait.

3. In Figure 1, I-1 and I-2 are the parents. The horizontal line that connects them is called a marriage line. The vertical line that extends down from the marriage line connects the children to the parents. Children are listed in order of their births from left to right. In other words, the oldest child is always placed on the extreme left. In this pedigree, persons II-1, II-2, II-3, II-4, and II-5 are the children of persons I-1 and I-2.

4. The trait being analyzed in Figure 1 is ear-lobe shape. There are two general ear-lobe shapes, free lobes and attached lobes. See Figure 2. The gene responsible for free ear lobes, represented by the capital letter E, is dominant over the gene for attached ear lobes, represented by the lowercase letter e. People with attached ear lobes are homozygous for the recessive trait and are represented as ee. In Figure 1, I-1 and II-5 are homozygous recessive (ee) and have attached ear lobes. The people represented by the unshaded symbols have two possible genotypes: EE or Ee.

Free ear lobe   Attached ear lobe

Figure 2

5. Use Figure 1 to complete questions 1 through 8 in Observations. Allow students to research any family they wish for Part B of the investigation. This will help to eliminate problems for those students who are adopted or whose family members may be absent at the time.

Part B. Constructing a Family Pedigree

1. In the space provided in Observations, draw the outline of a pedigree of your family or a family who lives near you. In the pedigree, include any grandparents, aunts, uncles, cousins, nieces, or nephews that live nearby. Number the generations and individuals.

2. The ability of a person to roll his or her tongue is the result of the dominant allele R. People who cannot roll their tongues have the genotype rr. People who can roll their tongues have the genotype RR or Rr. If you are developing a pedigree for your own family, determine if you can roll your tongue. See Figure 3.

Tongue roller

Non-tongue roller

Figure 3

3. If you cannot roll your tongue, enter the genotype rr in the space below your symbol on the pedigree.

4. If you can roll your tongue, enter the genotype R _ for the presence of the dominant gene in the space below your symbol on the pedigree.

5. If you are constructing a pedigree for your own family, survey additional members of your family for their ability to roll their tongue. If you are constructing a pedigree for another family, survey as many members of that family as possible.

6. Record the results of family members you tested in your pedigree.

Observations

1. What is the genotype of I-2? Explain your answer. _Ee. Because child II-5 has attached ear lobes_

   (ee), the mother must be Ee instead of EE. If she were EE, then all of the children would have free ear

   lobes (ee x EE = Ee).

2. What are the genotypes of II-1, II-2, II-3, and II-4? Explain your answer.

   Ee. They have free ear lobes and as a result their genotypes cannot be ee. They are all Ee because their

   father contributed the e and their mother contributed the E.

3. What are the possible genotypes for II-6? Explain your answer. *EE or Ee. She has free ear lobes*
and as a result could have either of the two genotypes.

4. If II-6 is EE, what is the genotype of her child with II-5? *Ee.*

5. What sex is the oldest child in generation II? *Female.*

6. Who is the youngest child in generation II? *II-5.*

7. Who is the daughter-in-law in this family? *II-6.*

8. How many generations are represented in this pedigree? *3.*

Use this space to construct the pedigree for the family you have chosen to study. Correctly number each generation and person. Shade in the symbols for those people who are homozygous recessive. Below the symbol for each person, write as much of the person's genotype as possible.

Answers will vary.

Analysis and Conclusions

1. Would you expect the other students in your class to have tongue-rolling pedigrees that are identical to yours? Explain your answer. No. Different families contain different numbers of members with unlike characteristics.

2. Explain why you are not always able to determine the exact genotype for a trait of a person when you construct a pedigree. A dominant genotype can be either homozygous or heterozygous. A pedigree does not show the difference between homozygous and heterozygous genotypes for a dominant trait.

3. If two parents are unable to roll their tongues, is it likely that they will have children who will be able to roll their tongues? Explain your answer. No. Both parents are homozygous recessive for the trait and will be unable to contribute a dominant allele to their children.

Critical Thinking and Application

1. Can the actual traits of an offspring be determined by knowing the traits of the parents? Explain your answer. No. Because genes combine purely by chance, it would be impossible to determine the actual traits of an offspring. But the possible combinations of genes can be determined.

2. A woman received the genes aBcD from her mother and AbCd from her father. Which of the following gene combinations could be present in her gametes: ABCD, abcd, ABCDD, aBccD, ABcd, AaBb? Explain your answer. The possible gene combinations are ABCD, abcd, and ABcd. The combinations ABCDD, ABccD, and AaBb are not possible because a normal gamete contains only one allele for each trait.

3. If a man who has long eyelashes (LL) marries a woman who has long eyelashes (Ll), what are the possible genotypes and phenotypes of their children? The possible genotypes of their children are LL and Ll. All children will have long eyelashes.

4. Complete the pedigree in the figure below. In the spaces below each symbol, write as much of the genotype of each individual as can be determined from the information provided. Assume the shaded symbols represent the homozygous recessive genotype rr.

Going Further

Design another pedigree for the family you used in Part B showing any of the following traits: hair on middle joint of fingers, straight little finger, cleft in chin, direction of hair whorl. Determine if each of these traits is dominant or recessive. Apply all appropriate symbols and labels with the possible genotypes of each person. Compare the different pedigrees you have constructed. What are the similarities? Differences?

22

Investigating Inherited Human Traits

You may want to refer students to pages 227–239 in the textbook for a discussion of the inheritance of traits.

Time required: 40 minutes.

Pre-Lab Discussion

Heredity is the passing on of traits, or characteristics, from parent to offspring. The units of heredity are called genes. Genes are found on the chromosomes in a cell. The combinations of genes for each trait occur by chance.

When one gene in a pair is stronger than the other gene, the trait of the weaker gene is masked, or hidden. The stronger gene is the dominant gene, and the gene that is masked is the recessive gene. Dominant genes are written as capital letters and recessive genes are written as lowercase letters. If both genes in a gene pair are the same, the trait is said to be *homozygous,* or pure. If the genes are not similar, the trait is said to be *heterozygous,* or hybrid. Sometimes genes are neither dominant nor recessive. The result of such a situation is a blending of traits.

The genetic makeup of an individual is known as its genotype. The observable physical characteristics of an individual that are the result of its genotype are known as its phenotype. In humans, the sex of an individual is determined by the particular combination of the two sex chromosomes. Individuals that have two X chromosomes (XX) are females, whereas those with an X and a Y chromosome (XY) are males.

In this investigation, you will observe how the results of different gene combinations produced certain traits.

Problem

How are traits inherited?

Explain to the students that the actual combination of genes is much more complicated than is indicated by this investigation. Some of the traits result from multiple alleles. In order to simplify the investigation, assume that all of the traits used are the result of the combination of two genes, or a gene pair.

Materials *(per pair of students)*

3 textbooks
2 coins
Pencil

To reduce the noise produced by flipping coins, have student use plastic disks used for bingo or tiddly-winks (available at toy or hobby shops). Have students place a small piece of masking tape on each side of the two disks. Mark one side of each disk "H" (heads) and the other side of each disk "T" (tails).

Procedure

1. Place the textbooks on the laboratory table so that they form a triangular well in which to toss the coins.

2. Determine which partner will toss for the female and which will toss for the male. Remember that there are two genes per trait.

3. Have the partner who is representing the male flip a coin into the well to determine the sex of the offspring. If the coin lands heads up, the offspring is a female. If the coin lands tails up, the offspring is a male. Record the sex of the offspring in Observations.

4. For all the coin tosses you will now make, heads will represent the dominant gene and tails will represent the recessive gene.

5. You and your partner should now flip your coins into the well at the same time. **Note:** *The coins should be flipped only once for each trait.*

6. Continue to flip the coins for each trait listed in the table in Figure 1. After each flip, record the trait of your offspring by placing a check in the appropriate box in the table.

7. Using the recorded traits, draw the facial features for your offspring in the space provided in Observations.

Traits	Dominant (both heads)	Hybrid (one head, one tail)	Recessive (both tails)
Shape of face	round (RR)	round (Rr)	square (rr)
Cleft in chin	absent (CC)	absent (Cc)	present (cc)
Hair	curly (HH)	wavy (Hh)	straight (hh)
Widow's peak	present (WW)	present (Ww)	absent (ww)
Spacing of eyes	close together (EE)	normal distance (Ee)	far apart (ee)
Shape of eyes	almond (AA)	almond (Aa)	round (aa)
Position of eyes	straight (SS)	straight (Ss)	slant upward (ss)
Size of eyes	large (LL)	medium (Ll)	small (ll)

Figure 1

Traits	Dominant (both heads)	Hybrid (one head, one tail)	Recessive (both tails)
Length of eyelashes	long (LL)	long (Ll)	short (ll)
Shape of eyebrows	bushy (BB)	bushy (Bb)	fine (bb)
Position of eyebrows	not connected (NN)	not connected (Nn)	connected (nn)
Size of nose	large (LL)	medium (Ll)	small (ll)
Shape of lips	thick (TT)	normal (Tt)	thin (tt)
Size of ears	large (LL)	normal (Ll)	small (ll)
Size of mouth	large (LL)	medium (Ll)	small (ll)
Freckles	present (FF)	present (Ff)	absent (ff)
Dimples	present (DD)	present (Dd)	absent (dd)

Figure 1 *(continued)*

Observations

Sex of offspring _Answers will vary._

Drawing of Offspring

Answers will vary.

Analysis and Conclusions

1. What percent chance did you and your partner have of "producing" a male offspring? A female offspring? Explain your answer. _There is a 50% chance of producing either a male or a female_ _offspring as there is a 50% chance of the coin landing either heads up or tails up._

2. Would you expect the other pairs of students in your class to have an offspring similar to yours? Explain your answer. _Because chance plays an important role in this investigation, it would be_ _almost impossible to have two similar offspring._

3. If a woman who is homozygous for almond-shaped eyes (AA) marries a man who is heterozygous for almond-shaped eyes (Aa), what are the possible genotypes and phenotypes of their children? _The possible genotypes are AA and Aa. All children will have almond-shaped eyes._

4. What are the possible genotypes of the parents of a child who has wavy hair (Hh)?
   HH and Hh; Hh and Hh; Hh and hh.

5. Which traits in this investigation showed a blending of genes? _Size of mouth, nose, ears, and eyes;_ _shape of lips; hair; spacing of eyes._

Critical Thinking and Application

1. Did you think that anyone in your class has all the same genetic traits that you have? Explain your answer. _No. You are a unique combination of many genetic traits passed on to you by your parents._ _Identical twins are an exception._

2. How might it be possible for you to show a trait when neither of your parents shows it?

Both parents might be heterozygous dominant and pass on the masked recessive gene to you. As a

homozygous recessive for that trait, you will display the recessive trait.

3. Do you think you would have some genetic traits similar to your grandparents? Explain your

answer. Yes. Your grandparents may have passed on a trait to your parents, who may have passed it on

to you.

4. There is a small village in a mountain valley in Spain where a large number of people are polydactyl (have more than five fingers or toes). Why does this trait tend to be passed on

from generation to generation? Isolated by the mountains, the people in the village tend to intermarry.

As a result, the gene, or genes, for polydactyly remains concentrated in the village population.

5. There have been cases in history where a king divorced his queen because she produced only daughters. Using your knowledge of genetics, explain why this was an incorrect move.

It is the male (father) who contributes the sex-determining X or Y chromosome in humans. If the male

contributes an X chromosome during fertilization, the child will be female. If the male contributes a Y

chromosome during fertilization, the child will be male.

Going Further

Repeat this investigation with your partner to "produce" your second offspring. After completing all of your tosses, make a drawing of the offspring. What similarities exist between your first and second offspring? What differences? Would you expect a third offspring to resemble either the first or the second offspring?

23

Cloning

You may want to refer students to pages 247–250 in the textbook for a discussion of breeding strategies.

Time required: 40 minutes plus 10 minutes for each of 3 weekly observations.

Pre-Lab Discussion

In recent years, plant breeders have produced new and improved varieties of plants by producing polyploid plants. A polyploid plant has one or more extra sets of chromosomes. In plants polyploidy is fairly common. Polyploid varieties of many garden plants are in demand commercially because they produce more foliage and larger fruits.

Once plants with desirable characteristics have been produced by inducing polyploidy, it is possible to obtain exact copies of the plants by *cloning* them. Cloning is the production of genetically identical organisms. Cloning is used to grow uniform and commercially desirable varieties of fruits, vegetables, and flowering plants. Cloning is not limited to plants alone, however. Certain animals such as frogs, toads, and salamanders can also be cloned. Animal cloning is particularly helpful to medical research on cancer and other diseases. It is also being used to understand how cells perform different tasks and how they build up immunities to various diseases.

In this investigation, you will clone a duckweed plant.

Problem

How is a plant cloned?

Materials *(per group)*

Glass-marking pencil
Distilled water
Tongs
Watch glass
Duckweed plant culture [1]
600-mL beaker
5 glass petri dishes
   (60 mm in diameter)
10% bleach solution [2]
Inoculating loop

Hand lens
Bunsen burner
Ring stand
Iron ring
Wire gauze
Plant growth medium [3]
Paper towels
Fluorescent light with timer
   (if available)

[1] Can be obtained from a biological supply house or a pet (aquarium) store.

[2] Add 100 mL liquid chlorine bleach to 900 mL distilled water.

[3] Add 1 g commercial household plant food to a 1000-mL flask. Then add 1 g sucrose (table sugar) and 1 L distilled water. Plug the flask with cotton and pasteurize the solution by gently heating the flask and solution in a water bath at 73°C for 20 minutes on 2 consecutive days. Cool and refrigerate the solution until it is needed.

Safety ⚗ 🥽 🧤 📦 👁

Put on a laboratory apron if one is available. Put on safety goggles. Handle all glassware carefully. Use extreme care when working with heated equipment or materials to avoid burns. Always use special caution when working with laboratory chemicals, as they may irritate the skin or cause staining of the skin or clothing. Never touch or taste any chemical unless instructed to do so. Note all safety alert symbols next to the steps in the Procedure and review the meanings of each symbol by referring to the symbol guide on page 10.

Procedure

1. Place a duckweed plant along with some water from its container into a watch glass. Examine the plant with a hand lens. Note the elongated flattened body, which consists of leaflike stems called fronds. The fronds float on the water's surface while the threadlike rootlets extend down into the water.

2. To set up a water bath, half fill a 600-mL beaker with distilled water. Bring the water to a gentle, rolling boil. **CAUTION:** *Be very careful when working with heated equipment or materials to avoid burns. Wear safety goggles.*

3. Place the lids and bottoms of the 5 glass petri dishes into the boiling water bath for 3 minutes.

4. After 3 minutes, use tongs to remove the lids and bottoms from the water bath. Place them upside down on paper towels to dry. **Note:** *Do not expose the inside of the dishes to the air.*

5. After the lids and bottoms have cooled, assemble the petri dishes and place them side-by-side in a row. With a glass-marking pencil, number the dishes 1 through 5. **Note:** *To keep from contaminating the dishes, remember to open the lids just enough to carry out the following steps without unnecessary exposure to the air.*

6. Half fill petri dish 1 with the 10% bleach solution. Half fill petri dishes 2, 3, and 4 with distilled water. Half fill petri dish 5 with the plant growth medium. **CAUTION:** *Be very careful when using a bleach solution. It is a strong base and may burn the skin or clothing. Wear safety goggles.*

7. Sterilize the inoculating loop by passing it through the flame of a Bunsen burner until its entire length is heated to a red glow. **CAUTION:** *Be very careful when using an open flame. Wear safety goggles.* Allow the inoculating loop to cool for a few seconds. Aseptic conditions are essential for successful plant cloning.

8. Using the inoculating loop, remove a duckweed plant from the watch glass and transfer it to petri dish 1. Submerge the plant in the 10% bleach solution for 10 minutes. This action will destroy any organisms that might be on the plant.

9. Transfer the plant to petri dish 2 to rinse off the bleach solution. To ensure the removal of the bleach, gently submerge and agitate the plant. Repeat this process in petri dishes 3 and 4. Then transfer the plant to petri dish 5. **Note:** *Sterilize the loop before each transfer and then pause a few seconds to allow the loop to cool before picking up the plant.*

10. With a hand lens, examine the plant in petri dish 5. Count the number of fronds that the plant has. Record this number in the Data Table.

11. Place petri dish 5 under a fluorescent light. The light should be regulated with a timer to provide 16 hours of light followed by 8 hours of darkness. If a fluorescent light is unavailable, place the petri dish on the ledge of a north-facing window.

12. Thoroughly wash and clean petri dishes 1 through 4, using a paper towel to remove the numbers from them.

13. Observe the duckweed plant each week for three weeks for signs of growth (number of fronds). Record this information in the Data Table.

Observations

Data Table

Number of Fronds on Duckweed Plant			
First Day	**After First Week**	**After Second Week**	**After Third Week**
	Answers will vary.		

Analysis and Conclusions

1. **What is a clone?** A clone is an exact genetic replica of an organism.

   _____

   _____

2. **Why is so much care taken to sterilize equipment in this investigation?**

   To avoid the contamination of the duckweed plant by organisms such as bacteria and fungi.

   _____

3. **How does cloning differ from sexual reproduction?** In sexual reproduction, the new organism

   receives traits from each parent. In cloning, the new organism is an exact genetic replica of only one parent.

   _____

4. **What happened to the old fronds in the duckweed plant as new ones appeared?**

   The old fronds separated from each other as new ones appeared. Some of the older fronds may have

   turned brown.

   _____

Critical Thinking and Application

1. **Of what value is cloning to someone working in a greenhouse?** Cloning allows a more rapid

   production of a particular type of plant. Plants in greater demand can be produced more quickly through

   cloning than through traditional methods.

2. How might cloning be useful in redeveloping a forested area that was destroyed by fire?

Trees and other types of foliage could be replaced more rapidly and evenly in the destroyed area by cloning than by natural replacement.

3. Explain why the new plant that develops from a stem of another plant is a clone.

The new plant is a clone because it is genetically identical to the parent plant.

4. Although the development of hybrid varieties of corn has tripled average corn yields in the United States since the 1930s, some plant breeders say that genetic uniformity (sameness) has become a problem in terms of plant disease. Why might disease be a problem for cloned plants?

Genetically identical plants are all equally susceptible to the same diseases. As a result, one of these diseases could destroy an entire population of these plants in a very short time. In a normal population, however, some plants would be less susceptible to the same disease and would survive.

5. Why has cloning been limited thus far to simple organisms and plants?

Simple organisms and plants are ideal for cloning because they reproduce fairly quickly, can be kept in the laboratory for study, produce many offspring, and contain fewer genes than more complex organisms.

Going Further

1. Research various techniques that are used for cloning plants. Then try to clone a mature fern from a few tissue cells taken from a leaflet of a frond.

2. Vegetative propagation is a cloning technique in which various parts of a plant such as leaves, stems, and roots are used to produce a new plant. Demonstrate the technique of vegetative propagation by cloning new plants from these plant parts.

24

Interpreting Events from Fossil Evidence

You may want to refer students to pages 278–282 in the textbook for a discussion of the fossil record.

Time required: 40 minutes.

Pre-Lab Discussion

A *fossil* is any evidence of life in the prehistoric past. Fossils can be actual remains of animals, impressions, carbon residues, or tracks left by a living organism. By using fossil records, scientists are able to piece together the story that fossils tell about the history of the Earth.

In this investigation, you will use some present-day knowledge and common sense to interpret fossil evidence.

Problem

How can fossils relate the history of an era?

Materials *(per student)*

Pencil

Procedure
Part A.

1. Observe the diagram of the fossil footprints in Figure 1.

Figure 1

2. Use Figure 1 to answer questions 1 through 6 in Observations.

3. Using the answers to these questions and some common sense, intepret the events that may have occurred in Figure 1. **Note:** *Your interpretation should be consistent with the diagram.*

Part B.

1. Observe the diagram of the fossil footprints in Figure 2.

Figure 2

2. Use Figure 2 to answer questions 7 through 9 in Observations.

3. Using the answers to these questions and some common sense, intepret the events that may have occurred in Figure 2. **Note:** *Your interpretation should be consistent with the diagram.*

Observations

Part A. Use Figure 1 to answer questions 1 through 6.

1. How can you tell in which direction the animals are walking? By examining the position of the claws.

2. How do footprints differ when an animal walks from when it runs?

Footprints are closer together when an animal walks and farther apart when it runs.

3. Did any of the animals change speed? When? Yes. When the animal in the upper left possibly smelled the large animal and fled; when the large animal left the attack area.

4. How many different types of animals are represented? Two or possibly three (students may suggest

only two because two sets of footprints are similar).

5. How did the animals interact with each other? One ran away; one attacked another.

6. How would footprints be formed and preserved? Students may suggest that animals made footprints

in soft soil or mud that hardened and lithified.

Part B. Use Figure 2 to answer questions 7 through 9.

7. Did any of the animals change speed? When? The animal on the far left moved faster, possibly when

it smelled or saw the middle animal.

8. How many different types of animals are represented? Three.

9. How did the animals interact with one another? The animal on the far right fled; the animals on the

left and in the middle attacked each other.

Analysis and Conclusions

Part A. Use Figure 1 to answer questions 1 through 4.

1. In what kind of environment did this all take place? In soft soil or mud.

2. If all the footprints were made within minutes of one another, which way was the wind

blowing? Explain your answer. Probably from south to north. One interpretation might be that the

animal in the upper left corner smelled the larger one and fled. The large animal smelled the smaller one on

the bottom right and attacked it.

3. What might the lines between the footprints of two of the organisms represent?

The animal possibly has a tail or is dragging an animal it has captured.

4. Write a paragraph interpreting the events in Figure 1. Support your interpretations with evidence from the diagram. Answers will vary. Accept any idea, even unusual ones that are supported by the fossil evidence in the diagram.

Part B. Use Figure 2 to answer questions 5 through 7.

5. Is it possible that the animals who made the footprints represented in the diagram never actually met each other at the same time? Explain your answer. Yes. Possibly a small animal left footprints while looking for food. A larger animal arrived later. It smelled the smaller animal's scent and came to investigate. Finding nothing, it flew away.

6. What might depth of a footprint tell an interpreter? The depth of a footprint might indicate the mass or foot structure of the animal.

7. Write a paragraph interpreting the events in Figure 2. Support your interpretations with

evidence from the diagram. _____ Answers will vary. Accept any ideas, even unusual ones, that are supported

by the fossil evidence in the diagram. ._____

_____

_____

_____

_____

_____

_____

_____

_____

_____

Critical Thinking and Application

1. In what type of rock would you be most likely to find fossils? Explain your answer.

Fossils will most likely be found in sedimentary rock. Most fossilized organisms were buried in sediments

after they died, and these sediments eventually changed to sedimentary rock.

_____

2. Would you be likely to find the fossil remains of a jellyfish or a worm? Explain your answer.

You would not be likely to find the fossilized remains of a jellyfish or a worm. Most invertebrate organisms

decay before leaving an imprint, and no hard body parts remain afterward.

_____

3. The exposed rock layers of the Grand Canyon are rich with fossil specimens. What does the presence of fossil coral, sponges, shellfish, and trilobites indicate about the past climate of the

Grand Canyon area? _____ The presence of sea-dwelling organism fossils indicates that at one time the area

was under water.

_____

4. How could paleontologists reconstruct our present-day environment 25,000 years from now if all written history were to be lost or destroyed? Paleontologists would be able to unearth buildings in urban environments much as we now do with ancient cities. Artifacts might also be found in these diggings. Prints from living organisms and vehicles might be analyzed. Core samples could be taken to determine soil and sediment types found in rock layers.

5. Scientists have found fossils of the same kind of organism on different continents. How might this have occurred? The continents may have at one time been connected to each other; seeds from a plant may have moved through the air to another continent; a flying animal may have moved from one continent to another.

Going Further

1. Make a cast of leaves, twigs, footprints, or bones, using plaster of Paris or clay. Relate this process to fossil formation.

2. Find out if there is a relationship between the depth of a footprint and the mass of a living thing. Have different people step in soft clay or soil. Measure the depth of the footprint and determine the relationship between the mass of the person and the depth of the footprint. Organize your information in a chart. Then interpret an "unknown" footprint.

25

Amino Acid Sequences and Evolutionary Relationships

You may want to refer students to pages 283–285 in the textbook for a discussion of similarities in body structure and chemical compounds.

Time required: 45 minutes.

Pre-Lab Discussion

Homologous structures—those structures believed to have a common origin but not necessarily a common function—provide some of the most significant evidence supporting the theory of evolution. For example, the forelimbs of vertebrates often have different functions and outward appearances, yet the underlying similarity of the bones indicates a common origin. Although homologous structures can be used to demonstrate relationships between similar organisms, they are of little value in determining evolutionary relationships among those structures that are dissimilar.

Another technique used to determine evolutionary relationships is to study the biochemical similarity of organisms. Though molds, aardvarks, and humans appear to have little in common physically, a study of their proteins reveals certain similarities. Biologists have perfected techniques for determining the sequence of amino acids in proteins. By comparing the amino acid sequences in homologous proteins of similar organisms and of diverse organisms, evolutionary relationships that might otherwise go undetected can be determined. Biologists believe that the greater the similarity between the amino acid sequences of two organisms, the closer their relationship. Conversely, the greater the differences, the more distant the relationship. Further, biologists have found that such biochemical evidence compares favorably with other lines of evidence for evolutionary relationships.

In this investigation, you will compare amino acid sequences in proteins of several vertebrates. You will also study amino acid differences and infer evolutionary relationships among some diverse organisms.

Problem

How do amino acid sequences provide evidence for evolution?

Materials *(per student)*

No special materials are needed.

Procedure
Part A. Comparing Amino Acid Sequences

1. Examine Figure 1, which compares corresponding portions of hemoglobin molecules in humans and five other vertebrate animals. Hemoglobin, a protein composed of several long chains of amino acids, is the oxygen-carrying molecule in red blood cells. The sequence shown is only a portion of a chain made up of 146 amino acids. The numbers in Figure 1 indicate the position of a particular amino acid in the chain.

	87	88	89	90	91	92	93	94	95	96	97	98	99	100	101
Human	THR	LEU	SER	GLU	LEU	HIS	CYS	ASP	LYS	LEU	HIS	VAL	ASP	PRO	GLU
Chimpanzee	THR	LEU	SER	GLU	LEU	HIS	CYS	ASP	LYS	LEU	HIS	VAL	ASP	PRO	GLU
Gorilla	THR	LEU	SER	GLU	LEU	HIS	CYS	ASP	LYS	LEU	HIS	VAL	ASP	PRO	GLU
Rhesus monkey	GLN	LEU	SER	GLU	LEU	HIS	CYS	ASP	LYS	LEU	HIS	VAL	ASP	PRO	GLU
Horse	ALA	LEU	SER	GLU	LEU	HIS	CYS	ASP	LYS	LEU	HIS	VAL	ASP	PRO	GLU
Kangaroo	LYS	LEU	SER	GLU	LEU	HIS	CYS	ASP	LYS	LEU	HIS	VAL	ASP	PRO	GLU

	102	103	104	105	106	107	108	109	110	111	112	113	114	115	116
Human	ASN	PHE	ARG	LEU	LEU	GLY	ASN	VAL	LEU	VAL	CYS	VAL	LEU	ALA	HIS
Chimpanzee	ASN	PHE	ARG	LEU	LEU	GLY	ASN	VAL	LEU	VAL	CYS	VAL	LEU	ALA	HIS
Gorilla	ASN	PHE	LYS	LEU	LEU	GLY	ASN	VAL	LEU	VAL	CYS	VAL	LEU	ALA	HIS
Rhesus monkey	ASN	PHE	LYS	LEU	LEU	GLY	ASN	VAL	LEU	VAL	CYS	VAL	LEU	ALA	HIS
Horse	ASN	PHE	ARG	LEU	LEU	GLY	ASN	VAL	LEU	ALA	LEU	VAL	VAL	ALA	ARG
Kangaroo	ASN	PHE	LYS	LEU	LEU	GLY	ASN	ILE	ILE	VAL	ILE	CYS	LEU	ALA	GLU

Human hemoglobin is being used as the standard for comparison.

Figure 1

2. In Data Table 1, notice that the abbreviated names of the amino acids in human hemoglobin are printed.

3. In the appropriate spaces in Data Table 1, write the abbreviated name of each amino acid in chimpanzee hemoglobin that is *different from* that in human hemoglobin. If there are no differences, leave the spaces blank.

4. For the remaining organisms, write the abbreviated names of the amino acids that do *not* correspond to those in human hemoglobin. **Note:** *Always be sure that you compare the amino acid sequence of each organism with that of the human and not the organism on the line above.*

5. Use Figure 1 to complete Data Table 2.

Part B. Inferring Evolutionary Relationships from Differences in Amino Acid Sequences

1. Another commonly studied protein is cytochrome *c*. This protein, consisting of 104 amino acids, is located in the mitochondria of cells. There it functions as a respiratory enzyme. Examine Figure 2. Using human cytochrome *c* as a standard, the amino acid differences between humans and a number of other organisms are shown.

Species Pairings	Number of Differences
Human–chimpanzee	0
Human–fruit fly	29
Human–horse	12
Human–pigeon	12
Human–rattlesnake	14
Human–red bread mold	48
Human–rhesus monkey	1
Human–screwworm fly	27
Human–snapping turtle	15
Human–tuna	21
Human–wheat	43

Figure 2

2. Using Figure 2, construct a bar graph on Graph 1 to show the amino acid differences between humans and other organisms.

3. Now examine Figure 3. In this figure the cytochrome *c* of a fruit fly is used as a standard in comparing amino acid differences among several organisms. Construct a bar graph on Graph 2 to show these differences.

Species Pairings	Number of Differences
Fruit fly–dogfish shark	26
Fruit fly–pigeon	25
Fruit fly–screwworm fly	2
Fruit fly–silkworm moth	15
Fruit fly–tobacco hornworm moth	14
Fruit fly–wheat	47

Figure 3

Observations

Data Table 1

87	88	89	90	91	92	93	94	95	96	97	98	99	100	101	102	103	104	105	106
Human																			
THR	LEU	SER	GLU	LEU	HIS	CYS	ASP	LYS	LEU	HIS	VAL	ASP	PRO	GLU	ASN	PHE	ARG	LEU	LEU
Chimpanzee																			
—	—	—	—	—	—	—	—	—	—	—	—	—	—	—	—	—	—	—	—
Gorilla																	LYS		
—	—	—	—	—	—	—	—	—	—	—	—	—	—	—	—	—	—	—	—
Rhesus monkey																	LYS		
GLN	—	—	—	—	—	—	—	—	—	—	—	—	—	—	—	—	—	—	—
Horse																			
ALA	—	—	—	—	—	—	—	—	—	—	—	—	—	—	—	—	—	—	—
Kangaroo																	LYS		
LYS	—	—	—	—	—	—	—	—	—	—	—	—	—	—	—	—	—	—	—

Data Table 1 (Continued)

	107	108	109	110	111	112	113	114	115	116
Human	GLY	ASN	VAL	LEU	VAL	CYS	VAL	LEU	ALA	HIS
Chimpanzee	—	—	—	—	—	—	—	—	—	—
Gorilla	—	—	—	—	—	—	—	—	—	—
Rhesus monkey	—	—	—	—	—	—	—	—	—	—
Horse	—	—	—	ALA	LEU	—	VAL	—	ARG	
Kangaroo	—	—	ILE	ILE	—	ILE	CYS	—	—	GLU

Data Table 2

Organisms	Number of Amino Acid Differences	Positions In Which They Vary
Human and chimpanzee	0	
Human and gorilla	1	104
Human and rhesus monkey	2	87,104
Human and horse	3	87,111,112,114,116
Human and kangaroo	7	87,104,109,110,112,113,116

176

Graph 1

Number of Differences

Species Pairings

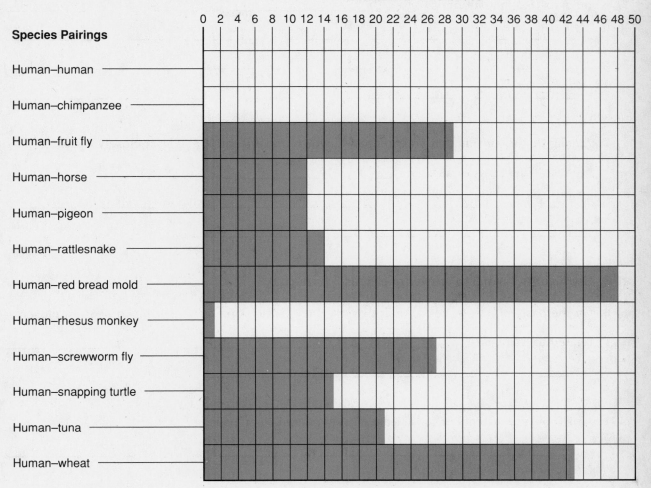

Graph 2

Number of Differences

Species Pairings

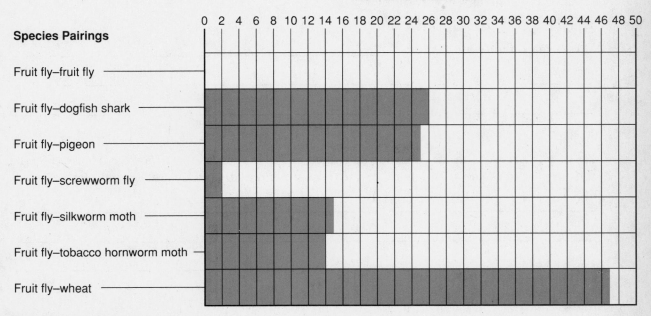

Analysis and Conclusions

Part A. Use Figure 1 to answer questions 1 and 2.

1. On the basis of the hemoglobin similarity, what organisms appear to be most closely related to humans? Explain your answer. Chimpanzees and gorillas appear to be most closely related to humans. In the sequence shown, the hemoglobin of the human and the chimpanzee are identical. The hemoglobin of the human and the gorilla differ with respect to only one amino acid. Thus these organisms show great biochemical similarity.

2. Among the organisms that you compared, which one appears to be least closely related to humans? Explain your answer. The kangaroo is least closely related. There are seven differences in the corresponding portions of their hemoglobin.

Part B. Use Figures 2 and 3 to answer questions 3 through 9.

3. On the basis of differences in their cytochrome *c*, which organisms appear to be most closely related to humans? Chimpanzee and rhesus monkey.

4. Which organisms appear to be least closely related to humans? Wheat and red bread mold.

5. Check the pair of organisms that appears to be most closely related to each other:

   _____ snapping turtle–tuna
   ___√___ snapping turtle–rattlesnake
   _____ snapping turtle–pigeon

   Give a reason for your answer. When compared to humans, the cytochrome *c* of the snapping turtle and rattlesnake differ by only one amino acid. There are slightly greater differences between the turtle's cytochrome *c* and that of the other two organisms.

6. Agree or disagree with the following statement and give reasons to support your answer. "Fruit flies appear to be more closely related to silkworm moths than they are to screwworm flies."
   Disagree; the cytochrome *c* of fruit flies and screwworm flies are more similar.

7. Name the pair of organisms that appears to be equally related to humans on the basis of cytochrome *c* similarity. _Pigeon and horse._ _____

_____

8. Is it possible that the organisms in question 7 could be equally related to humans but not equally related to each other? Explain your answer. _Yes; the cytochrome c of both pigeons and_

horses differs by 12 amino acids from that of humans, but these 12 amino acids may not be the same ones.

Therefore it cannot be said with certainty that the pigeon and horse are similar in terms of evolutionary

relationship.

_____

9. Agree or disagree with the following statement. "Fruit flies and humans have about the same evolutionary relationship to wheat." Explain your answer. _Agree; both differ from wheat by about_

the same number of amino acid sequences.

_____

Critical Thinking and Application

1. There is a difference of only one amino acid in one chain of the hemoglobin of humans and gorillas. What might have caused this difference? _A mutation probably occurred within the DNA of an_

ancestor common to both humans and gorillas.

_____

_____

2. If the amino acid sequences in the proteins of two organisms are similar, why will their DNA also be similar? _The sequence of amino acids in proteins is coded by the nucleotide base sequence in_

DNA. Like nucleotides in two organisms will code for the same amino acids and, hence, similar proteins.

_____

_____

_____

3. Many biologists believe that the number of differences between the proteins of different species indicates how long ago the species diverged from common ancestors. Why do these biologists believe that humans, chimpanzees, and gorillas diverged from a common ancestor only a few million years ago? _Their proteins, including hemoglobin and cytochrome c, differ by only a few amino acids._

4. Other proteins can be used to establish degrees of evolutionary relatedness between organisms. Would you expect to find roughly the same number of differences in the amino acid chains when comparing organisms? Explain your answer. _Yes; if organisms have a high degree of evolutionary relatedness, they should share about the same number of differences in the amino acid chains of other proteins. For example, chimpanzees and gorillas are closely related to humans when using either hemoglobin or cytochrome c as a standard._

Going Further

Conduct an investigation on the means by which amino acid sequences are used to construct *phylogenetic,* or *evolutionary, trees.* Then, using an appropriate reference, make a large bulletin-board drawing showing an example of a phylogenetic tree.

26

A Human Adaptation

You may want to refer students to pages 296–313 in the textbook for a discussion of variation.

Time required: 40 minutes.

Pre-Lab Discussion

Suppose that for some reason the only food source available to human beings was starch. Obviously, people who could digest starch would have a better chance of surviving than those who could not digest starch.

In human saliva, there is an enzyme called ptyalin that begins the digestion of starch in the mouth. If some people had more ptyalin in their saliva, they would be better suited to the new environment than those people who had very little ptyalin.

In this investigation, you will use a test to show the change of starch into the simple sugar glucose, determine how long it takes for your ptyalin to change starch into glucose, and find out whether other students in your class have the same amount of ptyalin. You will also determine if there is a genetic variation in your class population and whether the variation has a possible adaptive value.

Problem

What test is used to show the change of starch into the simple sugar glucose? Do people have similar amounts of ptyalin? If there is a genetic variation within a population, will this variation have an adaptive value?

Materials *(per group)*

Glass-marking pencil
10 test tubes
Test tube rack
50-mL graduated cylinder
Iodine solution   Add 5 g iodine and 10 g potassium iodide to 1 L water and stir. The color of the solution should be pale yellow. If it is not, add more water.
Water
2 150-mL beakers
Drinking straw
Starch solution_   Add 2 g cornstarch to 10 mL water. Add this to 1 L boiling water, stir for 2 minutes, and allow to cool.
Medicine dropper
Glass stirring rod

Safety ⚗ ▧ ◎

Put on a laboratory apron if one is available. Put on safety goggles. Handle all glassware carefully. Always use special caution when working with laboratory chemicals, as they may irritate the skin or cause staining of the skin or clothing. Never touch or taste any chemical unless instructed to do so. Use care when collecting and working with saliva. Note all safety alert symbols next to the steps in the Procedure and review the meanings of each symbol by referring to the symbol guide on page 10.

Procedure

1. With a glass-marking pencil, number the 10 test tubes from 1 to 10. Place them in a test tube rack.

2. Using the graduated cylinder, add 2 mL of iodine solution to each of the 10 test tubes.

3. To prepare a 6% saliva solution, add 17 mL of water to a beaker. Collect 1 mL of saliva by salivating through a drinking straw into the graduated cylinder. Pour the saliva into the water in the beaker and mix the solution.

4. Place 7 mL of starch solution in another beaker. To this solution, add 1 mL of the 6% saliva solution. Mix the solution by swirling the beaker. Note the exact time that you mixed the starch-and-saliva solution.

5. After 3 minutes, use a medicine dropper to remove a small amount of the starch-and-saliva solution from the beaker.

6. Add 2 drops of the starch-and-saliva solution to the first test tube containing the iodine solution. Be sure to return the rest of the contents of the medicine dropper to the starch-and-saliva solution.

7. Record the color of the iodine solution after adding the starch-and-saliva solution. **Note:** *In the presence of starch, the iodine solution will be blue-black in color. If no starch is present, because it has been broken down by ptyalin, the iodine solution's color will not change.*

8. At 3-minute intervals, add 2 drops of the starch-and-saliva solution to each of the 9 remaining test tubes of iodine solution.

Test tubes containing 2 mL of iodine solution

Figure 1

9. Record the color of each test tube in the proper place in Data Table 1. By observing the color of the solution, determine if the test tube contains starch or glucose and record this information as well.

10. In Data Table 2, record the total number of student groups that found a change in the starch solution within each given time interval. Have a member of each group place the data on the chalkboard to aid in tabulating the results of all the groups.

11. Prepare a line graph of the results recorded in Data Table 2 using the graph provided in Observations.

Observations

Data Table 1 Results of Group

3-minute Intervals	Color of Iodine Solution	Starch or Glucose Present?
0	Blue-black	Starch
3		
6		
9		
12	Answers will vary.	
15		
18		
21		
24		
27		
30		

Data Table 2 Results of Class

3-minute Intervals	Number of Student Groups Observing Change in Iodine
0	
3	
6	
9	
12	Answers will vary.
15	
18	
21	
24	
27	
30	

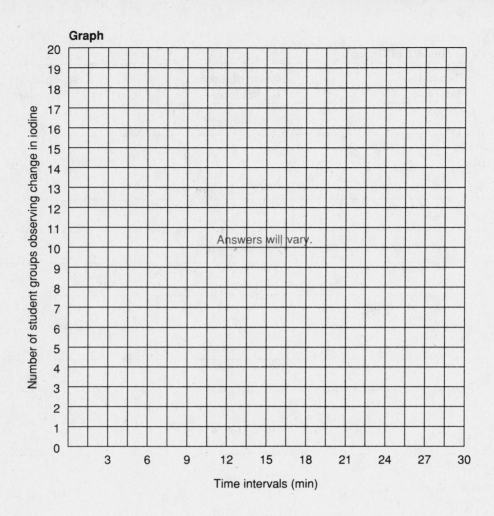

Graph

y-axis: Number of student groups observing change in iodine

x-axis: Time intervals (min)

Answers will vary.

1. In your group, how long did it take the saliva to digest the starch?

   Answers will vary.

2. How long did it take the majority of the student groups to digest the starch?

   Answers will vary.

3. What is the shape of the graph you have constructed? Ideally, there should be a bell-shaped distribution. However, data may be highly variable.

Analysis and Conclusions

1. If, indeed, starch were the only food source available to humans, which students would be more likely to survive? Explain your answer. Those with the shortest recorded time. A short time indicates the presence of a lot of ptyalin in the saliva. The more ptyalin there is, the more starch can be changed and digested into sugars.

2. Do the results of your class's groups show that there are various amounts of ptyalin in saliva? Explain your answer. Yes. Groups will show different time lengths needed for carbohydrate digestion.

3. a. Is the source of this chemical variation genetic? Yes.

b. Did this chemical variation occur before or during the experiment?

Before the experiment.

c. Do most variations occur before they are adaptive? Explain your answer.

Yes. Variations may not become evident until some environmental change occurs in the future.

4. Look at the shape of the graph you constructed. Suggest a reason for the shape.

If there is a bell-shaped distribution, students may note that natural selection "weeds out" extremes. Irregular

distribution of data might be attributed to the use of a small sample size.

Critical Thinking and Application

1. In addition to the amount of ptyalin found in saliva, list two other chemical variations

occurring within the human population that are helpful to survival.

Answers will vary, but may include immunity to disease, lack of allergies, low stomach acidity to prevent

ulcers, high metabolism rate, etc.

2. Describe three adaptations that would be most useful to a person who plays the piano.

Answers will vary, but may include finger length, hand span, arm length, limberness, dexterity, hand-eye

coordination, etc.

3. In prehistoric times, people had to struggle every day to survive. Why might a very smart person have an advantage? The person with the most intelligence would be more likely to survive, as he or she could use the ability to reason to help in a variety of life-threatening situations.

4. The ball-and-socket shoulder joint is an adaptation that is unique to primates. Why is this adaptation important to the survival of the human population? The ball-and-socket shoulder allows the human population to do many different physical tasks such as driving, building structures, swimming, using weapons, catching moving objects, etc.

Going Further

Gather data on several variations in humans, such as the width of the foot, the length of the little finger, or the ratio of standing height to sitting height. Graph each of the variations. Are the shapes of the graphs consistent with that of the ptyalin investigation?

Variation Within a Population

You may want to refer students to pages 296–302 in the textbook for a discussion of variation and natural selection.

Time required: 50 minutes.

Pre-Lab Discussion

The members of a species are not exactly alike. Small differences called variations exist in each member of a species. Variations are found in all plants and animals. Some variations may be passed on to the offspring of an organism through reproduction. Most inherited variations are neutral; that is, they do not affect the survival of the organism. Some variations are helpful. Helpful inherited variations are called adaptations. Harmful inherited variations will cause the organism to be less well-suited to its environment.

The process by which organisms with adaptations to the environment survive is called natural selection. Natural selection tends to allow well-adapted organisms to reproduce and pass the beneficial trait to their offspring. Organisms with harmful traits will die off. This process is sometimes referred to as "survival of the fittest."

In this investigation, you will observe variations that exist in two different types of plants. You will also observe variations that exist within a classroom population.

Problem

How can the variations within plant and animal populations be measured?

Materials *(per group)*

10 white kidney beans
10 maple leaves
Metric ruler
3 colored pencils

In Part A, the 10 maple leaves needed for each group should be taken from the same tree. In Parts A and B, it will be necessary to provide tables on the chalkboard for students to tabulate total class counts. After the entire class has placed measurements in the class tables, students can transfer the totals to the Data Tables in the laboratory investigation.

Procedure
Part A. Variation Within a Species of Plant

1. Obtain 10 white kidney beans and 10 maple leaves.

2. Measure the length of each kidney bean and maple leaf blade in millimeters. Record the measurements in Data Table 1.

3. Locate the petiole on the leaf as shown in Figure 1. Measure the length of the petiole of each leaf. Record the measurements in Data Table 1.

Blade length

Petiole length

Figure 1

4. Report the measurements for each of the plants to your teacher. Your teacher will record your measurements on the chalkboard.

5. Using the data from all groups in your class, record the range in lengths for the kidney beans, leaf blades, and petioles. Record your findings in Data Tables 2, 3, and 4, respectively. Fill in the first row of each table with the graduated lengths, beginning with the shortest length and ending with the longest.

6. Record the total class count for the lengths of the kidney beans, leaf blades, and petioles in the second row of the table in Data Tables 2, 3, and 4.

7. Using the data in Data Table 2, construct a line graph for the kidney bean lengths on Graph 1 provided in Observations.

8. Using the data in Data Tables 3 and 4, construct line graphs for the leaf blade lengths and the petiole lengths on Graph 2 provided in Observations. Use a different colored pencil to graph each set of data and be sure to include a key for each graph.

Part B. Variation Within a Classroom Population

1. Measure your hand span. The measurement should be made from the top of the thumb to the tip of the little finger as shown in Figure 2. Round off the measurement to the nearest centimeter. Record your hand span in the class chart on the chalkboard.

Measure this distance

Figure 2

2. After all your classmates have recorded their hand-span measurements in the class chart, transfer the class results to Data Table 5. Your results will show the total number of hands having the same hand span.

3. Construct a line graph of your results using Graph 3 provided in Observations.

Name _____ Class _____ Date _____

Observations

Data Table 1 Species Length Measurements

	Length of Samples (mm)									
	1	2	3	4	5	6	7	8	9	10
Kidney beans										
Leaf blades				Answers will vary.						
Petioles										

Data Table 2 Comparison of Kidney Bean Lengths (mm)

Length of kidney beans					Answers will vary.									
Total class count														

Data Table 3 Comparison of Leaf Blade Lengths (mm)

Length of leaf blades					Answers will vary.									
Total class count														

Data Table 4 Comparison of Petiole Lengths (mm)

Length of petioles					Answers will vary.									
Total class count														

Data Table 5 Comparison of Hand-span Lengths (mm)

	Measurement of Hand Spans (cm)															
	15	16	17	18	19	20	21	22	23	24	25	26	27	28	29	30
Total number of hand spans with the same measurement							Answers will vary.									

Graph 1

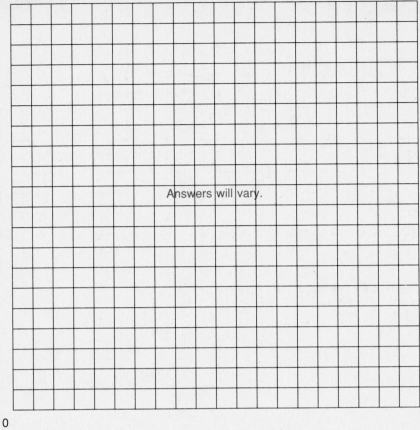

Total class count

Answers will vary.

0

Kidney bean lengths (mm)

Graph 2

Total class count

Answers will vary.

0

Leaf blade and petiole lengths (mm)

Graph 3

Number of students (y-axis): 0 1 2 3 4 5 6 7 8 9 10

Answers will vary.

Hand-span lengths (cm) (x-axis): 14 16 18 20 22 24 26 28 30

Analysis and Conclusions

1. **What is meant by the term variation?** Small differences in appearance that organisms of the same species may display.

2. **In what length range are most of the kidney beans? Most of the leaf blades? Most of the petioles?** Most samples should fall in the middle ranges.

3. **In what length range are the fewest beans? The fewest leaf blades? The fewest petioles?** The fewest samples should be at the extremes of the full-length range.

4. **What is the general shape of each line graph?** The shape of each graph should be a bell or upside-down U.

5. **What do the shapes of the graphs indicate about the lengths of the kidney beans, the lengths of the leaf blades, and the lengths of the petioles?** The shapes indicate that, although the lengths vary, most of the lengths are near the average, with fewer samples at both extremes.

6. **List two other variations that can be observed in the beans, leaf blades, and petioles.** Answers will vary, but might include width, thickness, petiole diameter, and coloration.

7. Are the hand spans of all students in your class the same? No. The lengths vary.

8. Which hand span occurs most often? Least often? Answers will vary, but the results should be based on Data Table 5 and Graph 3.

9. What is the general shape of the line graph? What does the shape of the line graph indicate about the hand spans of the students in your class? The graph should look similar to Graphs 1 and 2, indicating that most human measurements are near the average, with fewer measurements at both extremes.

Critical Thinking and Application

1. Why would having many seeds in a pod be a more useful adaptation to a bean plant than having only a few seeds? The more seeds a pod has the greater the possibility that some of them will germinate and grow into new bean plants.

2. Why would having a very short root system be a harmful adaptation to a desert cactus plant? A cactus plant with a short root system will have difficulty obtaining water. Thus it will have difficulty surviving in the desert.

3. How is the white coat color of certain arctic animals a helpful adaptation in the winter? The white coat color allows the animals to blend in with their white surroundings. This enables these animals to hide from their predators.

4. List two ways in which a large hand span might be a useful human adaptation. Answers will vary, but might include the playing of musical instruments, increased athletic ability, carrying large loads, and survival against predators.

Going Further

Investigate variations that occur in other types of plants. Make your measurements and graph the results as you did in this laboratory investigation. Do you think that all organisms of the same species exhibit variations for all of their traits? Explain your answer.

28

Classifying Organisms

You may want to refer students to pages 319–325 in the textbook for a discussion of classification.

Time required: 50 minutes.

Pre-Lab Discussion

Even early biologists developed classification systems in order to understand an organism and explain its relationships to other forms of life. The basis of the classification system in current use was developed in the 1700s by the Swedish botanist Carolus Linnaeus (1707–1778). Linnaeus used structural similarities as the basis of his system. Organisms were first placed in one of two large groups—the plant kingdom or the animal kingdom. Although all animals share certain similarities and all plants share certain similarities, individual members of each kingdom are quite different. Therefore, Linnaeus divided the two large groups (kingdoms) into smaller groups, and these groups, in turn, into still smaller groups.

In the Linnaean system, the largest groups are *kingdoms,* which are divided into smaller groups called *phyla* (singular, *phylum*). Phyla are then divided into *classes,* and classes are divided into many *orders.* Orders, in turn, are divided into *families,* families into *genera* (singular, *genus*), and genera into one or more *species.* Though most biologists generally classify organisms within these categories, they do not always agree on the criteria for placing an organism in a particular category. Because an organism can be observed from many viewpoints, the same organism may be classified differently by different biologists.

In this investigation, you will group and regroup a number of pictured objects according to similar characteristics. You will also classify a variety of monkeys and apes (primates) on the basis of their similarities and differences.

Problem

How can organisms be classified?

If students have difficulty in getting started, make a copy of Figure 4 on the chalkboard and elicit suggestions from the class as to how the figures can be divided into two groups and subsequently into smaller groups.

Materials *(per student)*

Scissors

Explain to students that in reality primates are classified by where they live, what they eat, whether they are social or live alone, and their internal structures—brain size, kinds and numbers of teeth, and so on. This investigation will enable students to classify only by the general appearance of the primates pictured.

Safety ▨

Be careful when handling sharp instruments. Note all safety alert symbols next to the steps in the Procedure and review the meanings of each symbol by referring to the symbol guide on page 10.

Procedure
Part A. Grouping Objects

1. Use scissors to cut along the dotted lines around each pictured object in Figure 4 on page 201. **CAUTION:** *Be especially careful if you are working with sharp pointed scissors.*

2. Place the group of objects you cut out in front of you. Then choose some characteristic to separate the objects into two groups of approximately equal numbers.

3. In Observations, make a branching chart similar to the one in Figure 1 to show how you divided the objects. Write the criterion you used to divide the group on the lines in your chart corresponding to line A1 and A2. Also list the numbers of the objects that belong on lines A1 and A2.

Figure 1

4. Next choose some characteristics to divide the objects in group A1 into two subgroups. Write their characteristics and numbers on your chart on the lines that correspond to lines B1 and B2 in Figure 1. Separate group A2 into two subgroups, and write their characteristics and numbers on the lines that correspond to lines C1 and C2.

5. Continue dividing each group until each pictured object is separated from all of the others. On your chart, continue to list the criterion you used for dividing each group. **Note:** *Your chart may not contain all of the branches shown in Figure 1. Also, you may need to extend your chart by adding branches not shown in Figure 1.*

Part B. Grouping Living Organisms

1. When classifying organisms, biologists must be very observant. Often only slight differences separate the members in one classification group from those in another. Study Figure 2, which shows some traits used for identifying primates.

Tail

No tail

Large eyes
for head size

Smaller eyes
for head size

Flat nails and
opposable thumb

Claws without
opposable thumb

Figure 2

2. Use the traits shown in Figure 2 and other traits to separate the primates in Figure 3 into two groups of approximately equal numbers. Use the space in Observations to make a branching chart similar to the one in Figure 1 to show how you separated the primates. Write the characteristics that you used to make your first division on the lines that correspond to lines A1 and A2 in Figure 1.

1 Mouse lemur

2 Fat-tailed lemur

3 Fork-marked lemur

4 Squirrel monkey

5 Aye-aye

6 Marmoset

7 Ring-tailed lemur

8 Proboscis monkey

9 Baboon

10 Chimpanzee

11 Gorilla

12 Orangutan

Figure 3

3. Continue to divide the primates into smaller groups until each is separated from all of the others. As you divide the primates into subgroups, complete your chart by listing the characteristics you used to separate them.

Observations

Branching Chart for Classifying Objects in Figure 4

Primate Branching Chart

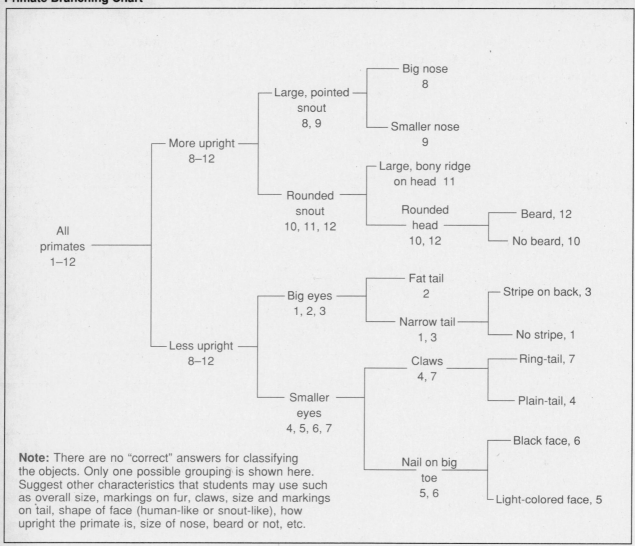

Note: There are no "correct" answers for classifying the objects. Only one possible grouping is shown here. Suggest other characteristics that students may use such as overall size, markings on fur, claws, size and markings on tail, shape of face (human-like or snout-like), how upright the primate is, size of nose, beard or not, etc.

Analysis and Conclusions

1. How is this investigation similar to the way in which biologists classify organisms?

   Biologists place organisms with common characteristics in the same group. Then on the basis of differences

   among group members, the organisms are subdivided into smaller groups.

2. Were either of your classification systems different from those developed by classmates? Why might this be possible? Answers will vary; different systems of classification are possible because

   students can use different criteria for grouping objects.

3. What characteristics did you find most useful for classifying the primates?

Answers will vary, but students will be likely to mention specific physical traits pertaining to the primate's

size and whether or not it has a tail.

4. What characteristics of the primates would not be especially useful for classifying them?

Traits that are very general or common to all primates, such as body hair, would not be useful.

5. Why should terms like *tall, short, large,* or *small* be avoided when describing traits of

organisms? These terms are relative. When classifying primates there is no common standard for

distinguishing small ones from large ones. Also, different sexes of the same species vary in size.

6. How does classification help you to better understand organisms? Grouping together organisms

that have similar physical traits enables one to see relationships among the organisms. Organisms with

similar traits are more closely related.

Critical Thinking and Application

1. Trees are usually identified by the characteristics of their leaves. Suggest two ways in which

trees could be identified during winter when they have no leaves. Trees can also be identified by

such traits as type of bark, stem, bud and root characteristics, types of fruit, and growth pattern.

2. Suppose you wanted to identify and classify all birds that came to a particular bird feeder during a spring day. What are some common characteristics you would use in classifying the

birds? Some characteristics that could be used are their color and markings, general body form, type of bill

and feet, and song.

3. Almost immediately after the invention of the microscope, taxonomists began to use it in their work. Why might a microscope be useful to a taxonomist? A microscope can be used to identify characteristics of an organism that are too small to be seen with the unaided eye.

4. Describe three ways in which pieces of clothing are classified in a department store.

Answers will vary. Clothing can be grouped by size, sex of the wearer, where on the body it is worn, age group wearing it, cost, and the type of activity for which it is intended.

Going Further

1. Devise a system to classify the different kinds of shoes your classmates wear. Make a chart similar to Figure 1 to show the different categories and characteristics used to group the shoes.

2. Make a list of ten or more household appliances. Exchange your list with a classmate. Classify the appliances into groups based on similar characteristics. Make a chart similar to Figure 1 to show the different categories and characteristics used to group the appliances.

Use Figure 4 to complete step 1 of Part A.

Figure 4

29

You may want to refer students to pages 319–329 in the textbook for a discussion of classification.

Time required: 45 minutes.

Using and Constructing a Classification Key

Pre-Lab Discussion

Suppose you find a large colorful wildflower while walking through the woods. Chances are the flower has already been named and classified, but how can you learn its identity? As an aid to help others identify unknown organisms, biologists have developed classification keys.

Many classification keys have been developed to help identify wildflowers and many other kinds of plants and animals. Although these keys may vary in purpose and complexity, they have certain features in common. These classification keys are often called *dichotomous keys*. The word dichotomous comes from the word *dichotomy*, meaning "two opposite parts or categories." A dichotomous classification key presents the user with two opposite statements about some trait of an organism. By choosing the statement that best describes the unknown organism, the user is led to further pairs of statements. By going from one set of statements to another, the name of the organism or its classification group is finally determined.

In this investigation, you will use a classification key to identify several organisms. You will then write a classification key for another group of organisms.

Problem

How can a classification key be used to identify organisms?

Materials (per student)

No special materials are needed

Procedure
Part A. Using a Classification Key

1. Examine the drawing of salamander 1 in Figure 1.

Figure 1

2. Read statements 1a and 1b in the classification key in Figure 2. One of these statements describes salamander 1; the other statement does not. Follow the directions in the statement that describes salamander 1 and continue following the correct statement directions until salamander 1 has been identified.

1	a	Hind limbs absent	*Siren intermedia,* siren
	b	Hind limbs present	Go to 2
2	a	External gills present in adults	*Necturus maculosus,* mud puppy
	b	External gills absent in adults	Go to 3
3	a	Large size (over 7 cm long in Figure 1)	Go to 4
	b	Small size (under 7 cm long in Figure 1)	Go to 5
4	a	Body background black, large white spots irregular in size and shape completely covering body and tail	*Ambystoma tigrinum,* tiger salamander
	b	Body background black, small round white spots in a row along each side from eye to tip of tail	*Ambystoma maculatum,* spotted salamander
5	a	Body background black with white spots	Go to 6
	b	Body background light color with dark spots and/or lines on body	Go to 7
6	a	Small white spots on a black background in a row along each side from head to tip of tail	*Ambystoma jeffersonianum,* Jefferson salamander
	b	Small white spots scattered throughout a black background from head to tip of tail	*Plethodon glutinosus,* slimy salamander
7	a	Large irregular black spots on a light background extending from head to tip of tail	*Ambystoma opacum,* marbled salamander
	b	No large irregular black spots on a light background	Go to 8
8	a	Round spots scattered along back and sides of body, tail flattened like a tadpole	*Triturus viridescens,* newt
	b	Without round spots and tail not flattened like a tadpole	Go to 9
9	a	Two dark lines bordering a broad light middorsal stripe with a narrow median dark line extending from the head onto the tail	*Eurycea bislineata,* two-lined salamander
	b	Without two dark lines running the length of the body	Go to 10
10	a	A light stripe running the length of the body and bordered by dark pigment extending downward on the sides	*Plethodon cinereus,* red-backed salamander
	b	A light stripe extending the length of the body, a marked constriction at the base of the tail	*Hemidactylium scutatum,* four-toed salamander

Figure 2

3. Write the scientific name and the common name of salamander 1 on the appropriate line provided in Observations.

4. Repeat steps 1 through 3 with each salamander until all the animals have been identified.

Part B. Constructing a Classification Key

1. Study Figure 3, which shows some common North American wildflowers. As you study the drawings of various flowers, note different characteristics in flower shape, number of petals, and leaf number and shape.

Large-flowered trillium

May apple

Broad-leaf arrowhead

Common blue violet

Red clover

Large-flowered bellwort

Figure 3

2. In the space provided in Observations, develop a classification key to identify each wildflower. Use the key to salamanders as a model for developing your wildflower key.

3. Check the usefulness of your wildflower key by letting another student see if he or she can use it to identify each pictured flower.

Observations
Part A. Using a Classification Key

Write the scientific and common names of each salamander in Figure 1 on the line that corresponds to its number.

1. *Plethodon glutinosus,* slimy salamander
_____

2. *Ambystoma jeffersonianum,* Jefferson salamander
_____

3. *Ambystoma maculatum,* spotted salamander
_____

4. *Triturus viridescens,* newt
_____

5. *Eurycea bislineata,* two-lined salamander
_____

6. *Necturus maculosus,* mud puppy
_____

7. *Ambystoma tigrinum*, tiger salamander
_____

8. *Hemidactylium scutatum*, four-toed salamander
_____

9. *Plethodon cinereus*, red-backed salamander
_____

10. *Siren intermedia*, siren
_____

11. *Ambystoma opacum*, marbled salamander
_____

Part B. Constructing a Classification Key

Use the space below to construct a wildflower classification key.

Wildflower Classification Key

A possible key follows:

1a	Flowers wth 3 petals	Go to 2
1b	Flowers with other than 3 petals	Go to 3
2a	Three oval-shaped leaves	Trillium
2b	Arrow-shaped leaves	Arrowhead
3a	Leaf divided into leaflets or lobes	Go to 4
3b	Leaf not divided into leaflets or lobes	Go to 5
4a	Leaf has 5 to 7 lobes	May apple
4b	Leaf made of 3-toothed leaflets	Red clover
5a	Bell-shaped flowers	Bellwort
5b	5-petaled flowers	Blue violet

Analysis and Conclusions

1. As you used the classification key to identify the salamanders, did you go from general to specific characteristics or from specific to general characteristics? _From general to specific._
_____

2. What two groupings do the scientific names of the salamanders represent?
Genus and species.
_____

3. Was the classification key you constructed exactly like those of other students? Explain why or why not. _Student keys will be likely to vary because different individuals will choose different traits around which to write their keys._
_____

4. If you were using actual wildflowers, what other characteristics could you use to identify them? Flower color, scent, and relative size of the flower parts, stems, and leaves might be used.

Critical Thinking and Application

1. Do you think that there may be some closely related species of organisms that cannot be identified with a classification key? Explain your answer. Yes. Some closely related species may not have easily distinguished physical traits. Therefore they may be extremely difficult or impossible to identify using a key. Also, the individuals of some species may be so variable that it would be impossible to delineate their traits in a key.

2. Why do you think biological classification keys always present two, rather than some other number, of choices at each step? Two opposing either/or choices call the user's attention to a few features at a time. Because of the complexity or similarity of some organisms, a greater number of choices in a key could lead to confusion. With only two choices, it is still sometimes difficult to decide which statement best describes a certain specimen.

3. What types of problems would scientists have today if Carolus Linnaeus had not developed his classification and naming system for organisms? Scientists who speak different languages would have different names for the same organism. This would make it very difficult for scientists to research and communicate information about a specific organism.

4. Explain what is meant by the statement "Classification systems are the inventions of humans; diversity is the product of evolution." Classification systems are our attempt to organize the many different types of life forms that have evolved from simpler forms of life.

Going Further

Use the key presented in this investigation as a model to construct a classification key to identify one or more of the following:
1. Instruments of a band or orchestra
2. Balls used in different kinds of sports (tennis ball, basketball, football, bowling ball, golf ball, and so on)
3. The students in your biology class

30

You may want to refer students to pages 342–346 in the text for a discussion of proto-life.

Time required: 45 minutes.

Making Coacervates

Pre-Lab Discussion

How did life on Earth begin? According to a hypothesis by Russian scientist Alexander Oparin, all life developed gradually from materials found in the oceans on primitive Earth. According to Oparin, prehistoric oceans probably consisted of a rich mixture of organic chemicals, including proteins and carbohydrates. If certain kinds of proteins and carbohydrates are mixed together with water, *coacervates,* or droplets showing lifelike characteristics, may form. Coacervates are not alive. However, in a manner similar to cells, coacervates appear to ingest materials, grow, and reproduce. Because of this, scientists have hypothesized that coacervates may have been the precursors of cells.

In this investigation, you will produce coacervates and observe their behavior.

Problem

How does a mixture of protein and carbohydrate molecules act like a living organism?

Materials *(per group)*

1 medium-sized test tube
1 rubber stopper that fits the test tube
1% gelatin solution   Dissolve 3.5 g gelatin in 346.5 mL distilled hot water. Refrigerate until needed.
1% gum arabic solution   Dissolve 0.75 g gum arabic in 74 mL distilled hot water.
1% hydrochloric acid solution   Slowly stir 1 mL concentrated hydrochloric acid into 99 mL distilled water.
pH test paper
2 medicine droppers   If gelatin or gum arabic is unavailable, these substitutes may work: alcohol added
Microscope   to gelatin in water; dilute sodium sulfate added to gelatin in water; sugar added
    to egg yolk in water; gum arabic, sucrose, or alcohol added to egg albumin in
Glass slide   water. First put the protein in water, and then add the carbohydrate to it.
Coverslip
10-mL graduated cylinder
Glass stirring rod

Safety ⚗ 🔥 👁

Put on a laboratory apron if one is available. Put on safety goggles. Handle all glassware carefully. Always use special caution when working with laboratory chemicals as they may irritate the skin or cause staining of the skin or clothing. Never touch or taste any chemical unless you are instructed to do so. Always handle the microscope with extreme care. You are responsible for its proper care and use. Use caution when handling glass slides as they can break easily and cut you. Note all safety alert symbols next to the steps in the Procedure and review the meanings of each symbol by referring to the symbol guide on page 10.

Procedure

⚠️ 🧪 **1.** Obtain a test tube and a rubber stopper that fits the test tube. Use the graduated cylinder to pour 6 mL of gelatin solution into the test tube. Next add 4 mL of gum arabic solution to the test tube. Mix the two solutions by *gently* inverting the test tube several times. **Note:** *Mix the solutions gently. Do not shake the test tube as this will hinder the formation of coacervates.*

⚠️ **2.** Coacervates will form only under specific environmental conditions. One important condition is the acidity of the environment. Unstopper the test tube and dip a glass stirring rod into the mixture. Touch a drop of the mixture onto a piece of pH paper. Compare the color of your pH paper to information given on the package of test papers or information supplied by your teacher. Record the pH under Trial 1 in the Data Table.

3. The cloudiness or clearness of the mixture may indicate the presence or absence of coacervates. Hold the test tube up to a light source. Record if the mixture is cloudy or clear under Trial 1 in the Data Table.

⚠️ **4.** Use a medicine dropper to put 2 drops of the mixture on a clean glass slide. Place a coverslip over the drops and examine them under low power. Coacervates, as shown in Figure 1, will look like droplets of material with tiny bubbles inside. **Note:** *You may not see coacervates until the pH (acidity) is adjusted, so do not get discouraged.* Observe the number, size, and movement of any coacervates present and record this information under Trial 1 in the Data Table. Clean the slide and coverslip.

Water molecules

Protein and carbohydrate molecules

Figure 1

🧪 **5.** Use a second medicine dropper to change the pH of the mixture by adding 3 drops of weak hydrochloric acid solution. **CAUTION:** *Hydrochloric acid can cause burns. If the acid touches your skin or clothes, immediately wash the area with water and notify your teacher.* Stopper the test tube and gently invert it once or twice to mix the solution.

6. Repeat steps 2 through 4, recording all information under Trial 2 in the Data Table.

7. Repeat step 5 four more times, adding 3 drops of weak hydrochloric acid each time. Test the pH mixture, observe and record the degree of cloudiness, and make observations of coacervates under the microscope. Record this information under Trials 3 through 6 in the Data Table.

210

Observations
Data Table

	Observation of Coacervates					
	Trial					
	1	**2**	**3**	**4**	**5**	**6**
pH			pH should become more acidic.			
Cloudy/clear			Mixture should be cloudy at a pH of approximately 4; solution will otherwise remain fairly clear.			
Microscopic observations			Answers will vary. Coacervates should be the largest and most abundant at a pH of approximately 4.			

Analysis and Conclusions

1. At what pH do coacervates appear to be the largest and most abundant?
   4.

2. At what pH or pHs do coacervates appear to be the smallest and least abundant?
   At pHs above or below 4.

3. How does the cloudiness of the solution relate to the presence or absence of coacervates?
   The cloudier the material in the test tube, the larger and more abundant the coacervates.

4. List two ways in which coacervates seem to be living organisms. They may appear to move, reproduce, ingest materials, and associate with one another. Accept various other student observations that indicate lifelike activity.

5. List two ways in which coacervates seem to be nonliving substances.
   Answers will vary, but may include the lack of nuclei and/or other cell organelles, inability to carry on metabolism, and inability to produce wastes.

Critical Thinking and Application

1. The word "coacervate" comes from the Latin word meaning "heap." How is this name suitable for describing the droplets you observed? Coacervates are droplets of material that tend to coalesce, or form globular "heaps," under certain environmental conditions.

2. Some scientists feel strongly that life may have evolved on other planets as well as on Earth. Why might they think so? If other planets contain organic raw materials and have environmental conditions similar to those of Earth, it might be possible for living organisms to have evolved in a way similar to those on Earth.

3. Do you think your coacervate investigation might have worked if you had substituted other proteins and carbohydrates? How could you test your hypothesis? Students will most likely answer that other raw materials could probably be used to produce coacervates. An investigation similar to the one just conducted could be set up to test other substances.

Going Further

Some scientists believe that microspheres may be another type of substance that may have been a precursor of the living cell. Conduct library research on the production and characteristics of microspheres. Refer to the work of American biochemist Sidney Fox.

31

Identifying Bacteria

You may want to refer students to pages 360–375 in the textbook for a discussion of bacteria.

Time required: 50 minutes.

Pre-Lab Discussion

Bacteria are divided into different groups based on a number of characteristics. One way to distinguish bacteria is by shape. Bacteria that resemble spheres are called *cocci*. *Bacilli* are bacteria that look like rods. Bacteria that resemble sprials are called *spirilla*.

Another way to distinguish bacteria is by their ability to accept a specific type of stain called a Gram stain. The Gram-staining method uses two stains—a dark purple stain and a light pink stain. Bacteria that are Gram-positive retain the dark purple stain. Bacteria that loose the dark purple stain and show only the light pink stain are called Gram-negative. The difference in staining characteristics is due to differences in the bacterial cell wall.

In this investigation, you will identify bacteria by their shape, mobility, and ability to accept a Gram stain.

Problem

How are different types of bacteria identified?

Provide prepared slides of at least three different species and shapes of bacteria. Be sure that every slide is labeled with the genus and species of bacterium. Prepared slides can be ordered from biological supply houses.

Materials *(per group)*

Microscope
Bunsen burner
Inoculating loop
Test tube rack
Glass-marking pencil
Flint striker or matches
2 glass slides
Slide holder
Staining tray
Wash bottle
Bibulous paper

Prepared slides of different-shaped bacteria
Cultures of:
 Escherichia coli
 Bacillus subtilis
Gram stain set of 4 dropper
 bottles:
 Crystal violet
 Gram's iodine
 95% ethyl alcohol
 Safranin

Annotations for preparation of cultures found after Going Further.

Dissolve 1.5 g crystal violet in 10 mL denatured alcohol. Stir until completely dissolved. Add 90 mL distilled water.
Dissolve 1 g iodine and 2 g potassium iodide in 300 mL distilled water. Stir until completely dissolved.
Dissolve 0.34 g of safranin in 10 mL 95% ethyl alcohol. Stir until completely dissolved. Add 90 mL distilled water.

Never culture pathogenic bacteria. However, treat all bacterial cultures as if they are pathogenic. Cultures should be killed before disposal. Autoclave all cultures and contaminated glassware at 15 pounds pressure per square inch (103.4 Pa). If a bacterial culture is accidentally spilled, flood the area with a disinfectant solution. Leave the disinfectant on the affected area and any broken glassware for at least 30 minutes before carefully wiping the area with moist paper towels. A clearly marked bottle of disinfectant should be placed on each worktable in case such accidents occur.

Safety 🧪 🥽 👆 📷 👁

Put on a laboratory apron if one is available. Put on safety goggles. Handle all glassware carefully. Use extreme care when working with heated equipment or materials to avoid burns. Always use special caution when working with laboratory chemicals, as they may irritate the skin or cause staining of the skin or clothing. Never touch or taste any chemical unless instructed to do so. Use special caution when working with bacterial cultures. Always handle the microscope with extreme care. You are responsible for its proper care and use. Use caution when handling glass slides as they can break easily and cut you. Note all safety symbols next to the steps in the Procedure and review the meanings of each symbol by referring to the symbol guide on page 10.

Procedure
Part A. Identifying Bacteria by Shape

🧪 1. Obtain prepared slides of different-shaped bacteria from your teacher. Bacteria have three characteristic shapes: round, or *coccus;* rod-shaped, or *bacillus;* and spiral-shaped, or *spirillum.* These three basic shapes can be arranged singly, in pairs (*diplo-*), or in chains (*strepto-*), and in clusters (*staphylo-*).

2. Observe a prepared bacteria slide under high power. Make a drawing of what you observe in the appropriate place in Observations. Write the name of the bacteria. Observe how the bacteria on this slide are arranged and record this information in Data Table 1.

3. Repeat step 2 with the other prepared slides obtained from your teacher.

Part B. Gram-Staining Bacteria

🧪 1. Obtain tubes of bacterial cultures A and B. **CAUTION:** *Use extreme care when working with bacterial cultures. Avoid spills. If a spill does occur, immediately call your teacher for assistance. Do not try to clean it up by yourself.* Place the tubes in an upright position in a test tube rack. With a glass-marking pencil, label one glass slide A and the other glass slide B.

🥽 2. Put on safety goggles. Light the Bunsen burner. **CAUTION:** *Use extreme care when working with*
👆 *or near an open flame. Tie back loose hair and clothing.*

🧪 3. Pick up test tube A and make a sterile transfer from the test tube to a clean glass slide in the
👆 following manner. Remove the plug and pass the mouth of the test tube through the flame of the Bunsen burner. Hold the inoculating loop in the flame until it is red hot. Allow the loop to cool for a few seconds. Pick up a loopful of bacterial culture from test tube A. Reflame the mouth of the test tube and replace the plug. Return the test tube to the test tube rack. Touch the loopful of bacterial culture to the center of slide A. Spread the bacteria into a circle about the size of a dime, as shown in Figure 1A. The area of bacteria on the slide is called a smear. Set slide A aside to air-dry. Flame the inoculating loop until it is red hot. **CAUTION:** *Do not touch the bacterial smear to determine if it is dry. Always avoid direct contact with bacterial cultures.*

4. Repeat step 3 making a transfer from test tube B to slide B.

🧪 5. Fasten a slide holder onto the end of slide A. Pass the slide, *smear side up,* three times through
👆 the flame of the Bunsen burner, as shown in Figure 1B. **CAUTION:** *Do not touch the hot glass slide. Handle it only with a slide holder.* Set the slide aside to cool. Repeat this procedure with slide B. Turn off the Bunsen burner. Passing the slide through the flame kills the bacteria and attaches, or fixes, the bacteria to the slide.

📷 6. Place both slides in the center of a staining tray. Find the dropper bottle marked "crystal violet." Flood the smears on both slides with crystal voilet, as shown in Figure 1C. **CAUTION:** *Handle the crystal violet with care. It is a stain and is difficult to remove from hands and clothing.* Leave the crystal violet on the smears for 60 seconds.

7. As shown in Figure 1D, use a wash bottle filled with water to rinse all excess crystal violet from the slides. **CAUTION:** *Do not let the water flow directly onto the smear.*

🔬 8. Place the slides between two sheets of bibulous paper, as shown in Figure 1E. Close the sheets and carefully press on the slides to blot them dry. **CAUTION:** *To avoid breaking the slides, use only gentle pressure.*

Figure 1

9. Steps 2 through 8 are the first steps in making a Gram stain. The result up to this step is called a *simple stain.*

10. Read steps 11 through 15 before you proceed with the Gram stain. The Gram stain is a differential stain; that is, it has one of two possible results. Gram-positive (Gram+) bacteria are stained violet or blue. Gram-negative (Gram-) bacteria are stained pink or red. You may want to stain only one slide at a time.

🔲 11. Replace the slide, smear side up, in the staining tray. Find the dropper bottle marked "Gram's iodine." Flood the smear with Gram's iodine. **CAUTION:** *Handle the Gram's iodine with care. It is a stain and is difficult to remove from hands and clothing.* Leave the Gram's iodine on the smear for 30 seconds.

12. With a wash bottle, wash away all excess Gram's iodine from the slide. **CAUTION:** *Do not let the water flow directly onto the smear.*

🔲 13. Find the dropper bottle marked "95% ethyl alcohol." Flood the smear with alcohol. Leave the alcohol on the smear for 10 seconds. Use a wash bottle to rinse away any excess alcohol. **CAUTION:** *Do not let the water flow directly onto the smear.* The alcohol removes the crystal violet from the Gram-negative bacteria. The Gram-negative bacteria are now colorless.

14. Find the dropper bottle marked "safranin." Flood the smear with safranin stain. **CAUTION:** *Handle the safranin with care. It is a stain and is difficult to remove from hands and clothing.* Leave the safranin on for 45 seconds. Wash away any excess safranin with a wash bottle. **CAUTION:** *Do not let the water flow directly onto the smear.* The safranin colors the Gram-negative bacteria pink or red.

15. Dry the slide between two sheets of bibulous paper.

16. Repeat steps 11 through 15 with the remaining slide.

17. Observe both slides under high power of a microscope. Record your observations in Data Table 2.

18. Return the slides and tubes of bacterial cultures to your teacher for proper disposal. Wipe the surface of your work area with disinfectant and allow it to air-dry. Thoroughly wash your hands with soap and water.

Observations

Prepared Slide 1

Magnification _____

Prepared Slide 2

Magnification _____

Answers will vary depending on prepared slides used.

Prepared Slide 3

Magnification _____

Data Table 1

Bacterium Name	Basic Shape	Arrangement (✓)				
		Single	Pair (diplo-)	Chain (strepto-)	Cluster (staphylo-)	Other (draw)
			Answers will vary depending on slides used.			

Data Table 2

Bacterium	Basic Shape	Color	Gram-Positive or Gram-Negative?
A (*Escherichia coli*)	bacillus	pink/red	Gram-negative
B (*Bacillus subtilis*)	bacillus	purple/blue	Gram-positive

Analysis and Conclusions

1. Why do you think you flame the slide with the smear facing away from the flame?

   To keep the flame from destroying the bacteria. _____

   _____

2. Why do you think you do not run water directly onto the smear?

   To keep from washing away the bacteria. _____

   _____

3. What are the two reasons for staining bacteria? To make the bacteria more visible under a

   microscope and to determine whether the bacteria are Gram-positive or Gram-negative.

   _____

4. Does a bacterium's Gram reaction seem to be directly related to its shape? How could you

   prove your hypothesis? Based on their limited observations in this investigation, students should answer

   no. More bacterial cultures could be observed and Gram stained to prove or disprove this hypothesis.

   _____

Critical Thinking and Application

1. Penicillin works by interfering with a bacterium's ability to build a cell wall. Using this information, explain why Gram-positive bacteria are more susceptible to destruction by penicillin than Gram-negative bacteria are. (*Hint:* Review the structural differences between Gram-positive and Gram-negative bacteria in your text.) Gram-positive bacteria have a cell wall made up of one layer and are therefore more susceptible to penicillin than Gram-negative bacteria, which have a cell wall made up of two layers.

2. You are given an unknown bacterial culture by your teacher. After completing the Gram-staining technique used in this investigation, you observe both pink and purple bacteria in the same smear. What could be a possible explanation for this? The culture was not pure at the beginning of the investigation. Also, contamination could have occurred during the investigation.

3. Occasionally after a flood or the breaking of a large water pipe, people living in the area are advised to boil their drinking water. Why is this done? Boiling the water will help to kill bacteria that may have contaminated the water supply.

4. It has been only in recent years that scientists have discovered fossilized bacteria. Why might this discovery have taken so long to occur? Bacteria are very small and thus difficult to see.

Going Further

1. Using the techniques for Gram staining that you used in this investigation, prepare a smear of bacteria that have been isolated from bacterial cultures prepared from various foods. Devise a system of research and chart your results.

2. Some scientists now think they have isolated a fourth bacterial shape—the bent rod. Conduct library research on this new finding and share your information with the class.

Pure cultures of *Escherichia coli* and *Bacillus subtilis* can be obtained from a biological supply house. Bacteria are easily cultured in tubes of nutrient broth. To prepare the nutrient broth, bring 350 mL distilled water to a boil in a 500-mL beaker. Slowly add 3 g dehydrated nutrient broth, stirring constantly. Pour the broth into small test tubes and insert a cotton plug into each tube. Sterilize the tubes of broth for 15 minutes at 15 pounds pressure in an autoclave or pressure cooker. The sterilized tubes can be stored in a refrigerator until they are needed. Transfer bacteria to the tubes of sterile nutrient broth using an inoculating loop and following sterile technique. Store inoculated tubes at room temperature for 2 or 3 days to allow the bacteria to grow. Tubes of bacteria can also be incubated at 37°C for 24 hours and then used immediately. Subcultures and dilutions of the cultures can be made at 2-week intervals. Cultures remain viable stored in a refrigerator for several weeks.

32

Controlling Bacterial Growth

You may want to refer students to pages 372–375 in the textbook for a discussion of bacteria.

Time required: 50 minutes plus a 15-minute observation period after 48 hours of incubation.

Pre-Lab Discussion

Chemical substances that either kill bacteria or inhibit bacterial growth are called *antimicrobial agents*. Antimicrobial agents are of three basic types: *antiseptics*, or chemicals used to inhibit the growth of or kill bacteria on living tissues; *disinfectants*, or chemicals used to inhibit the growth of or kill bacteria on nonliving things; and *antibiotics*, or chemical substances produced by living organisms, which inhibit the growth of bacteria.

The effectiveness of each type of antimicrobial agent is influenced by many factors. Some of these factors include the environmental conditions in which the agent is applied, the chemical properties of the agent, how long the agent has been stored, and the rate of deterioration of the agent.

In this investigation, you will test the effectiveness of disinfectants and antibiotics in inhibiting the growth of bacteria.

Problem

How can the growth of bacteria be controlled?

Materials *(per group)*

Annotations for the preparation of cultures are found after Going Further in Investigation 31.

Glass-marking pencil
Bunsen burner
Flint striker or matches
2 sterile cotton swabs
Beaker of water
Test tube rack
Sterile filter-paper disks
Sterile forceps
Distilled water
Metric ruler
Transparent tape

Culture of *Escherichia coli*
2 sterile nutrient agar plates
3 disinfectants chosen from the
    following: chlorine bleach,
    household cleaner, household
    disinfectant, lye, phenol
3 antibiotic disks chosen from the
    following: aureomycin,
    chloromycetin, penicillin,
    streptomycin, tetracycline,
    terramycin

Annotations for preparation of agar plates are found after Going Further in this investigation.

Antibiotic disks are available from biological supply houses.

Safety 🧪 📷 🥽 👁

Put on a laboratory apron if one is available. Put on safety goggles. Handle all glassware carefully. Tie back loose hair and clothing when using the Bunsen burner. Always use special caution when working with laboratory chemicals and bacterial cultures. Note all safety symbols next to the steps in the Procedure and review the meanings of each symbol by referring to the symbol guide on page 10.

Never culture pathogenic bacteria. However, treat all bacterial cultures as if they are pathogenic. Firmly seal with transparent tape any bacterial plates that are used for student inspection. For sterilization, use a high-temperature gas flame rather than an alcohol burner or candle flame. Cultures should be killed before disposal. Autoclave or pressure cook all cultures and contaminated glassware at 15 pounds pressure per square inch (103.4 Pa) for 20 minutes. Disposable plates should be incinerated.

Procedure
Part A. Inoculating a Sterile Nutrient Agar Plate

△ 1. Obtain two sterile nutrient agar plates. Carefully turn each plate over and lay it on your worktable. **CAUTION:** *Be very careful not to open the the petri dishes of sterile agar while handling them.*

Figure 1

2. With a glass-marking pencil, mark the bottom of each petri dish shown in Figure 1. Draw two lines at right angles to each other so that the dish is divided into four equal areas, or quadrants. Number the quadrants on each dish 1 through 4. **Note:** *Place the numbers near the edges of the dishes.* Near the top center of each dish write your initials. Carefully turn the petri dishes right side up.

△ 3. Obtain a test tube containing a bacterial culture of *Escherichia coli*. Place the test tube in a test tube rack. **CAUTION:** *Use extreme care when working with bacterial cultures. Avoid spills. If a spill does occur, immediately call your teacher for assistance.* Obtain two sterile cotton swabs. Carefully read steps 4 through 8 and study Figure 2 before you proceed. If a bacterial culture is accidentally spilled, flood the area with a disinfectant solution. Leave the disinfectant on the affected area and any broken glassware for at least 30 minutes before carefully wiping the area with moist paper towels. A clearly marked bottle of disinfectant should be placed on each worktable in case such accidents occur.

Figure 2

4. Put on your safety goggles and light the Bunsen burner. **CAUTION:** *Use extreme care when working with or near an open flame. Tie back loose hair and clothing.*

5. Pick up the test tube of *E. coli*. Remove the cotton plug. **Note:** *Do not let the cotton plug come in contact with any other object.* Pass the mouth of the tube back and forth through the burner flame.

6. Insert a sterile cotton swab into the bacterial culture. **Note:** *Shake off any excess liquid into the test tube.* Remove the cotton swab. **Note:** *Do not let the cotton swab come in contact with any other object.* Pass the mouth of the tube back and forth through the burner flame. Replace the cotton plug and return the test tube to the rack.

7. Slightly open a sterile nutrient agar plate. Place the tip of the cotton swab near the top center of the agar. Streak the agar as shown in Figure 3A. Lift the swab off the plate and turn the petri dish 90° to the right. Streak the agar again, as shown in Figure 3B. Close the petri dish.

8. Hold the top of the cotton swab in the flame of the Bunsen burner until it catches fire. Remove the swab from the flame and plunge it into a beaker of water.

9. Repeat steps 5 through 8 for the other sterile nutrient agar plate. **Note:** *Be sure to use a new sterile cotton swab for this transfer.* Turn off the Bunsen burner after you have completed the second plate.

10. The nutrient agar plates that you have just streaked, or inoculated, with bacteria will be used in part B of this investigation.

11. Return the test tube of *E. coli* to your teacher. Thoroughly wash your hands with soap and water.

A

B

Plate turned 90° to right

Figure 3

Part B. Controlling the Spread of Bacteria with Disinfectants and Antibiotics

1. Take one inoculated agar plate of *E. coli* that you prepared in Part A.

2. Select three disinfectants and three antibiotics, and record these selections in the Data Table. Carefully read steps 3 through 10 and study Figure 4 before you proceed.

A Pick up disk with forceps

B Soak disk in disinfectant

Disinfectant

Disk

C Place disk in quadrant 1

Forceps

Disk

D Flame forceps

Figure 4

3. Light the Bunsen burner. **CAUTION:** *Use extreme care when working with or near an open flame. Tie back loose hair and clothing.*

4. With sterile forceps, pick up a disk of filter paper. Insert the disk into disinfectant 1. Shake off any excess liquid.

5. Slightly open an inoculated agar plate. Position the filter-paper disk in the center of quadrant 1. With the tip of the forceps, gently press the disk against the agar until it sticks. Remove the forceps and close the petri dish.

6. Pass the forceps back and forth through the flame of the Bunsen burner several times. This procedure sterilizes the forceps. **CAUTION:** *If there is alcohol on the forceps, it will burn brightly and quickly. Stand back from the Bunsen burner when burning alcohol off the forceps.* Allow the forceps to cool before picking up the next filter-paper disk.

7. Repeat steps 4 through 6 with the remaining disinfectant-soaked disks in quadrants 2 and 3 of the inoculated plate of *E. coli*. **Note:** *Remember to sterilize the forceps after each use.*

8. In quadrant 4, place a filter-paper disk soaked in distilled water.

9. Repeat steps 4 through 8 with the other inoculated agar plate using antibiotic disks instead of disinfectants. You should have two inoculated agar plates as shown in Figure 5.

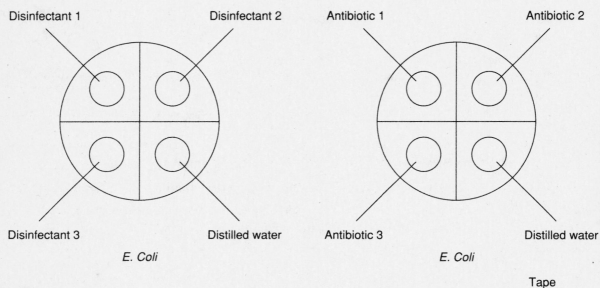

Disinfectant 1   Disinfectant 2   Antibiotic 1   Antibiotic 2

Disinfectant 3   Distilled water   Antibiotic 3   Distilled water

E. Coli   *E. Coli*

Figure 5

10. With transparent tape, tape the petri dishes closed, as shown in Figure 6. Turn the dishes upside down. Incubate the dishes for 48 hours at 37°C.

Tape

Figure 6

11. Observe the petri dishes after 48 hours. White or cloudy areas of the agar indicate bacterial growth. Notice any clear areas, called *zones of inhibition,* surrounding the filter-paper disks. A clear area indicates that the disinfectant or antibiotic inhibited bacterial growth. A lightly cloudy area surrounding a disk indicates that bacterial growth was slowed down. **Note:** *You may want to hold the petri dish to the light to see the zones of inhibition more clearly.*

12. With a metric ruler, measure to the nearest millimeter the size of the clear zone surrounding each disk. Record your measurements in the Data Table. If no clear zone is present, record the measurement as 0.

13. Return the petri dishes to your teacher for proper disposal. Thoroughly wash your hands with soap and water.

Observations

Data Table

Effects of Disinfectants and Antibiotics on Growth of *E. Coli*	
Disinfectant	**Zone of Inhibition** (mm)
1	
2	Answers will vary depending on disinfectants used.
3	
4 distilled water	
Antibiotic	**Zone of Inhibition** (mm)
1	
2	Answers will vary depending on antibiotics used.
3	
4 distilled water	

Analysis and Conclusions

1. Why is it important not to open the sterile nutrient agar plates? To prevent the plates from

becoming contaminated by airborne microorganisms.

_____

2. Why do you think it is so important to write the numbers and initials near the edges of the

petri dish? So that the writing will not obstruct the view of the bacteria growing in the petri dish.

_____

3. Why is it important to use sterile techniques while inoculating the agar plate?

Sterile techniques should always be used when working with bacteria to prevent contamination of the

environment and of the bacteria being studied.

4. What is the purpose of the disk soaked in distilled water in each inoculated petri dish?

The disk serves as a control.

_____

5. What is the purpose of taping closed the lids of the petri dishes? To keep the lids from coming

open and allowing contamination of the inoculated plates.

_____

6. Which disinfectant was most effective in preventing the growth of *E. coli?*

Answers will vary depending on the disinfectants used.

7. Which antibiotic was most effective in preventing the growth of *E. coli?*

Answers will vary depending on the antibiotics used.

8. How do you know that any inhibition you have observed is due to the disinfectants and

antibiotics on the disks? There should be no inhibition around the control disks.

Critical Thinking and Application

1. Pretend that a serious staphylococcus infection has developed in the locker room of your school's gym. Assume that you are responsible for getting rid of the staph contamination.

How would you do so? Use a sterile inoculating loop to collect a sample of suspected sources of the

bacteria. Culture the bacteria with disinfectant disks. Scrub the area with the most effective disinfectant.

2. Scientists have observed that an antibiotic seems to lose its effectiveness against a particular population of bacteria after a prolonged period of time. What do you think is responsible for

this phenomenon? The antibiotic kills the susceptible bacteria in the population. The surviving bacteria will

have mutated to a form that is immune to the antibiotic and will produce offspring that will inherit this immunity.

3. Why are the different disinfectants not equally effective against all species of bacteria?

Species of bacteria differ from one another and therefore react differently to various disinfectants.

4. Suppose that your doctor diagnoses your condition as a bacterial infection and prescribes an antibiotic. Your doctor cautions you to take the antibiotic for 10 days even though you may feel fine after a few days. Explain why you should follow your doctor's orders.

After a few days, the antibiotic will probably have destroyed most of the bacteria. Thus, you will feel better.

However, some bacteria will still remain and will reproduce. The infection will begin again. Taking the antibiotic

for 10 days almost certainly ensures that all of the bacteria will be destroyed.

Going Further

1. You may want to conduct the following experiment dealing with the origin of antibiotics. Stir a handful of soil into about 100 mL of water. Allow the soil to settle. Dip filter-paper disks into the soil water. Set the disks aside to dry. Use the procedures of this investigation to test for the presence of natural antibiotics.

2. Using the procedures presented in this investigation, test other species of bacteria—such as *B. subtilis, P. vulgaris,* and *S. lutea*—for their resistance or sensitivity to various disinfectants and antibiotics.

To prepare nutrient agar plates, mix 3 g beef extract, 5 g peptone, and 15 g agar in 1 L distilled water. Bring mixture to a boil, stirring constantly to avoid burning. Heat until liquid is clear. Sterilize in containers covered with cotton plugs in autoclave or pressure cooker for 15 minutes at 15 pounds pressure. Recipe makes about 50 petri dishes. Refrigerate. Nutrient agar can also be purchased from biological supply houses.

33

Adaptations of the Paramecium

You may want to refer students to pages 384–386 in the textbook for a discussion of the paramecium.

Time required: 50 minutes.

Pre-Lab Discussion

Paramecia are animallike single-celled organisms that belong to the phylum *Ciliata*. In nature, paramecia can be found swimming freely in fresh water. The paramecium, like any other living organism, has certain metabolic requirements for survival. The activities that fulfill these requirements are accomplished by certain cell organelles. These cell structures, like the tissues of more complex multicellular organisms, perform specialized tasks. Paramecia are relatively large protozoans with easily identifiable organelles, making them especially useful for study in the biology laboratory.

In this investigation, you will examine the structure and function of the various organelles of the paramecium. You will also observe adaptations of a paramecium that help it survive.

Problem

How is a paramecium structured for survival?

Materials *(per group)*

Culture of *Paramecium caudatum* [1]
Methyl cellulose solution [2]
Carmine solution [3]
Yeast suspension [4]
Congo red solution [5]
Glass slide
Coverslip
Cotton ball
Microscope
Toothpick or glass rod
Medicine dropper

[1] Annotations for the preparation of *Paramecium* culture are found after Going Further.

[2] Dissolve 10 g methyl cellulose in 90 mL distilled water. Stir until dissolved. Pour into dropper bottles for student use.

[3] Dissolve 1 g carmine red in 100 mL distilled water. Stir until dissolved. Pour into dropper bottles for student use.

[4] Mix 1 package active dry yeast in 1 L lukewarm tap water. Mix to dissolve. Use within 2 days.

[5] Dissolve 30 mg Congo red powder in 10 mL distilled water. Pour into dropper bottles for student use.

Safety 👤 🧰

Put on a laboratory apron if one is available. Put on safety goggles. Handle all glassware carefully. Always use special caution when working with laboratory chemicals, as they may irritate the skin or cause staining of the skin or clothing. Never touch or taste any chemical unless you are instructed to do so. Always handle the microscope with extreme care. You are responsible for its proper care and use. Use caution when handling glass slides as they can break easily and cut you. Note all safety alert symbols next to the steps in the Procedure and review the meanings of each symbol by referring to the symbol guide on page 10.

Procedure
Part A. Paramecium Structure and Movement

⚠️ **1.** With a toothpick or glass rod, place a ring of methyl cellulose on a clean glass slide, as shown in Figure 1. The toothpick should be held in a vertical position while the methyl cellulose is being put into place. Laying the toothpick on its side causes smearing.

Figure 1

📷 **2.** Use a medicine dropper to place a drop of paramecium culture within the ring of methyl cellulose. The methyl cellulose is thick like syrup and will slow the paramecia down to make observations easier. **CAUTION:** *Be careful not to spill the methyl cellulose. It can irritate your skin.*

3. Pull a few fibers from the cotton ball and place them over the paramecia and methyl cellulose.

4. Cover the paramecium culture with a coverslip. Cotton ball fibers can be used alone if methyl cellulose is not available.

5. Observe the paramecium culture under the low-power objective of the microscope. Look for slipper-shaped paramecia that are relatively motionless or trapped near a cotton fiber.

6. Carefully switch to the high-power objective.

7. Adjust the diaphragm to permit a low level of light to enter the lens. This will allow a better contrast for observing organelles.

8. Observe one paramecium for a few minutes.

9. In the space provided in Observations, draw a single paramecium as you observe it in the microscope. Include the organelles that you see. Indicate which end is the posterior (rear) end and which is the anterior (front) end.

10. Refer to Figure 2 to label the organelles you see in your specimen.

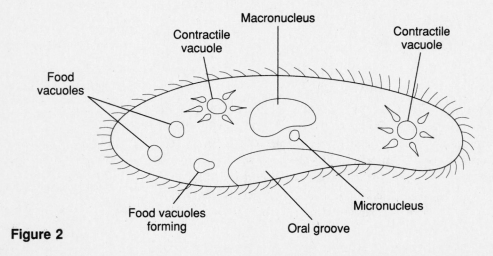

Figure 2

11. Observe the motion of the paramecium and answer question 1 in Observations.

12. Observe how the paramecium reacts when it bumps into a cotton fiber. Answer question 2 in Observations.

13. Look for hairlike structures on the outer surface of the organism. These are called cilia. Answer questions 3 and 4 in Observations.

14. Carefully lift the coverslip and add a drop of carmine solution to the paramecium culture. **CAUTION:** *Carmine solution is a dye that can stain your clothing and skin. Be careful.*

15. Replace the coverslip and refocus a single paramecium under high power.

16. Observe the way in which the particles of the carmine solution are moved around the paramecium. Answer question 5 in Observations.

17. Carefully wash and dry the slide and coverslip.

Part B. Ingestion and Digestion in the Paramecium

1. Prepare a second slide of paramecia and methyl cellulose.

2. Add a drop of yeast suspension that has been stained with Congo red to the paramecium culture on the slide. Congo red is a pH indicator. It turns blue in acidic conditions, pink in neutral conditions, and red in basic conditions. **CAUTION:** *Congo red is a dye that can stain your clothing and skin. Be careful.*

3. Cover the slide with a coverslip.

4. Locate a single paramecium under low power and then focus under high power.

5. Look for red yeast cells being drawn into the paramecium.

6. Look for the formation of a food vacuole at the end of the paramecium's gullet. See Figure 2. Continue your observations of the paramecium feeding for several minutes. Answer questions 6 and 7 in Observations.

7. Observe what happens to the food vacuole when it becomes full. Answer question 8 in Observations.

8. Continue observing "older vacuoles" full of yeast. Note any color change in the yeast. Answer questions 9 and 10 in Observations. [1]

9. While observing the food vacuoles, also look for star-shaped organelles toward the anterior and posterior ends of the paramecium. These are called contractile vacuoles. Notice that the yeast cells are not in contact with the contractile vacuoles.

10. Continue observing the contractile vacuoles. Note that the contractile vacuoles occasionally shrink and almost disappear.

11. Time the intervals between contractions of this vacuole. Answer question 11 in Observations.

12. Carefully wash and dry the slide and coverslip.

You may want to make the following observations with freshly prepared slides if the materials are available. Use methyl green to observe the macronucleus. Methylene blue will stain both nuclei. India ink will aid observation of the pellicle and cilia. A drop of acetic acid or dilute HCl will cause the trichocysts to be discharged.

[1] Initially, the food vacuole should be red because it is basic. As the digestive enzymes are secreted, the pH becomes more acidic and the food vacuole turns blue due to a change in the indicator. During digestion carbon dioxide is formed, which forms carbonic acid as it combines with water. The color of the food vacuole may return to red as its contents are completely digested and the carbon dioxide diffuses out of the cell. The undigested material in the food vacuole leaves the organism through the anal pore.

Observations

Paramecium

Answers will vary but should resemble Figure 2.

---

1. Describe the motion of the paramecium as it moves throughout the microscope field.

   It moves quickly using its cilia.

2. How does a paramecium react when it bumps into a cotton fiber?

   It keeps turning until its way is unobstructed.

3. Describe the movement of the cilia on a paramecium. Cilia move somewhat like oars in a rowboat.

   There is a power motion and a return motion. The cilia move in unison. Each cilium bends on its return

   stroke so that it offers the least possible resistance to the water.

4. Are the cilia located only on the perimeter of the paramecium? No, they completely cover the

   organism.

5. How are the particles of the carmine solution affected by the paramecium?

   Carmine solution can be observed going into the oral groove and leaving near a spot below the oral groove.

   Some of the solution may swirl around the outside of the paramecium.

6. How did the yeast cells end up in the gullet of the paramecium? The cilia swept the food into the

   gullet.

7. Describe how a food vacuole forms as yeast cells are ingested by a paramecium.

   The cytoplasm at the end of the gullet engulfs the food by phagocytosis, forming a vacuole.

8. What happens to the food vacuole when it becomes full? It moves in a clockwise direction through the paramecium, getting smaller as the food is digested. Wastes eventually will be excreted at a point near where the food was ingested.

9. What is the initial color of the yeast cells in the food vacuole? Red.

10. What color do the yeast cells eventually change to after a period of time in a vacuole? Blue.

11. What was the time interval between contractions of the contractile vacuole? Answers will vary.

Analysis and Conclusions

1. Why is methyl cellulose necessary for observing paramecia? It is necessary to use methyl cellulose to slow the paramecia down so they can be seen.

2. What is the function of the cilia on a paramecium? The function of the cilia is for movement and to sweep food particles into the oral groove.

3. What does a color change in the food vacuoles containing the yeast cells indicate? As digestion occurs, the food vacuoles become more acidic.

4. What is the function of the food vacuole? To digest the food taken in by the paramecium.

5. Paramecia are constantly taking in water. What natural processes cause the water to move in and out of a paramecium? Elimination of metabolic wastes and water causes the paramecium to constantly take in more water.

6. What is the function of the contractile vacuole? To collect excess water and to expel it from the cell.

Critical Thinking and Application

1. The trachea in your throat is lined with ciliated cells. Based on your observations of the paramecium's cilia, explain how the function of the cilia in your throat is similar to the function of the cilia of the paramecium. _The cilia in a human throat move particles of dirt upward away from the lungs in one direction. The cilia in the trachea function in a similar way as the cilia on a paramecium._

2. If a paramecium were to live in a saltwater environment, would it need to have a contractile vacuole? Explain your answer. _No. A contractile vacuole moves excess water out of a paramecium. Salt water would cause the water inside the paramecium to diffuse out of it. This is because the concentration of water would be greater inside the paramecium, and diffusion occurs from a greater concentration to a lesser concentration. Because a freshwater paramecium in a saltwater environment would lose water by diffusion, it would not need a contractile vacuole._

3. Although protozoans are unicellular organisms, parts of their cells exhibit a high degree of specialization. List three cell parts of a paramecium that show specialization within the cell. Relate each cell part in the organism to an organ in the human body.
Answers will vary, but may include: oral groove–mouth; food vacuole–stomach or small intestine; contractile vacuole–kidneys; cilia–sense organs.

Going Further

1. Changes in the environment may produce changes in paramecium behavior. Set up an experiment to observe a paramecium's response to changes in: the salt concentration of water; the pH of water; the temperature of water; and light.

2. Cilia are embedded in the pellicle, or outer membrane, of the paramecium. Embedded in the pellicle are trichocysts, which normally are not visible. To find this organelle, add a drop of weak acetic acid to a slide of paramecium culture. The trichocysts will protrude from the pellicle and appear as clusters of long fibers or hairs. Report your findings to your teacher and class.

Preparation of *Paramecium* Culture:

Paramecia can be successfully cultured in an infusion of dried lettuce leaves. To prepare the infusion, remove several large outer leaves from a head of lettuce. Place the leaves in an oven at low temperature for several hours to dry. Remove the lettuce leaves when they have become crisp and brown. Discard any blackened or charred leaves. Grind the dried leaves with a mortar and pestle. The ground leaves can be stored almost indefinitely in a tightly sealed glass container. In an Erlenmeyer flask, add 1.5 g powdered lettuce leaves to 1 L boiling distilled water. Boil for 5 minutes. Filter the infusion into smaller Erlenmeyer flasks. Seal the flasks with cotton plugs. Sterilize the flasks for 15 minutes at 15 pounds pressure in an autoclave or pressure cooker. Allow the infusion to stand overnight. Using sterile pipettes and flasks, add two parts of lettuce infusion to one part distilled water. Add several drops of a pure concentrated *Paramecium* culture to each flask. Stopper the flasks with cotton plugs. Set the cultures in dim light at room temperature for one to two weeks.
Paramecia need to be subcultured every month. Place several drops of the existing culture into flasks of dilute lettuce infusion. *Paramecium* cultures are available from biological supply houses.

34

Comparing Protists

You may want to refer students to pages 381–401 in the textbook for a discussion of protists.

Time required: Part A–30 minutes
Part B–30 minutes

Pre-Lab Discussion

Kingdom *Protista* includes algal protists, animallike protists, and fungal protists. Protists are often thought of as simple organisms, but a closer examination reveals that they possess a variety of specialized structures. Protists are eukaryotic, which means they have a nucleus enclosed in a membrane. Protists also possess other organelles that perform different functions. Although most protists are one-celled organisms, a few are multicellular. Protists are usually found in damp or watery environments.

In this investigation, you will study several algal and animallike protists.

Problem

What are some characteristics of protists?

Materials *(per group)*

Culture of mixed diatoms   Instructions for preparation of protist cultures are found on
Culture of *Euglena gracilis*   pages T 21 and T 22.
Culture of *Amoeba proteus*
Culture of *Stentor coeruleus*
Microscope
2 glass slides
2 coverslips
Medicine dropper
Methyl cellulose   Dissolve 10 g methyl cellulose in 90 mL distilled water. Stir until dissolved.
Index card   Pour into dropper bottles for student use.
Scissors
Toothpick

Safety 🔺 ⬛ ▦

Put on a laboratory apron if one is available. Put on safety goggles. Handle all glassware carefully. Always use special caution when working with laboratory chemicals, as they may irritate the skin or cause staining of the skin or clothing. Never touch or taste any chemical unless instructed to do so. Always handle the microscope with extreme care. You are responsible for its proper care and use. Use caution when handling glass slides as they can break easily and cut you. Note all safety symbols next to the steps in the Procedure and review the meanings of each symbol by referring to the symbol guide on page 10.

Procedure
Part A. Observing Algal Protists

🧪 **1.** Prepare a wet-mount slide of a mixed diatom culture.

2. Observe the diatoms under the low-power objective of a microscope. Note the variety of colors, shapes, and sizes. Locate an area containing two or three different diatoms.

3. Switch to the high-power objective and focus on one individual diatom at a time. All diatoms have a two-part cell wall, or shell, made of silica. Observe the ridges and patterns in the diatoms' shells.

4. Notice the grooves in the shell. These grooves connect with pores that open to the outside environment. Look for other structures within the diatoms. In the appropriate place in Observations, draw a sketch of two diatoms that you observed. Record the magnification of the microscope.

5. Look for movement of the diatoms. Answer question 1 in Observations.

🧪 **6.** Prepare a wet-mount slide of *Euglena gracilis* culture. Add a drop of methyl cellulose to the culture before placing the coverslip on the slide. Methyl cellulose will slow down the euglena's movement. **CAUTION:** *Be careful not to spill the methyl cellulose. It can irritate your skin.*

7. Mount the slide onto the microscope and focus under low power. Locate several euglenas.

8. Switch to high power and focus on one euglena. Observe the shape of the euglena and distinguish its anterior (front) end from its posterior (rear) end.

9. Note the chloroplasts, which are greenish structures that enable a euglena to make its own food.

10. Locate the euglena's outer covering, or pellicle. The pellicle is flexible and allows the euglena to change its shape. Notice the two flagella, or taillike structures. The longest flagellum helps the organism move. Find the flask-shaped groove called the reservoir, where the flagella are attached.

11. Find the contractile vacuole, which collects extra water and discharges it from the cell. Locate the nucleus.

12. Locate the red eyespot, which is sensitive to light. From an index card, cut a strip the size of a glass slide. Then cut a slit about 1.5 mm long in the center of the card. Place the card with the slit under the slide on the microscope stage. After several minutes, carefully remove the card and examine the euglenas again. Answer question 2 in Observations.

13. In the appropriate place in Observations, draw and label one euglena. Label the following parts: pellicle, flagellum, reservoir, chloroplasts, contractile vacuole, eyespot, and nucleus. Record the magnification of the microscope.

14. Carefully wash and dry your slides and coverslips.

Part B. Observing Animallike Protists

🝮 **1.** Prepare a wet-mount slide of *Amoeba proteus* culture.

2. Mount the prepared slide under the microscope and focus under low power. Use the diaphragm to cut down the amount of light entering the lens. An ameba is easier to observe in low light. Move the slide back and forth to search for the organism. Ameba are somewhat transparent and very irregular in shape.

3. Locate one ameba and switch to high power. Observe the organism closely for several minutes. Locate the two kinds of cytoplasm: endoplasm, a clear outer layer near the cell membrane; and ectoplasm, the granular interior cytoplasm that contains organelles.

4. Notice the movement of the ameba's cytoplasm. Classified as a sarcodine, the ameba moves with **psuedopodia (false feet), or cell extensions.**

5. Observe the organelles such as the nucleus and the contractile vacuole.

6. Carefully remove the coverslip from the slide and add a drop of *Stentor* culture. Mix the two cultures with a toothpick and carefully replace the coverslip. Observe what happens when an ameba comes in contact with a *Stentor*.

7. In the appropriate place in Observations, draw and label one ameba. Label the following structures: ectoplasm, endoplasm, pseudopod, nucleus, contractile vacuole, and food vacuole. Answer questions 3 and 4 in Observations.

🝮 **8.** Prepare a wet-mount slide of *Stentor coeruleus* culture.

9. Mount the slide under the microscope and focus under low power. Examine the size and shape of the *Stentor*.

10. Switch to the high-power objective. Notice the narrow posterior end of the *Stentor*. It may be attached to debris or algae particles. Normally the organism is free-swimming, but when feeding it attaches its posterior end to an object.

11. Locate the hairlike cilia. The *Stentor* is a ciliate protist that moves by means of cilia. Observe the organism for a few minutes. Notice if it changes shape.

12. Note the shape and location of the mouth opening and the cilia that surround the mouth. The *Stentor* sucks in food by setting up water currents with these cilia.

13. Find the gullet, where food is taken into the organism. Also locate the long thin nucleus.

14. In the appropriate place in Observations, draw and label one *Stentor*. Label the following structures: cilia, gullet, and nucleus.

15. Carefully wash and dry your slides and coverslips.

Observations

Magnification _____

Magnification _____

Diatoms

Euglena

Magnification _____

Magnification _____

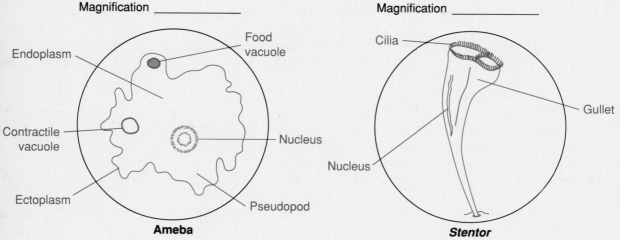

Ameba

Stentor

1. Describe any kind of diatom movement that you discovered. <u>Some diatoms move slowly by</u> extending a stream of cytoplasm through the grooves on the surface of the cell walls.

2. Where did you find the euglenas after removing the index card? <u>Euglenas are concentrated in the</u> area of the slide where light passed through the slit.

3. Does an ameba retain a constant shape? Explain your answer. <u>No. Because of movement of the</u> cytoplasm into the pseudopodia, the cell shape is constantly changing.

4. Describe what happens when an ameba meets some food. <u>The pseudopodia move the cytoplasm to</u> surround the food and take it into a food vacuole, which digests the food.

5. Which protist moved the slowest? <u>The ameba.</u>

Analysis and Conclusions

1. Why do you think diatoms show colors of green, yellow, and brown?

Diatoms are algal protists and contain chlorophyll and other pigments.

2. How do the eyespot and the chloroplasts work together to help the euglena survive?

The eyespot draws the euglena toward light, which is used by chloroplasts for photosynthesis.

3. What characteristics of an animal does the euglena possess? A cell membrane and a flagellum.

4. What are the functions of cilia in *Stentor*? Locomotion and food getting.

Critical Thinking and Application

1. Some of the white blood cells in your body show ameboid movement. What does this mean?

They move slowly, one part at a time, and often surround microorganisms in order to destroy them.

2. Why is it important for a photosynthetic organism such as a diatom to live near the surface of a body of water? At the surface, ample light is available for the diatom to conduct photosynthesis.

3. Euglenas are generally autotrophic organisms. Why does this characteristic make the euglena a good choice for use in the biology laboratory? Because euglenas can produce their own food, they are easier to culture and maintain in the laboratory. They do not need to be fed often, as do other protists.

4. Why are ground-up diatoms sometimes added to powdered cleansers?

The silica in the shells of diatoms makes the cleanser more abrasive and thus a more powerful cleaner.

Going Further

Obtain a sample of pond water, or prepare a hay infusion for culturing protists. To make a hay infusion, boil a few pieces of timothy hay stalks in about 200 mL of spring water. **CAUTION:** *Wear safety goggles.* Transfer the mixture to a jar, add a few grains of boiled rice, and allow it to stand for two days. If you add pond water instead, let the culture stand for several days. The culture will become cloudy and then will become clear. When it is clear, make several slides from drops of water taken from different levels of the pond water or the hay infusion. Examine the culture or pond water for protists and identify them. Attempt to outline a food web based on the organisms found.

35

The Structures of Fungi

You may want to refer students to pages 407–423 in their textbook for a discussion of fungi.

Time required: Part A–15 minutes
Part B–15 minutes
Part C–15 minutes

Pre-Lab Discussion

Fungi include a variety of organisms that are widely distributed in many different habitats. Fungi are heterotrophs that secrete enzymes to break down materials outside their body. Then they absorb these products of digestion and use them as food. Most fungi are saprophytes that live on dead organisms; some are parasites that feed on living organisms; and a few are symbionts that live in association with other organisms.

Most fungi have a "body" made up of tangled filaments called a *mycelium*. A mycelium is, in turn, made up of filaments called *hyphae*. The mycelium attaches to a food source, and the hyphae, although microscopic, present a large surface area through which food can be absorbed.

In this investigation, you will observe and identify the structures and characteristics of several different types of fungi.

Problem

What structures and characteristics of fungi can be identified in a slime mold, mushroom, bracket fungus, and lichen?

Materials *(per group)*

Cultures of *Physarum polycephalum* with growth medium can be obtained from biological supply houses.

Physarum polycephalum culture and prepared slides
Slime mold slides are made from a culture of *Physarum polycephalum*. Use an inoculating loop or a cotton swab to obtain an oat grain with slime mold attached. Place the mold on a piece of wet filter paper in a pan or petri dish. Place a coverslip next to the paper. Wait one half hour or more for the mold to grow onto the coverslip. Place a drop of water on a glass slide and lay the coverslip, mold side down, on the slide.

Hand lens
Microscope
Agaricus campestris *Agaricus campestris* is an edible mushroom that can be obtained at the grocery store.
Bracket fungus Bracket fungus can be obtained from biological supply houses or from a nearby forest or wooded area. Caution students never to eat fungi that are collected from nature.
2 glass slides
2 coverslips
Forceps
Medicine dropper
Lichen Specimens of lichen can be obtained from biological supply houses.
Probe

Safety 🔼 ▨

Before beginning the procedure, check with students to see if any of them have allergies to molds or yeasts. Students with allergies should be excused from this laboratory investigation.

Put on a laboratory apron if one is available. Put on safety goggles. Handle all glassware carefully. Be careful when handling sharp instruments. Always handle the microscope with extreme care. You are responsible for its proper care and use. Use caution when handling glass slides as they can break easily and cut you. Note all safety alert symbols next to the steps in the Procedure and review the meanings of each symbol by referring to the symbol guide on page 10.

Procedure

Part A. Observing a Slime Mold

🔺 1. Use a hand lens to observe a culture of *Physarum polycephalum*. Record your observations.

🔺 2. Obtain a prepared slide of *Physarum polycephalum* and observe it under the low-power objective of a microscope. Record your observations.

Part B. Examining Basidiomycetes—Mushroom and Bracket Fungus

1. Obtain an *Agaricus campestris* mushroom.

2. Examine the structure of the mushroom. Locate the stalk, the umbrella-shaped cap, and the rows of gills on the underside of the cap. Record your observations.

3. Using forceps, carefully remove one gill from the mushroom cap.

🔺 4. Place the gill in a drop of water on a glass slide and cover with a coverslip.

5. Use the microscope to observe the gill under both low and high power. Each gill has thousands of extensions called basidia. Under the microscope most of the cells of the gill will appear as rectangles. On the edge of the gill, locate the club-shaped basidia and the attached basidiospores. In *Agaricus,* each basidium contains four spores. (You may not see all four spores on each basidium.) Record your observations.

6. Obtain a specimen of bracket fungus, a basidiomycete that grows on trees.

🔺 7. Use a hand lens to examine the underside of the fungus. Record your observations.

Part C. Identifying Parts of a Lichen

1. Obtain a lichen specimen.

🔺 2. Use a hand lens to examine your lichen. Powdery masses on the surface of the lichen may be spore cases. Record your observations.

🔺 3. Place a small section of the lichen on a glass slide. Add a drop of water.

▰ 4. Gently tease the lichen apart with a probe. Add a coverslip.

5. Observe the lichen under low power.

6. Switch to high power and again examine the lichen. Note the greenish cells enmeshed in the whitish filaments. The greenish cells may be a green alga or a cyanobacterium. The white filaments are the hyphae of the fungus. Record your observations.

Observations

Part A. Observing a Slime Mold

1. Describe the appearance of the slime mold. <u>Yellowish, fan-shaped mass.</u>

2. What characteristic of an animal did you observe in the slime mold?

   <u>Ameboid movement.</u>

3. What characteristic of a fungus did you observe in the slime mold?

Answers will vary. Some slides may show fruiting bodies that produce spores.

_____

Part B. Examining Basidiomycetes—Mushroom and Bracket Fungus

1. Draw and label the parts of a mushroom that you observed.

Agaricus Structures

2. Draw and label several basidia with basidiospores from the gill you observed under the microscope.

Magnification _____

Agaricus Basidia

3. Did you observe the mycelium of the mushroom? Explain your answer.

No, the mycelium of a mushroom is located underground. The mushroom itself is the reproductive structure.

It is actually made up of a mass of hyphae packed together.

4. Did you observe the mycelium of the bracket fungus? Explain your answer.

No, the mycelium of the bracket fungus is located under the bark of the tree.

5. Describe the appearance of the bracket fungus. White; soft; spongy on the underside; rings on the topside.

Part C. Identifying Parts of a Lichen

1. Describe the appearance of your lichen. Answers will vary.

2. Draw and label the parts of the lichen you observed using the microscope.

Magnification _____

Algae

Fungus

Lichen

Analysis and Conclusions

1. Why are slime molds difficult organisms to classify? Because they exhibit characteristics of fungi as well as animallike protists.

2. Why would you not always be able to see all four spores on each basidium of a mushroom gill? Some spores may have already been shed; others may not be fully developed.

3. Which parts of a mushroom are normally eaten? Cap, gills, stalk.

4. Which fungus in this investigation is a parasite? Explain your answer.

Bracket fungus. The mycelium grows under the tree's surface and enzymes are used to break down

cellulose from the tree for food.

5. Which fungus is actually a symbiotic relationship between two different organisms? How does

each organism benefit? Lichen. The alga produces food through photosynthesis for the fungus, and the

fungus provides support and nutrients for the alga.

Critical Thinking and Application

1. Why is it an advantage for a mushroom to develop under ground and produce many spores?

Developing under ground increases chances for survival. The production of many spores increases the

chance the species will survive.

2. Lichens are very sensitive to sulfur dioxide, an air pollutant. How might the study of lichens

benefit human health? Lichens can be used as an indicator of sulfur dioxide air pollution and air quality

in an area.

3. *Agaricus campestris* is an edible mushroom. Is it safe to eat all types of mushrooms? Explain

your answer. No. Some species of mushrooms are poisonous and can cause severe illness or death. It is

extremely difficult to tell safe and dangerous mushrooms apart.

Going Further

1. Purchase a mushroom-growing kit from a biological supply company and grow your own mushrooms. Once growth starts, mushrooms should continue to appear for several weeks. Examine and describe the growth stages of the emerging mushrooms. Make a drawing of the life cycle of a mushroom.

2. Go on a fungi scavenger hunt. Locate, but do not disturb, examples of slime molds, mushrooms, bracket fungi, and lichens in your neighborhood.

36

Mold Growth

You may want to refer students to pages 407–423 in the textbook for a discussion of fungi.

Time required: 30 minutes
Daily observations–
5 minutes

Pre-Lab Discussion

Fungi provide us with food and return important nutrients to the environment for future use. But when fungi appear on our food as mold, they are definitely not welcome!

One of the most commonly purchased food items in a grocery store is bread. Bread has a relatively short shelf-life (the time it takes for food to spoil). And bread is often spoiled by the presence of mold. Food producers have developed chemical additives that help to extend the shelf-life of many foods. For example, to extend the shelf-life of bread, producers often add calcium propionate to bread to prevent the growth of mold.

In this investigation, you will test the resistance of different types and brands of bread to the growth of mold.

Problem

To give students the opportunity to design their own experiment, you can provide them with the Pre-Lab Discussion, Problem, and Materials list.

Which type of bread shows the greatest resistance to mold growth?

Materials *(per group)*

Petri dishes   Self-sealing plastic bags can be used in place of petri dishes.
Forceps
Medicine dropper
Glass-marking pencil
Bread—a variety of different   You can include commercially produced as well as bakery breads. Home
    types and brands   baked breads can also be used. You might also include diet and "all-
        natural" breads.

Safety ⚗ Students with allergies to mold should be excused from this laboratory investigation.

Put on a laboratory apron if one is available. Handle all glassware carefully. Note all safety alert symbols next to the steps in the Procedure and review the meanings of each symbol by referring to the symbol guide on page 10.

Procedure

The day before the lab, expose a variety of types and brands of old bread (3–4 days) to mold spores by wiping slices of each bread across the floor or countertop. Cut each slice of bread into fourths. Each lab group should be responsible for testing one type of bread and reporting their observations to the class.

Use the type of bread provided by your teacher to perform the following procedure.

⚗ 1. Use forceps to place a 1/4 slice of bread in a petri dish.

2. Use the medicine dropper to moisten the bread with 20 drops of water.

3. Close the petri dish and place it in a warm location along with the petri dishes from other lab groups. Label the petri dish with a glass-marking pencil or place it on a sheet of paper with your group's name and class.

4. Observe the bread daily for a week. Record your observations in Data Table 1.

5. At the end of the week report your observations to the class and complete Data Table 2.

Observations

Data Table 1

Day	Appearance of Bread
1	
2	Answers will vary.
3	
4	
5	

Data Table 2

Brand	Day on Which Mold Was First Observed
	Answers will vary.

1. Calcium propionate is an additive put in bread to prevent mold growth. Using the list of ingredients on the bread packages, which breads contained calcium propionate?

   Answers will vary depending on the type of breads used.

2. Which bread was the first to show the growth of mold? Answers will vary, but breads without calcium propionate should show mold growth first.

3. How did the appearance of the mold change during the week? Answers will vary but may include: grew larger, color changed.

4. Why were all the petri dishes placed in the same location? To keep the experimental conditions the same except for the variable being tested.

Analysis and Conclusions

1. Why did mold grow on the bread in the closed petri dishes? Mold spores were on the bread before the petri dishes were closed.

2. What conditions favor the growth of mold? Moisture, warmth.

3. Would you expect homemade breads or commercially produced breads to have a longer shelf-life? Explain your answer. Commercially produced breads would have a longer shelf-life because they usually contain additives that inhibit mold growth.

Critical Thinking and Application

1. Many dehydrated foods do not contain chemical additives. Would you expect mold to grow on dehydrated foods? Explain your answer. No, the lack of moisture would prevent mold growth.

2. Some molds that grow on bread are green. Can bread mold produce its own food through photosynthesis? Explain your answer. _No, bread mold is a fungus and fungi are heterotrophs._

_____

Going Further

Chemical additives are used in many foods. Using reference materials, identify the purpose of adding each of the following chemicals to foods: ammonium sulfate, calcium sulfate, monocalcium phosphate, potassium bromate, ethoxylated mono- and diglycerides.

37

Characteristics of Green Algae

You may want to refer students to pages 435–438 in the textbook for a discussion of green algae.

Time required: 50 minutes.

Pre-Lab Discussion

Green algae are members of phylum Chlorophyta and contain chlorophylls *a* and *b* within their chloroplasts. It is these chlorophylls that give the algae their green color. Green algae may live as single cells or they may be multicellular. Green algae are found mainly in moist areas on land and in fresh water. Some species, however, live in the oceans.

In this investigation, you will observe some characteristics of several different types of green algae.

Problem

What are some characteristics of green algae?

Materials *(per group)*

Microscope
4 glass slides
4 coverslips
4 medicine droppers

Cultures of:
Chlamydomonas
Volvox
Ulothrix
Ulva

Cultures are available from biological supply houses. Prepared slides of the organisms may be used instead of cultures.

Safety 🔺

Put on a laboratory apron if one is available. Handle all glassware carefully. Use caution when handling laboratory cultures. Always handle the microscope with extreme care. You are responsible for its proper care and use. Use caution when handling glass slides as they can break easily and cut you. Note all safety alert symbols next to the steps in the Procedure and review the meanings of each symbol by referring to the symbol guide on page 10.

Procedure
Part A. Unicellular Green Algae

 1. Prepare a wet-mount slide of a *Chlamydomonas* culture.

2. Place the slide on the stage of the microscope and focus under the low-power objective, locating several *Chlamydomonas.*

3. Switch to the high-power objective and focus on one *Chlamydomonas.* Observe the shape of the *Chlamydomonas.* Notice the two flagella, or taillike structures. Locate the large cup-shaped chloroplast that surrounds the centrally located nucleus.

4. Find the small organelle called the pyrenoid at the base of the chloroplast. The pyrenoid synthesizes and stores starch. Note the eyespot, which enables the *Chlamydomonas* to sense bright light or darkness.

5. In the appropriate place in Observations, sketch one *Chlamydomonas*. Include the following labels on your sketch: cell wall, flagellum, chloroplast, nucleus, pyrenoid, and eyespot if visible. Record the magnification.

Part B. Colonial Green Algae

1. Prepare a wet-mount slide of a *Volvox* culture.

2. Place the slide on the stage of the microscope and observe the *Volvox* colony under the low-power objective.

3. In the appropriate place in Observations, sketch several cells in the *Volvox* colony. Include the following labels on your sketch: cell wall, chloroplast, cytoplasm, and flagellum. Record the magnification.

4. Switch to the high-power objective. Note any differences in the cells of the colony.

Part C. Filamentous Green Algae

1. Make a wet-mount slide of a *Ulothrix* culture. *Ulothrix* is a filamentous green alga. With the exception of the cell at the base, the cells of each filament are similar. The cell at the base, called the holdfast cell, is modified to hold the plant to stones and other objects.

2. Place the slide on the stage of the microscope and observe a filament of *Ulothrix* under the low-power objective.

3. Switch to the high-power objective. Note the green, horseshoe-shaped chloroplast.

4. In the appropriate place in Observations, sketch a portion of the *Ulothrix* filament. Include the following labels on your sketch: cell wall, chloroplast, and nucleus. Record the magnification.

Part D. Multicellular Green Algae

1. Prepare a wet-mount slide of an *Ulva* culture.

2. Place the slide on the stage of the microscope and focus under the low-power objective.

3. Switch to the high-power objective. To determine the number of cell layers present in *Ulva*, slowly focus up and down while observing the slide under the high-power objective.

4. In the appropriate place in Observations, sketch two or three cells of *Ulva*. Include the following labels on your sketch: cell wall, cytoplasm, chloroplast, and nucleus. Record the magnification.

5. Carefully clean and dry the slides and coverslips you have used.

Observations

1. How does a *Volvox* colony move? <u>A *Volvox* colony moves with a rolling and tumbling motion caused</u>

<u>by the beating of its flagella.</u>

2. Were any of the cells in the *Volvox* colony different from the others? If so, how were they

different? <u>Students will most likely observe that *Volvox* cells vary in size.</u>

3. How many cell layers does *Ulva* have? <u>*Ulva* has two layers of cells.</u>

High-power objective

Magnification _____

Eyespot

Flagellum

Chloroplast

Nucleus

Pyrenoid

Cell wall

Chlamydomonas

High-power objective

Magnification _____

Flagellum

Cytoplasm

Cell wall

Chloroplast

Volvox

High-power objective

Magnification _____

Chloroplast

Nucleus

Cell wall

Ulothrix

High-power objective

Magnification _____

Cytoplasm

Nucleus
Cell wall

Chloroplast

Ulva

Analysis and Conclusions

1. How is *Chlamydomonas* animallike? How is it plantlike? _Chlamydomonas_ is animallike because it possesses flagella and therefore can move; it is plantlike because it has a cell wall, chloroplast, and pyrenoid.

2. How is *Volvox* animallike? How is it plantlike? _Volvox_ is animallike because it possesses flagella and therefore can move; it is plantlike because it has a cell wall and chloroplasts.

3. List three ways in which the green algae you observed in this investigation are different.

The green algae vary in size, shape, and form. Some algae are microscopic single cells, whereas others are large and multicellular. Their chloroplasts differ in shape. Some green algae are capable of movement, whereas others are not.

4. List two ways in which the green algae you observed in this investigation are similar.

All the green algae contain cell walls, chloroplasts, chlorophyll, cytoplasm, and a nucleus. Also, their color is similar.

Critical Thinking and Application

1. Are unicellular organisms necessarily simple organisms? Explain your answer.

Unicellular organisms are not necessarily simple; they often possess a variety of organelles that have very specialized functions within the cell.

2. Why are algae not able to grow on land to any great extent? Algae lack an internal system of tubes to move water and other materials throughout their cells; thus they must be constantly surrounded by an external source of water.

3. What is the advantage of a holdfast to an alga, such as *Ulva,* that lives in coastal waters?

The holdfast enables the *Ulva* to cling tightly to rocks despite the constant motion of turbulent coastal waters.

4. Suppose a new species of unicellular green algae containing chlorophyll and an eyespot is discovered. Would you expect this type of algae to have either flagella or cilia? Explain.

This type of algae would be expected to have flagella or cilia to help it move toward a light source in order to conduct photosynthesis.

Going Further

1. Obtain samples of red and brown algae for observation. How are red and brown algae similar to green algae? How are they different?

2. Survey some of the foods in your local supermarket. Which contain products made from algae? Identify the products. To which group of algae do they belong? What role do the algal products play? Prepare a report or poster on your findings to be presented to your class.

38

Examining an Algal Bloom

You may want to refer students to pages 433–443 in the textbook for a discussion of algae.

Time required:

Part A – 15 minutes
Part B – 30 minutes (one week later)

Pre-Lab Discussion

When pollutants, such as phosphate-containing detergents and fertilizers, are dumped into ponds and lakes, the algae population greatly increases. This sudden massive growth of algae is called an *algal bloom* and appears as a thick, green covering on the surface of the water.

Although the algae on the water's surface flourish, those lying below the surface do not. These algae die because they are shaded from the sun by the masses of algae above them. The dead algae sink to the bottom of the pond or lake, taking their nutrients with them. Thus a large amount of organic matter accumulates on the bottom.

Because the dead organic matter serves as food for bacteria, there is a tremendous increase in the growth of these organisms. As the bacteria grow, they use up the oxygen in the water. Eventually, fishes and other aquatic organisms suffocate and die. This oxygen-depletion process is called *eutrophication*.

In this investigation, you will observe the ability of some detergents and fertilizers to cause algal blooms.

Problem

If possible, have each group test a different type of detergent or fertilizer. Groups can then compare their data at the end of the investigation.

How is the growth of algae affected by chemical pollutants?

Materials *(per group)*

Green algae culture [1]
Pond water [2]
1% pollutant solution [3]
Microscope
Glass slide
Coverslip
Medicine dropper
Glass-marking pencil
3 250-mL Erlenmeyer flasks
100-mL graduated cylinder
10-mL graduated cylinder
3 cotton balls
Sheet of translucent tissue
  paper

[1] *Closterium* is recommended because of its large unicellular structure, hardiness, and tolerance to pollution. However, other varieties of algae may be used.

[2] Pond water is recommended for this investigation, but if it is not available, use tap water that has been aged for 24 hours.

[3] Place 10 g powdered detergent that contains phosphates and is biodegradable or 10 mL liquid plant fertilizer in a flask containing 1 L pond water or aged tap water. Add 5 g nonsterile soil and mix. Stopper the flask with cotton and leave it in a dark place where it will remain undisturbed for one week. Filter mixture before using.

Jars or similar containers may be substituted as long as they can be stoppered.

Safety ⚗ 🔥

Put on a laboratory apron if one is available. Put on safety goggles. Handle all glassware carefully. Always use special caution when working with laboratory chemicals, as they may irritate the skin or cause staining of the skin or clothing. Never touch or taste any chemical unless instructed to do so. Always handle the microscope with extreme care. You are responsible for its proper care and use. Use caution when handling glass slides as they can break easily and cut you. Note all safety alert symbols next to the steps in the Procedure and review the meanings of each symbol by referring to the symbol guide on page 10.

Procedure

Part A. Preparing Algal Cultures

⚗ **1.** With the glass-marking pencil, mark one flask "Control," the second flask "0.5% pollution," and the third flask "1% pollution."

2. Measure out 100 mL of pond water and place it in the flask marked Control. Use the 10-mL graduated cylinder to add 5 mL of the green algae culture to the flask. **Note:** *To make sure that there is an equal amount of algae in each 5-mL sample, gently swirl the container containing the green algae culture before pouring each sample.*

🔥 **3.** Obtain the 1% pollutant solution from your teacher. Measure out 50 mL of the pollutant solution and place it in the flask marked 0.5% pollution. Then add 50 mL of pond water and 5 mL of green algae to the flask.

4. Measure out 100 mL of the 1% pollutant solution and place it in the flask marked 1% pollution. Then add 5 mL of the green algae culture to the flask.

5. Gently swirl the flasks to mix the algae with the other solutions. Plug the flasks with cotton balls.

6. If a fluorescent light is available, place the flasks about 60 centimeters from the light for one week. If a fluorescent light in not available, place the flasks in a window. To protect the algae from heat, cover the flasks with a sheet of translucent tissue paper.

Part B. Observing Algal Cultures

1. After one week, observe the cultures in the flasks. Look for a greenish tint or cloudiness in the flasks.

⚗ **2.** Gently swirl the Control flask and make a wet-mount slide from one drop of the culture.

3. Place the slide on the stage of the microscope and focus under low power. Count the number of algal cells in each of the three fields of view shown in Figure 1. Record the numbers in the appropriate places in the Data Table. Record the average number of algal cells.

Figure 1

4. Repeat steps 2 and 3 with the two other flasks. Record the information in the appropriate places in the Data Table.

5. Using the graph provided in Observations, plot the average number of algal cells found in the Control, in the 0.5% pollution solution, and in the 1% pollutant solution. Connect the points on the graph.

6. Place your data in the data table provided by your teacher on the chalkboard.

Provide a large data table so that student groups can pool their results for analysis.

Observations

Data Table

Field of View	Number of Algal Cells		
1	Control	0.5% Pollution	1% Pollution
2			
3		Answers will vary.	
Average			

Graph

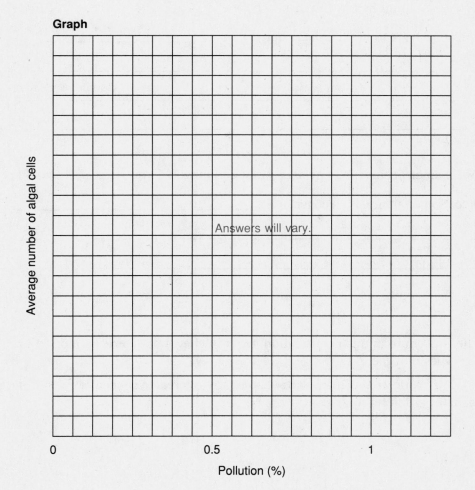

Average number of algal cells

Answers will vary.

Pollution (%)

0   0.5   1

Analysis and Conclusions

1. Why is a light source necessary in this investigation? Light is necessary for the algae to conduct photosynthesis.

2. According to your data, which pollution solution caused the least algal growth?
   0.5% pollution solution.

3. According to your data, which pollution solution caused the greatest algal growth?
   1% pollution solution.

Critical Thinking and Application

1. How might algae be an indicator of the amount of water pollution in a body of water?
   The presence of a large amount of algae in a body of water might indicate a large amount of chemical pollution in the water. The opposite might also be true.

2. Do you think it would be an easy task to bring a body of water that has undergone eutrophication back to life? Explain your answer. No. Algae from both the surface and the floor of the body of water would have to be removed. The chemical pollutants would have to be removed or neutralized also. Plants and animals would then have to be reintroduced into the environment.

3. If you were an environmental engineer, what action would you suggest to avoid the eutrophication of an aquatic ecosystem? Laws could be made to prevent water pollution and contamination; detergents that did not add nutrients to the water could be made and used; better purification methods for polluted water could be introduced in water treatment plants.

Going Further

1. Using the Procedure in this investigation, test the effects of detergent and fertilizer pollutants on other types of algae.

2. Repeat this investigation using pollutant solutions of greater concentrations to determine if they promote or inhibit algal growth.

   ### An Alternate Investigation:

   To simplify this investigation, have each group fill a one-gallon jar about two-thirds full of pond water or aged tap water. Have each group add 2 g of a detergent or fertilizer to the water. Make sure that each group uses a different detergent or fertilizer. Add 25 g of a *Spirogyra* culture to each jar. Be sure that one group acts as the control and adds no pollutant. Then have each group find the mass of the jar and water. Cover the jars with plastic wrap and place near a light source.

   After two weeks, have the groups find the mass of each jar and its water. Which jars experienced the most algal growth? The least? Explain. Have the students compare and analyze their results.

39

Comparing Marine and Land Nonvascular Plants

You may want to refer students to pages 433–443 and pages 449–454 in the textbook for a discussion of algae, mosses, and liverworts.

Time required:
Part A–30 minutes
Part B–30 minutes

Pre-Lab Discussion

Nonvascular plants that live in water are called *algae*. Algae can be unicellular or multicellular. Most are multicellular. Some species of multicellular algae are commonly seen along the shoreline or washed up on the beach. These algae are called seaweeds. Seaweeds come in a variety of colors, including green, brown, and red. The brown alga *Fucus* is one of the more familiar seaweeds and is often seen attached to rocks and wharf pilings at the intertidal zone. At the intertidal zone, the seaweed is exposed at low tide and under water at high tide.

Nonvascular plants that live on land include the liverworts and the mosses. These plants are generally found in moist environments because they lack the water-conducting tubes that are found in higher plants.

In this investigation, you will compare a marine nonvascular plant (alga) and a land nonvascular plant (moss).

Problem

Although this investigation involves algae, which are discussed in Chapter 20, their inclusion here provides an opportunity for students to compare algae with their evolved land plants—the mosses.

How do marine and land nonvascular plants compare?

Materials *(per group)*

Large shallow bowl	Coverslip
Sea water	Dissecting needle
Microscope	Forceps
Dissecting microscope	Brown alga, *Fucus*
Hand lens	Moss, *Polytrichum*
Dissecting tray	Prepared slide of moss protonema
Scissors	Prepared slide of moss antheridia
Scalpel	and archegonia
Glass slide	

Fucus vesiculosus is also called rockweed. It can be purchased from biological supply houses.

Other mosses such as *Funaria hygrometria, Mnium affine, Physcomitrium pyriforme,* or *Catharinea undulata* may be substituted.

Safety 🔺 ▨

Put on a laboratory apron if one is available. Always handle the microscope with extreme care. You are responsible for its proper care and use. Use caution when handling glass slides as they can break easily and cut you. Be careful when handling sharp instruments. Note all safety alert symbols next to the steps in the Procedure and review the meanings of each symbol by referring to the symbol guide on page 10.

Procedure
Part A. Adaptive Structures and Reproduction of *Fucus*

1. Place the *Fucus* in a large shallow bowl. Cover the plant with sea water.

2. Carefully remove a piece of *Fucus* from the bowl and place in on the dissecting tray.

Figure 1   *Fucus*

3. Look for the main stem. At its base, notice a tough, fibrous pad of tissue called the holdfast.

4. Feel the stems in their midregions until you come across a small lump. This is the air bladder. Air bladders sometimes come in pairs on either side of the midrib.

5. Using the scissors, cut out a small section of the stem containing an air bladder. Place it back in the bowl and observe what happens.

6. Look at the leaflike structures on the seaweed. Find the flattened forked stem tips. Special cells called apical cells located at the tips divide by mitosis and produce the forked branching pattern.

7. Examine the stem tips for swollen areas called receptacles. Receptacles contain eggs and sperm.

8. Look for the most swollen receptacles because they are the most mature and are the best ones for examination. Orange-yellow receptacles contain gametes that are ready to be dispersed.

9. With a hand lens, notice the tiny bumps on the surface of a receptacle. For a closer look, use the dissecting microscope.

10. In order to examine the gametes, you will have to open the receptacles and look inside. Using a scalpel, carefully cut out a very thin cross section of the receptacle. See Figure 2. **CAUTION:** *Use extreme care when using a sharp instrument.*

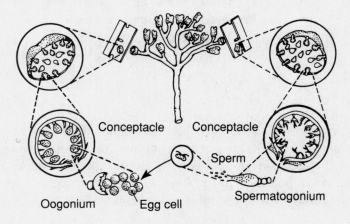

Figure 2

Life Cycle of *Fucus*

🔺 **11.** With the forceps, place the thin section of the receptacle on the glass slide and prepare a wet mount.

12. Observe the section of the receptacle under the low power of the microscope. **Note:** *It may take a little practice to cut the section thin enough so that it can be viewed under the microscope.* If the students are having difficulties slicing the receptacle thin enough to prepare a wet mount, suggest that they try viewing it under the dissecting microscope without a coverslip.

13. Inside the receptacle, look for several small, round chambers that come into contact with the receptacle. These chambers are called conceptacles. Notice whether a conceptacle has an opening to the outside wall. A female conceptacle has several round oogonial sacs, each of which contains 8 egg cells. A male conceptacle has spermatogonial sacs containing many orange dots. Each dot is a sperm cell. In *Fucus,* fertilization and development are external. In the appropriate place in Observations, sketch and label the conceptacle. Record the magnification.

Part B. Adaptive Structures and Reproduction of *Polytrichum* Moss

1. Examine a small clump of *Polytrichum* moss under the dissecting microscope. Use Figure 3 to identify the structures of a moss.

Capsule containing spores
Antheridia
Gametophytes
Archegonia
Leaflike structures
Stemlike structures
Rootlike structures (rhizoids)

Figure 3

2. Carefully separate a sporophyte from a gametophyte. A sporophyte consists of one stalk with a capsule on it. The green "leafy" part is the female gametophyte. Notice that the capsule has a cap on it.

🔺 **3.** To examine the contents of the capsule, carefully remove the cap. Then place a drop of water on a glass slide and squeeze the contents of the capsule into the water. Cover with a coverslip and locate the capsule's contents under low power. Then observe under high power. **CAUTION:** *When turning to the high-power objective lens, always look at the objective from the side of the microscope so that the objective lens does not hit or damage the slide.* In the appropriate place in Observations, sketch what you see. Record the magnification.

4. Examine a prepared slide of moss protonema. A protonema is a mass of tangled green filaments that germinate and grow from a spore.

5. Examine a prepared slide of moss antheridia and archegonia. These reproductive organs are found in the upper tips of the gametophytes.

6. Study Figure 4, which shows the life cycle of a moss. Compare the similarities and differences in the life cycles of *Fucus* and *Polytrichum.*

Sperm from male gametophyte reaches egg cell in archegonium of female gametophyte

Fertilization occurs

Diploid sporophyte

Mature gametophyte

Haploid spores released

Haploid protonema

Life Cycle of Polytrichum

Figure 4

Observations

Magnification _____

Fucus Conceptacle

Magnification _____

Polytrichum Spores

1. What structure enables *Fucus* to attach itself to rocks and wharf pilings?
Holdfast.

2. What happens when you put the *Fucus'* air bladder in water? It floats.

3. Is the conceptacle male or female? Explain your answer. Answers will vary. A female conceptacle
has several round, large sacs. A male conceptacle has numerous small sacs with orange dots.

4. What are the structures inside the moss capsule called? Spores.

5. Does the protonema contain any structures? If so, what might they be?
Yes. Possibly chloroplasts.

6. What is the female gametophyte called? The male gametophyte? Female—archeoginum;
male—antheridium.

Analysis and Conclusions

1. What is the adaptive value of the holdfast on an alga? It prevents the alga from being washed
ashore or out to sea.

2. What is the adaptive value of the air bladder on an alga? An air bladder provides buoyancy and
holds the "leaves" near the water's surface for increased light.

3. Of what value is the flat, branching system of seaweed? The larger, flat blades can receive a greater
amount of light for a more efficient photosynthetic process.

4. How does a moss capsule disperse its contents? When the capsule dries out, it opens and disperses the spores into the air.

5. Compare the similarities and differences in the life cycles of *Fucus* and *Polytrichum*.

In *Fucus*, the female part of the plant forms an oogonium and the male part forms a spermatogonium. The egg and sperm unite externally and form the new plant. In the moss, however, there is a stage in which the spores divide by mitosis and grow into a gametophyte plant that develops gametes. They, in turn, develop into male and female portions that produce haploid gametes and then produce a zygote. The life cycle of a moss is more complex than the life cycle of an alga.

Critical Thinking and Application

1. What structural differences allow the moss to be more successful on land than the alga?

The moss has an ability to absorb water through rhizoids and to store water in its storage tissues. The alga cannot do this and therefore is not adapted for life on land.

2. Why is moss not usually found growing in areas of little rainfall? Because moss lacks water-conducting vessels, it is not able to obtain water from deeper levels within the soil.

3. Why do moss plants grow close to the ground? Moss plants cannot grow high off the ground because they do not have conducting structures that help move water upward through the plant.

4. Gardeners often add sphagnum moss to soil. How might this be helpful?

Sphagnum moss helps the soil retain water. It also helps to decompose organic matter, thereby adding nutrients to the soil.

Going Further

1. Using references in the library, find out about the kelp (seaweed) forests that grow off the California coast. What types of kelps grow there? How large are they? What other organisms live within the kelp community? What advantages do the kelps provide to other organisms? What effects would harvesting the kelps have on the environment?

2. Examine the external and reproductive structures of another land nonvascular plant, the liverwort *Marchantia*. Sketch and label what you see.

Name _____ Class _____ Date _____

40

Special Characteristics of Ferns

You may want to refer students to
pages 455–461 in the textbook
for a discussion of ferns.

Time required: Part A–40 minutes
Part B–40 minutes

Pre-Lab Discussion

Ferns belong to a group of plants that are "true" land plants. These plants have
specialized tissues called *vascular tissues* that transport water and the products of
photosynthesis throughout the plant. For this reason, these plants are called vascular
plants. Vascular plants can grow much larger than plants without vascular tissues. When
comparing cellular organization, ferns lie between mosses and more complex vascular
plants, such as trees.

In this investigation, you will observe some of the characteristics of ferns. You will
also examine how ferns reproduce.

Problem

What are some special characteristics of ferns?

Materials *(per group)*

Whole bracken fern sporophyte
    plant
Bracken fern frond with sori
Dissecting microscope or
    hand lens
2 glass slides
2 coverslips
Medicine dropper
Dissecting tray
Scalpel or razor blade
Forceps
Ethyl alcohol
Microscope

The bracken fern *(Pteridum aquilinum)* is available from biological
supply houses.

For a 70% solution, add 70 mL 95% ethyl alcohol to a graduated cylinder. Fill to the 95-mL
mark with distilled water.

Safety 🧪 ⬛ ▨

Put on a laboratory apron if one is available. Handle all glassware carefully. Always
handle the microscope with extreme care. You are responsible for its proper care and
use. Use caution when handling glass slides as they can break easily and cut you. Always
use special caution when working with laboratory chemicals, as they may irritate the skin
or cause staining of the skin or clothing. Never touch or taste any chemical unless
instructed to do so. Be careful when handling sharp instruments. Note all safety alert
symbols next to the steps in the Procedure and review the meanings of each symbol by
referring to the symbol guide on page 10.

Procedure
Part A. Characteristics of the Sporophyte Fern

1. Examine a whole sporophyte fern plant. Use Figure 1 to identify the structures of a fern.

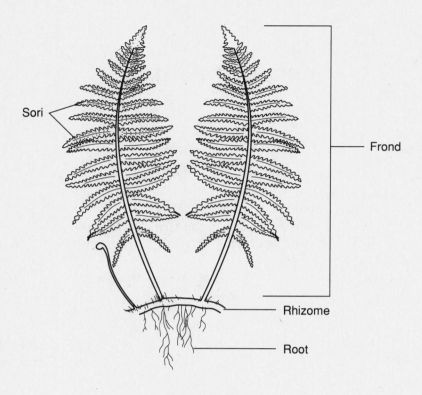

Figure 1

2. Locate the horizontal stem structure called the rhizome.

3. Notice how the fern leaves, or fronds, arise from the rhizome. Note the shape of the frond and the presence of veins in the stem part.

4. Examine the underside of the frond for brownish-yellow spots. These spots are called sori (singular, sorus).

5. With the scalpel, cut off a 0.5-cm piece of rhizome from the fern. **CAUTION:** *Use extreme care when using a sharp instrument.* Place the rhizome in the dissecting tray. While holding the rhizome with the forceps, cut a very thin cross section of the rhizome with the scalpel.

6. Prepare a wet-mount slide of the rhizome cross section. If it is too thick, place it on a glass slide without the coverslip. Place the slide onto the stage of the microscope and observe it under low power. Note the epidermis and the vascular tissue: xylem (water and mineral conduction) surrounded by phloem (organic material transport). In the space provided in Observations, sketch and label the cross section of the rhizome. Label the following structures on the sketch: epidermis, xylem, and phloem. Record the magnification of the microscope.

Part B. Characteristics of the Gametophyte Fern

1. Obtain the fern frond that contains sori.

2. Use the dissecting microscope or hand lens to examine a single sorus.

3. Place a drop of water on a clean glass slide. Then, as shown in Figure 2, use the scalpel to gently scrape a sorus into the drop of water on the slide. **CAUTION:** *Use extreme care when using a sharp instrument.*

Scalpel   Glass slide

Figure 2

4. Examine the sorus under the low power of the dissecting microscope. Locate the club-shaped structures that were scraped from the sorus. These structures are called sporangia and contain spores. In the appropriate place in Observations, sketch a single sporangium. Record the magnification of the microscope.

5. Prepare a second slide of only spores by removing a few sporangia from a sorus onto a clean, dry slide. Add one drop of ethyl alcohol to the sporangia on the slide. **CAUTION:** *Be very careful when working with laboratory chemicals.*

6. Examine the sporangia under the low power of the dissecting microscope. Observe what happens to the spore cases of the sporangia. In the appropriate place in Observations, sketch a few of the spores that were ejected from the sporangia.

7. Examine the life cycle of a fern in Figure 3.

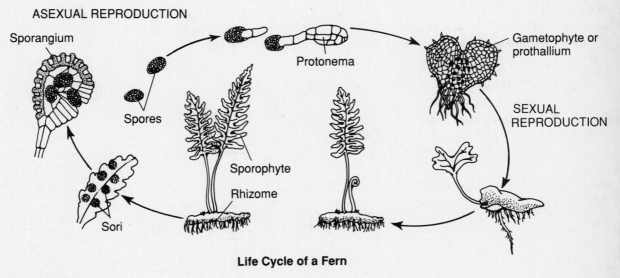

Life Cycle of a Fern

Figure 3

Observations

Magnification _____

Xylem

Phloem

Epidermis

Rhizome

Magnification _____

Sporangium

Magnification _____

Spores

1. **How are the vascular tissues arranged in the fern rhizome?** In intermediate ferns, the vascular

   tissues form a U-shaped cylinder in the center of the fern.

   _____

   _____

2. **Is the gametophyte plant haploid or diploid? Explain your answer.**

   The gametophyte is haploid because it produces sperm and egg, each of which has one-half the required

   number of chromosomes.

Analysis and Conclusions

1. **How are ferns similar to mosses and liverworts?** Ferns, mosses, and liverworts all have a male and

   a female gametophyte and undergo alternation of generations.

   _____

   _____

2. How are ferns similar to woody trees? Ferns and woody trees both have supportive tissues, a vascular system, and veins in their leaves.

3. Fern fronds are difficult to snap or tear from the main part of the plant. Explain why this is so.

Each frond grows out of a horizontal underground stem called a rhizome. It is difficult to "pick" a fern because its roots grow laterally under ground.

4. Why are ferns larger than mosses and liverworts? Mosses and liverworts do not have a vascular system or supportive tissue like the ferns. Therefore, they cannot conduct food and water up the plant effectively and must remain close to the ground.

5. Describe the life cycle of a fern. Ferns have a sporophyte stage during which they produce spores. The spores fall to the ground, grow into the gametophyte stage, and produce gametes (egg and sperm). The resulting zygote grows into a sporophyte, and the cycle begins again.

Critical Thinking and Application

1. Why are ferns found in a greater range of habitats than mosses or liverworts?

Ferns are better adapted to land than mosses or liverworts because they are vascular, have tough leaves, and can retain water. Mosses and liverworts do not have these characteristics. Ferns have roots that can penetrate the soil and take up water, while their leaves can thrust into the air and compete for sunlight.

2. Considering the large number of spores that are produced by a single frond of a fern plant, why do you think there are not more fern plants growing on Earth?

The spores must find favorable growing conditions. Many of the spores die before this occurs.

3. Why is it advantageous for the spores to be located on the bottom surface of the fern fronds?

When the sporangium opens, spores will drop out and fall to the ground where they may find a suitable

place to grow.

4. Many flowering plants have leaves that are very similar in appearance to fern fronds. Although these plants are not true ferns, some of them are called ferns. The asparagus fern is an example. How would you determine whether such a plant was a fern?

You could look for the presence of sori and sporangia. These structures are not present in flowering plants.

Going Further

1. Grow your own fern prothallia. Tightly pack peat moss into a small, clay-type plant container. Place the container of peat moss in boiling water for 5 to 10 minutes. With tongs, remove the container and set the bottom of it in a petri dish of water. The peat moss will soak up the water and provide a source of moisture. Place a few sections of fronds containing ripe sori on the peat moss for a few days. Cover the entire surface of peat moss and fronds with a glass plate to retain moisture. Set it in a shaded area. Prothallia should appear within 4 to 6 weeks.

2. After collecting several types of fern fronds, set up an exhibit to show how ferns are identified. How are fronds classified? What are the names of the leaflets of fronds? Illustrate the different locations of sori. If possible, show the locations of fertile and nonfertile leaflets.

41

Seed-Bearing Plant Tissues

You may want to refer students to pages 467–481 in the textbook for a discussion of seed plants.

Time required: 45 minutes.

Pre-Lab Discussion

The seed-bearing plants of the subphylum Spermopsida are more complex structurally than the plants of any other grouping. Plants in this subphylum reproduce sexually by means of seeds. Based on the appearance of their seeds, seed-bearing plants are divided into two classes. The seeds of the *angiosperms,* or the flowering plants, are enclosed in protective structures called fruits. The seeds of the *gymnosperms,* or coniferous plants, are found unprotected on structures called cones.

The seed-bearing plants developed specialized plant tissues. For the most part, these tissues are similar in both angiosperms and gymnosperms. Each type of specialized tissue has a specific function. Epidermal tissue is the outer covering of plants and protects the tissues beneath it. Meristematic tissue is found at the tips of roots and stems and contains cells that undergo rapid cell division. Vascular tissues (phloem and xylem) conduct water and nutrients throughout the plant. Sclerenchyma tissue, which may contain fiber cells or stone cells, strengthens and supports parts of the plants.

In this investigation, you will identify several specialized plant tissues in seed-bearing plants.

Problem

What is the structure of some specialized plant tissue in seed-bearing plants?

Materials *(per group)*

Plant leaf
Forceps
Glass slide
Coverslip
Medicine dropper
Microscope
Prepared slides of longitudinal sections of:
    coleus stem tip
    Mature stem of *Aristolochia*
    sycamore stem

These prepared slides are available from biological supply houses.

Put on a laboratory apron if one is available. Always handle the microscope with extreme care. You are responsible for its proper care and use. Use caution when handling glass slides as they can break easily and cut you. Note all safety alert symbols next to the steps in the Procedure and review the meanings of each symbol by referring to the symbol guide on page 10.

Procedure
Part A. Examining Epidermal Tissue

1. Examine the upper and lower sides of the plant leaf.

2. Carefully tear the leaf in half. Using the forceps, remove a small section of the lower epidermis, or the thin transparent covering of the leaf.

⚗ 3. Prepare a wet-mount slide of the epidermis. Examine it under the low power of the microscope. Observe the shape and arrangement of the epidermal cells. In the appropriate place in Observations, sketch and label a section of the epidermis. Record the magnification of the microscope.

Part B. Examining Meristematic Tissue

⚗ 1. Examine the prepared slide of the coleus stem tip under the low power of the microscope. Locate the tip of the stem and then find an area that contains many cells in various stages of mitosis.

2. Switch to the high-power objective. **CAUTION:** *When switching to the high-power objective lens, always look at the objective from the side of the microscope so that the objective lens does not hit or damage the slide.* In the appropriate place in Observations, sketch and label some of the cells you observe under high power. Record the magnification of the microscope.

Part C. Examining Vascular Tissue

⚗ 1. Examine the prepared slide of *Aristolochia* (Dutchman's pipe vine) under the low power of the microscope.

2. Switch to the high-power objective. Locate the sieve-tube element, which is a long tubelike structure, and the companion cells next to the sieve-tube element. Together these structures compose the phloem. In the appropriate place in Observations, sketch and label the sieve-tube element and a few companion cells. Record the magnification of the microscope.

⚗ 3. Examine the prepared slide of the sycamore stem under the low power of the microscope.

4. Switch to the high-power objective. Locate a few wide tubular cells called vessel elements, which compose the xylem. Observe the pitted appearance of the side walls of the vessel elements. In the appropriate place in Observations, sketch and label a few vessel elements.

Part D. Examining Supporting (Sclerenchyma) Tissue

⚗ 1. Examine the prepared slide of *Aristolochia* under the low power of the microscope. Locate the long narrow cells with thick cell walls. These cells are the fibers.

2. Switch to the high-power objective. In the appropriate place in Observations, sketch and label a few of these fiber cells. Record the magnification of the microscope.

Name _____ Class _____ Date _____

Observations

Magnification _____

Leaf Epidermis

Magnification _____

Meristematic Tissue of Coleus

Magnification _____

Phloem of *Aristolochia*

Magnification _____

Xylem of Sycamore Stem

Magnification _____

Fiber Cells of *Aristolochia*

1. How do the upper and lower sides of the leaf differ in appearance?

The upper side is waxy and shiny, whereas the underside is dull.

2. Describe epidermal tissue. Epidermal tissue is made up of closely packed cells that cover tissues

beneath it. In most plants, the epidermal tissue is one cell thick.

3. Describe meristematic cells. Meristematic cells are small and cube-shaped. They have thin walls and

many vacuoles.

4. What part of a plant contains the most meristematic cells? The tips of growing stems and roots.

5. What major cell structure is absent in fiber cells? The nucleus.

6. What part of a plant contains fiber cells? The xylem and phloem of stems.

Analysis and Conclusions

1. What is the function of epidermal tissue? Epidermal tissue covers and protects internal tissues.

2. What is the function of meristematic tissue? Meristematic tissue undergoes frequent cell division,

providing for the growth of plant tissues.

3. What is the function of the phloem? The phloem transports food to the various parts of the plant.

4. What is the function of the xylem? The xylem transports water and minerals to the various parts of the

plant.

5. Why do the walls of the vessel elements have pits? The pits permit material to pass through the

walls to neighboring cells.

6. What is the function of the fiber cells? The fiber cells provide strength and support for certain parts of

the plant.

Critical Thinking and Application

1. Describe how each of the following characteristics of meristematic cells would be an advantage in rapid cell division.

   a. thin cell walls Thick walls would be a tremendous waste of energy as they would have to be torn down almost as soon as they were built.

   b. no vacuoles Vacuoles are primarily storage organelles. Because meristematic cells do little but divide, they would have no need to store anything.

   c. much smaller size than mature cells Small cells have a high ratio of surface area to volume. Oxygen and food would quickly diffuse into these cells.

2. In some forests, porcupines do much damage to young trees as they chew off the bark, which contains the phloem. Soon the trees' roots die, and then the trees themselves. Explain why this happens. Removing the ring of bark, which contains the phloem, from each tree prevents food manufactured in the leaves from reaching the roots. As a result, the roots die. Soon the rest of the tree dies because water and minerals cannot be absorbed into the tree by the dead roots.

3. A cross section of a cactus leaf, or needle, shows that it has a thick epidermis. How does this adaptation help the cactus leaf to survive in hot climates? The thick epidermis protects the leaf from losing too much water and dying of dehydration.

Going Further

1. Prepare an illustrated report on the seed plants that live in one of the following environments: arctic, swamp, desert, temperate forest. Describe the special adaptations that these plants have in order to survive there. Include drawings or photographs of these plants.

2. Make wet-mount slides of the pollen grains from three different types of flowers. Examine the pollen grains under the low power and the high power of a microscope. What are some differences among these pollen grains? What are some similarities?

42

Comparing Monocots and Dicots

You may want to refer students to pages 473–475 in the textbook for a discussion of monocots and dicots.

Time required: 45 minutes.

Pre-Lab Discussion

Angiosperms, or flowering plants, are divided into two subclasses: monocots and dicots. The simplest difference between monocots and dicots is the number of *cotyledons*, or first leaves developed by the embryo plant. Monocots, such as grasses, orchids, irises, lilies, and palms, have one cotyledon. Dicots, such as cacti, roses, maples, peas, and oaks, have two cotyledons. In addition to the number of cotyledons, monocots and dicots have several other differences in structure.

In this investigation, you will observe some of the characteristics of monocots and dicots.

Problem

What are some of the structural differences between monocots and dicots?

Materials (*per group*) Florists will often donate flowers that have lost their freshness and cannot be sold.

2 monocot flowers with leaves Lilies, irises, amaryllis, narcissus, and orchids make good monocot specimens.
2 dicot flowers with leaves Roses, violets, buttercups, daisies, larkspurs, apple blossoms, and
Prepared slide of a cross section of a strawberry blossoms make good dicot specimens.
   monocot stem Available from biological supply houses.
Prepared slide of a cross section of a
   dicot stem
Microscope

Safety ⚗

Put on a laboratory apron if one is available. Always handle the microscope with extreme care. You are responsible for its proper care and use. Use caution when handling glass slides as they can break easily and cut you. Note all safety alert symbols next to the steps in the Procedure and review the meanings of each symbol by referring to the symbol guide on page 10.

Procedure

1. Examine the leaves of the monocot and dicot specimens and observe any differences in the pattern of veins on the leaves. In the appropriate place in Observations, sketch one monocot leaf and one dicot leaf. Be sure to include the vein patterns in the sketches.

The students will be more likely to discover the number of flower parts if they are provided with several monocot and dicot specimens for examination.

2. Count the number of petals on each of the monocot flowers and the dicot flowers.

3. Carefully examine the center of each flower. The centrally located stalklike structure is called the pistil. The pistil is surrounded by several other stalklike structures called the stamens. Each stamen contains a pollen sac. Count the number of stamens in each monocot and dicot flower.

4. Examine the prepared slide of the monocot stem under the low power of the microscope. Notice that xylem and phloem tissues are gathered into vascular bundles. Observe the arrangement of the vascular bundles. In the appropriate place in Observations, sketch the monocot stem. Record the magnification of the microscope.

5. Repeat step 4 using the prepared slide of the dicot stem. In the appropriate place in Observations, sketch the dicot stem. Record the magnification of the microscope.

Observations

Monocot Leaf

Dicot Leaf

Magnification _____

Magnification _____

Monocot Stem

Dicot Stem

1. How do the veins in a monocot leaf differ from those in a dicot leaf?

The veins in a monocot leaf usually lie parallel to one another. The veins in a dicot leaf form a branching or netted pattern.

2. Compare the number of petals on a monocot flower to the number on a dicot flower.

Monocot petals usually occur in threes or multiples of three. Dicot petals occur in fours or fives or multiples of four or five.

3. Compare the number of stamens on a monocot flower to the number on a dicot flower.

Monocot stamens usually occur in threes or multiples of three. Dicot stamens occur in fours or fives or multiples of four or five.

4. How does the arrangement of vascular bundles in a monocot stem differ from the arrangement in a dicot stem? In monocot stems, vascular bundles are scattered throughout the stem. In dicot stems, the vascular bundles are arranged in a ring near the outside of the stem.

Analysis and Conclusions

1. What are two functions of the vascular bundles found in the stems of angiosperms?

Vascular bundles transport water and minerals from the roots to the other parts of the plant. They also transport sugar and other nutrients formed during photosynthesis from the leaves to the other parts of the plant.

2. What are three differences between monocots and dicots? Differences between monocots and dicots include different venation patterns, different numbers of petals and stamens, different vascular bundle arrangements, and different numbers of cotyledons.

Critical Thinking and Application

1. A newly discovered fossil plant has 8 petals. Using this information, predict the type of venation (vein arrangement), the number of stamens, and whether the plant is a monocot or a dicot. Because the plant has 8 petals (a multiple of four), it should also have branching venation, should have a multiple of four stamens, and should be a dicot.

2. The lima bean is the seed of the lima bean plant. Each half of the bean is a cotyledon, or seed leaf. Based on this seed structure, is this plant a monocot or a dicot? Explain your answer. Because the lima bean has two cotyledons, it is a dicot. Monocots have only one cotyledon.

3. What characteristics of angiosperms have made them so successful in a variety of environments? Answers might include flowers that contain both male and female sex organs, a vascular system for the efficient transport of water and food, cotyledons that provide nutrients for the embryo, strong supporting tissue, and seeds contained within protective structures.

Going Further

1. Start growing bean plants from seeds. Separate the seedlings into three groups. Allow one group of seedlings to remain undisturbed. Remove one cotyledon from each seedling in the second group. Remove both cotyledons from the seedlings in the third group. Compare the growth of each group of seedlings over a period of time. Construct a data table to present your results.

2. Make a collection of the different types of leaves found in your area. Examine each type of leaf and classify it as a monocot or a dicot. Use a reference book to determine how accurate your classifications are.

43

Root and Stem Structures

You may want to refer students to pages 491–508 in the textbook for a discussion of roots and stems.

Time required: 45 minutes.

Pre-Lab Discussion

The first structures to appear on a germinating seed are the roots. The initial root to grow from a seed is the primary root, which is then followed by secondary roots that branch out from the primary root. In a *taproot system,* the primary root grows longer and thicker than the secondary roots. In a *fibrous root system,* the secondary roots continue to grow, and eventually all the roots are of equal or nearly equal size.

Roots have several functions. They anchor the plant in place, absorb water containing dissolved minerals from the environment, and act as storage areas for excess food. Some roots even develop into new plants. *Adventitious roots* grow from parts of the plant other than the roots. *Aerial,* or *prop, roots* are roots that are suspended in the air.

Plant structures that grow between the roots and the leaves are called stems. Although stems usually grow above the ground in vertical positions, they can also grow under the ground in horizontal positions. All stems begin growing as soft, tubelike structures. If the stem remains soft, and usually green, for the entire life of the plant, it is a *herbaceous stem.* A *woody stem* becomes hard and often turns brown.

The primary function of stems is to conduct water and dissolved minerals from the roots to the leaves and, at the same time, to conduct food from the leaves to the rest of the plant. Stems may also function as food storage areas, supporting structures, and places for the growth of new plants.

In this investigation, you will examine the structures of roots and stems. You will also observe the structural differences between some monocot and dicot roots and stems.

Problem

What are some structures of roots and stems?

Materials *(per group)*

2-week-old radish seedlings
Hand lens or dissecting microscope
Microscope

To prepare the sprouting radish seedlings, soak seeds in water overnight and then place them in a moist paper towel for about 3 days.

Carrot
Methylene blue stain

Large old carrots are best for showing stele and cortex. It may be easiest for students to handle part of a carrot. A 10-cm piece would be a good size.

Ethyl alcohol
Scalpel or single-edged razor blade
Dissecting tray
Forceps
Glass slide

To make a 70% ethyl alcohol solution, add 70 mL 95% ethyl alcohol to a graduated cylinder. Fill to the 95-mL mark with distilled water.

150-mL beaker
Prepared slides of cross section of: Prepared slides are available from biological supply houses.

    Helianthus root
    Zea root
    Helianthus stem
    Zea stem

Safety

Put on a laboratory apron if one is available. Put on safety goggles. Handle all glassware carefully. Always handle the microscope with extreme care. You are responsible for its proper care and use. Use caution when handling glass slides as they can break easily and cut you. Always use special caution when working with laboratory chemicals, as they may irritate the skin or cause staining of the skin or clothing. Never touch or taste any chemical unless instructed to do so. Be careful when handling sharp instruments. Note all safety alert symbols next to the steps in the Procedure and review the meanings of each symbol by referring to the symbol guide on page 10.

Procedure
Part A. External and Internal Structures of a Root

1. Examine Figure 1 and identify each root as being taproot, fibrous, adventitious, or aerial.

Grass   Dandelion   Orchid   Corn

Types of Roots

Figure 1

2. Examine the two-week-old radish seedling. Note the basic structures of the seedling: leaves, stem, and roots.

3. With a hand lens or dissecting microscope, examine the delicate root hairs extending from the root.

4. Place the carrot in the dissecting tray. As shown in Figure 2, hold the carrot steady with one hand while you cut it in half lengthwise with the scalpel or single-edged razor blade. **CAUTION:** *Always cut in a direction away from yourself. Because the carrot is very hard, be careful not to let the scalpel or razor blade slip and cut you.*

Figure 2

5. Examine the two halves of the carrot. Each half is a longitudinal section. Notice the stele in the center. The stele contains the xylem and the phloem. Surrounding the stele is the food-storing cortex. In the appropriate place in observations, sketch a longitudinal section of the carrot. Label the stele and the cortex.

6. To make a cross section of the carrot, place one of the longitudinal sections cut side down on the dissecting tray. About 4 cm from the end of the carrot, cut straight down using the razor blade. Discard the small piece. **CAUTION:** *Be careful when handling a sharp instrument.*

7. Make another cut straight down, as close as possible to the one you just made. See Figure 3. With the forceps, carefully remove the carrot cross section from the razor blade and place it on a glass slide.

Figure 3

8. Place the slide over the mouth of the beaker. Then cover the carrot cross section completely with methylene blue stain. Allow the stain to set for 1 minute. **CAUTION:** *Methylene blue stain is a permanent stain. Be careful not to get it on your hands or clothing.*

9. After 1 minute, slowly pour alcohol over the carrot cross section until no more stain washes away.

10. Observe the cross section of the carrot with a hand lens or under a dissecting microscope. In the appropriate place in Observations, sketch the cross section of the carrot. Label the stele and the cortex.

11. Place the prepared slide of the sunflower *(Helianthus)* root cross section under the low power of the microscope. The sunflower is a dicot.

12. Locate the epidermal cells that form the outer edge of the root. Examine different areas on the glass slide. Notice some root hairs, which are extensions of single epidermal cells.

13. Find the cortex, which is located within the epidermis. The cells of the cortex are large and thin walled.

14. Locate the star-shaped pattern formed by xylem cells at the center of the root. Switch to the high-power objective and focus on one xylem cell. Note its thick cell wall. **CAUTION:** *When switching to the high-power objective, always look at the objective from the side of the microscope so that the objective does not hit or damage the slide.*

15. Observe the smaller and thinner-walled phloem cells within the arms of the star. This distinctive pattern of xylem and phloem is typical of dicot roots. In the appropriate place in Observations, label the xylem, phloem, cortex, epidermis, and root hair.

16. Examine the corn *(Zea)* root cross section under the low power of the microscope. Corn is a monocot.

17. Notice that groups of xylem cells are scattered within the central area of the root. Move the glass slide around until you find the phloem cells, which are also scattered in bunches through the central area of the root.

18. Notice that the cortex and epidermis are similar in both the sunflower root and the corn root. In the appropriate place in Observations, label the xylem, phloem, cortex, epidermis, and root hair in the corn root.

Part B. Internal Structures of Stems

1. Observe the prepared slide of a cross section of a sunflower *(Helianthus)* stem under low power of the microscope. The sunflower has a herbaceous, or nonwoody, stem. Notice that the vascular bundles are arranged in a ring within the stem. Switch to the high-power objective and focus on a single vascular bundle. Observe the thick-walled xylem cells. Notice the smaller, thinner-walled phloem cells within the bundle.

2. Switch back to the low-power objective and observe the arrangement of cells within the stem cross section. The pith is the large area within the ring of vascular bundles. Surrounding the ring is the cortex. The outermost layers are epidermis. In the appropriate place in Observations, label the vascular bundle, xylem, phloem, pith, cortex, and epidermis.

3. Observe the prepared slide of a cross section of a corn *(Zea)* stem under the low-power objective of the microscope. Note the general arrangement of the cell and the position of the xylem and phloem.

4. Examine the epidermis, cortex, and pith in the corn stem cross section. In the appropriate place in Observations, label the vascular bundle, xylem, phloem, epidermis, cortex, and pith.

Observations

Longitudinal Section of Carrot

Cross Section of Carrot

Sunflower Root   **Corn Root**

Sunflower Stem   **Corn Stem**

Analysis and Conclusions

1. Next to the name of each plant, identify the type of root.

   a. Grass _Fibrous_____

   b. Dandelion _Taproot_____

   c. Orchid _Aerial_____

   d. Corn _Adventitious_____

2. Based on its root structure, is the carrot a monocot or a dicot? _The carrot is a dicot.____

   _____

3. Of the fibrous and taproot, which is best adapted for food storage? _Taproot._____

   _____

4. Which does the shape of the root hair increase—the volume or the surface area of the root?

Surface area.

5. How do monocot and dicot root structures differ? In the dicot root, the xylem is arranged in a star-shaped pattern with the phloem between the arms of the star. In the monocot root, groups of xylem and groups of phloem cells are scattered surrounding the pith.

6. Compare the pattern of xylem and phloem in dicot stem and root. In the dicot stem, xylem and phloem are within vascular bundles. In the dicot root, xylem and phloem are separated.

7. Both roots and stems have a layer of epidermis that forms the outer layer of cells. How do the epidermal cells differ in function in roots and stems? The epidermal cells of roots absorb water, whereas the epidermal cells of stems keep water in the stem.

Critical Thinking and Application

1. Why is it advisable to prune a plant when it is transplanted? Root hairs are destroyed in the process of the move. The plant is trimmed to reduce the plant's requirements from the weakened root system.

2. Would plants with fibrous roots or taproots be more suitable for planting in a windy area? Explain your answer. Fibrous roots spread out over a larger area of the soil than do taproots. As a result, fibrous roots would be able to anchor more soil and thus prevent erosion of soil by wind.

3. What types of roots, fibrous or taproot, are most commonly found on desert plants? Explain your answer. Fibrous roots are most commonly found on desert plants because fibrous roots branch out as they grow. This branching out of the roots enables them to spread over a larger area, making the roots more apt to come in contact with any water in the dry soil.

4. Some giant sequoia trees that have had an automobile tunnel cut through their woody stems continue to grow. How is this possible? In extremely old trees, such as the giant sequoias, the xylem dies. The growth of living tissues therefore takes place in the outer portion of the stems.

5. What advantages do plants with woody stems have over plants with herbaceous, or nonwoody, stems? Plants with woody stems can support large vertical growth and therefore are more likely to get unobstructed sunlight. They can also withstand strong winds and trampling by animals and humans.

Going Further

1. To observe how materials are transported up through a stem, cut the stem of a white carnation in half lengthwise. Measure out 50 mL of water into each of two beakers. Add 5 drops of red food coloring to one beaker and 5 drops of blue food coloring to the other beaker. Place the beakers side by side and carefully place one half of the carnation stem in each beaker. Allow the beakers to remain undisturbed for 24 hours. After 24 hours, observe the color of the carnation flower. Half of the carnation should turn red and the other half should turn blue.

2. To determine the regions of greatest growth in new roots and stems of bean seedlings, germinate some been seeds in a petri dish lined with wet filter paper. Using a waterproof pen, mark 1-mm intervals on the root when it reaches 1 cm in length. Periodically examine the roots to determine which areas show the most growth. Repeat this procedure on stems of seedlings planted in soil.

44

Leaf Structures

You may want to refer students to pages 502–505 in the textbook for a discussion of leaves.

Time required: Part A–15 minutes
Part B–30 minutes
Part C–30 minutes

Pre-Lab Discussion

Leaves are specialized organs found on the stems of plants. The most important function of the leaf is to carry out the process of photosynthesis. All of the necessary raw materials for photosynthesis come together in the leaf. The *xylem* conducts water to the leaf. Carbon dioxide in the air enters through the *stomata* (singular, stoma), or pores, in the leaf. The *chloroplasts* in the leaf capture the light energy needed to convert water and carbon dioxide into food.

Most leaves have large, thin, flattened sections called *blades*. The blade is attached to the stem by a thin structure called the *petiole*. Leaf blades occur in a variety of shapes and sizes. *Simple leaves* have only one blade and one petiole. *Compound leaves* have several blades, or leaflets, that are joined together and to the stem by several petioles. The leaflets of some compound leaves spread out like fingers on a hand. The leaflets of others grow in pairs along a long central petiole. The leaflets of still others are arranged on petioles, which, in turn, are arranged around a long central petiole.

In this investigation, you will identify some of the specialized structures in a leaf. You will also see how leaves vary in size and shape.

Problem

What are some structures of a leaf?

Materials *(per group)*

Leaf selection should vary in type, margin, arrangement of veins, and arrangement on stem. Note that the last category must include several leaves on a stem. It is important that at least 2 out of the 10 leaves be monocots. You might ask students to bring in leaves. If leaves are in short supply, they can be copied in a photocopy machine.

Dicot leaf
Monocot leaf
Conifer (pine) leaf
10 leaves (include simple and compound
    leaves, monocots and dicots)
Prepare slide of a cross section of privet
    leaf or a lilac leaf
Hand lens
Reference books
Microscope

Safety 🔬

Handle all glassware carefully. Always handle the microscope with extreme care. You are responsible for its proper care and use. Use caution when handling glass slides as they can break easily and cut you. Note all safety alert symbols next to the steps in the Procedure and review the meanings of each symbol by referring to the symbol guide on page 10.

Procedure
Part A. Observing External Leaf Structure

1. Note the color of the upper and lower surfaces of the dicot leaf.

⚠ 2. Identify the blade and the petiole. Use a hand lens to observe the midrib, or large central vein that runs the length of the leaf. Look for smaller veins that branch out from the midrib to all parts of the blade. In the appropriate place in Observations, sketch the dicot leaf and label the blade, petiole, midrib, and smaller veins.

3. Observe the shape of the monocot leaf. Use a hand lens to examine the leaf veins. Note that the lower edge of the leaf blade surrounds the stem, forming a sheath. In the appropriate place in Observations, sketch the monocot leaf and label the blade, sheath, stem, and veins.

4. Examine the shape of the pine leaf. Pine leaves are found in clusters that are enclosed by a scaly sheath. Pine leaves grow in groups of two, three, and five needles. In the appropriate place in Observations, sketch the pine leaf and label the blades and the sheath.

Part B. Classifying Leaves

1. Using reference books, identify each of the 10 different leaves. Record each leaf name in the appropriate place in the Data Table.

2. Classify each leaf as simple or compound. Compound leaves may be further classified into palmately compound leaves, which have several leaflets that arise from the tip of the petiole, and pinnately compound leaves, which have leaflets that run along opposite sides of an extension of the petiole. Use Figure 1 to identify each leaf type. Record the leaf type for each leaf in the appropriate place in the Data Table.

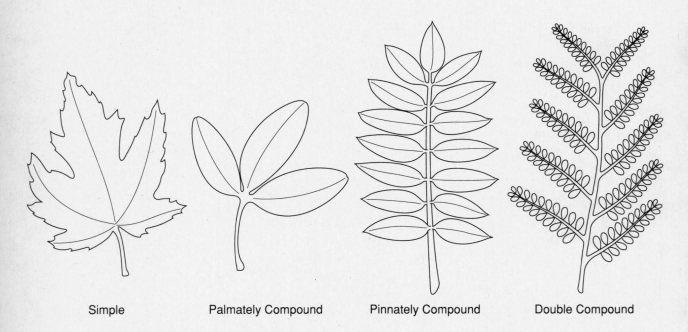

Simple   Palmately Compound   Pinnately Compound   Double Compound

Figure 1   Leaf Types

⚠ 3. Observe the venation, or vein pattern, of each leaf. In parallel venation, several main veins run the length of the leaf. Most monocots have parallel venation. In net venation, a netlike pattern of veins spreads throughout the leaf. Most dicots have net venation. To identify the vein pattern, hold each leaf specimen up to the light and use a hand lens to see the veins. Record the type of venation for each leaf in the Data Table. Note that leaf venation is not illustrated because stud will have drawn both types of venation in Part A.

4. Observe the pattern of leaf margin for each leaf. Use Figure 2 to identify types of leaf margins. Record the type of leaf margin in the Data Table.

Figure 2   **Leaf Margin Types**

5. Observe the arrangement of the leaves or leaflets on the stem of each leaf. In an opposite arrangement, the leaves are arranged opposite each other on the stem. In an alternate arrangement, the leaves are attached at alternate positions on the stem. In a whorled arrangement, several leaves arise together around one part of the stem. Use Figure 3 to identify leaf or leaflet arrangements. Record the leaf arrangement for each leaf in the Data Table.

Figure 3   **Leaf Arrangement**

Part C. Examining a Cross Section of a Dicot Leaf

🔺 1. Examine a prepared slide of a privet or lilac leaf cross section under the low-power objective of the microscope. Notice the arrangement of the various layers of the leaf. Identify the upper epidermis, or the top layer of the leaf. Locate the lower epidermis, or the bottom layer of the leaf. Epidermal hairs, which cut down the intensity of bright light and slow down water evaporation, may be present. These hairs may make the leaf surface feel fuzzy.

2. Switch to the high-power objective. **CAUTION:** *When switching to the high-power objective, always look at the objective from the side of the microscope so that the objective does not hit or damage the slide.* Locate the upper and lower epidermis. Note the size of the epidermal cells. Cells in the epidermis secrete a substance called cutin, which covers the whole leaf and prevents the leaf from drying out. Label the upper and lower epidermis and cutin on the leaf diagram in Observations.

3. Move the slide so that you can focus on the lower epidermis. Look for stomata, or pores, in the epidermis. Locate some guard cells that border each stoma. These specialized cells control the opening and closing of the stomata. On the leaf diagram in Observations, label a stoma and its guard cells. Investigation 45 will cover leaf stomata in more detail. Inform students that the stomata will appear colorless when open. Closed stomata will show the guard cells close together.

4. Locate a layer of elongated rectangular cells just below the upper epidermis. These cells are called palisade parenchyma cells. They contain many chloroplasts, which appear as tiny green bodies in the cells. Label a palisade parenchyma cell and a chloroplast on the leaf diagram in Observations.

5. Observe the irregularly shaped spongy parenchyma cells just below the palisade cells. Spongy parenchyma cells contain fewer chloroplasts than the palisade parenchyma cells. The spongy cells form a honeycomb pattern with intercellular air spaces, which connect with the stomata in the lower epidermis. Together, the palisade and spongy parenchyma cells make up the mesophyll layer. Label a spongy parenchyma cell, the mesophyll layer, and an air space on the leaf diagram in Observations.

6. Move the slide sideways and locate the circular structure called a vascular bundle in the mesophyll layer. Label a vascular bundle on the leaf diagram in Observations.

7. Locate some xylem and phloem cells within the vascular bundles. Xylem cells generally have thick walls and are bunched near the top of a leaf vein. Phloem cells are thinner and are located near the bottom of a leaf vein. Surrounding and supporting a vascular bundle are cells forming bundle sheaths. Label the xylem, phloem, and bundle sheath on the leaf diagram in Observations. Explain that a cross section of a monocot leaf or conifer leaf would look different from the dicot cross section. If possible, obtain one of these cross sections for your students' observation under the microscope.

Name _____ Class _____ Date _____

Observations

Dicot Leaf

Monocot Leaf

Conifer Leaf

Data Table

Leaf Name	Leaf Type	Type of Venation	Leaf Margin	Leaf Arrangement
		Answers will vary.		

Leaf Cross Section

Analysis and Conclusions

1. **Which surface of the leaf, upper or lower, contains the most chlorophyll? Explain why.**

   The upper surface is the darker shade of green and contains more chlorophyll because more light strikes this surface so that photosynthesis can occur.

2. **How is the structure that attaches the leaf to the stem different in monocots as compared to dicots?** The dicot leaf is attached to the stem by a petiole. Part of the monocot leaf forms a sheath that encircles the stem.

3. **How are the veins important to the leaf's function?** Veins contain vascular bundles that move food, water, and other materials to and from the leaf.

4. **How does the conifer (pine) leaf differ from the dicot leaf?** The conifer leaf is needle-shaped instead of being flat and broad.

5. **Consult your Data Table. How many dicot leaves did you examine?**

   Answers will vary.

6. How do the stomata and air spaces in the spongy parenchyma work together to help the leaf

survive? Carbon dioxide from the air passes through the stomata into the air spaces, where it is used by

the cells. Oxygen and water vapor pass from the cells through air spaces into the stomata and thus out of

the leaf.

Critical Thinking and Application

1. A cross section of a pine leaf would show a thickened cutin and a thickened epidermis. How does this design help the pine leaf survive in the northern parts of the United States?

The thickened outer structure protects the pine leaf from extreme dryness and cold.

2. Some people mist their house plants with water. Do you think the plant can absorb the water

through its leaves? Explain your answer. No. Water is taken into a plant through the roots and cannot

be absorbed through its leaves.

3. The gypsy moth, *Lymantria dispar,* is an insect that is responsible for damaging millions of kilometers of trees in the northeastern United States. The larval stage of this insect is a caterpillar that feeds on the leaves of trees, particularly oak and apple. How do you account for the fact that after a few years of repeated defoliation by these insects, trees often die?

When the gypsy moth caterpillars eat the leaves of a tree, the tree is unable to get energy through

photosynthesis. Most trees can survive a few years of this defoliation by restricting growth. However,

after repeated defoliation, the trees become so weakened, they die.

4. In order to keep your house plants healthy, why should you periodically remove dust from

their leaves? Dust forms a covering over the top layer of the leaf, preventing light and carbon dioxide

from entering the leaf. As a result, photosynthesis does not occur and the plant soon dies.

Going Further

Examine some examples of leaf adaptations. Leaf adaptations occur when the leaf changes its form for protection, storage, support, or some other need. Look for the following specially adapted leaves: an onion or flower bulb, a spine or prickle from a cactus, a tendril on a climbing plant, and a leaf from a succulent plant such as a jade. Also visit a greenhouse or a florist for an example of an insect-eating plant such as a Venus' flytrap. Use reference materials in the library to find photographs of plants that are carnivorous. Try to determine what function each of these different leaf adaptations serves for the plant.

45

Estimating the Number of Stomata in a Leaf

You may want to refer students to pages 502–508 in the textbook for a discussion of leaf structure and transpiration.

Time required: Part A—45 minutes
Part B—30 minutes

Pre-Lab Discussion

The leaf is the main organ through which water is given off by a plant. As a plant absorbs water through its roots, the water is carried through the stem to the leaves. Some of the water is used in the leaves during photosynthesis. However, more water is taken in and transported to the leaves than can be used during photosynthesis. The excess water evaporates into the atmosphere through the *stomata,* or pores, in a process called *transpiration.*

Stomata are openings generally found on the undersides of leaves. They are formed by two specialized epidermal cells called *guard cells.* Guard cells regulate the passage of water vapor, oxygen, and carbon dioxide into and out of the leaf.

In this investigation, you will observe guard cells in a fresh lettuce leaf. You will also estimate the total number of guard cells in a lettuce leaf.

Problem

How can the number of stomata in a leaf be estimated?

Materials *(per group)*

Small piece of crisp lettuce in cold water
Small piece of wilted lettuce
Microscope
2 glass slides
2 coverslips
Medicine dropper
Forceps
Calculator (optional)
Transparent plastic metric ruler
Probe

Safety

Always handle the microscope with extreme care. You are responsible for its proper care and use. Use caution when handling glass slides as they can break easily and cut you. Be careful when handling sharp instruments. Note all safety alert symbols next to the steps in the Procedure and review the meanings of each symbol by referring to the symbol guide on page 10.

Procedure

Part A. Observing Guard Cells and Stomata in a Lettuce Leaf

🔺 1. Place a drop of water in the center of a glass slide.

2. Locate a large rib in the crisp lettuce leaf. As shown in Figure 1, bend the lettuce leaf against the curve until it snaps.

A

Lettuce leaf
lower epidermis

B

Bend leaf
against curve

C

Remove
lower epidermis

Coverslip

Glass slide

D

Prepare a wet mount

Figure 1

▦ 3. With the forceps, carefully remove the thin layer of epidermis from the piece of lettuce. Spread the epidermis out as smoothly as possible in the drop of water on the slide. **Note:** *If the epidermis becomes folded on the slide, use a probe to gently unfold and flatten it.* Add a coverslip.

4. Observe the lettuce epidermis under the low-power objective of the microscope. **Note**: *It may be necessary to adjust the diaphragm so that there is sufficient light passing through the cells.* Notice the irregular shapes of the epidermal cells. Notice the guard cells, which are pairs of kidney-shaped cells scattered throughout the epidermis. The spaces between the guard cells are the stomata.

5. Center a single stoma-guard cell unit in the center of the field of view under low power. Switch to high power and focus on the single stoma-guard cell unit. **CAUTION:** *When switching to the high-power objective, always look at the objective from the side of the microscope so that the objective does not hit or damage the slide.*

6. In the appropriate place in Observations, sketch a single stoma-guard cell unit as seen under high power of the microscope. Label the guard cells, stoma, and chloroplasts. Record the magnification of the microscope.

7. Set the wet-mount slide of the lettuce epidermis aside for now. It will be used in Part B of the investigation.

8. Repeat steps 1 through 6 using the wilted lettuce leaf.

Part B. Estimating the Number of Stomata

🔺 **1.** Observe the slide of the crisp lettuce leaf epidermis under low power of the microscope. Count the number of stoma-guard cell units you see in the low-power field of view. Record the number in Data Table 1.

2. Carefully switch to high power. Count the number of stoma-guard cell units you see in the high-power field of view. Record the number in Data Table 1.

3. Using the transparent plastic metric ruler, measure the diameter of the low-power field of view in millimeters. **Note:** *See Laboratory Investigation 4 for step-by-step directions on how to measure the diameter of a field of view.* Calculate the diameter of the high-power field of view. Record the radii of the low-power and high-power fields of view in Data Table 2. The radius is equal to one half of the diameter.

4. Calculate the area of the low-power and high-power fields of view using the formula:

$$area = \pi r^2$$

Record this information in the appropriate place in Data Table 2.

5. To determine the number of stomata in a square centimeter of lettuce leaf epidermis, use the following formula:

$$stomata/cm^2 = \frac{total\ number\ of\ stomata}{area\ (cm^2)}$$

Calculate the number of stomata in a square centimeter for low power and high power. Record this information in the appropriate place in Data Table 2.

6. With the metric ruler, measure the size of the entire lettuce leaf. Calculate the area of the lettuce leaf using the following formula:

$$area\ (cm^2) = width\ (cm) \times length\ (cm)$$

Estimate the number of stomata in the lettuce leaf. Record this information in the appropriate place in Data Table 2.

Observations

Magnification _____   Magnification _____

Crisp Lettuce Leaf   **Wilted Lettuce Leaf**

Data Table 1

	Low Power	High Power
Number of Stomata	Answers will vary.	

Data Table 2

Measurement	Low Power	High Power
Radius (mm)		
Radius^2 (mm^2)		
$\pi \times r^2$	3.14 x	3.14 x
Area (mm^2)		
Area in cm^2 (Area in cm$^2 = \dfrac{\text{area in mm}^2}{100}$)	Answers will vary.	
Stomata / cm^2 = $\dfrac{\text{Total number of stomata}}{\text{area in cm}^2}$		
Area of lettuce leaf (cm^2) = width (cm) x length (cm)		
Number of stomata/leaf = area of lettuce leaf x stomata/cm^2		

Analysis and Conclusions

1. Compare the sizes of the stomata in the crisp and wilted lettuce leaves.

   The stomata in the crisp lettuce leaf are larger than the stomata in the wilted lettuce leaf.

2. Explain the size difference between the stomata in the crisp lettuce leaf and the stomata in the wilted lettuce leaf. The wilted leaf contains little water. The guard cells lose their turgor pressure and cause the stomata to decrease in size, preventing further water loss.

3. What is the function of the guard cells? To control the size of the stomata for the regulation of water

loss.

4. Is the low-power estimated number of stomata close to the high-power estimated number?

Why might the numbers be different? Answers will vary. Differences can be attributed to errors in

measurement under high power.

Critical Thinking and Application

1. Where would you expect to find stomata on the leaves of a floating water lily plant? Explain

your answer. The stomata on a water lily plant will be on the upper surface to allow for water loss and

gas exchange.

2. Why do you think the stomata of a plant are open during the day and closed at night?

During the day, when there is adequate water and when an exchange of gases is necessary, as during

photosynthesis, the stomata are open. At night, when there is little light and no photosynthesis is taking

place, the stomata are closed.

3. What would happen to a plant if its leaves were completely coated with petroleum jelly?

Explain your answer. Coating a plant with petroleum jelly would prevent the diffusion of carbon dioxide,

an ingredient for photosynthesis, into the plant. The jelly would also prevent the release of oxygen and

water vapor. As photosynthesis stopped, the plant would eventually die.

4. Would you expect the leaf of a desert cactus or the leaf of a water lily to have more stomata?

Explain your answer. The leaf of a water lily plant will have more stomata. Whereas the water lily plant

must rid itself of much extra water, the desert cactus will try to retain as much water as possible. Fewer

stomata will aid in water conservation in a hot, dry climate.

Going Further

1. Design and conduct an experiment to show the effects of temperature, time of day, light, and soil moisture on stomata opening and closing. How will you know whether the stomata are open or closed?

2. Outline a leaf, such as that of a bryophyllum or African violet, on a sheet of graph paper. Determine the area of the leaf by counting the squares inside the outline. Using the procedure described in the investigation, count the number of stomata in one square centimeter. Calculate the total number of stomata on the leaf surface.

46

Plant Hormones

You may want to refer students to pages 521–527 in the textbook for a discussion of plant hormones.

Time required:
Steps 1–5–30 minutes
Steps 6–12–40 minutes
Daily measurements: 5 to 10 minutes

Pre-Lab Discussion

Both plants and animals produce hormones, one type of which regulates growth. Plant hormones are often called phytohormones. Gibberellins are a group of phytohormones that affect plant growth. The effects of these hormones were first observed in the 1920s in rice plants that were attacked by a fungus. The rice plants grew unusually tall and spindly. Japanese scientists discovered that the plants' extraordinary growth was caused by a substance produced by the fungus *Gibberella fujikuroi*. The substance, later called gibberellin, or gibberellic acid, was named after the fungus that produced it.

In 1956, gibberellins were also found in the bean plant *Phaseolus vulgaris*. Now scientists believe that gibberellins are produced by all higher plants. Some plants have a mutation that causes dwarfism. This mutation is thought to interfere with a plant's ability to produce gibberellic acid.

In this investigation, you will observe the effects of gibberellic acid on the growth of normal and dwarf pea plants.

Problem

What is the effect of gibberellic acid on the growth of normal and dwarf pea plants?

Materials *(per group)*

4 large flower pots
Small stones
Soil-and-sand mixture
4 plastic bags
4 twist ties
Scissors
25 toothpicks
Metric ruler
Wooden stakes
Sheet of unlined white paper
Cotton swabs
Masking tape
Red and black pens or pencils
16 Little Marvel pea seeds   Soak all peas overnight in water. Soaking will help to soften the
16 Alaska pea seeds   seed coat and hasten germination.

Gibberellic acid solution   Dissolve 100 mg gibberellic acid powder in 2 mL 70% ethyl alcohol. Stir until completely dissolved. Mix dissolved powder with 1L distilled water. Refrigerate after making. Use immediately after preparation. Pour solution into dropper bottles for student use.

It is useful to add a wetting agent such as polyoxyethylene sorbitan monolaurate (commercially known as Tween 20) to the gibberellic acid solution. The wetting agent prevents the solution from running off the leaves. Add 1 mL wetting agent to 1 L gibberellic acid solution.

Put on a laboratory apron if one is available. Put on safety goggles. Handle all glassware carefully. Always use special caution when working with laboratory chemicals, as they may irritate the skin or cause staining of the skin or clothing. Never touch or taste any chemical unless instructed to do so. Be careful when handling sharp instruments. Note all safety alert symbols next to the steps in the Procedure and review the meanings of each symbol by referring to the symbol guide on page 10.

Procedure

⚗ **1.** Using strips of masking tape, label the four large flower pots as shown in Figure 1. Also include the name of one person in your group and the date on each flower-pot label.

| Little Marvel peas treated with water | Little Marvel peas treated with gibberellic acid | Alaska peas treated with water | Alaska peas treated with gibberellic acid |

Figure 1

2. For drainage, place stones in the bottom of each flower pot. Then fill the flower pots two-thirds full with a mixture of soil and sand. Moisten the soil-and-sand mixture.

3. In each of the two pots labeled "Little Marvel peas," scatter eight Little Marvel pea seeds along the surface of the soil. Cover the seeds with a thin layer of soil. Moisten the seeds.

4. In each of the pots labeled "Alaska Peas," scatter eight Alaska pea seeds along the surface of the soil. Cover the seeds with a thin layer of soil. Moisten the seeds.

5. Place each pot in a plastic bag and seal the bag with a twist tie. Store the pots in a warm, dark place where they will remain undisturbed for four days.

6. When the seedlings begin to emerge from the soil, open the plastic bags and place the pots in a warm, sunny place. Add water as needed to keep the soil moist but not wet.

7. When the seedlings are about 3 cm tall (after about eight days), select five of the healthiest plants. With your thumb and index finger, pinch off the remaining seedlings at the soil line.

8. To identify each seedling, cut out small "flags" from the unlined white paper. Number the flags 1 through 5. Attach these flags to the ends of toothpicks as shown in Figure 2. Place a toothpick in the soil next to each seedling.

9. Using a metric ruler, measure the initial stem length of each seedling in millimeters. As shown in Figure 3, measure the stem length as the distance from the first pair of true leaves to the tallest part of the plant. Record these measurements in the appropriate places in the Data Table.

10. Using a cotton swab, apply water to the leaves and shoot tips of the seedlings in pots 1 and 3.

11. Using a clean cotton swab, carefully apply gibberellic acid solution to the leaves and shoot tips of the plants in pots 2 and 4. **CAUTION:** *Handle gibberellic acid with care to avoid spills.*

12. Arrange the pots so that each one receives the same quantity of light. Give each pot the same amount of water. As the plants grow taller, use wooden stakes to support them.

13. Each day for the next eight school days, measure the stem length of each plant to the nearest millimeter. Record the date and the measurements in the appropriate places in the Data Table. Find the average stem length of the five seedlings in each pot and record the average in the appropriate place in the Data Table.

Figure 2

Measure this distance

Figure 3

14. Using the averages in the Data Table, plot stem length versus number of days of growth on the graph in Observations. **Note:** *Because you have not recorded eight consecutive days of growth (you did not record on the weekend), you must account for these gaps on your graph. Leave space on the graph for the days when measurements could not be taken.*

Observations

Data Table

Plant Variety	Pot Number	Treatment	Plant Number	Stem Length (mm)							
				Day 1 Date:	Day 2 Date:	Day 3 Date:	Day 4 Date:	Day 5 Date:	Day 6 Date:	Day 7 Date:	Day 8 Date:
Little Marvel	1	Water	1								
			2								
			3								
			4								
			5								
			Average								
	2	Gibberellic acid	1								
			2								
			3								
			4								
			5								
			Average								
Alaska	3	Water	1								
			2								
			3								
			4								
			5								
			Average								
	4	Gibberellic acid	1								
			2								
			3								
			4								
			5								
			Average								

Students' measurements will vary. In general, untreated Little Marvel pea plants (dwarf plants) will grow most slowly and will always be the shortest plants. Treated Little Marvel pea plants will achieve nearly the height of treated Alaska pea plants. Treated Alaska peas will grow more rapidly than untreated Alaska peas.

Graph

Answers will vary, but should reflect the information in the Data Table.

Students will not be able to measure the change in stem length each day for eight consecutive days. Therefore, have them record the dates of the measurements. Make sure they take into account the gaps in measurements when they graph their results. Remind students that the plants will be growing on the weekends even though no record will be made of their growth. Thus, an accurately constructed graph should reflect these gaps. For example, suppose the last measurements were made on day 5 and no measurements were made on days 6 and 7. The next point to be plotted on the graph would be at day 8.

Analysis and Conclusions

1. Why was water applied to the leaves and stem tips of the plants in pots 1 and 3?

Pots 1 and 3 are used as controls. Use of water establishes that any increase in stem length is due to the

gibberellic acid and not to the water or to the swabbing.

2. Based on the graph you constructed, explain which group of plants showed the fastest rate of

growth. Little Marvel pea plants treated with gibberellic acid should show the fastest growth rate.

3. Compare the growth of Little Marvel pea plants and Alaska pea plants with and without treatment with gibberellic acid. When treated with water, Little Marvel pea plants remain short. When treated with gibberellic acid, they grow to about the same height as the treated Alaska pea plants. Untreated Alaska pea plants are somewhat taller than the untreated Little Marvel pea plants.

4. Which variety of pea plants studied is the dwarf variety? Little Marvel peas.

5. What caused the rapid growth of the Little Marvel pea plants? The application of gibberellic acid.

6. On the last day measurements were taken, what was the difference in average stem length between the untreated and the treated Little Marvel plants? Answers will vary, but the treated Little Marvels should be significantly taller than the untreated Little Marvels.

7. Develop a hypothesis to explain the growth demonstrated in this investigation.
If gibberellic acid causes the lengthening of stems and if dwarf plants cannot make gibberellic acid, then the application of gibberellic acid should make both normal and dwarf plants grow taller than untreated varieties of both.

Critical Thinking and Application

1. Suggest how a commercial plant grower might apply knowledge of the effects of gibberellic acid. If customers were interested in having especially tall plants, commercial growers could apply gibberellic acid to develop plants of the desired height.

2. A head of lettuce is actually a rosette of leaves on a very short stem. Explain what might happen if a lettuce head were treated with gibberellic acid. The stem would elongate dramatically and the leaves would be spaced out on the stem. The lettuce would no longer have a "head."

3. The word hormone comes from a Greek word meaning "to arouse." How is this name suitable for the function of hormones? Hormones are responsible for triggering and controlling the growth and development of plants.

4. How might a knowledge of plant hormones be useful to a commercial gardener who supplies florists with fresh flowers for holidays even though some of these holidays do not coincide with the natural growing period of the plants in demand? The gardener could use certain hormones to cause plants to grow and flower at times other than their natural growing periods.

Going Further

1. In the investigation you just completed, the gibberellic acid solution was applied directly to the leaves and stem tips of the plants. Design an experiment in which the gibberellic acid enters the plant through a route other than the leaves and stem tips. Perform the experiment and compare the results with those obtained in this investigation.

2. Gardeners often pinch off the stems of plants to enhance the plants' growth. This pinching off is related to the production of certain hormones. Determine which hormones are involved. Find out the mechanism of action of these hormones. Then design an experiment that shows the effect of pinching back the stem tips. Use four healthy plants — two experimental plants and two control plants.

47

Germination Inhibitors

You may want to refer students to pages 521–527 in the textbook for a discussion of plant hormones.

Time required: 40 minutes and observation period of 8 days.

Pre-Lab Discussion

As a seed germinates, new cells are produced. As they grow larger, they differentiate into plant organs, such as roots, stems, leaves, and flowers. Eventually, a mature plant results.

Tomato seeds will usually germinate when exposed to the proper amounts of moisture and oxygen and a fairly warm temperature. Yet inside the tomato, where these conditions are also met, tomato seeds do not germinate. Why? Plants contain certain hormones that control their metabolism and growth processes.

In this investigation, you will observe the effects of a hormone called a germination inhibitor.

Problem

What are the effects of a germination inhibitor on tomato seeds? What effect does a germination inhibitor from one kind of tomato have on other kinds of tomatoes?

Materials *(per group)*

Tomatoes (2 different varieties)
Filter paper
Strainer
Mortar and pestle (or bowl and spoon)
Funnel
Beaker
4 petri dishes
Plastic wrap
Glass-marking pencil

Safety ⚠

Put on a laboratory apron if one is available. Handle all glassware carefully. Note all safety alert symbols next to the steps in the Procedure and review the meanings of each symbol by referring to the symbol guide on page 10.

Procedure

Part A. Observing the Effects of a Germination Inhibitor

 1. With the glass-marking pencil, label the petri dishes 1 through 4.

2. Using a mortar and pestle, crush one whole tomato (Variety A). Strain the crushed tomato and collect the extract in the beaker. With a glass-marking pencil, label the beaker "Extract A" and set it aside for now.

3. From the tomato pulp, remove about 20 seeds and wash them.

4. Line petri dishes 1 and 2 with filter paper. Place 10 seeds in each dish.

5. Moisten petri dish 1 with water and petri dish 2 with the tomato extract. Cover the petri dishes with plastic wrap. Observe the seeds for several days, adding more water or tomato extract as needed to keep the filter paper moist.

6. Record the total number of seeds that germinate daily in each petri dish in the appropriate place in Data Table 1.

Part B. Comparing the Effects of Germination Inhibitors

 1. Line petri dishes 3 and 4 with filter paper.

2. Using a mortar and pestle, crush a different kind of tomato (Variety B) and obtain 20 seeds from the tomato pulp. Wash the seeds and place 10 seeds in each petri dish

3. Moisten petri dish 3 with water. Moisten petri dish 4 with the extract in the beaker labeled Extract A, which you collected during Part A.

4. Cover the petri dishes with plastic wrap. Observe the seeds for several days. Record the total number of seeds that germinate daily in each petri dish in the appropriate place in Data Table 2.

5. Using the graph in Observations, construct four different line graphs representing the number of seeds that germinated in each of the four petri dishes. Label each of the line graphs.

Observations

Data Table 1

Petri Dish	Day 1	Day 2	Day 3	Day 4	Day 5	Day 6	Day 7	Day 8
1 (Variety A with water)				Answers will vary.				
2 (Variety A with extract A)								

Data Table 2

Petri Dish	Day 1	Day 2	Day 3	Day 4	Day 5	Day 6	Day 7	Day 8
3 (Variety B with water)				Answers will vary.				
4 (Variety B with extract A)								

Graph

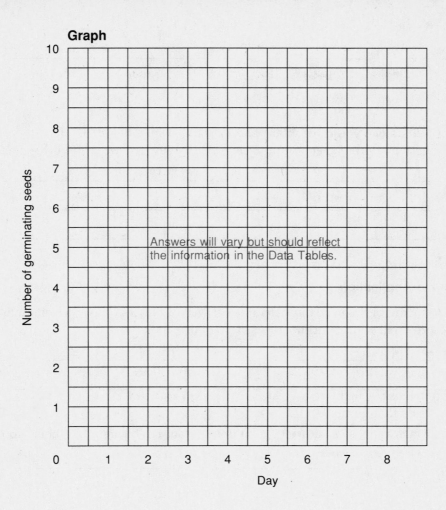

Number of germinating seeds

Answers will vary but should reflect
the information in the Data Tables.

Day

Analysis and Conclusions

1. What is the purpose of petri dishes 1 and 3? Petri dishes 1 and 3 act as controls for the experiment.

_____

2. What is seed germination? Germination is the early growth of a new plant from a seed. Usually the root

is the first part of the plant to emerge.

_____

3. Explain how you can determine whether or not a seed has germinated.

When a root appears, the seed has germinated.

_____

_____

4. What conclusion can you draw after observing the results of Part A? Do tomatoes contain a germination inhibitor? Give evidence to support your answer. Students should report the number of seeds germinating in each case. No seeds, or very few, should germinate in the tomato extract, indicating that tomatoes do contain inhibitors.

5. What conclusions can you draw after observing the results of Part B? Is Extract A effective in preventing germination of seeds from Variety B? Give evidence to support your answer. Answers may vary depending on the varieties used. However, answers should be consistent with data collected. Most inhibitors are specific to the variety from which they were collected.

Critical Thinking and Application

1. Explain why some of the seeds in petri dishes 1 and 3 may not have germinated, even though they were provided with all of the necessary conditions for growth.
Some seeds that were used in the experiment may have been dead.

2. Explain why many seeds in nature that do not contain inhibitors might begin to germinate during late spring. During the late spring, in many areas, the necessary conditions for seed germination —warmth and moisture—become available.

3. In addition to tomatoes, what are some fruits and/or vegetables that you think may contain germination inhibitors? Answers will vary. Examples could include apples, oranges, watermelons, squash, cucumbers, peppers, etc.

Going Further

1. Test the effectiveness of the germination inhibitor on additional varieties of tomatoes as well as on other kinds of plants. You might want to try flax or tobacco seeds because they are in the same family as the tomato.

2. Is the germination inhibitor a protein? If it is, it will lose its effectiveness when boiled. Repeat Part A of this investigation using boiled tomato extract. What happens?

48

Observing Plant Responses

You may want to refer students to page 525 in the textbook for a discussion of tropisms.
Time required:
    Part A–15 minutes, with an observation after 5 days.
    Part B–15 minutes, with an observation after 3 days.
    Part C–15 minutes.

Pre-Lab Discussion

The movement of a part of a plant in response to environmental stimuli such as light, gravity, water, or touch is called a *tropism*. The growth of a plant stem toward a light stimulus is called *phototropism*. The growth of a root downward toward the center of the Earth (gravity) is called *gravitropism*. The growth of a plant toward water is called *hydrotropism*. A plant's growth movement in response to touch is called *thigmotropism*.

When the plant part responds to a stimulus by growing toward the stimulus, the response is known as a *positive tropism*. When the plant part responds by growing away from the stimulus, the response is known as a *negative tropism*. Thus, stems show a positive tropism to light and a negative tropism to gravity. Roots, on the other hand, show a negative tropism to light and a positive tropism to gravity. In many tropisms, certain plant hormones called *auxins* regulate plant growth and help a plant respond to some stimuli.

Plant movements that are independent of the direction of the stimulus are not classified as tropisms. Instead, they are called *nastic movements*. While tropisms take a fairly long time to occur and are not easily reversed, nastic movements occur rapidly and are quickly reversible.

In this investigation, you will observe the processes of gravitropism and phototropism. You will also investigate the nastic movements of the *Mimosa* plant.

Problem

How do plants respond to external stimuli?

Materials *(per group)*

4 corn seeds	Soak all seeds in	Toothpick
4 bean seeds	water for 24 hours	Stopwatch or clock with
Petri dish	before investigation	second hand
2 paper cups	begins.	Metric ruler
Paper towels		Large cardboard box with
Masking tape		slit (one box for the
Glass-marking pencil		entire class)
Clay		Soil
Scissors		Protractor
Potted *Mimosa pudica* plant	Available from biological supply houses.

Put on a laboratory apron if one is available. Handle all glassware carefully. Be careful when handling sharp instruments. Note all safety alert symbols next to the steps in the Procedure and review the meanings of each symbol by referring to the symbol guide on page 10.

Procedure
Part A. Observing Gravitropism

🔥 **1.** Arrange the four soaked corn seeds in a petri dish as shown in A of Figure 1. The pointed end of each seed should face the center of the petri dish. One seed should be placed at the 12 o'clock position, and the other seeds should be at the 3, 6, and 9 o'clock positions, respectively.

▦ **2.** Cut a circle of paper towel the size of the petri dish and place it over the seeds. Then carefully pack the petri dish with enough pieces of paper towel so that the seeds are held firmly in place when the other half of the petri dish is put on. See B of Figure 1. **CAUTION:** *Be careful when using scissors.*

Figure 1

3. Moisten the paper towels with water. Cover the petri dish and seal the two halves together with strips of masking tape.

4. With a glass-marking pencil, draw an arrow on the lid pointing toward 12 o'clock. Label the lid with the name of one member of your group and the date.

5. As shown in C of Figure 1, prop the petri dish up with pieces of clay so that the arrow is pointing upward. Place the petri dish in a dark place and allow it to remain undisturbed for about 5 days.

6. After 5 days, remove the petri dish from the dark place. In the appropriate place in Observations, make a sketch of the seeds in the petri dish.

Part B. Observing Phototropism

1. Punch four holes in the bottom of each paper cup. Label the cups A and B and put the name of one member of your group on each cup.

2. Fill the cups nearly full with soil. Then plant two bean seeds about 4 cm apart in each cup and cover with about 1 cm of soil. Water the seeds and allow them to grow until they are about 5 cm high.

3. After the seedlings have reached a height of about 5 cm, place the cup labeled A in an area of the room that gets the same amount of light from all sides.

4. Place the cup labeled B in the cardboard box that your teacher prepared. Note that a small slit has been cut out on one side of the box. Place the cup in the box as shown in Figure 2.

Figure 2

5. After each group has placed their cups in the cardboard box, it will be closed so that light enters only through the slit. Allow the cups to remain undisturbed in the box for 72 hours.

6. After 72 hours, observe the plants in in cups A and B. Use the protractor to measure the angle at which the plant bends in relation to the soil. See Figure 3. Record the information in the appropriate places in the Data Table. Also in the Data Table, record any observations on the height, color, stem and leaf shape, and leaf arrangement of each plant.

Figure 3

Part C. Observing Nastic Movements

1. Without touching them, observe the petiole and leaflets of the *Mimosa* plant. In the appropriate place in Observations, sketch these structures.

2. Position the toothpick between your index finger and thumb. Then as shown in Figure 4, allow the toothpick to spring forward so that it touches a leaflet. Observe the response of the leaflet to touch. Have one group member determine how long it takes the leaflet to respond to the stimulus and how long it takes the leaflet to return to its original position.

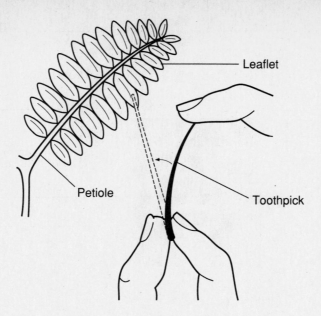

Leaflet

Petiole

Toothpick

Figure 4

3. Repeat step 2 touching the petiole instead of the leaflet. Determine how long it takes the petiole to respond to the stimulus and how long it takes the petiole to return to its original position.

Observations

Germinating Corn Seeds

Mimosa Leaf

Data Table

Cup	Plant	Angle of Bending	Observations
A	1		
	2		Answers will vary.
B	1		
	2		

1. How did the leaflet respond when you touched it with the toothpick?

The leaflet folds up when it is touched.

2. How long did it take for the leaflet to respond to the stimulus and then to return to its original position? Answers will vary.

3. How did the petiole respond when you touched it with the toothpick?

The petiole droops or bends downward from the stem when it is touched.

4. How long did it take for the petiole to respond to the stimulus and then to return to its original position? Answers will vary.

Analysis and Conclusions

1. Which part(s) of the germinating corn seeds showed positive gravitropism? Which part(s) showed negative gravitropism? The roots of the seeds showed positive gravitropism. The stems and leaves of the seeds showed negative gravitropism.

2. Why were the corn seeds placed in the dark instead of near a light source?

Seeds do not need light in order to germinate.

3. Why was it important that the petri dish in Part A be kept in an upright position throughout the investigation? Changing the position of the petri dish would change the variable being studied (the effect of gravity on the growth of a plant).

4. Do plant leaves and stems show a positive or a negative phototropism? Give evidence to support your answer. Plant leaves and stems show a positive phototropism. The plants that received light from all directions grew straight up, while the plants that received light from only one direction grew in that direction.

5. Why are *Mimosa* plants said to have nastic movements instead of negative or positive

thigmotropism? The plants moved independently of the direction of the stimulus. Their movements were

also very rapid and quickly reversible.

Critical Thinking and Application

1. If an insect landed on a *Mimosa* plant, how do you think the leaflets would respond? How

might this response be helpful to the plant? The leaflets would fold up quickly. This response would

most likely frighten the insect away, preventing the insect from damaging the plant.

2. Why do many people regularly turn or rotate their houseplants? Positive phototropism usually

causes plant stems to bend toward the light. Some people rotate their houseplants to prevent them from

having a "lopsided" look.

3. Certain types of vines display a positive thigmotropism by climbing on or clinging to objects
such as stakes or fences. How is this an advantage in the process of photosynthesis?

Plants with a positive thigmotropism can climb over or around objects, giving them a better chance of

getting light for photosynthesis.

4. How is a plant root's positive gravitropism an advantage for the survival of the plant?

Positive gravitropism allows the root to grow downward into the soil. As the root grows deeper, it is better

able to absorb water from the deeper layers of soil, which have better water retention.

Going Further

1. Design an experiment to observe another type of tropism such as hydrotropism or
chemotropism.

2. Are bean seedlings responsive to white light only? Design and conduct an experiment to find
out.

49

Reproductive Structures in a Flower

You may want to refer students to pages 533–539 in the textbook for a discussion of flower structure.

Time required: 45 minutes.

Pre-Lab Discussion

Flowers are the reproductive organs of angiosperms, or flowering plants. Flowers vary in size, color, and arrangement. All flowers, regardless of variety, have the function of seed formation and the production of more plants. Flowers contain both nonreproductive and reproductive structures.

In this investigation, you will examine a flower and identify its nonreproductive and reproductive parts. You will also observe the male and female sex cells produced by a flower.

Problem

How is a flower adapted for sexual reproduction?

Materials *(per group)*

Variety of fresh flowers
Stamens and pistil from a
    dissected flower
Hand lens
Forceps
Scalpel or single-edged razor
    blade
Dissecting tray
Dissecting needle
Scissors
Microscope
2 glass slides
2 coverslips
Medicine dropper
Sheet of unlined white paper

Day-old fresh flowers are generally available for free or at a reduced cost from local florists or nurseries. Obtain a variety of flowers such as tulips, lilies, violets, apple blossoms, or gladioli.

Safety 🔬 ✂

Put on a laboratory apron if one is available. Handle all glassware carefully. Be careful when handling sharp instruments. Always handle the microscope with extreme care. You are responsible for its proper care and use. Use caution when handling glass slides as they can break easily and cut you. Note all safety alert symbols next to the steps in the Procedure and review the meanings of each symbol by referring to the symbol guide on page 10.

Procedure

Part A. Observing the External Anatomy of a Flower

1. Refer to Figure 1 as you examine each flower. Identify the receptacle, or structure to which all other flower parts are attached. Note the sepals, which are small, leaflike structures above the receptacle. All of the sepals together are called the calyx. Observe the brightly colored petals inside the calyx. All of the petals together are called the corolla. These structures make up the nonreproductive structures of a flower.

2. As you observe each flower, note the number and color of both the sepals and the petals. Record this information in the appropriate place in the Data Table.

Figure 1

Part B. Reproductive Structures of a Flower

1. Choose one flower. Using Figure 2, identify the male reproductive structures, or stamens. Each stamen consists of an anther and a filament. Identify the female reproductive structure, or pistil. Each pistil consists of an ovary, a stigma, and a style.

2. In the appropriate place in Observations, sketch the flower you observed. On the sketch, label the stamen, anther, filament, pistil, ovary, stigma, and style.

3. With a scissors or forceps, remove the petals from the flower. **CAUTION:** *Be careful when handling sharp instruments.* Be very careful not to destroy any of the reproductive structures of the flower.

Figure 2

4. With a forceps, remove the stamens and place them on a sheet of unlined white paper. Set the stamens aside for use in Part C. In the appropriate place in Observations, sketch a stamen that you removed from the flower. Label the anther and the filament.

318

5. Using a scalpel or single-edged razor blade, carefully remove the pistil. Cut the ovary in half at its widest part as shown in Figure 3. **CAUTION:** *Be careful when handling sharp instruments. Always cut in a direction away from your hands and body.* Observe the inside of the ovary. Note the number and arrangement of the ovary chambers. The white, oval objects inside the chambers are the ovules, or eggs.

6. In the appropriate place in Observations, sketch a cross section of the ovary showing the number and arrangement of the chambers. Label the ovules, ovary walls, and chambers. Set the pistil aside for use in Part C.

Figure 3

Part C. The Gametes of a Flower

1. With a forceps, remove an ovule from the dissected ovary. Place the ovule in a drop of water in the center of a clean glass slide and add a coverslip. Observe the ovule under the low-power objective of a microscope. In the appropriate place in Observations, sketch the ovule as seen through the microscope. Record the magnification of the microscope.

2. Gently brush an anther from one of the stamens across the stigma of the pistil. With a hand lens, look for pollen grains that may have stuck to the stigma.

3. Gently touch the point of a dissecting needle to one of the anthers. Transfer some pollen grains to a drop of water in the center of a clean glass slide. Add a coverslip. Examine the pollen grains under the high-power objective of a microscope. **CAUTION:** *When switching to the high-power objective, always look at the objective from the side of the microscope so that the objective does not hit or damage the slide.* The pollen grains may appear to be moving. This is due to the movement of water under the coverslip.

4. In the appropriate place in Observations, sketch several pollen grains as seen through the microscope. Record the magnification of the microscope.

Observations

Data Table

Flower Name	Number of Sepals	Color of Sepals	Number of Petals	Color of Petals
		Answers will vary.		

Reproductive Structures of a Flower

Flower Stamen

Flower Ovary Cross Section

Name _____ Class _____ Date _____

Magnification _____   Magnification _____

Drawings will vary
depending on
type of flower
observed.

Ovule   **Pollen Grains**

1. How many stamens are in the flower you dissected? <u>Answers will vary depending on the kind of</u>
flower observed.
_____

2. How many pistils are in the flower you dissected? One.
_____

3. Approximately how many ovules do you think are in the ovary? (Make an educated guess.)
Approximately 200 or more.
_____

Analysis and Conclusions

1. The flower parts of monocot flowers usually occur in multiples of three. The flower parts of
dicot flowers usually occur in multiples of four or five. From this information, identify the
flower you dissected as a monocot or a dicot. <u>Answers will vary depending on the kind of flower</u>
observed.
_____

2. List the function of each of the following flower parts and note whether the parts comprise the
pistil or the stamen.
   a. anther <u>produces pollen grains (stamen)</u>
   b. filament <u>supports anther (stamen)</u>
   c. ovary <u>contains ovules (pistil)</u>
   d. ovule <u>contains egg (pistil)</u>
   e. pollen <u>contains sperm (stamen)</u>
   f. stigma <u>collects pollen grains (pistil)</u>
   g. style <u>path through which pollen tubes grow (pistil)</u>

3. Why does a flower have more pollen grains than ovules? Pollen is carried by wind or insects, and much of it never reaches the stigma. For this reason, more pollen is produced than ovules.

Critical Thinking and Application

1. Explain why a heavy rainfall on a fruit orchard in the spring might result in a poor fruit yield in the fall. The heavy rainfall washes the pollen grains off the stigmas of the flowers. As a result, fertilization is decreased and there is a reduction in fruit production.

2. For what biological reason do farmers object to people picking apple blossoms during the apple blossom season? Farmers planted the apple trees to harvest fruit. When blossoms are picked, the reproductive structures are removed from the plants. This reduces the fruit-producing ability of the plants.

3. Flowers that are pollinated by the wind have smaller petals and sepals than flowers that are pollinated by insects or animals. Why are small petals and sepals an advantage to these flowers? A plant with small petals and sepals is more likely to pick up pollen distributed by the wind. Large petals and sepals could act to deflect the pollen grains and fertilization would not occur.

4. Why do flowers that are pollinated by insects have large, brightly colored petals?
Large, brightly colored petals are easily visible and attractive to insects. As insects investigate the inside parts of the flowers, they often pick up pollen grains. These pollen grains are then transferred to other flowers where fertilization occurs.

Going Further

Germinate pollen tubes from the pollen of a mature stamen in a 10% sucrose solution. Prepare a wet mount of the pollen solution in a depression slide and allow it to set for a few days in a warm place. Examine the pollen under low power and high power of a microscope. Look for pollen tubes and sets of three nuclei in the pollen tubes.

50

Fruits and Seeds

You may want to refer students to pages 538–542 in the textbook for a discussion of fruits and seeds.

Time required: 45 minutes.

Pre-Lab Discussion

The ripened ovary, with its enclosed seeds, and other associated parts form the *fruit*. Associated parts include sepals, petals, and the receptacle. The term "fruit" not only refers to the apples, pears, and peaches that are commonly found in the supermarket, but it also includes such things as string beans, peanuts, tomatoes, chestnuts, and cucumbers.

In the life cycle of a flowering plant, the fruit is essential to the dispersal of seeds. For example, animals may eat the fruit and thereby carry the seeds far from the parent plant. The seeds often pass unchanged through the animal's body. When the seeds pass out of the animal's body, they are dropped in places were they may germinate. Some fruits burst open, thus releasing their enclosed seeds and dispersing them some distance from the parent plant. Other fruits float in water and can be carried hundreds of kilometers from where they originate. Still other fruits are adapted to being carried by the wind.

A *seed* is made up of a seed coat, stored food, and an embryo. Each seed contains one or more *cotyledons,* or seed leaves, that store and digest foods. A plant that has two cotyledons is called a *dicot,* whereas a plant that has one cotyledon is called a *monocot.* Some monocot seeds have an *endosperm,* which makes up a large portion of the seed. The endosperm stores food for the embryo plant.

In this investigation, you will examine some of the major structures of some common fruits and seeds.

Problem

What is the structure of some common fruits and seeds?

Materials *(per group)*

Various fruits may be substituted for those listed here. Plums may be substituted for peaches, grapefruits or lemons may be substituted for oranges, and pears may be substituted for apples.

Scapel	Kidney bean seed All seeds should be soaked overnight.
Dissecting tray	Corn seed
Peach	Single-edged razor blade
Apple	Hand lens
Orange	

Safety 🔬 ▦

Put on a laboratory apron if one is available. Handle all glassware carefully. Be careful when handling sharp instruments. Note all safety alert symbols next to the steps in the Procedure and review the meanings of each symbol by referring to the symbol guide on page 10.

Part A. Examining the Parts of the Pericarp

1. Using a scalpel, carefully cut the peach lengthwise. Do not cut into the pit. **CAUTION:** *Be careful when handling sharp instruments. Always cut in a direction away from your hands and body.*

2. Observe the ripened ovary wall, which is called the pericarp. The pericarp may be fleshy or dry, hard or soft. A pericarp is made up of three layers: the exocarp, or outer layer; the mesocarp, or middle layer; and the endocarp, or inner layer. Because the thickness and texture of these layers vary in different types of fruits, the variations are used to classify the different types of fruits. Examine Figure 1, which shows a stone fruit and its pericarp layers. A stone fruit is a type of fruit in which the endocarp is stony or hard. Find the parts labeled in Figure 1 in the peach. In Data Table 1, describe the three different layers of the pericarp.

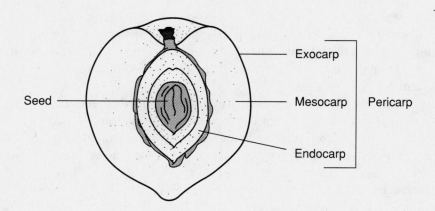

Figure 1

Part B. Examining Some Simple Fruits

1. Examine the peach that you cut open in Part A. Because the peach develops from a single pistil, it is known as a simple fruit. A simple fruit in which all or most of the pericarp is fleshy is called a simple fleshy fruit.

2. Notice that the pericarp of the peach has three distinctly different layers. A simple fleshy fruit with a pericarp divided into three distinct layers is called a drupe.

3. Place the orange in the dissecting tray. Using a scalpel, cut the orange in half so that you can see it in cross section. **CAUTION:** *Be careful when handling sharp instruments. Always cut in a direction away from your hands and body.* Look for small oil glands just below the surface of the skin, which together with the rind forms the pericarp. The large fleshy portion of the fruit, which contains the liquid, is called the juice sac. The orange, which has a pericarp that is entirely fleshy, is called a berry. In the appropriate place in Observations, sketch the cross section of the orange and label the pericarp, oil gland, juice sac, and seed.

4. Using a scalpel, cut through the center of the apple. The apple is an example of a pome. A pome is a simple fleshy fruit whose pericarp is surrounded by a fleshy, tasty floral tube. The floral tube is formed from the fused bases of the petals, sepals, and stamens.

5. Study Figure 2. In the appropriate place in Observations sketch the cross section of the apple and label the floral tube, exocarp, mesocarp, and endocarp.

Figure 2

6. Complete Data Table 2 based on your observations.

Part C. Structure of Seeds

1. Locate the hilum, or oval scar, on the side of the kidney bean seed. The hilum is the point of attachment of the ovule. Look for a small dot called the micropyle directly above or below the hilum. The micropyle is the opening through which the pollen tube enters the ovule. Examine the seed coat, or thick outer covering. In the appropriate place in Observations, label the hilum, micropyle, and seed coat.

2. Carefully remove the seed coat from the bean seed with a single-edged razor blade. **CAUTION:** *Be careful when handling a sharp instrument. Always cut in a direction away from your hands and body.*

3. Separate the seed into two equal halves. Each of these halves is a cotyledon, or seed leaf, which stores food for the developing embryo plant.

4. Use a hand lens to observe the stemlike structure located near the edge of one of the cotyledons. The upper portion of this structure is the hypocotyl, which forms the stem of the plant. Observe the lower portion of the hypocotyl, which is called the radicle and forms the primary root. Locate the epicotyl, or small leaflike structure connected to the hypocotyl. The epicotyl forms the first leaves of the plant. In the appropriate place in Observations, label the cotyledons, hypocotyl, radicle, and epicotyl.

5. Examine the seed coat of the corn seed and identify the silk scar, which is a tiny pointed structure at the top of the kernel. In the appropriate place in Observations, label the seed coat and silk scar.

6. With the single-edged razor blade, carefully cut the corn seed in half from top to bottom. **CAUTION:** *Be careful when handling a sharp instrument. Always cut in a direction away from your hands and body.* The cotyledon is the whitish area in which the embryo is embedded. The epicotyl is the part of the embryo formed by the two leaves rolled into a spear. The hypocotyl is the small shaft of tissue below the epicotyl. The lower tip of the hypocotyl is the radicle. The endosperm occupies the remainder of the kernel outside of the cotyledon. In the appropriate place in Observations, label the hypocotyl, epicotyl, radicle, cotyledon, and endosperm.

Observations

Data Table 1

Pericarp Layer	Description
Exocarp	skinlike, fuzzy exterior, orange-brown color
Mesocarp	fleshy, juicy, fragrant, orange color
Endocarp	hard or stony, brown color, rough surface

Orange Cross Section

Apple Cross Section

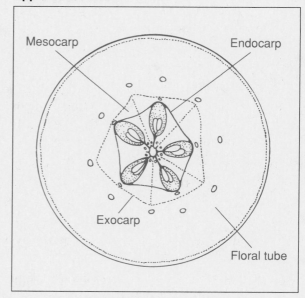

Data Table 2

Type of Fruit	Description	Examples
Berry	Entire pericarp is fleshy	tomato, grape, date, cucumber
Drupe	Pericarp is formed of three distinct layers— exocarp, mesocarp, and endocarp (stony)	cherry, peach, almond, plum, coconut
Pome	Pericarp is surrounded by floral tube, which becomes fleshy and tasty	apple, pear, quince

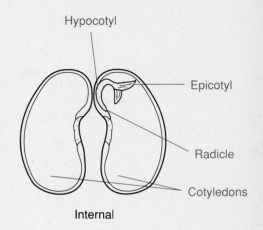

Kidney Bean Seed

Figure 4

Corn Seed

Figure 5

Analysis and Conclusions

1. Why do flower structures dry up as fruits develop? After fertilization, the flower parts are no longer

needed.

2. A fleshy fruit with a rind is called a hesperidium. Other than the orange name a common

hesperidium. Lemon, lime, grapefruit.

3. From your observations, what is one difference between a drupe and a berry?

A drupe contains a hard pit, which is surrounded by a fleshy portion and outer skin. A berry has a thick skin,

a fleshy portion, and many ovules.

4. From your observations, what is one difference between a drupe and a pome?

A drupe contains a pericarp that consists of three distinct layers, the inner layer being hard. A berry contains

a pericarp that is entirely fleshy.

5. a. Is the kidney bean seed a monocot or a dicot? Explain your answer.

The kidney bean seed is a dicot because it has two cotyledons.

b. Is the corn seed a monocot or a dicot? Explain your answer.

The corn seed is a monocot because it has one cotyledon.

6. What is the function of the cotyledons? They provide food for the growing plant until it can carry on

photosynthesis.

Critical Thinking and Application

1. People sometimes get into a dispute about whether a tomato is a fruit or a vegetable. As a

botanist, how could you settle this argument? Botanically speaking, a tomato is a fruit (actually, a

berry) because it is the ripened ovary of the flower.

2. How are seeds structurally adapted to life on land? Seeds have tough exterior coats that protect

plant embryos and endosperms from injury and dryness. These hard coverings are not necessary in moist

or wet environments.

3. Why is seed dispersal essential to the survival of a plant species?

Seed dispersal methods account for the spreading of seed plants across the Earth. Although seed dispersal

is not important to an individual plant, it is essential for survival of the plant species.

4. List two examples of fruits in which the seed is eaten and the fruit is discarded.

Sunflowers, peas, beans, peanuts, and other types of nuts.

Going Further

1. Fruits that develop from several flowers whose ovaries ripen and develop as one mass are known as multiple fruits. Find out which fruits are multiple fruits. Cut some multiple fruits lengthwise so that you can see the internal organization of the fruit. Make labeled sketches of what you see.

2. Seeds have various structures that assure their dispersal to environments that are suitable for their germination and growth. Using reference materials, make a chart of the different dispersal methods. Include drawings or photographs showing the types of seed dispersal.

51

Germination and Seedling Development

You may want to refer students to pages 540–542 in the textbook for a discussion of seed development.

Time required: 20 minutes on the first day, plus a 30-minute observation period on each of the next 2 days.

Pre-Lab Discussion

When conditions are suitable, a seed undergoes *germination,* or the development of an embryo into a seedling. For germination to occur, water, warmth, and oxygen must be available in the proper amounts. The amounts vary from species to species.

Germination can occur only in *viable seeds,* or seeds in which the embryo is alive. Not all viable seeds will germinate, even when given the proper amounts of water, warmth, and oxygen. Many seeds must go through a period of *dormancy,* or a period during which the embryo is alive but not growing. Dormancy is an adaptation that prevents germination of the seed until conditions are suitable. Once dormancy is complete and all the needed environmental conditions are met, germination begins.

In this investigation, you will observe some of the processes associated with seed germination and seedling development.

Problem

What changes occur in a seed during germination and seedling development?

Materials *(per group)*

10 *Brassica rapa* seeds
Petri dish
Forceps
Hand lens
Filter paper
Base of a 2-L soft-drink bottle
Metric ruler
Pencil
2 colored pencils
Fluorescent plant light (if available)

The *Brassica rapa* seed is a fast-growing variant of wild mustard, which is ideal for a short-term investigation of seed germination and seedling development. Rapid-cycling *Brassica rapa* seeds are available from Carolina Biological Supply Company.

Filter paper should fit snugly into the petri dish.

The base of the plastic soft-drink bottle can be removed by filling the bottle with hot tap water and twisting off the base. The holes in the base should be covered with black electrical tape.

Safety 🔺 ◖▮

Put on a laboratory apron if one is available. Handle all glassware carefully. Observe proper laboratory procedures when using electrical appliances. Note all safety alert symbols next to the steps in the Procedure and review the meanings of each symbol by referring to the symbol guide on page 10.

Procedure

1. As shown in Figure 1, use a metric ruler and pencil to draw a line across the filter paper about 3 cm from the top edge. Label the bottom edge of the filter paper with the seed type, date, and name of one member of your group. **Note:** *Be sure to use pencil to label the filter paper because ink will smear when water is added.*

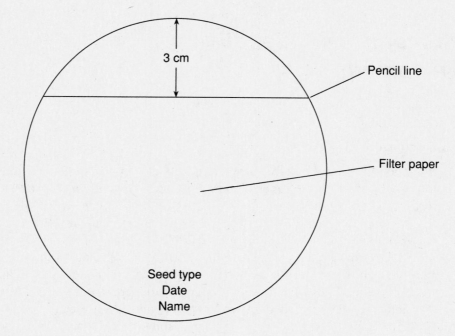

3 cm

Pencil line

Filter paper

Seed type
Date
Name

Figure 1

2. Place the filter paper in the top of a petri dish. Thoroughly wet the filter paper.

3. With a forceps place 10 *Brassica rapa* seeds on the line you drew on the filter paper. Space the seeds out evenly across the line as shown in Figure 2.

Seeds

Petri dish
bottom

Petri dish
top

Pencil line

Moistened
filter paper

Figure 2

4. Cover the seeds with the bottom half of the petri dish.

5. Carefully place the petri dish in the base of the 2-liter soft-drink bottle so that the seeds are positioned at the top and the petri dish is angled slightly. See Figure 3. Make sure that none of the seeds have fallen from their original positions. Slowly add water to the soft-drink-bottle base from the side until the water reaches a depth of about 2 cm.

Water should be added to the soft-drink-bottle base every one to two days. Be sure that you or the students add water from the side of the base only. Adding water over the tops of the petri dishes will wash the seeds from the filter paper.

Petri dish bottom

Petri dish top

Moistened filter paper

Seed

Soft-drink-bottle base

2-cm depth of water

Figure 3

6. Place the soft-drink-bottle base under a fluorescent light. If a fluorescent light is not available, place the base near the best source of light in the room.

7. After 24 hours, observe the germination of the seeds. If necessary, use the hand lens to observe the germinating seeds. Note the number of seeds that have a split seed coat, an emerging radicle, hypocotyl, or epicotyl, or the appearance of a primary root and root hairs. Record the information in Data Table 1.

8. Measure the primary root length of each of the 10 seeds in millimeters and record this information in Data Table 2. If no primary root has emerged from a seed, record its length as 0 mm. Calculate the average root length for each of the 10 seeds and record this information in Data Table 2.

9. Measure the hypocotyl length of each of the 10 seeds in millimeters and record this information in Data Table 3. If no hypocotyl has emerged from a seed, record its length as 0 mm. Calculate the average hypocotyl length for each of the 10 seeds and record this information in Data Table 3.

10. Repeat steps 8 and 9 after two more 24-hour periods. Record the information in Data Tables 1, 2, and 3.

11. On the graph in Observations, construct a line graph showing the average root length over the 72-hour observation period. On the same graph, construct a line graph showing the average hypocotyl length over the 72-hour observation period. Use pencils of different colors to construct the two line graphs. Label each line graph.

12. In the appropriate place in Observations, sketch one of your 72-hour-old seedlings. Label the hypocotyl, primary root, root hairs, and cotyledons.

Observations

Total number of seeds in petri dish = _____10_____

Data Table 1

Time	Number of Seeds					
	Split Seed Coat	Radicle	Primary Root	Root Hairs	Hypocotyl	Epicotyl
After 24 hours						
After 48 hours			Answers will vary.			
After 72 hours						

Data Table 2

Time	Root Length (mm)										
	Seed 1	Seed 2	Seed 3	Seed 4	Seed 5	Seed 6	Seed 7	Seed 8	Seed 9	Seed 10	Average
After 24 hours											
After 48 hours				Answers will vary.							
After 72 hours											

Data Table 3

Time	Hypocotyl Length (mm)										
	Seed 1	Seed 2	Seed 3	Seed 4	Seed 5	Seed 6	Seed 7	Seed 8	Seed 9	Seed 10	Average
After 24 hours											
After 48 hours				Answers will vary.							
After 72 hours											

Graph

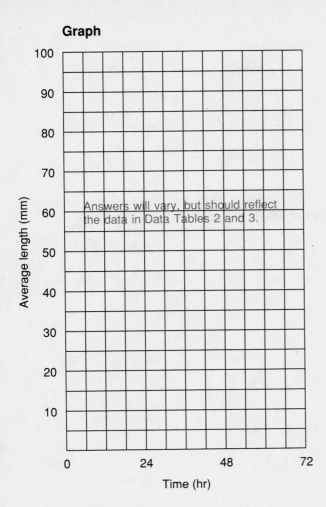

Average length (mm) vs Time (hr)

100
90
80
70
60
50
40
30
20
10
0

0   24   48   72

Answers will vary, but should reflect the data in Data Tables 2 and 3.

***Brassica* Seedling**

Cotyledons

Hypocotyl

Primary root

Root hairs

Analysis and Conclusions

1. Why might some of the *Brassica* seeds not germinate? Some of the seeds may not have absorbed

enough water or may not have been viable. Also, some of the seeds may not have been mature.

2. Why is it important for the dry seed to absorb water before it begins germination?

The dry seed absorbs water and swells. The increase in volume helps to weaken the seed coat. The water

also causes the growth of the radicle inside of the seed coat, causing the seed coat to break open.

3. What is the first structure to emerge from inside the seed? What is the function of this

structure? The radicle is the first structure to emerge from inside the seed. As the radicle grows, the

primary root and root hairs develop. These roots anchor the plant and absorb water needed for the growth

of the seedling.

4. What is the function of the cotyledons? The cotyledons provide stored food for the embryo and can carry on photosynthesis until the young plant leaves develop and are capable of producing their own food.

5. In which part of the seedling will photosynthesis eventually occur? Photosynthesis occurs in the leaves of the seedling.

Critical Thinking and Application

1. Several seeds are put in a moist, airtight container, and the container is placed in a dark closet. The seeds begin to germinate and then die. Offer an explanation for the death of the seeds. The seeds use the stored food from the cotyledons to begin the germination process. When this food is used up, the young plants must have light in order to carry on photosynthesis. Without a light source for photosynthetic activity, the seeds will die.

2. How is dormancy an adaptation for plant survival? Some species of plants can remain dormant for long periods of time. This adaptation allows plants to postpone germination until the proper environmental conditions for growth are present.

3. If certain seeds require six weeks of prolonged cold before dormancy ends, what prevents them from germinating in the middle of January after a particularly cold November and December? Germination will not occur until suitable environmental conditions are met. As long as the temperature remains low, the seeds will remain in a dormant state. This dormancy can be for an indefinite period of time depending on the plant species.

Going Further

1. To observe the effect of light on seed germination and seedling development, prepare two petri dishes using the procedure described in this investigation. Completely cover one of the petri dishes with aluminum foil and allow the other petri dish to remain uncovered. Compare the rate of germination and the lengths of the primary roots and hypocotyls of the two sets of seeds. Construct data tables and line graphs to record your observations.

2. To observe the effect of temperature on seed germination and seedling development, prepare three petri dishes using the procedure described in this investigation. Keep one petri dish at room temperature, place another in an area that is warmer than room temperature, and put the remaining one in the refrigerator. The three dishes need to receive equal amounts of light; if it is not possible to provide light for the seeds in the warm and cold environments, cover all of the petri dishes so that none of the seeds receive any light. Compare the germination rates and lengths of the primary roots and hypocotyls of the three sets of seeds. Construct data tables and line graphs to record your observations. Are the seeds that were kept in the cold environment dead or merely dormant? Design and conduct an experiment to find out.

52

Sponges and Hydras

You may want to refer students to pages 560–569 in the textbook for a discussion of sponges and cnidarians.

Time required: 45 minutes.

Pre-Lab Discussion

Sponges and cnidarians are simple invertebrates. Sponges make up the phylum Porifera, which means "pore-bearing." The phylum is named for the many pores that cover the body of a sponge. Cnidarians are members of the phylum Cnidaria. Hydras, jellyfishes, and sea corals are types of cnidarians.

Sponges have no true tissues or organs, no digestive tract, and no nervous system. Their bodies are loosely organized into two cell layers. Support comes from hard structures called *spicules* or from flexible material called *spongin*. Some sponges have both spicules and spongin.

Cnidarians have true tissues. Their bodies consist of two layers—an outer epidermis and an inner gastrodermis. Each cnidarian also has a body cavity where food is digested. Cnidarians have a simple nervous system that allows them to respond to stimuli.

In this investigation, you will examine the characteristics of sponges and cnidarians.

Problem

What are some characteristics of a sponge and a hydra?

Materials *(per group)*

Preserved whole specimen   Slides and preserved specimens are available from biological supply houses.
    of *Grantia*
Prepared slide of *Grantia,*
    longitudinal section
Hand lens
Microscope
Scalpel or single-edged razor blade
Glass slide
Coverslip
Chlorine bleach solution
Toothpick
2 medicine droppers
Prepared slide of hydra, whole   Slides are available from biological supply houses.
    mount
Prepared slide of hydra,
    longitudinal section

Put on a laboratory apron if one is available. Put on safety goggles. Handle all glassware carefully. Always use special caution when working with laboratory chemicals, as they may irritate the skin or cause staining of the skin or clothing. Never touch or taste any chemical unless instructed to do so. Always handle the microscope with extreme care. You are responsible for its proper care and use. Use caution when handling glass slides as they can break easily and cut you. Be careful when handling sharp instruments. Note all safety alert symbols next to the steps in the Procedure and review the meanings of each symbol by referring to the symbol guide on page 10.

Procedure
Part A. Examining the Anatomy of a Sponge

🏺 1. With a hand lens, examine the external structure of the simple marine sponge *Grantia*. Find the osculum, which is a large opening at the top through which water flows out of the sponge. Locate several ostia (singular, ostium), or pore cells. Water flows into the sponge through the ostia. Note the long, straight spicules that encircle the osculum and project through the outer surface of the sponge. In the appropriate place in Observations, sketch what you see. Label the osculum, ostia, and spicules.

2 Under the low-power objective of a microscope, examine a prepared slide of a longitudinal section of *Grantia*. Note the two cell layers. The outer cell layer is called the ectoderm and the inner cell layer is called the endoderm. Look for the flagellated cells called collar cells in the endoderm. Collar cells collect food particles from the water that passes through the sponge's body cavity, or spongocoel. Between the ectoderm and endoderm is mesenchyme, or a jellylike material containing some cells. Observe the spicules, hard structures made of calcium carbonate. In the appropriate place in Observations, sketch the sponge you have observed under low power. Label ectoderm, mesenchyme, collar cell, flagellum, spicules, and spongocoel. Record the magnification of the microscope.

▦ 3. Using a scalpel or a single-edged razor blade, cut a small piece from the *Grantia* specimen. **CAUTION:** *Be very careful when handling sharp instruments. Always cut in a direction away from your hands and body.*

🏺 4. Put on safety goggles. Place the piece of *Grantia* on a glass slide. With a medicine dropper,
⬚ add two drops of chlorine bleach solution to the piece of sponge. **CAUTION:** *Be very careful*
👁 *when using chlorine bleach. It may burn your skin or clothing.* Using a toothpick, gently stir the sponge and chlorine bleach solution.

5. Using another medicine dropper, add a drop of water to the slide. Then cover with a coverslip. Observe the *Grantia* spicules under the low-power objective of the microscope. In the appropriate place in Observations, sketch several spicules. Record the magnification of the microscope.

Part B. Examining the Anatomy of a Hydra

1. Under low power of the microscope, examine a prepared, whole mount slide of a hydra. Locate the basal disk at the posterior end of the body. The basal disk is the part with which the hydra attaches itself to surfaces. At the anterior end is the mouth. Look for several long tentacles. In the appropriate place in Observations, sketch the hydra under low power. Label the mouth, tentacle, body, and basal disk.

2. Under low power of the microscope, examine a prepared slide of a longitudinal section of a hydra. Locate the three layers: the outer epidermis, the inner gastrodermis, and the mesoglea, or thin layer of jellylike material between the epidermis and gastrodermis. Note the body cavity called the gastrovascular cavity.

3. Locate one of the hydra's tentacles. Notice the small bumps on the tentacle. They contain stinging structures called nematocysts.

4. Most species of hydra have separate male and female animals. However, some species contain both male and female reproductive structures. Look for the testes, or cone-shaped structures found on the upper half of the body, and the ovary, found on the lower half of the body. Examine the hydra to see if it has testes or an ovary (or both). In the appropriate place in Observations, sketch the hydra under low power. Label the mouth, tentacle, nematocyst, testis (if present), ovary (if present), bud (if present), epidermis, mesoglea, gastrodermis, and gastrovascular cavity.

Observations

Grantia

Magnification _____

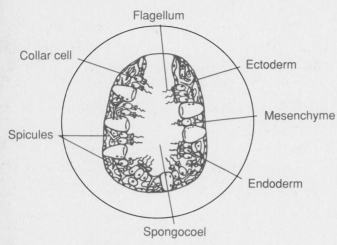

Flagellum

Collar cell

Ectoderm

Mesenchyme

Spicules

Endoderm

Spongocoel

Grantia, **Longitudinal Section**

Magnification _____

Grantia **Spicules**

Magnification _____

Tentacle

Mouth

Basal disk

Body

Hydra, Whole Mount

Magnification _____

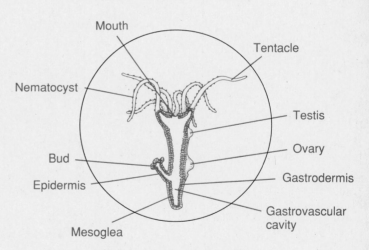

Mouth

Tentacle

Nematocyst

Testis

Ovary

Bud

Gastrodermis

Epidermis

Gastrovascular cavity

Mesoglea

Hydra, Longitudinal Section

Analysis and Conclusions

1. How does a sponge get oxygen and food? The sponge gets oxygen and food from the water flowing through and around it.

2. What is the function of the spicules of a sponge? They provide support for soft body tissue.

3. What was the purpose of the chlorine bleach solution in Part A of the investigation?

The chlorine bleach solution dissolves the cells of the sponge, thus enabling the observer to see the spicules distinctly.

4. What body structures make the sponge well adapted for living in water?

The sponge has pores, an osculum, spicules for support, and flagella.

5. What is the function of the gastrovascular cavity of a hydra? The gastrovascular cavity aids in the circulation of materials and the digestion of food.

6. Compare the sponge and the hydra in terms of body symmetry and tissue structure.

Both the sponge and the hydra have radial symmetry. The sponge does not have true tissues, whereas the hydra does.

Critical Thinking and Application

1. How do sponges differ from flagellate protists? Protists are unicellular and motile, and their flagella appear on the exterior surfaces of their bodies. Sponges are multicellular and sessile, and their flagella are on the interior surfaces of their bodies.

2. Why do you think a *Grantia* sponge should not be used to wash cars or porcelain sinks?

The glasslike spicules in *Grantia* could easily scratch the paint on the car or the porcelain. Most commercial sponges contain spongin or are synthetic.

3. How did the discovery and production of artificial sponges change the population of natural

sponges? The natural population of sponges has increased because fewer sponges are harvested from the

ocean.

.

4. "Cnid" is the Greek word for nettle, or stinging hair. Is the phylum name Cnidaria appropriate to the group of organisms such as hydra and jellyfishes? Explain your answer.

The cnidoblasts on the tentacles of hydras and jellyfishes are capable of stinging, making the phylum name

Cnidaria, to which these organisms belong, quite appropriate.

Going Further

1. Obtain and examine several different types of natural sponges, as well as a commonly used synthetic sponge. Note any similarities and differences between the sponges.

2. To examine the feeding habits of the hydra, place several drops of a hydra culture that has remained unfed for 24 hours in a watch glass. Add a drop of *Daphnia* culture to the watch glass. Place the watch glass under a dissecting microscope for observation. Describe what you see.

53

Flatworms and Roundworms

You may want to refer students to pages 570–578 in the textbook for a discussion of unsegmented worms.

Time required: 40 minutes.

Pre-Lab Discussion

Flatworms are classified in the phylum Platyhelminthes. The phylum name is derived from the Greek words *platy,* meaning flat, and *helminth,* meaning worm. The worms in this phylum have flat bodies and no body cavity. Most flatworms are parasites, or organisms that live on or in other living things. Some flatworms, however, are free-living organisms. Although most free-living flatworms live in the oceans, some live in fresh water or in soil.

Roundworms are classified in the phylum Nematoda. The worms in this phylum have long, slender bodies that taper to points at both ends. There are more species of roundworms than any other kind of worm. Roundworms are found in nearly every kind of environment, including deserts, arctic regions, hot springs, and oceans. Like flatworms, some roundworms are parasitic, whereas others are free-living.

In this investigation, you will observe some of the characteristics of parasitic and free-living flatworms and roundworms.

Problem

What are some characteristics of flatworms and roundworms?

Materials *(per group)*

Microscope
Prepared whole-mount slides of: Prepared slides are available
  Planarian *(Dugesia)*   from biological supply houses.
  Pork tapeworm *(Taenia)*, with view
    of scolex and proglottids
  Vinegar eel *(Turbatrix aceti)*
  Trichina worm *(Trichinella)*, encysted
    in a muscle

Safety 🔬

Handle all glassware carefully. Always handle the microscope with extreme care. You are responsible for its proper care and use. Use caution when handling glass slides as they can break easily and cut you. Note all safety alert symbols next to the steps in the Procedure and review the meanings of each symbol by referring to the symbol guide on page 10.

Procedure
Part A. Observing Flatworms

 1. Examine a prepared whole-mount slide of a planarian *(Dugesia)* under the low-power objective of a microscope. Planarians are free-living, freshwater flatworms that have a definite head with a simple brain. Locate the two eyespots in the head region. They are used to find a light source.

2. Locate the mouth in the middle of the body on the ventral, or lower, surface. Note a long tube, called the pharynx, that draws food from the mouth into the gastrovascular cavity. In the appropriate place in Observations, sketch a planarian under low power. Label the eyespots, mouth, pharynx, and gastrovascular cavity. Record the magnification of the microscope.

3. Examine a prepared whole-mount slide of a tapeworm *(Taenia)* under low power. Locate the head, called the scolex. Note the presence of several suckers and a ring of hooks.

4. Behind the scolex is a narrow neck. The remainder of the tapeworm's body is made up of nearly square sections called proglottids, which grow from the neck. Thus the youngest proglottids are closest to the neck. Proglottids contain the male and female reproductive organs. In the appropriate place in Observations, sketch the tapeworm under low power. Label the scolex, suckers, hooks, young proglottids, and older proglottids. Record the magnification of the microscope.

Part B. Observing Roundworms

 1. Examine the prepared whole-mount slide of a vinegar eel *(Turbatrix aceti)* under low power. This roundworm is named for the liquid in which it is normally found. Locate the mouth at its anterior, or front, end and the anus at its posterior, or tail, end. Note the bulblike pharynx and long intestine.

2. If the vinegar eel is a female, eggs will be found lined up in the uterus. If it is a male, it will contain a single testis. In the appropriate place in Observations, sketch the vinegar eel under low power. Label the mouth, pharynx, intestine, anus, eggs (if female), and testis (if male). Record the magnification of the microscope.

3. Examine a prepared whole-mount slide of a trichina worm *(Trichinella)* larva encysted in muscle tissue under low power. In the appropriate place in Observations, sketch what you see. Label the trichina worm larva, cyst, and muscle tissue. Record the magnification of the microscope.

Observations

Magnification _____

Magnification _____

Planarian *(Dugesia)*   **Tapeworm *(Taenia)***

Name _____ Class _____ Date _____

Magnification _____   Magnification _____

Vinegar eel *(Turbatrix aceti)*

Trichinella encysted in muscle tissue

Analysis and Conclusions

1. How do flatworms and roundworms differ in body structure? Flatworms are flat, have no anus, and can reproduce sexually and asexually. Roundworms are round, have an anus, and can reproduce only sexually.

2. How are flatworms similar to roundworms in body structure? They are both invertebrates, have bilateral symmetry, are unsegmented, and have free-living and parasitic forms.

3. Why are structures for locomotion lacking in parasitic flatworms and roundworms?

Parasitic worms do not need to move around in search of food once they have attached themselves to a host.

4. Would the nervous and digestive systems be more complex in the free-living forms or the parasitic forms of the flatworms and roundworms? Explain your answer.

The nervous and digestive systems of free-living worms are more complex. Unlike parasites, these worms are responsible for locating and digesting their own food.

Critical Thinking and Application

1. Why is the term "eyespot" instead of "eye" used when refering to the structure at the anterior end of the planarian body? <u>The eyespot on a planarian is only photosensitive; that is, it only responds to light. Organisms with true eyes are able to see images.</u>

2. List two advantages that parasitic worms have over free-living worms.
   <u>Hosts supply parasites with oxygen, a constant optimum temperature for growth, a well-protected moist environment, a steady supply of predigested food, and a mechanism for reproduction.</u>

3. Why is it rare that an individual parasite will kill its host? <u>If the parasite kills its host, it will also die unless it is able to quickly find another host organism.</u>

4. You have taken a job as a product inspector in a large meat-packing company. As your first assignment, you must inspect pork for the presence of trichina worms. What should you look for? <u>You should check the pork carefully for the presence of small cysts. These cysts might contain trichina worm larvae.</u>

5. A person infected with a tapeworm will display symptoms such as weight loss, weakness, and a low blood count. How can a doctor be certain that a patient has a tapeworm and not some other illness with similar symptoms? <u>The doctor could check the feces for the presence of proglottids, which have torn away from the body of the tapeworm.</u>

Going Further

1. To collect planarians, tie a piece of string around a piece of liver and lower it into a pond or lake. After a few hours, raise the string. Why does the liver attract planarians?

2. Fill a clear glass petri dish with pond water. Cover half of the petri dish with cardboard, so that it will be in darkness. Place planarians in the exposed side of the petri dish. After an hour, determine in which side of the petri dish the planarians are found. Do your observations show planarians to have a positive or a negative response to light?

54

You may want to refer students to pages 585–593 in the textbook for a discussion of mollusks.

Time required: 40 minutes.

Examining a Clam

Pre-Lab Discussion

The phylum Mollusca has many species, including clams, snails, slugs, octopi, and squids. Mollusks are soft-bodied invertebrates that have a muscular foot and a mantle. In most mollusks, the mantle secretes a hard shell. The many different types of mollusks may swim freely, float, or burrow into the sand or mud. Although most mollusks are marine, or sea-living, some mollusks live in fresh water, and others live on land. For thousands of years, people have eaten many types of mollusks, such as clams, scallops, oysters, and squids. Other kinds of mollusks have been used to make buttons, ornaments, tools, money, and dyes.

One representative mollusk is the clam. Clams are pelecypods, or bivalves, and have a two-part hinged shell. They are found in fresh water in streams, ponds, and lakes. They are also commonly found burrowed into the mud of ocean mud flats.

In this investigation, you will observe the behavior of a clam. You will also examine the internal and external structures of a clam.

Problem

What are some structures of a clam?

Materials (per group)

Order preserved clams or mussels of the genera *Anodonta*, *Lampsilis*, *Ellipto*, *Quadrula*, or *Mercenaria* from a biological supply house. You may also purchase specimens from a local seafood market or collect living specimens from oceans, streams, or lakes. Clams must be stored in plastic bags in a refrigerator.

Live freshwater clam
Fresh or preserved clam
One valve of a clam shell
Large beaker containing water and sand
Carmine solution in dropper bottle   Dissolve 1 g carmine red in 100 mL distilled water. Stir until dissolved. Pour into dropper bottles for student use.
Glass stirring rod
10% hydrochloric acid in dropper bottle   Slowly and carefully pour 10 mL concentrated hydrochloric acid into 90 mL distilled water. Pour into dropper bottles for student use.
Dissecting tray
Scalpel
Paper towels

Safety 🔬 🥽 🧤 👁 ▥ 🧫

Put on a laboratory apron if one is available. Put on safety goggles. Handle all glassware carefully. Always use special caution when working with laboratory chemicals, as they may irritate the skin or cause staining of the skin or clothing. Never touch or taste any chemical unless instructed to do so. Be careful when handling sharp instruments. Follow your teacher's directions and all appropriate safety procedures when handling live animals. Note all safety alert symbols next to the steps in the Procedure and review the meanings of each symbol by referring to the symbol guide on page 10.

Procedure
Part A. Observing a Live Clam

1. Place a live clam on its side in a large beaker of water (or an aquarium) with at least 4 cm of sand on the bottom. Observe what happens. Record your observations in the Data Table. Continue to observe the clam for several minutes without disturbing it. Answer question 1 in Observations.

2. Locate the incurrent and excurrent siphons on the live clam. These are the areas where water enters and exits the body of the clam. Obtain a dropper bottle of carmine solution. Place one or two drops of carmine solution near the siphons. **CAUTION:** *Handle the carmine solution with care because it stains the skin and clothing.* Observe what happens to the carmine solution. Record your observations in the Data Table.

Figure 1

3. Locate the mantle on the live clam. See Figure 1. With a glass stirring rod, carefully and gently touch the clam on different parts of the mantle. Record your observations in the Data Table.

4. Return the live clam in the beaker to your teacher when you have completed your observations.

Part B. External Anatomy of the Clam

1. Thoroughly rinse a preserved clam to remove excess preservative. **CAUTION:** *The preservative used on the clam can irritate your skin. Avoid touching your eyes while working with the preserved clam.* Place the clam in a dissecting tray. Observe the bivalve shell. Notice the hinge ligament. Answer question 2 in Observations.

2. Locate the small, pointed area near the hinge ligament. This is the umbo, which is the oldest part of the clam. Note that the umbo is on the dorsal side toward the anterior end of the clam. Notice the concentric growth lines. They represent alternating periods of slow and rapid growth. Answer question 3 in Observations. Locate the posterior, anterior, dorsal, and ventral surfaces of the clam shell. Hold the clam shell with the anterior end up and the hinge facing toward you. Locate the hinge, right valve, and left valve of the clam shell. In the appropriate place in Observations, label the surfaces of the clam shell as they appear. Also label the hinge and right and left valves.

3. Hold the clam in the dissecting tray as shown in A of Figure 2. With a scalpel, carefully expose the middle layer by scraping away some of the horny outer layer of the shell. **CAUTION:** *Be careful when handling sharp instruments. Scrape in a direction away from your hand to avoid cutting yourself.*

Figure 2

4. The shell of a clam is made up of three layers: the horny outer layer; the thick, middle layer called the prismatic layer; and the innermost layer called the pearly layer. Place one drop of hydrocholoric acid on the exposed prismatic layer, as shown in B of Figure 2. **CAUTION:** *Be careful when handling acids as they can burn the skin.* The bubbling of the acid indicates that calcium carbonate is present in the shell. Answer question 4 in Observations.

5. Follow your teacher's directions for storing the clam for further use or properly disposing of the clam.

6. Observe a valve of an opened clam shell. Note the inner surface of the valve and the pearly layer. Answer question 5 in Observations. Locate the "scars" left by the anterior and posterior adductor muscles on the inner surface of the valve. In the appropriate place in Observations, label the anterior adductor muscle, posterior adductor muscle, mantle, and umbo.

Observations

Data Table

	Observations
Clam placed on side	Answers will vary. However, a healthy clam will bury itself in the sand.
Movement of carmine solution	Enters incurrent siphon and exits through excurrent siphon.
Touching mantle with glass rod	Mantle withdraws, shell closes tightly.

Clam Shell

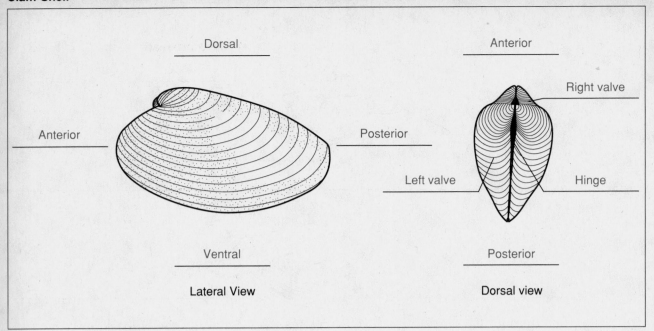

Dorsal

Anterior

Right valve

Anterior

Posterior

Left valve

Hinge

Ventral

Posterior

Lateral View

Dorsal view

Clam Shell Valve

Umbo

Anterior
adductor
muscle

Posterior
adductor
muscle

Mantle

1. Describe how a clam moves and buries itself in the sand. Answers will vary, however most clams

will turn upward to bury themselves in the sand.

_____

_____

2. Describe the location of the hinge ligament in relation to the two halves of the shell.

The hinge ligament is found between the two valves of the shell.

_____

_____

3. How many growth lines did you count on your clam shell? Answers will vary. _____

4. Describe what happened when acid was placed on the exposed prismatic layer of the clam shell. _The prismatic layer of the clam shell bubbled._ _____

_____

5. Describe the inner layer of the clam shell. _The inner layer of the clam shell is pearly, iridescent, and_

multicolored. _____

Analysis and Conclusions

1. Why is it important for a clam to take in water through the incurrent siphon?

The clam removes oxygen and microorganisms from the incoming water.

_____

2. Why is it important for a clam to expel water through the excurrent siphon?

Water is expelled through the excurrent siphon so that the clam can bring in a new supply of water through

the incurrent siphon.

3. What is the function of the hinge ligament? _The hinge ligament attaches the two valves of the clam's_

shell. _____

4. Why would the number of growth lines vary among clams? _The size, age, and species of clam will_

cause the number of growth lines to vary. _____

5. Of what is the prismatic layer of a clam's shell composed? _The prismatic layer is composed of_

calcium carbonate. _____

6. In addition to the valve you observed, where else would adductor muscles be found?

Adductor muscles would be found on the inner surface of the other valve opposite the scars on the valve

you observed.

Critical Thinking and Application

1. The nervous system of a clam is very simple. How can a clam function with such a simple nervous system? The clam has few sense receptors and leads an extremely sessile life. It does not require a complex nervous system.

2. List one advantage and one disadvantage of the shell surrounding a clam.

   The shell protects the clam from the environment or predators, but the shell's weight makes it difficult for the clam to move.

3. Why is it important for the hinge ligament and the adductor muscles of the clam to be very strong? The strong ligament and muscles keep the valves tightly closed. This acts as a protective mechanism for the clam.

4. Clams reproduce by releasing eggs and sperm into the water. Would you expect clams to release large or small numbers of eggs and sperm? Explain your answer.

   Because eggs and sperm can find each other only by chance in open water, enormous numbers of them are released by clams. If only small numbers were released, fertilization would rarely occur.

5. Why are fossils of mollusks more abundant than those of the worm phyla?

   The hard shells of the mollusks are much more likely to be preserved over millions of years than the soft body parts of worms. Soft body parts are much more likely to decay over time.

Going Further

1. Examine the gills from a preserved clam under a dissecting microscope. Remove some of the gill tissue and prepare a wet mount of it for examination under the microscope. Sketch what you see.

2. Shell collecting is an interesting hobby. Many books on shell collecting and identification are available in bookstores and libraries. If you live near the ocean, or if you vacation at the seashore, you may wish to start a shell collection.

55

The Earthworm

You may want to refer students to pages 594–600 in the textbook for a discussion of the earthworm.

Time required:
Parts A and B–35 minutes
Part C–50 minutes

Pre-Lab Discussion

The earthworm, *Limbricus terrestris*, is a member of the phylum Annelida. An earthworm is quite well-adapted to a life of burrowing through the soil. Its streamlined shape helps it move through the soil. A coating of mucus secreted by the skin lubricates the earthworm as it passes through the soil. The mucus coating also helps oxygen pass through the earthworm's skin while it is in the air or under the water. The earthworm moves through the soil by sucking the soil in its path into its mouth with the aid of its muscular pharynx. As material passes through the tubelike digestive system, sand grains in the gizzard help grind the food, which is then digested and absorbed in the intestine.

In this investigation, you will examine the external and internal structure of the earthworm.

Problem

How is the earthworm's body adapted to its environment?

Materials *(per group)*

Preserved earthworm
Dissecting tray
Scalpel
Scissors
Medicine dropper
Probe
Dissecting pins
Forceps
Hand lens
Resealable plastic bag
Paper towels

Order preserved earthworms from a biological supply house. The same earthworm is to be used in Parts A and B of this investigation. Have groups store their earthworms in tightly sealed plastic bags labeled with their names and the date.

The surface of the earthworm's epidermis is covered by a noncellular cuticle. The cuticle contains many pores through which mucus secreted by the epidermis is released to the outer surface of the earthworm's body. You may want to strip off a small piece of the iridescent cuticle and place it on a microscope slide with a drop of water and a coverslip for students to observe. Minute pores in the cuticle will be visible.

Safety 🔺 ▣

Put on a laboratory apron if one is available. Handle all glassware carefully. Be careful when handling sharp instruments. Note all safety alert symbols next to the steps in the Procedure and review the meanings of each symbol by referring to the symbol guide on page 10.

Procedure

Part A. The Technique of Animal Dissection

1. Dissection is the technique of exposing the internal structures of an organism for observation. Dissection is commonly used in the study of large and complex plants and animals. The opportunity to dissect an animal should be thought of as a unique opportunity to gain firsthand knowledge of an animal you know little about. As you dissect an animal, you should think in terms of structure related to function.

2. Obtain the following tools and instruments needed for dissection: dissecting tray, scalpel, scissors, probe, dissecting pins, and forceps. **CAUTION:** *The scalpel, scissors, and probe are sharp. Use extreme caution when handling these instruments to avoid cuts. Always cut in a direction away from your hands and body.* Become familiar with these tools and instruments used in dissection.

3. Most cutting in dissection is done with scissors rather than a scalpel. Most of the actual dissection involves the forceps, probe, and fingers. These instruments are used to tear, separate, and move or lift parts instead of cutting them.

4. Read the following rules for dissection.

   - Before beginning a dissection, identify all external parts.

   - Determine the proper order in which internal structures are to be exposed.

   - Identify which structures could be easily damaged if dissection is not done properly.

   - Do not completely remove any body part unless instructed to do so. If a body part is to be removed, leave a small portion of it attached as a reference point.

   - When making the first cut, insert the point of the scissors just below the skin. Cut with short, clipping motions. Keep the lower blade of the scissors pointing upward, away from the internal structure of the animal being dissected.

Part B. External Anatomy of the Earthworm

1. Rinse a preserved earthworm thoroughly with water to remove excess preservative. Place the earthworm in a dissecting tray lined with moist paper towels. Turn the earthworm over and observe the difference between the darker-colored dorsal side and the lighter-colored ventral side of the cuticle (outer layer). With your fingers, feel the shape of the dorsal and ventral surfaces. **CAUTION:** *The preservative used on the earthworm can irritate your skin. Avoid touching your eyes while working with the preserved earthworm.* Answer question 1 in Observations.

2. Locate the slightly pointed anterior end and the blunt posterior end of the earthworm's body. Notice the somites, or segments, of the body. Count the total number of segments in the earthworm. The segments of an earthworm are counted from anterior to posterior. In the anterior portion of the earthworm identify the clitellum, the light brown enlarged band around the body. The clitellum functions in reproduction by secreting the cocoon into which eggs are deposited. Answer question 2 in Observations.

3. Locate the mouth on the ventral side of the anterior end of the earthworm. The flap of skin overhanging the mouth is the prostomium. **Note:** *The prostomium is not counted as the first segment in the earthworm's body.* Locate the anus, the opening in the last segment of the posterior end. The mouth and anus are the two openings of the tubelike digestive system.

4. Slide your fingers along the ventral surface of the earthworm from anterior to posterior and feel the bristlelike setae. The setae anchor the earthworm to the ground and function in movement. Then slide your fingers along the dorsal surface of the worm from anterior to posterior. With a hand lens, observe the location and number of setae on each segment of the earthworm's body. Answer question 3 in Observations.

5. Use a hand lens to find the openings of the seminal receptacles, which are located on the ventral surface in the grooves between segments 9 and 10 and segments 10 and 11. The seminal receptacles receive sperm from another earthworm during reproduction. On the sides of segment 14, locate the openings of the oviducts. These openings are pores through which eggs are released. On the side of segment 15, locate the openings of the sperm ducts. These openings are pores through which sperm are released and are surrounded by swollen "lips." You may be able to observe slight ridges that run posteriorly from the sperm duct openings to the clitellum. These ridges direct sperm into the clitellum.

6. In the appropriate place in Observations, label the following structures of the earthworm's external anatomy: anterior end, posterior end, mouth, prostomium, setae, segments, seminal receptacles, oviduct openings, sperm duct openings, clitellum, and anus. Give the number(s) of the segment(s) in which each structure appears.

Part C. Internal Anatomy of the Earthworm You may wish to dissect an earthworm and set it up under a dissecting microscope for students to refer to throughout their dissections.

1. Place the preserved earthworm in the dissecting tray with the dorsal surface up. Slightly stretch out the earthworm's body. With dissecting pins, pin the first and last segments of the earthworm to the bottom of the dissecting tray. Locate the dorsal blood vessel, a dark line that runs along the midline of the dorsal surface. The vessel runs from the anterior end to the posterior end. Insert the tip of a pair of scissors just to the right of the dorsal blood vessel and about 10 segments from the posterior end. Cut along the blood vessel to the anterior end as shown in Figure 1. Keep the scissors parallel to the bottom of the dissecting tray. **CAUTION:** *When using scissors, cut in a direction away from your hand and body to avoid cutting yourself.* Keep the cut as shallow as possible. The body wall of the earthworm is very thin, and the internal organs lie just inside. **Note:** *The major internal organs of the earthworm are anterior to the clitellum. Be very careful when cutting in this area.*

Dorsal blood vessel

Figure 1

2. When the cut is complete, carefully open the body wall. Notice that the coelom is not one large cavity but is separated into segments by septa (singular, septum), or thin partitions of tissue. The septa are continuations of the external segments. Beginning at the anterior end, use a probe or dissecting pin to carefully tear the septa from the anterior to the posterior end. Place dissecting pins in segments 5, 15, 25, 35, and 45 to hold open the body wall. Place the pins at an angle as shown in Figure 2. Placing pins in every tenth segment will help you locate the major internal organs that are located in specific segments. Use a medicine dropper to place several drops of water on the exposed organs of the earthworm. **Note:** *Throughout the dissection, add water to the earthworm to keep it from drying out.*

3. Trace the digestive system of the earthworm from the mouth to the anus. The mouth is located in the first three segments. Locate a slight swelling, the muscular-walled pharynx, posterior to the mouth in segments 3 to 6. The slender esophagus, located in segments 6 to 14, empties into the thin-walled crop, located in segments 15 and 16. The crop temporarily stores food. Examine the gizzard, a grinding organ located in segments 17 and 18. The gizzard mixes food with sand from the soil and physically breaks the food into smaller pieces. Use a probe to feel the difference in the walls of the crop and gizzard. Locate the intestine, or straight tube

A   B

45
40
30
25
20
15
10
5

Figure 2

leading from the gizzard to the anus. Near the posterior end of the earthworm, cut out a 1-cm section of the intestine and observe it with a hand lens. Locate the dorsal fold of tissue in the inside of the intestine. This tissue fold is the typhlosole. Answer question 4 in Observations.

4. In the appropriate place in Observations, label the following parts of the earthworm's digestive system: mouth, pharynx, esophagus, crop, gizzard, and intestine.

5. Trace the earthworm's closed circulatory system by following the dorsal blood vessel anteriorly along the midline to the five aortic arches, located in segments 7 to 11. In the posterior section use a probe to carefully move aside the intestine. Locate the ventral blood vessel. The aortic arches connect the dorsal blood vessel with the ventral blood vessel.

6. In the appropriate place in Observations, label the following parts of the earthworm's circulatory system: aortic arches, dorsal blood vessel, and ventral blood vessel.

7. In the appropriate place in Observations, sketch the plan of the earthworm's circulatory system as seen from the side. Label the aortic arches, dorsal blood vessel, and ventral blood vessel. Include arrows that indicate the flow of blood in each vessel.

8. Locate the brain, which is a white mass of tissue found in the third segment anterior and dorsal to the pharynx. With a probe, gently push aside the pharynx and esophagus to expose the white ventral nerve cord. The ventral nerve cord runs along the inner ventral surface from segment 3 to the last segment. With a hand lens, you may be able to see the two branched nerves that run from the brain around the esophagus to the ventral nerve cord. In each segment, locate a mass of nerve cells, or ganglia, attached to the ventral nerve cord.

9. In the appropriate place in Observations, label the following parts of the earthworm's nervous system: brain, ventral nerve cord, and ganglion.

10. With a probe, push aside the intestine in a region just posterior to the clitellum. With a hand lens, look for the white, coiled nephridia (singular, nephridium). A pair of nephridia occur in every segment except the first three segments and the last segment. Each nephridium collects wastes from the coelom and carries them to the outside of the body through pores, or openings, in the body wall of each segment.

11. In the appropriate place in Observations, label the nephridia, or structures of the earthworm's excretory system.

12. An earthworm has both male and female reproductive organs and can produce both eggs and sperm. Use a hand lens during the remainder of the dissection. First locate the male reproductive organs. Find the two seminal vesicles in segments 9 to 13. The seminal vesicles are three-lobed, light-colored organs along the sides of the esophagus. Two small pairs of testes are located in segments 10 and 11. The female reproductive organs include a pair of small, spherical seminal receptacles, located in segments 9 and 10, and a pair of ovaries, located in the septum between segments 12 and 13. With the exception of the seminal vesicles, most of the reproductive organs are small and difficult to see in preserved specimens.

13. In the appropriate place in Observations, label the following parts of the earthworm's reproductive system: seminal vesicles, testes, seminal receptacles, and ovary.
Do not let students become discouraged at not being able to locate the small reproductive organs. If a student does find any of these small organs, point them out to the whole class.

14. Follow your teacher's instructions for storing the earthworm for further use or properly disposing of the earthworm and its parts. Thoroughly wash and dry your dissecting tray, scissors, pins, probe, and any other equipment you may have used. Wash your hands with soap and water.

Observations

External Anatomy of the Earthworm

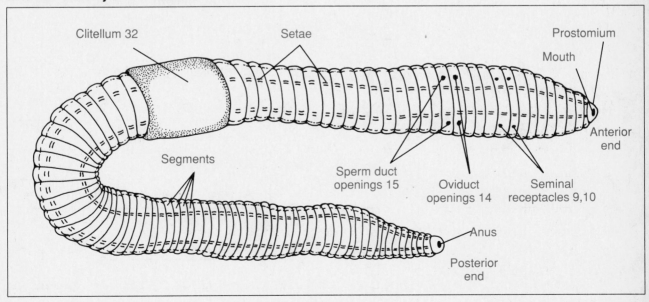

© Prentice-Hall, Inc.

Circulatory System of the Earthworm

Internal Anatomy of the Earthworm

1. Describe the shape of the dorsal and ventral surfaces of the earthworm's body.

   The dorsal surface of the earthworm is slightly rounded, and the ventral surface is flat.

2. **a.** How many segments are in your earthworm? Answers will vary with the earthworm, but should range from 100 to 150.

   b. In which segments is the clitellum located? The clitellum is located from segments 31 (or 32) to 37.

3. **a.** Where are setae located on the earthworm? The setae are located on the ventral surface only.

   b. How many setae are on each segment? There are 4 pairs of setae on each segment.

4. Compare the walls of the crop and the gizzard. The crop has thin walls and the gizzard has thicker, muscular walls.

Analysis and Conclusions

1. Why is it important not to make a deep cut with the scissors when dissecting your earthworm specimen? By making a shallow cut into the specimen you can avoid destroying underlying organs and tissues.

2. What do you think is the function of the typhlosole? The typhlosole increases surface area in the intestine for more absorption of digested food.

3. How does the earthworm's digestive system adapt it to filtering food out of the soil?
Soil containing food enters the digestive system through the mouth and passes into the gizzard where the food is ground up. Then, as the soil continues through, food is digested and absorbed in the intestine.

4. Describe two ways in which an earthworm's body is adapted to life in the soil.
The earthworm's long, thin shape helps it pass easily through the soil. The setae aid in this movement by gripping the soil. The one-way digestive system enables the earthworm to dig a path with its mouth as soil and food pass through.

Critical Thinking and Application

1. Imagine an assembly line for disassembling things instead of putting them together. Compare the earthworm's tubelike digestive system to such a "disassembly line." What is the advantage of a tubelike digestive system over a saclike digestive system?
Food passes through the earthworm's digestive system in much the same way as material moves through an assembly line. Everything moves in a continuous stream in one direction past every point in the digestive system where it can be further disassembled. It enters the mouth; it is stored in the crop, ground in the gizzard, and chemically digested and absorbed in the intestine; and feces leave through the anus. This orderly approach to the breakdown of food allows more complex substances to be digested.

2. Describe one way in which an earthworm is poorly adapted to life on land.

Because the earthworm absorbs oxygen through its moist skin, it dehydrates easily.

3. How might an earthworm's lack of appendages be an adaptation to burrowing?

A lack of appendages gives the earthworm a streamlined shape so that it can pass through the soil more

quickly and without injury.

4. Explain how an earthworm enriches and aerates the soil, thus improving it for plant growth.

The burrows created by the earthworm aerate the soil. Organic wastes that are the result of earthworm

digestion return essential organic substances to the soil. These organic substances act as fertilizers for

plants.

Going Further

1. With a probe, carefully tear open each organ of the digestive system and observe its contents.

2. Observe a prepared transverse section of an earthworm through a dissecting microscope. Make a sketch of the section and label the following parts: dorsal blood vessel, ventral blood vessel, ventral nerve cord, intestine, typhlosole, nephridia, setae, circular muscle fibers, longitudinal muscle fibers, and cuticle.

3. Set up a terrarium with live earthworms and observe their burrowing, feeding, and mating behavior.

4. Obtain earthworm cocoons from a biological supply house or collect them outdoors. Place the cocoons on moist paper towels in a covered petri dish. Watch for 12 to 20 earthworms to hatch in 1 to 30 days. Describe what you observe.

The Grasshopper

You may want to refer students to pages 607–631 in the textbook for a discussion of arthropods.

Time required: 45 minutes.

Pre-Lab Discussion

Grasshoppers are members of the phylum Arthropoda and the class Insecta. The class Insecta contains more than 900,000 species, which is about five times as many species as in all the other animal groups combined. Insects are mainly land animals and occupy almost every environmental habitat on land. The development of wings gave insects such distinct advantages over other land invertebrates as greater dispersal, access to more food supplies, and more efficient methods of escape from predators.

Insects have an exoskeleton composed of chitin. They have three pairs of jointed legs and three distinct body regions. These regions are the head, thorax, and abdomen. Usually two pairs of wings are attached to the thorax. As members of the class Insecta, grasshoppers have one pair of antennae and one pair of large compound eyes. They also have a tracheal tube-spiracle system for gas exchange. The efficient respiratory system of insects provides oxygen for the rapid movement of muscles. The high reproductive capacity and relatively short reproductive cycle of grasshoppers enables them to increase their populations at a rapid rate.

In this investigation, you will observe the behavior and movement of a live grasshopper. You also will examine the external features of the grasshopper and identify parts of its anatomy.

Problem

What are the parts of a grasshopper?

Materials *(per group)*

Live grasshopper in glass jar
Preserved grasshopper
Paper towels
Dissecting tray
Probe
Scalpel
Hand lens
Lettuce
Dissecting microscope
Glass slide
Medicine dropper

Students can be asked to collect living specimens. Keep live grasshoppers in glass jars with air holes punched in the lids. Provide twigs or sticks for perching and lettuce or other green leafy vegetables for food. If necessary, crickets can be substituted. They are available from biological supply houses or pet stores. Preserved specimens are available from biological supply houses.

Put on a laboratory apron if one is available. Handle all glassware carefully. Always handle the microscope with extreme care. You are responsible for its proper care and use. Use caution when handling glass slides as they can break easily and cut you. Be careful when handling sharp instruments. Always use special caution when working with laboratory chemicals, as they may irritate the skin or cause staining of the skin or clothing. Never touch or taste any chemical unless instructed to do so. Follow your teacher's directions and all appropriate safety procedures when handling live animals. Note all safety alert symbols next to the steps in the Procedure and review the meanings of each symbol by referring to the symbol guide on page 10.

Procedure
Part A. Observing the Reactions of a Live Grasshopper

🐾 1. Referring to Figure 1, locate the head, thorax, abdomen, three pairs of legs, and two pairs of wings of a live grasshopper in a glass jar. Observe the grasshopper for several minutes without disturbing it. Notice how the grasshopper moves and note which legs it uses when walking. Gently tap the side of the jar to make the grasshopper jump. Observe which legs are used in jumping. Answer questions 1 and 2 in Observations.

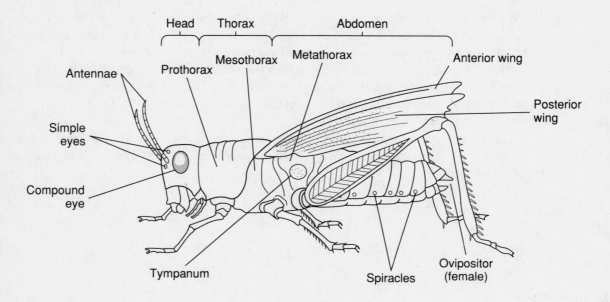

Figure 1

⚗ 2. Observe the position and movements of the grasshopper when it is at rest. Use the hand lens to observe the movements of the abdomen that are associated with respiration. Answer question 3 in Observations.

3. Tear off a small piece of lettuce and offer it to the grasshopper. Notice how the animal eats. Closely observe the movement of the mouthparts. Answer question 4 in Observations.

4. Return the grasshopper to your teacher when you have completed your observations.

Part B. Observing the External Anatomy of the Grasshopper

📷 1. Rinse the preserved grasshopper with water to remove excess preservative. Place the grasshopper in a dissecting tray. Touch the chitinous exoskeleton and apply gentle pressure. **CAUTION:** *The preservative used on the grasshopper can irritate your skin. Avoid touching your eyes while working with the preserved grasshopper.* Answer question 5 in Observations.

⚠ 2. Locate the three body segments of the grasshopper: the head, the thorax, and the abdomen. Use the hand lens to examine the head. Notice two long antennae, the sensory organs for touch, located at the front top of the head. Closely examine the antennae with a hand lens. Three simple eyes, or ocelli, are located in the head—one at the base of each antenna and one in the center front of the head. The head also contains two compound eyes, one located on each side of the head. Simple and compound eyes are sensory organs for vision. Answer question 6 in Observations.

⚠ 3. With a scalpel, carefully cut off a portion of the compound eye and place it on a clean glass slide with a drop of water. **CAUTION:** *When using a scalpel, cut in a direction away from your hand and body to avoid cutting yourself.* Observe the piece of the eye through low power of a dissecting microscope. The compound eye is made up of over 2000 facets, or surfaces, that allow the grasshopper to see almost all of its surroundings. In the appropriate place in Observations, sketch the compound eye as it appears through low power. Record the magnification of the microscope. Answer question 7 in Observations.

4. Closely examine the mouthparts with a hand lens. Identify the following parts as shown in Figure 2: the labrum (upper lip), the mandibles (jaws), the maxillae with sensory palps for tasting, the labium (lower lip) with sensory palps for tasting, and the hypopharynx, the tonguelike structure inside the mouth. Figure 2 also shows what each individual mouthpart looks like.

Figure 2

5. Locate the thorax. Notice that the thorax is divided into three segments. One pair of legs is attached to each segment. Observe the two front legs, or forelegs, and the third and largest pair of legs, the jumping legs, or hindlegs. Notice that each leg is composed of the coxa, trochanter, femur, tibia, and tarsus, as shown in Figure 3. Answer question 8 in Observations.

Figure 3

6. Observe the two pairs of wings, which also are located on the thorax. Use your fingers to gently spread open the wings. Notice the difference between the forewings and the hindwings. The leathery forewings protect the membranous and delicate hindwings, which are used for flying.

7. Locate the abdomen and notice its segments. On the first segment of the abdomen, locate the drum-shaped tympanum (eardrum). The tympanum is the sensory organ for sound. On the lateral surface of each segment of the abdomen, locate the small openings called spiracles. The spiracles are openings into the gas-exchange, or respiratory, system of the grasshopper. Note that the last segment of the abdomen is different in males and females. In females, the last segment, the ovipositor, is modified into a clawlike structure with four points used to dig a hole where eggs are laid. The female's abdomen is longer than the male's. In males, the last segment is blunt and curved upward. See Figure 4. Answer question 9 in Observations.

Spiracles are often difficult for students to locate. Circulate throughout the lab and point out the spiracles to each group.

Female   Male

Figure 4

8. In the appropriate place in Observations label the external anatomy of the grasshopper.

Observations

Magnification _____

Grasshopper Compound Eye

Grasshopper

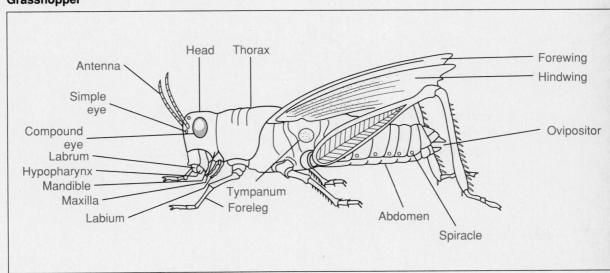

1. Describe the color of the grasshopper. Greenish-brown color; patterned surface.

_____

2. Which legs are used for walking or crawling? For jumping? The front legs (or forelegs) are used for

walking or crawling and the hindlegs are used for jumping.

_____

3. Describe the movements of the grasshopper's abdomen associated with respiration.

The entire abdomen expands or contracts at the same time.

_____

4. Compare the movement of the grasshopper's jaws to those of humans.

Grasshoppers' jaws move sideways; humans' jaws move up and down.

5. Describe the texture of the grasshopper's exoskeleton. The exoskeleton is hard, smooth, and resistant to pressure.

6. Describe the appearance of the antennae as seen through a hand lens.

The surfaces of the tips are covered with tiny hairs and pores.

7. How do simple and compound eyes differ? The simple eye has only one lens; the compound eye has many lenses.

8. Compare the forelegs and the jumping legs in terms of structure and size.

The basic parts and structure are similar. In the jumping legs, the femur is larger; the tibia is longer and has larger spines; and the tarsus is larger.

9. What sex is your grasshopper? How can you tell? Answers will vary. The female has a longer abdomen and an ovipositor; the male has a shorter, blunt-tipped abdomen.

Analysis and Conclusions

1. How is the color of a grasshopper an adaptation to where it lives?

It is the same color as grass, which provides camouflage for the grasshopper.

2. List two characteristics of chitin that make it a good material for the exoskeleton and wings of arthropods. Chitin is firm, strong, flexible, and lightweight.

3. How is the grasshopper adapted to detect moving objects in the environment?

The grasshopper can see movement through its eyes, can feel movement through its antennae, and can hear movement through its tympanum.

4. What are the mouthparts of a grasshopper adapted to do? The mouthparts are adapted to tear and

chew leaves.

5. Of the three body regions of the grasshopper, which one is specialized for locomotion?

The thorax region, with its three pairs of legs, is specialized for locomotion.

6. What do you think is the function of the spinelike structures found on the tibia and tarsus?

They help to hold the grasshopper to blades of grass and other surfaces.

Critical Thinking and Application

1. How can a grasshopper's exoskeleton be both an advantage and a disadvantage?

The exoskeleton is smooth and firm, and provides protection for the grasshopper. It also restricts its

movement and must be shed to allow for growth.

2. List three structures of the grasshopper that are adaptations for life on dry land.

Answers will vary, but may include the chitinous exoskeleton, which keeps the grasshopper from drying out,

wings for flying, well-developed legs for walking and jumping, and spiracles for breathing air.

3. Most insects are small as compared to most vertebrates. Do you think being small is more of an advantage or a disadvantage to insects? Give evidence to support your answer.

It is more of an advantage because insects are able to hide from predators and need only small amounts of

food. They can also be inadvertently transported around the world, either by wind or by hiding in export

cargo.

4. Can you drown a grasshopper by holding its head under water? Explain your answer.

No. Because the respiratory organs, or spiracles, are located on the abdomen, the grasshopper could still

breathe even if its head was being held under water.

Going Further

1. Study other behaviors of living grasshoppers by setting up experiments to determine whether grasshoppers can live in close quarters with other species of insects, what foods grasshoppers prefer, and whether grasshoppers react to certain stimuli, such as light.

2. Obtain preserved specimens from as many of the classes of arthropods as possible. Compare the characteristics of each, such as the number of body regions, number of legs, types of mouthparts, and types of respiratory organs. Record your observations in a data table.

57

Isopod Environments

You may want to refer students to pages 620–621 in the textbook for a discussion of crustaceans.

Time required: 45 minutes.

Pre-Lab Discussion

The phylum Arthropoda is made up of several different subphyla. The subphylum Crustacea contains over 35,000 species. Animals in the subphylum Crustacea include crabs, lobsters, crayfishes, and shrimps. The crustaceans are familiar as food sources for people. In general, crustaceans are characterized by a hard exoskeleton, two pairs of antennae, and mouthparts called mandibles. Although most are aquatic, a few crustaceans, such as the isopods, live on land. The pill bug and the sow bug are examples of isopods.

In this investigation, you will examine the external anatomy of a pill bug. You will also observe the behavior of pill bugs.

Problem

What are some characteristic structures of a pill bug? What type of environment is preferred by the pill bug?

Materials *(per group)*

6 live pill bugs in a glass jar
Paper towels
Sheet of black construction paper
Petri dish and cover
Masking or transparent tape
Pen or pencil
Scissors
2 meduim-sized paper cups
Ice cubes
Warm water
Hand lens

Pill bugs are easily found under rocks or in other damp areas in the spring or fall, but are difficult to find in the winter. Live pill bugs *(Oniscus)* are available from biological supply houses.

Safety ⚗ ▦ 🖐

Put on a laboratory apron if one is available. Handle all glassware carefully. Be careful when handling sharp instruments. Follow your teacher's directions and all appropriate safety procedures when handling live animals. Note all safety alert symbols next to the steps in the Procedure and review the meanings of each symbol by referring to the symbol guide on page 10.

Procedure

Part A. Observing the Behavior of a Pill Bug

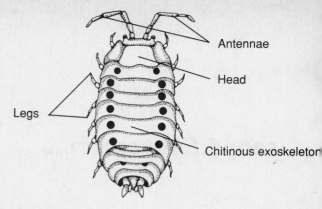

1. Referring to Figure 1, locate the head, antennae, chitinous exoskeleton, and seven pairs of legs of live pill bugs in a glass jar.

2. Open the jar and gently touch one of the pill bugs as it walks across the bottom of the jar. Answer questions 1 and 2 in Observations.

3. Use a hand lens to observe a pill bug as it walks across the jar. Answer question 3 in Observations.

Figure 1

Part B. The Pill Bug's Response to Texture

1. Place the bottom of a petri dish on a paper towel. Using the pencil or pen, trace the bottom of the petri dish on the paper towel.

2. Use scissors to cut out the paper outline of the petri dish. Then fold the outline in half. **CAUTION:** *Be careful when handling sharp instruments.*

3. As shown in Figure 2, place the folded paper towel in the bottom of the petri dish. Tape the paper towel in place along all sides. **Note:** *Place the petri dish on top of a paper towel. This will provide a background color that is similar on both sides of the petri dish.*

4. Place 6 isopods from the glass jar in the center of the petri dish. Cover the petri dish and allow the pill bugs to remain there undisturbed for 5 minutes.

Figure 2

5. After 5 minutes, examine the petri dish. Count the number of pill bugs that moved onto the toweled side and the number of pill bugs that moved onto the untoweled side. Record this information in the appropriate place in the Data Table.

6. Return the pill bugs to the glass jar.

Part C. The Pill Bug's Response to Moisture

1. Repeat steps 1 and 2 of Part B. Place the folded paper towel on the other side of the bottom of the petri dish used in Part B. As shown in Figure 3, moisten one of the folded paper towels with water.

2. Place 6 pill bugs into the center of the petri dish. Cover the petri dish and allow the pill bugs to remain there undisturbed for 5 minutes.

3. After 5 minutes, examine the petri dish. Count the number of pill bugs that moved onto the moistened side of the petri dish and the number of pill bugs that moved onto the dry side of the petri dish. Record this information in the appropriate place in the Data Table.

4. Return the pill bugs to the glass jar and remove the paper towels and tape from the petri dish.

Tape

Moistened paper towel

Dry paper towel

Figure 3

Part D. The Pill Bug's Response to Light

1. Repeat step 1 of Part B.

2. Use scissors to cut out the paper towel outline of the dish. **CAUTION:** *Handle scissors with care.*

3. Place the paper towel circle in the bottom of the petri dish and moisten the entire circle with water.

4. As shown in Figure 4, cover one-half of the top of the petri dish with black construction paper. Use tape to keep the construction paper in place.

Top
of
petri dish

Tape

Moistened
paper towel

Black
construction paper

Figure 4

5. Position another paper towel under the petri dish. Add 6 pill bugs to the center of the bottom of the petri dish. Cover the petri dish and allow the pill bugs to remain there undisturbed for 5 minutes.

6. After 5 minutes, examine the petri dish. Count the number of pill bugs that moved onto the dark side of the petri dish and the number of pill bugs that moved onto the lighted side of the petri dish. Record this information in the appropriate place in the Data Table.

7. Return the pill bugs to the glass jar. Remove the black construction paper and tape from the top of the petri dish, but allow the moistened paper towel to remain in the bottom of the dish.

Part E. The Pill Bug's Response to Temperature

1. Fill one cup with ice cubes and fill the other cup with warm water.

2. Place the two cups side by side, as shown in Figure 5. Place the petri dish on top of the cups. Make sure that the center of the petri dish is over the area where the two cups touch each other.

Center of petri dish

Paper cup containing
ice cubes

Paper cup containing
warm water

Figure 5

3. Place 6 pill bugs in the center of the petri dish. Cover the petri dish and allow the pill bugs to remain there undisturbed for 5 minutes.

4. After 5 minutes, examine the petri dish. Count the number of pill bugs found on the cold side of the petri dish and the number of pill bugs found on the warm side of the petri dish. Record this information in the appropriate place in the Data Table.

5. Return the pill bugs to the glass jar and follow your teacher's instructions for storing the pill bugs for further use.

6. Remove the moistened paper towel from the petri dish and discard the towel properly.

Data Table

Side of Petri Dish	Number of Pill Bugs
Toweled	
Untoweled	
Moist	
Dry	Answers will vary.
Dark	
Light	
Cold	
Warm	

Observations

1. Describe the texture and appearance of the pill bug's exoskeleton.

The pill bug's grayish-black exoskeleton is hard, smooth, and pressure resistant.

2. What response does the pill bug show when touched? When touched, the pill bug will turn over on its back and curl up into a ball.

3. Describe the way in which the pill bug moves. The seven pairs of legs work together to move the bill bug across a surface at an even pace.

Analysis and Conclusions

1. What is the function of the pill bug's exoskeleton? The exoskeleton protects the pill bug and keeps it from drying out.

2. Of what advantage to the pill bug is its response to touch? By rolling over and curling up, the pill bug is able to protect its soft underside.

3. Does the pill bug prefer a rough-textured or a smooth-textured environment?
Answers should reflect the students' data. Pill bugs should prefer a rough texture to a smooth one.

4. Does the pill bug prefer a dry or a moist environment? Why would a pill bug prefer this type of environment? Answers should reflect the students' data. Pill bugs should prefer a moist environment. This environment helps to keep the pill bug from drying out and dying.

5. Does the pill bug prefer a light or a dark environment? Why would a pill bug prefer this type of environment? Answers should reflect the students' data. Pill bugs should prefer a dark environment. A dark environment is more likely to be moist than a lighted one. A dark environment will also provide more protection from predators.

6. Does the pill bug prefer a warm or a cold environment? Answers should reflect students' data. Pill bugs should not have a preference for either a warm or a cold environment.

Critical Thinking and Application

1. Like other crustaceans, pill bugs use gills to breathe. Do the results of this investigation seem to support this information? Explain your answer. Answers will vary. Because the gills must retain a covering film of moisture to function properly, pill bugs require and seek out a moist environment.

2. The word *isopod* comes from Greek words meaning "same feet." How is this name appropriate for the pill bug? Pill bugs have seven pairs of identical legs, so this name is quite appropriate.

3. How would a permeable exoskeleton on a land-living arthropod affect the type of environment in which you would find this arthropod? A permeable exoskeleton would limit the arthropod to certain environments. For example, hot, arid conditions would cause the arthropod to dry out and die.

Going Further

To observe another crustacean, obtain a fiddler crab from a local pet store. Place the crab in the middle of a shoe box containing a layer of sand 5 cm deep and some small and medium-sized stones. Where does the crab go? Why is this reaction of value to the crab? Next, place the crab in a small aquarium filled with water to a depth of 10 cm. Gently touch the feelers of the crab with a pencil. Observe what happens. Use a net to remove the crab from the water. Compare the behavior of the crab in water with its behavior on land. Make an oral presentation to your class.

58

The Starfish

You may want to refer students to pages 637–644 in the textbook for a discussion of echinoderms.

Time required: 30 minutes.

Pre-Lab Discussion

The starfish, or sea star, is a spiny-skinned marine invertebrate that is a member of the phylum Echinodermata. Echinoderms are animals whose bodies are often covered with hundreds of small spines. Brittle stars, sand dollars, sea cucumbers, and sea urchins are also types of echinoderms.

Starfish are the most familiar echinoderms. They are found in coastal waters and along rocky seashores. They feed on oysters, clams, snails, barnacles, and worms. Starfish are known for their characteristic star-shaped bodies. They typically have five rays, or arms, branching out from a central disk. Because of their division into five parts, starfish are said to have pentaradial symmetry. If a ray breaks off, the starfish is able to regenerate, or grow back, a new one.

In this investigation, you will examine the external structures of a starfish.

Problem

How is the anatomy of a starfish adapted to life in a marine environment?

Materials (per group)

Preserved starfish   Available from biological supply houses.
Dissecting tray
Hand lens

Safety ⚗ 🧰

Put on a laboratory apron if one is available. Handle all glassware carefully. Always use special caution when working with laboratory chemicals, as they may irritate the skin or cause staining of the skin and clothing. Never touch or taste any chemical unless instructed to do so. Note all safety alert symbols next to the steps in the Procedure and review the meanings of each symbol by referring to the symbol guide on page 10.

Procedure

1. Rinse the starfish thoroughly with water to remove any extra preservative. **CAUTION:** *The preservative used on the starfish can irritate your skin. Avoid touching your eyes while working with the preserved starfish.*

2. Place the starfish in the dissecting tray with its aboral, or top, surface facing up. Notice that the starfish's body plan consists of 5 rays radiating out from a central disk. Although most starfish have 5 rays, sun stars have 7 to 14 rays, and some sea stars have 15 to 24 rays.

3. Using a hand lens, examine the skin on the aboral surface. Notice the many coarse spines that cover the entire aboral surface. The epidermis is spiny and irregular because parts of the endoskeleton protrude through the skin. Around the base of the spines are pedicellariae, which are jawlike structures. They capture small animals and keep the epidermis free of foreign objects. The skin gills are soft projections from the aboral surface that are lined by tissue of the inner cavity. They provide a large, moist area across which oxygen can be removed from the water. The skin gills are protected by the pedicellariae.

4. Referring to Figure 1, use a hand lens to locate a spine and the pedicellariae around it. Locate skin gills near some pedicellariae. Answer question 1 in Observations.
   Skin gills and pedicellariae may be difficult to find on preserved specimens.

Aboral Surface of Starfish

Figure 1

5. Study the aboral surface of the central disk. Answer question 2 in Observations.

6. Locate a small red or yellow buttonlike structure on the central disk. This structure is the madreporite, or sieve plate. The madreporite contains many tiny pores through which water enters the water-vascular system. The water-vascular system is a system of water-filled canals and appendages that function primarily in locomotion and feeding.

7. Try to find the anus in the center of the central disk. The anus, which opens out from the intestine, is the opening through which solid wastes are eliminated from the body.
   The anus may be difficult to find on preserved specimens.

8. In the appropriate place in Observations, label the following structures on the aboral side of the starfish: central disk, rays, spines, madreporite, and anus.

9. Turn the starfish over so that its oral, or bottom, surface is facing up.

10. With the hand lens, examine the mouth, an opening in the middle of the central disk through which food is taken in. Notice the small spines that surround the mouth. Many types of starfish feed by pushing part of the stomach out through the mouth. The stomach secretes enzymes that digest prey.

11. Find the ambulacral groove that begins at the mouth and extends down the center of each ray. Find the small tube feet that line the groove. The tube feet are part of the water-vascular system. The tube foot is a hollow, thin-walled cylinder with a bulblike structure called the ampulla at one end and a sucker at the tip. Fluid-pressure changes caused by muscle contractions in the ampulla and tube foot create suction in the tip of the tube foot. The suction enables the starfish to pull itself along a surface or to grasp prey. Answer question 3 in Observations.

12. Locate the eyespots, which are tiny red or pink dots that are found on the oral surface of a small tentacle at the tip of each ray. An eyespot is made up of 80 to 200 ocelli, which contain granules of red pigment. The eyespots are sensitive to light but are not capable of forming images.   The eyespot may be difficult to locate on a preserved specimen.

13. In the appropriate place in Observations, label the following structures on the oral side of the starfish: ambulacral groove, mouth, tube feet, oral spines, and ray spines.

Observations

Aboral Side of Starfish

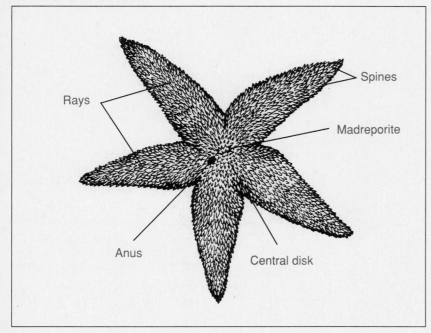

Spines

Rays

Madreporite

Anus

Central disk

Oral Side of Starfish

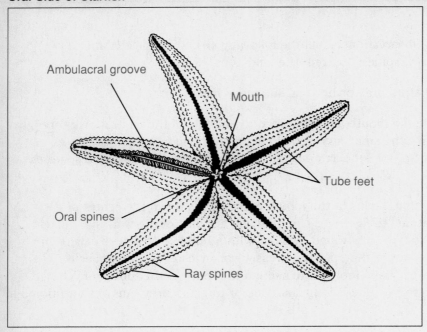

Ambulacral groove

Mouth

Tube feet

Oral spines

Ray spines

1. **Describe the feel of a starfish's spines.** _The spines have a rough, bumpy texture and are hard to the_ touch.

2. **How does the number of spines in the central disk compare to the number of spines in a ray?** Answers will vary with the specimens used. Many species of starfish have fewer spines in the central disk than in the rays.

3. **How many rows of tube feet does your specimen have?** _Answers will vary. Starfish generally have 2_ or 4 rows per ray.

Analysis and Conclusions

1. **What is the function of a starfish's spines?** _The spines on a starfish provide protection against_ predators.

2. **What kind of body plan does a starfish have?** _The body plan is pentaradial—it is organized into fives._

3. **What are two functions of the tube feet?** _The tube feet are used in locomotion, food-getting, and_ respiration.

4. How does a starfish take in food? In many species, the starfish everts part of its stomach and partially

digests its prey. It may then pull its stomach and prey back into its body and complete digestion internally.

5. How does respiration occur in the starfish? Respiration in the starfish occurs through the gills and the

tube feet.

6. List two adaptations of the starfish that make it well adapted to life in marine waters.

Answers will vary, but may include gills, a water-vascular system with tube feet, and pedicellariae.

Critical Thinking and Application

1. Starfish produce large numbers of eggs and sperm. How is this production an adaptive

advantage? Because fertilization occurs in the water, the production of large numbers of eggs and sperm

makes for a greater likelihood that fertilization will occur.

2. When a starfish pries open the shell of a clam or oyster, the mollusk resists. Even if the shell
opens only slightly, the starfish will get its meal. How does this occur?

Because the starfish's stomach is a thin, membranous structure, it can enter an opening less than one

millimeter wide. The stomach partially digests the soft body of the mollusk and then it can easily be pulled

from its shell into the starfish's body.

3. Because starfish were eating many clams and oysters, divers were hired to go out and chop
the starfish into pieces. After this, fishermen found even more empty clam and oyster shells

than before. Why did this occur? A starfish can regenerate an entire new body from a small part of

the central disk and a single ray. Each starfish piece regenerated a new body resulting in an increase, not a

decrease, of the starfish population.

4. Why can a starfish move equally well in any direction? Because of its radial symmetry, a starfish

can move equally well in any direction. The starfish does not have an anterior or a posterior end.

5. Many echinoderms, which are bottom-dwellers as adults, have free-swimming larvae. What advantage do free-swimming larvae provide for the echinoderms?

Free-swimming larvae are able to move around and search for the best possible environment in which to

settle as an adult.

Going Further

1. Sand dollars, sea urchins, sea lilies, sea cucumbers, and brittle stars belong to the same phylum as starfish. Obtain preserved specimens of these animals. Compare their external structures with those of the starfish.

2. Set up a saltwater aquarium in your classroom. Obtain a live starfish and other types of echinoderms and observe their behavior in the aquarium.

59

Comparing Invertebrate Body Plans

You may want to refer students to pages 654–657 in the textbook for a discussion of invertebrate body plans.

Time required: 45 minutes.

Pre-Lab Discussion

Invertebrates, like all other organisms, are divided into groups based on certain distinguishing characteristics. Two characteristics that are examined when grouping invertebrates are cell layers and body cavities.

The number of cell layers making up the body varies among invertebrates. Cnidarians—jellyfishes and sea anemones, for example—possess only two cell layers in their body wall: an inner gastroderm and an outer epidermis. More advanced invertebrates—worms, mollusks, arthropods, and echinoderms, to name a few—have three basic cell layers: an inner endoderm, a middle mesoderm, and an outer ectoderm.

The animals that possess three basic cell layers can be divided into groups based on the structure of their body cavity. The body cavity, if present, is a fluid-filled hollow in the body wall that is located between the endoderm and the ectoderm. Animals that lack a body cavity are called acoelomates. Animals that have a body cavity that is only partially lined with mesoderm are called pseudocoelomates. And animals that have a body cavity that is completely lined with mesoderm are called coelomates.

In this investigation, you will compare the body plans and structures of invertebrates from four different phyla.   The terms endoderm, mesoderm, and ectoderm are generally reserved for describing embryos. However, these terms are used here for the sake of simplicity and to avoid confusing students with additional terminology.

Problem

What are the differences in body plans and structures of the cnidarians, flatworms, roundworms, and annelids?

Materials (per group)

Microscope
Prepared slides of cross sections of: Prepared slides are available from biological supply houses.
   Cnidarian (Hydra)
   Flatworm (Dugesia)
   Roundworm (Ascaris lumbricoides)
   Earthworm (Lumbricus terrestris)

Safety 🔺

Handle all glassware carefully. Always handle the microscope with extreme care. You are responsible for its proper care and use. Use caution when handling glass slides as they can break easily and cut you. Note all safety alert symbols next to the steps in the Procedure and review the meanings of each symbol by referring to the symbol guide on page 10.

Procedure

Part A. Examining the Body Plan and Structures of the Cnidarian

1. Study Figure 1, which shows the basic body plans of the four invertebrates you will be examining.

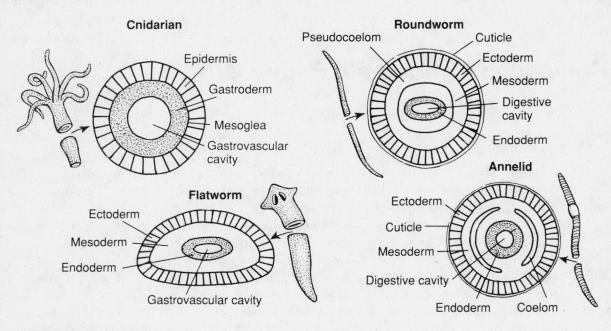

Figure 1

2. Examine a prepared slide of a cross section of a cnidarian under the low-power objective of a microscope. Look at the body layers. Switch to high power to see the specific structures in greater detail. **CAUTION**: *When switching to the high-power objective, always look at the objective from the side of the microscope so that the objective does not hit or damage the slide.*

3. Locate the epidermis, or outer layer of cells. Try to find some barbed cells called cnidocytes, each of which contains a stinging structure called a nematocyst.

4. Locate the gastroderm, or inner cell layer. Notice how some of the cells in the gastroderm have flagella. These flagellated cells help to circulate food and other materials within the gastrovascular cavity.

5. Locate the gastrovascular cavity in the center of the cross section of the cnidarian. Food digestion occurs within the gastrovascular cavity.

6. Locate the mesoglea, which is a noncellular jellylike material between the epidermis and the gastroderm.

7. In the appropriate place in Observations, label the following structures on the cross section of the cnidarian *(Hydra)*: epidermis, mesoglea, gastroderm, cnidocyte, nematocyst, and gastrovascular cavity.

Part B. Observing the Body Plan and Structures of the Flatworm

1. Examine a prepared slide of a cross section of a flatworm under low power. Locate the ectoderm, endoderm, and gastrovascular cavity.

2. Find the middle cell layer, or mesoderm, between the ectoderm and the endoderm. The mesoderm makes up most of the flatworm and consists of muscles, glands, organs, loose cells, and many other kinds of structures. Notice the absence of a body cavity.

3. In the appropriate place in Observations, label the following structures on the cross section of the flatworm: ectoderm, mesoderm, endoderm, and gastrovascular cavity.

Name _____ Class _____ Date _____

Part C. Examining the Body Plan and Structures of the Roundworm

 1. Examine a prepared slide of a cross section of a roundworm under low power. Locate the thick outer covering called the cuticle. This tough coating keeps a parasitic roundworm from being digested by its host. Just inside of the cuticle is the ectoderm, a thin layer of cells. Locate the mesoderm, the fiberlike layer just inside the epidermis.

2. Toward the center of the roundworm, look for the endoderm. The space inside the endoderm is the inside of the roundworm's digestive tract. The space between the endoderm and the mesoderm is called a pseudocoelom.

3. In the appropriate place in Observations, label the following structures on the cross section of the roundworm: cuticle, ectoderm, mesoderm, endoderm, and pseudocoelom.

Part D. Examining the Body Plan and Structures of the Earthworm

1. Examine a prepared slide of a cross section of an earthworm. Find the thin protective outer layer called the cuticle. Just below the cuticle, look for the layer of cells of the ectoderm.

2. Inside the ectoderm are two muscle layers. The outer layer contains the circular muscles, which run circularly around the earthworm. The thick inner layer contains the longitudinal muscles, which run the length of the worm. These two layers of muscle make up the mesoderm.

3. Study the center of the slide. You will see a round or horseshoe-shaped space that is the inside of the digestive tract. The layer of cells that surrounds the space is the endoderm. Surrounding the endoderm is another set of circular and longitudinal muscles.

4. Notice a relatively open space between the muscles surrounding the digestive tract and the muscles just inside the epidermis. This body cavity is called a coelom.

5. Locate a long, fiberlike structure inside the coelom. This structure, called a nephridium, is involved in excretion. There should be one nephridium on each side of the earthworm's body.

6. On the outer surface of the earthworm, find some bristly structures called setae. The earthworm uses the setae to help move its body through the soil.

7. In the appropriate place in Observations, label the following structures on the cross section of the earthworm: cuticle, ectoderm, circular and longitudinal muscles (both sets), endoderm, coelom, nephridium, and setae.

Observations

Cross Section of Cnidarian *(Hydra)*

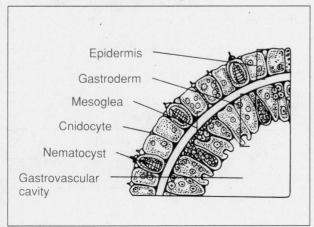

Cross Section of Flatworm *(Dugesia)*

Cross Section of Roundworm (Ascaris)

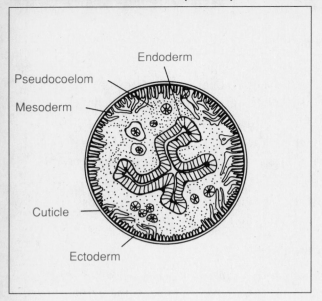

Cross Section of Earthworm (Lumbricus)

Analysis and Conclusions

1. What structures in the cnidarian correspond to the digestive cavity, ectoderm, and endoderm in the earthworm? The gastrovascular cavity, epidermis, and gastroderm, respectively.

2. How is the body plan of the cnidarian different from the body plan of the flatworm?
   Whereas the cnidarian has only two cell layers in its body, the flatworm has a third body layer (mesoderm).

3. How is the body plan of the flatworm similar to the body plan of the roundworm?
   Both the flatworm and the roundworm have three body layers: the ectoderm, the mesoderm, and the endoderm.

4. How is the body plan of the flatworm different from the body plan of the roundworm?
   Whereas the flatworm has no body cavity (is an acoelomate), the roundworm has a pseudocoelom.

5. How is the body plan of the earthworm different from the body plans of the other three organisms you examined? Of the four organisms studied in this investigation, only the earthworm has a true coelom, that is, a body cavity that is completely lined with mesoderm.

Critical Thinking and Application

1. Suppose a newly discovered organism is found to have three body layers. Scientists think that it is a worm but disagree as to the group in which it should be placed. How could they assign it to the proper group based on body structure? _Scientists could look at a cross section of the_ _organism to determine if it is an acoelomate, a pseudocoelomate, or a coelomate._

_____

_____

2. What are two advantages of the presence of a coelom in an organism?

A coelom allows for movement of the organs within the body and enables an animal to move around more

freely. The fluid-filled coelom also provides support for the organism and allows for the development of

more complex organs and organ systems.

3. Suppose a new phylum of invertebrates is discovered. These invertebrates have a gastrovascular cavity and a very thin layer of mesodermal cells but show no organ development. Where would you place this new phylum with respect to the ones studied in this investigation? Explain your placement. _Because this phylum's organisms have a mesodermal layer they should be_ _placed above the cnidarians. Because the organisms show no organ development, they should be placed_

before the flatworms, which do display some organ development.

_____

Going Further

Construct or draw a new form of invertebrate having characteristics of one existing phylum or intermediate characteristics of two related phyla. From your completed model or drawing, your classmates should be able to identify the animal's symmetry, locomotion, nervous system, method of circulation, excretory system, and type of digestive system and, based upon its gas-exchange structure, whether your new "species" is terrestrial or aquatic.

60

Identifying Invertebrates

You may want to refer students to pages 653–668 in the textbook for a discussion of invertebrate characteristics.

Time required: 50 minutes.

Pre-Lab Discussion

Invertebrates are an extremely diverse group of organisms. For example, invertebrates perform the function of movement in many different ways. Hawk moths zip and hover agilely in the air; snails creep slowly over the ground; soft-bodied earthworms burrow in the dark, damp soil; brittle stars thrash their arms to move across the ocean floor; jellyfishes pulse through the water; sponges do not move at all. The ways in which invertebrates carry out their other life functions are also quite varied.

Because invertebrates are so different from one another, it is necessary to classify them, or place them into groups that share certain key characteristics. This makes it easier to study them and to organize information about them in a coherent way.

In this investigation, you will identify the phylum to which each of a number of unknown invertebrate specimens belongs.

Problem

What external characteristics can be used to identify unknown invertebrates?

Materials *(per group)*

Unidentified preserved
    invertebrate specimens
Dissecting tray
Hand lens

Specimens such as sponges, cnidarians, flatworms, roundworms, mollusks, annelids, arthropods, and echinoderms are available from biological supply houses. You should have representative specimens from as many of these groups as possible. Try to choose specimens that have easily observed external structures.

Safety 🔺 🖾

Put on a laboratory apron if one is available. Handle all glassware carefully. Always use special caution when working with laboratory chemicals, as they may irritate the skin or cause staining of the skin or clothing. Never touch or taste any chemical unless instructed to do so. Note all safety alert symbols next to the steps in the Procedure and review the meanings of each symbol by referring to the symbol guide on page 10.

Procedure

1. Rinse an unidentified invertebrate specimen thoroughly with water in order to remove any excess preservative. **CAUTION:** *The preservative used on the specimen can irritate your skin. Avoid touching your eyes while working with the preserved specimen.*

2. Throughout this investigation, you will be examining a number of invertebrate specimens for the presence or absence of certain characteristics and structures. Use the hand lens whenever you need to see a characteristic more clearly. Record all of your observations in the appropriate place in the Data Table in Observations. If an organism does not display a particular characteristic, write the word "none" in the appropriate place in the Data Table.

3. Examine your specimen carefully. Some of the structures may be difficult for the students to find. You shoul circulate throughout the lab to help students locate these structures.

   - Does the animal have no symmetry, radial symmetry, or bilateral symmetry?

   - Does the animal have a hard body or a soft body?

   - Does the animal have a hard exoskeleton?

   - Does the animal's body show segmentation?

   - Is the animal motile, or free to move around, or is it sessile, or not free to move around?

   - If the animal is motile, what is its method of locomotion?

   Record the observations in the appropriate places in the Data Table.

4. Observe the external structures of the organism's digestive system.

   - Does the animal have a mouth?

   - Does the animal have an anus?

   Record the observations in the appropriate place in the Data Table.

5. Observe the external structures of the organism's respiratory system.

   - Does the animal have gills?

   - Does respiration occur through the external surface of the organism?

   Record the observations in the appropriate place in the Data Table.

6. Observe any external evidence of reproductive structures on the organism.

   - Is the animal a hermaphrodite, having the ability to produce both male and female sex cells, or are the sexes separate?

   Record the observations in the appropriate place in the Data Table.

7. Are there any other external characteristics that might help you to identify this animal? Record the observations in the appropriate place in the Data Table.

8. Review all your observations. Based on your observations, write the name of the phylum to which this organism belongs in the last column of the Data Table.

9. Repeat steps 3 through 8 for all of the other specimens provided by your teacher.

Observations

Data Table

Specimen	Type of Symmetry	Hard or Soft Body	Hard Exoskeleton	Segmentation	Motile or Sessile	Method of Locomotion	Mouth	Anus	Type of Respiratory System	Hermaphrodite or Single Sex	Other Characteristics	Phylum
1												
2												
3												
4							Answers will vary depending on the specimens used.					
5												
6												
7												
8												

Analysis and Conclusions

1. Why should you examine the same characteristics in each animal that you are trying to identify? By examining the same characteristics, you will be better able to compare the organisms and correctly classify them.

2. What characteristics should you examine if you were asked to determine whether the organism was terrestrial or aquatic? You could look for certain respiratory structures such as gills or spiracles. You could also look at the organism's method of locomotion.

3. What is one advantage of using a preserved specimen instead of a live specimen in this investigation? A preserved specimen is easier to examine for long periods of time because it does not move. Also, a preserved specimen will not display any protective behaviors such as pinching, stinging, or biting.

4. What is one disadvantage of using a preserved specimen instead of a live specimen in this investigation? With a preserved specimen you are unable to observe the form of locomotion or any behavioral characteristics. Also, some of the identifying structures on the organism may be changed or destroyed by the chemical preservative.

5. If you were unsure of one of your classifications, what could you further examine to make sure of your identification? You could dissect the organism to inspect its internal anatomy, or look at a prepared slide of a cross section of the organism to observe its internal structures.

Critical Thinking and Application

1. What adaptations in body form are found in motile organisms that are not found in sessile organisms? Many motile organisms have bilateral symmetry and a body with a definite head region. This streamlining of the body may make movement easier. In many organisms, the head region has specialized sense organs and a brain. This aids in food and predator detection.

2. How might radial symmetry be advantageous? Radial symmetry might enable invertebrates to receive stimuli from all directions and to move in all directions.

3. How might bilateral symmetry be advantageous? Bilateral symmetry allows for the formation of an anterior, or head, region. Organisms with bilateral symmetry have a more complex nervous system and are better able to react to external stimuli.

4. How is being a hermaphrodite an advantage to certain invertebrates?

It allows the invertebrate to mate any time it encounters another mature adult of the same species.

It eliminates the need to search for a mate of the opposite sex when conditions for reproduction are right.

5. List two ways in which invertebrates are of benefit to humans. Mollusks are commonly used as a food source for humans, and for the production of materials such as pearls. Earthworms are useful in soil aeration. Many invertebrates are used in scientific research.

6. List two ways in which invertebrates are harmful to humans. Some invertebrates are parasites that feed off human hosts. Many invertebrate species do extensive damage to agricultural crops. Invertebrates such as starfish eat clams and other mollusks that are used as human food sources. Some invertebrates produce toxins that can cause painful or deadly stings.

Going Further

1. Collect living specimens of some of the different invertebrate phyla. Observe differences in their means of locomotion, food preferences, feeding behaviors, and other behavioral characteristics. Construct a data table to record your observations.

2. Invertebrates are incredibly diverse organisms. Prepare a report on one type of invertebrate that was not discussed in Chapters 26 through 30 of your textbook. What characteristics does this organism have that make it similar to other invertebrates? What characteristics does this invertebrate have that make it unusual or unique? Report your findings to the class.

61

The Fish

You may choose to use models, charts, or videos as an alternative to an actual fish dissection. Refer to the section on Handling Ethical Issues in the front matter of this book.

You may want to refer students to pages 679–692 in their textbook for a discussion of fishes.

Time required: 45 minutes.

Pre-Lab Discussion

Fishes are members of the phylum Chordata and subphylum Vertebrata. The largest class of fishes, class Osteichthyes, contains fishes with skeletons made of bone. Fishes exhibit many adaptations for life in an aquatic environment. The perch and the goldfish are representative members of the class Osteichthyes.

In this investigation, you will observe the movement and behavior of a live goldfish. You will also identify the external parts of a perch.

Problem

How are the structures of a fish adaptations for living in an aquatic environment?

Materials *(per group)*

Live goldfish   Available from a local pet store.
Preserved perch   Available from biological supply houses.
Large glass jar or beaker
Water from an aquarium
Fish net
Stopwatch or clock with second hand
Dissecting tray
Probe
Forceps
Hand lens
Glass slide
Coverslip
Paper towels
Medicine dropper
Dissecting microscope

Safety 🔬 ⬚ ▨ 🐟

Put on a laboratory apron if one is available. Always handle the microscope with extreme care. You are responsible for its proper care and use. Use caution when handling glass slides as they can break easily and cut you. Handle all glassware carefully. Always use special caution when working with laboratory chemicals, as they may irritate the skin or cause staining of the skin or clothing. Never touch or taste any chemical unless instructed to do so. Be careful when handling sharp instruments. Follow your teacher's directions and all appropriate safety procedures when handling live animals. Note all safety alert symbols next to the steps in the Procedure and review the meanings of each symbol by referring to the symbol guide on page 10.

Procedure

Part A. Observing the Behavior of a Live Fish

1. Fill a large glass jar or beaker three-quarters full with water from an aquarium.

2. With a fish net, carefully remove one live goldfish from the aquarium. Immediately place the fish into the glass jar filled with aquarium water. Steps 1, 2, and 6 can be eliminated if groups of students are given a live fish already in its own container.

3. Observe the goldfish. Using a stopwatch or clock with a second hand, count how many times the fish opens and closes its mouth in one minute. Count how many times the gill covers move in one minute. Answer question 1 in Observations.

4. Observe how the goldfish swims. Carefully watch the movements of the body, fins, and tail. Answer question 2 in Observations.

5. Locate the goldfish's dorsal, caudal, pectoral, pelvic, and anal fins. Answer question 3 in Observations. Complete the Data Table in Observations after you have observed the function of each fin as the fish swims.

6. With a fish net, carefully return the goldfish to the aquarium.

Part B. Examining the External Anatomy of a Fish

1. Obtain a preserved perch. Rinse the fish under running water to remove excess preservative. **CAUTION:** *The preservative used on the fish can irritate your skin. Avoid rubbing your eyes while working with the fish. Leave a piece of wet paper towel at your work area to wipe your fingers after contact with the fish.* Dry the fish with paper towels and place it in a dissecting tray. Position the fish in the tray with the dorsal surface away from you and the head of the fish pointing left.

2. Observe the coloring of the fish. Compare the color of the dorsal and ventral surfaces. Answer question 4 in Observations.

3. Locate the three regions of the fish's body: the head, the trunk, and the tail.

4. Locate the eye and the nostrils on the head of the fish. Carefully insert a probe into one of the nostrils to determine where the nostrils lead. Answer question 5 in Observations.

5. Insert a probe into the mouth. Carefully pry open the mouth. Locate the upper jaw, or maxilla, and the lower jaw, or mandible. The perch possesses powerful jaws and strong teeth for catching and eating prey.

6. Carefully insert your index finger into the open mouth. Feel the location of the teeth and the texture and location of the tongue. **CAUTION:** *Touch the teeth very gently. They are very sharp.* Answer question 6 in Observations.

7. Locate the operculum, the protective bony covering over the gills. With a probe, carefully lift the operculum away from the gills lying underneath. Observe the flat, scalelike bones supporting the operculum.

8. While holding the operculum back, use a hand lens to examine the gills carefully. Locate the spaces between the gills. Also locate the gill arch—a cartilage support for each gill, the gill filaments—soft, fingerlike projections that make up the gills, and the gill rakers—hard projections located on the inner surface of the gill arch. In the space provided in Observations, draw and label a gill. Label the gill arch, gill filaments, and gill rakers.

9. Observe the scales that cover the fish's body. With forceps, carefully remove a single scale. Prepare a wet-mount slide of the scale and observe it under a dissecting microscope. Observe the growth rings on the scale. As a fish grows, the scales grow larger. Each growth ring on the scale represents one year's growth. Answer question 7 in Observations. In the space provided in Observations, draw a scale as seen under a dissecting microscope. Label the growth rings on your drawing. Record the magnification of the microscope.

10. Locate the lateral line system—a series of sensory pits forming a line on each side of the body from the operculum to the tail.

11. Locate the anus, a small opening anterior to the anal fin. In a male perch, a small opening called the urogenital pore is located behind the anus. Sperm cells produced by the testes are released through the urogenital pore. In a female perch, the genital pore is located behind the anus. Eggs from the ovaries are released through the genital pore. The female fish also has a separate urinary pore located behind the genital pore.

12. On the diagram in Observations, label the following regions and parts of the external anatomy of a perch: head, trunk, tail, anterior dorsal fin, posterior dorsal fin, anal fin, caudal fin, pectoral fin, pelvic fin, eye, nostril, mouth, maxilla, mandible, operculum, gills, lateral line system, anus, urogenital pore, and scales.

13. When you have finished examining your specimen, follow your teacher's instructions for storing the perch for further use.

Observations

Data Table

Type of Fin	Function
Anterior dorsal	Keeps fish from rolling over while swimming
Posterior dorsal	
Anal	
Caudal	Propels fish through water
Pectoral	Used in steering; helps fish to stop
Pelvic	

Perch Gill

Perch Scale

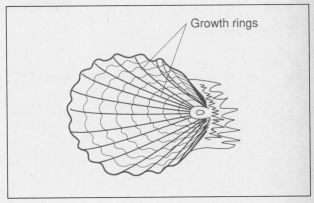

Magnification _____

External Anatomy of the Perch

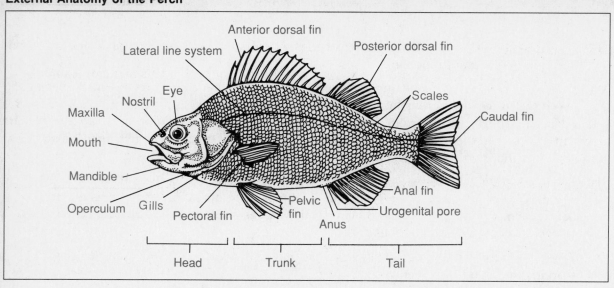

1. **a.** How many times does the fish open and close its mouth in one minute?

   Answers will vary.

   b. How many times do the gills move in one minute? Answers should be the same number as for 1a.

2. Describe the motion of the fish as it swims. Answers should include that the body bends from side to side as the fish swims.

3. **a.** How many individual fins are there on the goldfish? There are seven fins on the goldfish.

   b. Which fins occur in pairs? The pectoral fins and the pelvic fins occur in pairs.

4. Compare the color of the dorsal and ventral surfaces of the fish. The dorsal surface is darker than the ventral surface.

5. Where do the perch's nostrils lead? Into the nasal cavity.

6. Describe the location and texture of the perch's teeth. The teeth are located on both jaws, are very sharp, and are slanted backward/inward.

7. How old is your fish? Answers will vary.

394

Analysis and Conclusions

1. What is the relationship between the number of times the mouth opens and closes and the number of times the gill covers move? The number is the same, indicating that the movements are related.

2. How is the fish's body shape an adaptation to its environment? The thin, streamlined body enables easier and more rapid movement through the water.

3. How does the coloring of the dorsal and ventral surfaces of the fish provide protection against predators? The dark dorsal surface blends in with the dark bottom of a pond, etc., when seen from above looking down. The light ventral surface blends in with the light sky when seen from below looking up.

4. How are the perch's teeth adapted to their function? Because the perch is a carnivore, its teeth are adapted to catch and hold its prey.

5. What is the function of the gill rakers of a perch? Gill rakers strain out particles that enter the mouth and prevent them from getting on or impairing the function of the gill filaments.

6. What is the function of the lateral line of a perch? The lateral line, sensitive to pressure waves in the water, senses the movement of other animals in the vicinity. This helps the perch in avoiding predators and catching prey.

7. What structures on the perch make it adapted for living in an aquatic environment? Answers may include gills, fins, operculum, and lateral line system. Internal structures such as the air bladder may also be mentioned.

Critical Thinking and Application

1. While many invertebrates have an exoskeleton, or hard shell covering, vertebrates such as fishes have an endoskeleton. Of what advantage to the fish is the endosketeton?

   An endoskeleton can support a larger body than can an exoskeleton. Also, the endoskeleton grows as the

   organism grows, eliminating the need for molting.

2. The perch possesses a gas-filled internal structure called the swim bladder. What is the function of the swim bladder? The swim bladder is responsible for adjusting the fish's specific gravity, which permits the fish to sink or rise in the water without swimming.

3. Certain species of fishes that live deep in ocean waters have chemicals within their skin that make them luminescent, or glow-in-the-dark. Of what advantage is this characteristic to these fishes? Answers will vary but may include that this light may enable fishes to see in dark water, distract predators, attract prey, or find a mate.

4. The perch fertilizes its eggs externally and leaves the eggs exposed on rocks. The guppy fertilizes its eggs internally and gives birth to live young. Which fish probably produces fewer eggs? Compare the survival rate of these two species. Because the perch leaves its eggs exposed on rocks, it is reasonable to assume that its eggs are more vulnerable to being eaten by predators or destroyed. To compensate for this loss, the perch probably produces large numbers of eggs. The young of guppies are fully developed at birth. Guppies, therefore, probably produce fewer young with the higher survival rate of the two fish.

Going Further

1. Examine the skeleton of a large bony fish. To do so, boil the fish in water to make the flesh easier to remove. Then carefully remove the flesh and reassemble the skeleton. Sketch the fish's skeletal system and, using reference materials, label all of the bones.

2. Obtain a preserved shark or other cartilaginous fish. Compare the external structures with those of the perch.

3. Find out what you can about *Latimeria*, a lobe-finned fish that is called a coelacanth. Write a report on its discovery.

62

You may choose to use models, charts, or videos as an alternative to an actual frog dissection. Refer to the section on Handling Ethical Issues in the front matter of this book.

The Frog

You may want to refer students to pages 695–701 in the textbook for a discussion of frogs.

Time required: Part A–20 minutes
Part B–20 minutes
Part C–60 minutes

Pre-Lab Discussion

Frogs belong to the class Amphibia. Amphibians have adaptations for living in terrestrial as well as aquatic environments. Frogs are among the most commonly studied organisms in biology. Although many differences exist between humans and frogs, the basic body plans are similar. Humans and frogs both belong to the phylum Chordata. By studying the anatomy of the frog, you will be better able to understand your own body.

In this investigation, you will observe the behavior of a live frog. You will examine the external features of a frog and identify parts of its external anatomy. In addition, you will dissect a preserved frog to observe its internal anatomy.

Problem

How is a frog structured for survival?

Materials *(per group)*

Live frog
Large glass jar
Aquarium with water
Preserved frog
Dissecting tray
Scissors
Probe
Forceps
Hand lens
Plastic bag
Scalpel
Dissecting pins
Dissecting needle
Paper towels
Medicine dropper
Clock with second hand

Only a few live frogs are needed to do Part A. Students can work in groups to make their observations. Keep live frogs in an aquarium with some dry surfaces exposed.

Preserved frogs are available from a biological supply house. The same frog is to be used for Parts B and C of this investigation. Have students store their frogs in tightly sealed plastic bags labeled with their names.

Safety 🔬 🧤 ✂️ 🧪

Put on a laboratory apron if one is available. Handle all glassware carefully. Be careful when handling sharp instruments. Always use special caution when working with laboratory chemicals, as they may irritate the skin or cause staining of the skin or clothing. Never touch or taste any chemical unless instructed to do so. Follow your teacher's directions and all appropriate safety procedures when handling animals. Note all safety alert symbols next to the steps in the Procedure and review the meanings of each symbol by referring to the symbol guide on page 10.

Procedure
Part A. Observing a Live Frog

1. Line a large glass jar with moist paper towels. Place a live frog in the jar. Cover the jar so that the frog will not escape. **Note:** *Do not let the paper towels become dry. Sprinkle water on the towels if they begin to dry out.* The glass jar should be large enough to allow for some movement of the frog.

2. Observe the frog without disturbing it. Answer question 1 in Observations.

3. Closely observe the movement of the throat and nostrils as the frog breathes. Also observe the sides of the body. Answer questions 2 and 3 in Observations.

4. With your fingers, gently prod the frog and observe how it jumps. Observe the function of the front and back legs as the frog jumps and lands. Answer questions 4 and 5 in Observations.

5. Moisten your hands with water. Carefully pick up the frog and place it in an aquarium partially filled with room-temperature water. Observe how the frog swims and floats. Answer questions 6 through 10 in Observations.

6. Return the live frog to your teacher when you have completed your observations.

Part B. External Anatomy of the Frog

1. Obtain a preserved frog. Rinse the frog with water to remove excess preservative. **CAUTION:** *The preservative used on the frog can irritate your skin. Avoid touching your eyes while working with the frog.* Dry the frog with paper towels and place it in a dissecting tray.

2. Identify the dorsal and ventral surfaces and the anterior and posterior ends of the frog. Answer question 11 in Observations.

3. Locate the forelegs and the hindlegs. Each foreleg, or arm, is divided into four regions: upper arm, forearm, wrist, and hand. Each hindleg also has four regions: thigh, lower leg, ankle, and foot. Identify the parts of the forelegs and hindlegs. Examine the hands and feet of the frog. If the hands have enlarged thumbs, the frog is a male. Answer questions 12 through 14 in Observations.

4. Locate the two large, protruding eyes. Lift the outer eyelid using a probe. Beneath the outer lid is an inner lid called the nictitating membrane. Answer question 15 in Observations.

5. Posterior to each eye is a circular region of tightly stretched skin. This region is the tympanic membrane, or eardrum. Locate the tympanic membranes on both sides of the head.

6. Anterior to the eyes, locate two openings called the external nares (singular, naris), or nostrils.

7. In the appropriate place in Observations, label the following external areas and structures of a frog: anterior, posterior, dorsal, ventral, forelimb, hand, hindlimb, foot, tympanic membrane, external nares, eye, nictitating membrane, and mouth.

8. Hold the frog firmly in the dissecting tray. Using scissors, make a small cut at each of the hinged points of the jaw, as shown in Figure 1. **CAUTION:** *To avoid injury, cut in a direction away from your hands and body.* Open the mouth as much as possible. Under running water rinse away any excess preservative.

Cut jaws on both sides along the dotted line. Cut away from hands and body to avoid injury.

Figure 1

9. The tongue is the most noticeable structure in the mouth. Observe where the tongue is attached and note the two projections at the free end. Answer question 16 in Observations.

10. At the back of the mouth, locate the large horizontal opening, the gullet opening. In front of the gullet opening, find a vertical slit, the glottis.

11. Look for two openings on the back sides of the floor of the mouth. These are the openings to the vocal sacs. They are present in male frogs but not in female frogs.

12. Examine the roof of the mouth. Near the front center of the roof of the mouth are two small bumps. These bumps are the vomerine teeth. On either side of the vomerine teeth are the openings of the internal nares. Behind the vomerine teeth, observe two large bulges. These bulges are the eye sockets. Run your fingers along the top jaw. The teeth you feel are the maxillary teeth. The openings of the Eustachian tubes are on either side near the back of the mouth. Insert a probe into an opening of one Eustachian tube. Note where the probe stops.

13. In the appropriate place in Observations, label the following parts of a frog's mouth: vomerine teeth, internal nares, maxillary teeth, eye sockets, openings to Eustachian tubes, tongue, gullet opening, glottis, and openings to vocal sacs.

Part C. Internal Anatomy of the Frog

You may want to dissect a frog and display it for students to refer to throughout the dissection.

1. Place your preserved frog in a dissecting tray with the ventral surface up. With dissecting pins, securely pin the frog's feet and hands to the bottom of the dissecting tray as shown in Figure 2. Angle the pins away from the body of the frog so that they will not interfere with your dissection.

Figure 2

2. With forceps, lift the loose skin of the abdomen. Carefully insert the tip of a pair of scissors beneath the skin. **CAUTION:** *To avoid cutting yourself, cut in a direction away from your hands and body.* Cut the skin along line *AB* as shown in Figure 2. Using forceps and scissors, continue cutting the skin along lines *CD* and *EF*.

3. With your fingers, carefully separate the skin from the underlying muscles. Open the flaps of skin as far back as possible and pin them to the bottom of the dissecting tray. Angle the pins away from the body of the frog so that they will not interfere with your dissection. Notice the blood vessels branching throughout the inner lining of the skin. Observe the abdominal and pectoral muscles. Note the direction of the muscle fibers.

4. Carefully lift the abdominal muscles with the forceps. Cut a second *AB* incision. **Note:** *Keep the cut through the muscles shallow so as not to damage underlying organs.* As the incision is made in the chest, or pectoral area, you will need to cut through bone. This bone is part of the pectoral girdle. **Note:** *Use extra force with the scissors when cutting through the bone. Be careful not to damage any of the internal organs below the bone.* Make cuts *CD* and *EF* through the abdominal muscle.

5. Remove the pins holding the skin in place. Stretch the abdominal opening as much as possible. At this time the hands and feet of the frog may need to be repinned.

6. Study the positions of the exposed organs. Notice that most of the organs are held in place by thin, transparent tissues called mesenteries.

7. If the frog is a mature female, the most obvious organs will be the ovaries. The ovaries are white sacs swollen with tiny black-and-white eggs. Carefully lift the ovaries from the body cavity, cut the attachments with scissors, and remove the ovaries from the frog. **Note:** *Be careful not to rupture the ovaries with the scissors. If the ovaries are ruptured, they can spill out a mess of eggs.*

8. The large reddish-brown organ in the upper part of the abdominal cavity is the liver. Answer question 17 in Observations.

9. With your fingers or a probe, lift and separate the lobes of the liver upward. Behind the middle lobe, look for a greenish, finger-shaped gland. This gland is the gallbladder. You may be able to locate the bile duct leading from the liver to the gallbladder.

10. With scissors, carefully remove the liver and gallbladder from the body. The remaining organs of the digestive system are easier to see with the liver removed.

DIGESTIVE SYSTEM

11. Locate the esophagus, which is a white tube leading from the mouth and connecting to the upper part of the white, muscular stomach. Notice the shape of the stomach. Look for a constriction at the lowest part of the stomach. This constriction is the pylorus. The pylorus leads into the long, coiled small intestine. Pull the loops of small intestine away from the body. Notice the mesentery that holds the intestines in place. Inside the first loop of the small intestine near the stomach, locate a thin, white organ called the pancreas. Also in the intestinal mesentery, locate a brown bean-shaped organ called the spleen. **Note:** *The spleen is an organ of the circulatory system.* Answer questions 18 and 19 in Observations.

12. The small intestine ends in a large bag-shaped organ, the large intestine. The last organ of the digestive system is the cloaca, a saclike organ at the end of the large intestine. Undigested food leaves the frog's body through an opening called the anus.

13. With scissors, cut the esophagus near the stomach. Cut through the large intestine just above the cloaca. With your fingers, carefully remove the digestive system from the body.

14. Stretch out the digestive system on the dissecting tray. With scissors, cut open the stomach along its outside curve. Open the stomach and examine its structure and contents. Answer questions 20 through 22 in Observations.

15. Dispose of the digestive system, liver, and ovaries according to your teacher's instructions.

16. In the appropriate place in Observations, label the following parts of the frog's digestive system and related organs: esophagus, stomach, pylorus, small intestine, large intestine, cloaca, liver, gallbladder, pancreas, mesentery, anus, and spleen.

UROGENITAL SYSTEM

17. The reproductive system and urinary system of the frog are closely connected and can be studied as the combined urogenital system. The two kidneys are reddish-brown organs located on the dorsal posterior wall of the abdominal cavity. The kidneys lie on either side of the backbone. **Note:** *The kidneys may be covered with a thin membrane. If so, carefully tear open the membrane with the point of a dissecting needle.* The yellow, fingerlike lobes attached to the kidneys are fat bodies. A small, twisted tube called the ureter leads from each kidney into the saclike urinary bladder. The bladder is connected to the cloaca.

18. Locate the reproductive organs of the frog. If your frog is a male, it possesses testes, tiny white or yellow oval organs found on the ventral surface of the kidneys.

19. If your frog is female, it possessed egg-filled ovaries that were removed in step 7. If your frog is an immature female, the pale oval ovaries are located ventral to the kidneys. Leading from each ovary is a long, coiled tube called the oviduct. The oviduct extends along the side of the body cavity. The oviduct eventually joins the cloaca.

20. In the appropriate place in Observations, label the following parts of the male and female urogenital systems: kidney, fat body, ureter, urinary bladder, cloaca, testes, ovary filled with eggs, and oviduct.

RESPIRATORY SYSTEM

21. Locate the two lungs. They are small, spongy brown sacs that lie to the right and left of the heart. Look for the bronchial tubes that extend from the anterior part of the lungs and join with the trachea, or windpipe.

22. Insert a dropper into the glottis of the frog. Pump air into the lungs and observe what happens. Answer question 23 in Observations.

23. With scissors and forceps, carefully remove the lungs from the frog's body. Dispose of the lungs according to your teacher's instructions.

CIRCULATORY SYSTEM

24. Locate the heart. The heart is encased in a membranous sac called the pericardium. With the tip of the scissors, carefully cut open the pericardium.

25. Note the vessels attached to the heart. The large artery on the ventral surface of the heart is the coronary artery. **Note:** *If the frog has been injected with red and blue latex paint, the veins and arteries will be obvious.*

26. Carefully cut the blood vessels leading to and from the heart. Remove the heart from the frog. Place the heart in the dissecting tray with the dorsal surface facing up. Identify the right and left atria and the ventricle. Touch and compare the walls of the two atria and the ventricle. Answer question 24 in Observations.

27. Observe the dorsal surface of the heart. Locate the thin-walled triangular sac called the sinus venosus. Locate the two veins leading from the top and the one vein leading from the bottom of the sinus venosus.

28. With a scalpel, cut the heart into anterior and posterior halves. Note the thickness of the walls and the types of heart chambers. **CAUTION:** *Be careful when using a scalpel. Always cut in a direction away from your hands and body.*

29. In the appropriate place in Observations, label the following structures of the frog's heart: right atrium, left atrium, ventricle, coronary artery, and sinus venosus.

MUSCULAR SYSTEM

30. Remove the pins from the frog's feet and hands.

31. Cut the skin completely around the upper thigh of one leg, as if cutting off the leg of a pair of pants. With forceps, carefully pull the skin downward to the foot. Expose the thigh muscles, the knee, and the calf muscles.

32. Move the lower leg up and down to simulate the leg movement during a jump. Observe the various leg muscles involved in the leg movement. Answer question 25 in Observations.

33. Follow your teacher's instructions for storing the frog for further use or properly disposing of the frog and its parts. Thoroughly wash, dry, and put away your dissecting tray and tools. Wash your hands with soap and water.

Observations

External Anatomy of the Frog

Mouthparts of the Frog

Eye socket

Gullet
Glottis

Tongue

Maxillary teeth

Internal naris (nostril)

Vomerine teeth

Opening to Eustachian tube

Opening to vocal sacs

Digestive System and Other Parts of the Frog

Esophagus

Gallbladder
Mesentery
Pancreas

Small intestine

Large intestine

Liver

Stomach

Spleen
Pylorus

Cloaca

Anus

Urogenital System of the Frog

The Frog Heart

1. **Describe how the eyes of a frog close.** Lids close from the top and bottom and meet in the center of the eye. The eyeball is pressed into the mouth when the eye is closed.

2. **a. How many times do the nostrils open and close in one minute?** Answers will vary.

   b. How many times does the throat move up and down in one minute?
   Answers should be the same as 2a.

3. **Describe the movements of the sides of the frog's body during breathing.**
   The sides of the frog move in and out.

4. **Describe how a frog jumps.** The hindlegs project the frog; the forelegs absorb the shock of the landing.

5. a. Are the hindlegs or forelegs more important in jumping? The hindlegs are more important in
jumping.

b. Are the hindlegs or forelegs more important in landing? The forelegs are more important in
landing.

6. Is the skin of the frog smooth or rough? Moist or dry? The skin of the frog is smooth and moist.

7. Why is the frog difficult to hold? The frog's moist, slippery skin makes it difficult to hold.

8. Describe the position of a frog when it floats. The head, specifically the eyes and nostrils, are above
water. The rest of the body hangs down with the front and back legs extended.

9. What parts of the body remain above the surface when the frog floats?
The eyes and nostrils remain above water.

10. How does the frog use its legs while swimming? The back legs provide power for swimming.
The front legs are not actively involved.

11. Describe the color of the dorsal and ventral surfaces of the frog. The dorsal side is green and
brown spotted; the ventral side is white or cream-colored.

12. How many digits are on each of the frog's hands? A frog's hand has 4 digits.

13. How many digits are on each of the frog's feet? A frog's foot has 5 digits.

14. Is your frog male or female? How can you tell? Answers will vary. Males have enlarged thumbs;
females have normal-sized thumbs.

15. Where is the nictitating membrane attached? The nictitating membrane is attached at the bottom of the eye.

16. Where is the tongue attached to the mouth? The tongue is attached to the front of the lower jaw.

17. How many lobes does the liver contain? The liver has 3 lobes.

18. What is the shape of the stomach? The frog's stomach has a J-shape.

19. Describe the mesentery that holds the intestines. The mesentery contains many blood vessels.

20. Describe the general shape, or plan, of the frog's digestive system.
The frog's digestive system is one long, continuous tube.

21. Describe the inside wall of the stomach. The inside wall of the stomach is ridged and muscular.

22. Describe the contents of the frog's stomach. Answers will vary, depending on individual frogs.

23. What happens when air is pumped into the lungs? The lungs become inflated.

24. Compare the walls of the two atria and the ventricle. The walls of the atria are thinner and less muscular than the walls of the ventricle.

25. Describe the movement of the leg muscles as the leg is bent and straightened.
Muscles work in opposing pairs with one muscle stretched while the other muscle is contracted.

Analysis and Conclusions

1. How does the number of times the nostrils open and close in one minute compare with the number of times the throat moves up and down in one minute? The numbers are the same, indicating a relationship between the movement of the nostrils and the throat.

2. How are the feet of a frog adapted for swimming? Frogs have long, flipperlike feet with webbing between the toes.

3. How is the coloration of the frog an adaptation to its habitat? The dark dorsal surface provides camouflage in swamps, ponds, and grass. The light ventral surface provides camouflage in water as seen from below.

4. How is the location of the nares an adaptation to living in water? The position of the nares enables the frog to breathe while being partly submerged under water.

5. The tip of the tongue in a live frog is sticky. What would be the advantage of this? The frog's sticky tongue would be useful for holding insects and catching prey.

6. How does the length of the small intestine relate to its function in absorbing digested food? Because the small intestine is so long, there is a large amount of surface area to absorb digested food.

7. Explain why in a frog's heart the ventricle has a thicker wall than the atrium. The ventricle is the chamber that pumps blood to all parts of the body, so the ventricle must have enough muscle to do so.

Critical Thinking and Application

1. Frogs are insect eaters. How is the frog's tongue designed for the type of food it eats? Because the frog's tongue is attached at the front of its mouth, the frog is able to flip out its tongue to catch insects. The surface of the tongue is also sticky, which enables it to better hold its prey.

2. List three adaptations that permit the frog to live on land successfully.

Answers might include protective coloration, jumping legs, strong backbone, 3-chambered heart, and lungs.

3. List three adaptations that permit the frog to live in water successfully.

Answers may include webbed feet, white ventral side, wet skin through which it breathes, nictitating membrane, and the ability to float with nostrils and eyes above water.

4. The frog's sense organs are located on top of the head. How does this help the frog when it is in the water? The frog can keep its sense organs above the water while it is swimming. This could be useful in catching prey or avoiding a predator.

Going Further

1. Construct a terrarium with a habitat that is favorable to a frog. Obtain a live frog and place it in the terrarium. Feed the frog several live insects and observe its feeding behavior.

2. Examine the skeleton of a preserved frog. To do this, carefully remove the skin, muscles, and organs of the frog. Work in one area of the body at a time until the bones are exposed. Using reference materials, identify as many bones as possible.

3. Carefully remove the brain and spinal cord of a preserved frog. To do this, remove the skin from the dorsal surface of the frog. Using a probe and a dissecting needle, carefully chip away the bone of the cranial cavity and the vertebral column. **Note:** *To remove the brain and spinal cord in one piece, work slowly and carefully.* Using reference materials, identify the parts of the brain. Sketch and label the parts of the brain.

Frog Brain

63

Adaptations in Lizards

You may want to refer students to pages 707–719 in the textbook for a discussion of reptiles.

Time required: 50 minutes.

Pre-Lab Discussion

Members of class Reptilia, which are called reptiles, are ectothermic, or "cold-blooded," vertebrates that are covered with dry scaly skin. They are adapted for reproduction on land. Most species are land-dwelling, but some species spend much time in water. Turtles, snakes, lizards, crocodiles, and alligators are reptiles. Reptilian skin is dry, thick, and waterproof, protecting the body from drying out even in very arid climates. The skin is covered by tough scales that protect the animal from injury.

Anolis carolinensis, or the anole or American chameleon, is a common lizard found throughout the southern United States. It can be found on shrubs, trees, and fences and on the ground. Often it is found around homes, and it seems to thrive in areas inhabited by humans. The anole is best known for the variability of its skin color, which can change from green to brown or gray. This change in skin color is thought to be stimulated by changes in light intensity, temperature, and emotional state.

In this investigation, you will observe the external structures of an anole. You will also observe its response to environmental change.

Problem

What are the external structures of a lizard? What changes occur in a lizard's coloration in different environments?

Materials *(per group)*

Preserved anole Available from biological supply houses.
Live anole
Aquarium or large glass jar
6 sheets of construction paper (green,
   yellow, brown, red, black, and white)
Metric ruler
Dissecting tray
Paper towels

Live anoles are available from biological supply houses or they can be collected in nature. Anoles will not drink water from a container. Set up a terrarium and each day spray the plants with water so that the anoles can lick the water droplets.

Safety ⚗ 📷 🧪

Put on a laboratory apron if one is available. Handle all glassware carefully. Always use special caution when working with laboratory chemicals, as they may irritate the skin or cause staining of the skin or clothing. Never touch or taste any chemical unless instructed to do so. Follow your teacher's directions and all appropriate safety procedures when handling live animals. Note all safety alert symbols next to the steps in the Procedure and review the meanings of each symbol by referring to the symbol guide on page 10.

Procedure
Part A. External Anatomy of the Anole

1. Obtain a preserved anole. Rinse the anole with water to remove excess preservative. **CAUTION:** *The preservative used on the anole can irritate your skin. Avoid touching your eyes while working with the anole.* Dry the anole with paper towels and place it in a dissecting tray.

2. Measure the entire body length of the anole in centimeters. Record this measurement in Data Table 1. Also measure the length of the tail alone in centimeters. Record this measurement in Data Table 1. Obtain the measurements of four other groups of students and record this information in Data Table 1. Determine the average length of the five anoles and their tails and record this information in Data Table 1.

3. Observe the texture and color of the anole's skin. Answer questions 1 and 2 in Observations.

4. Identify the sex of your anole. Males are generally larger than females and have a dewlap, or fold of skin under the neck. Females have only a small, primitive dewlap. Answer question 3 in Observations.

5. Locate the head, trunk, and tail of the anole.

6. Examine the head of the anole. Look for the presence of eyelids and external ear openings. Look for the presence of nostrils.

7. Open the mouth of the anole. Look for the presence of teeth.

8. Examine the feet of the anole.

9. In the appropriate place in Observations, label the following external structures of the anole: head, trunk, tail, dewlap, foot, nostrils, and external ear opening.

10. Follow your teacher's instructions for storing the anole for further use.

Part B. Protective Behavior of an Anole

1. Place a sheet of white construction paper on the floor of an aquarium or a large glass jar.

2. Obtain a live anole. Place the anole in the aquarium or jar on the sheet of paper. Record the original color of the anole in Data Table 2. Observe any color changes in the skin of the anole. Record your observations in Data Table 2. **Note:** *Allow the anole to calm down for several minutes before observing any changes in color.*

3. Repeat steps 1 and 2 for each of the colored sheets of paper.

4. Return the anole to your teacher.

Observations

External Anatomy of the Anole

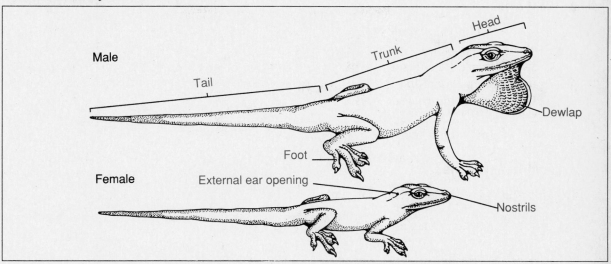

Data Table 1

Anole	Entire Body Length (cm)	Tail Length Only (cm)
1		
2		
3	Answers will vary.	
4		
5		
Average		

Data Table 2

Background Color	Original Color of Anole	Anole Color After Several Minutes
	Answers will vary.	

1. Describe the texture and appearance of the anole's skin. The anole's skin has a rough surface that is covered with horny epidermal scales.

2. What is the color of your anole? Answers will vary, but the anole will probably be green or brown.

3. What is the sex of your anole? How can you tell? Answers will vary. Students should look for the absence or presence of a dewlap.

Analysis and Conclusions

1. How does the anole's average tail length compare to its average body length?
Answers will vary, but students should find that the tail is as long if not longer than the trunk and the head combined.

2. What is a possible function of the dewlap? Students might answer that it aids in courtship or mating behavior. They might also mention that, when flared, its menacing appearance helps to frighten predators.

3. What is the function of the eyelids on the anole? Because anoles live in hot, dry climates, the eyelids function to shield the eyes from the sun, much as our eyelids do.

4. What is the function of the teeth of the anole? The teeth are used to grind insects or other food for the anole.

5. How are the anole's feet adapted for life on land? The anole does not have webbed feet. This aids the anole in running and climbing on land.

6. In what way do bright and dark background colors affect the intensity of reflected light?
Bright colors will reflect more light, whereas darker colors tend to absorb more light.

7. In general, what color does the anole become when placed against dark backgrounds? Against

light backgrounds? Answers will vary, but students should find that the anole changes to a lighter color

against light backgrounds and to a darker color against dark backgrounds.

Critical Thinking and Application

1. The anole has the ability to lose its tail and then regenerate a new one. How is this a useful

adaptation for the anole? If the anole is grabbed by a predator, it can lose its tail and escape. Later the

anole will grow a new tail.

2. Only two species of lizard are poisonous. Why do most lizards not need to produce poisonous

venom for survival? Because lizards prey on insects and other small animals, they do not need to use

venom to immobilize their prey. The two poisonous species of lizard are large, carnivorous animals.

3. Name three adaptations that anoles have for living on land. Answers may include tough, thick skin,

nonwebbed feet, lungs, protective coloration, eyelids, nostrils, and teeth.

4. Why are reptiles not found in arctic regions? Because reptiles are ectothermic, they obtain most of

their body heat from the environment. In arctic areas, the temperature is too low and does not provide

sufficient warmth for the reptiles to carry on their metabolic processes.

Going Further

1. Observe living anoles for several weeks. Record and compare the behaviors of males and females. Observe movements, social structure, territoriality, and feeding habits.

2. Obtain a liquid-crystal temperature strip. Under the supervision of your teacher, hold the strip against the skin of a live anole. Record the surface temperature of the anole. Place the anole in the sun for 5 minutes and check the temperature again. Carry out the same procedure with a small mammal such as a gerbil or hamster and compare the results.

64

Examining Bird Adaptations

You may want to refer students to pages 723–731 in the textbook for a discussion of birds.

Time required: 50 minutes.

Pre-Lab Discussion

All birds are grouped in the class Aves. Birds are endothermic, or warm-blooded, vertebrates. The streamlined shape of their feather-covered bodies enables them to fly efficiently. Although a number of modern birds cannot fly, all birds are descended from ancestors that were capable of flight. The forelimbs of birds are wings, which are used for flight in most birds. Birds also have a four-chambered heart and a closed circulatory system.

There are many different types of birds. Each type of bird has special adaptations that enable it to live successfully in its environment. The mouth of a bird is formed by a toothless projecting beak. The various shapes and sizes of beaks are adaptations for eating different kinds of foods. The structure of a bird's legs and feet also exhibits adaptations based on the bird's native environment. Birds can also have different types of feathers. These feathers, which are actually modified scales, serve many different functions.

In this investigation, you will examine some of the general characteristics of birds. You will also observe how the feathers, legs, feet, and beaks of various birds enable them to survive in their environments.

Problem

In what ways are various birds adapted to different environments?

Materials *(per group)*

Contour feather   Feathers can be obtained from local craft stores.
Down feather
Pinfeather
Hand lens
Chicken leg bone (femur)   Have students save and clean chicken leg bones whenever
Scalpel or single-edged razor blade   they have chicken to eat at home.

Safety 🔺 ▦

Put on a laboratory apron if one is available. Handle all glassware carefully. Be careful when handling sharp instruments. Note all safety alert symbols next to the steps in the Procedure and review the meanings of each symbol by referring to the symbol guide on page 10.

Procedure
Part A. Examining Feathers

1. Obtain a contour feather. Use Figure 1 to locate the different parts of the feather. The shaft of the feather has two parts: the quill and the rachis. Observe that the rachis supports the hairlike barbs that make up the vane. Notice that the portion of the vane on one side of the shaft is narrower than the vane portion on the other side of the shaft. In a bird's wing, the narrow portion of the vane on one feather overlaps the wide portion of the vane on the feather next to it. This slight overlap allows for a smooth, continuous wing surface.

Figure 1

2. Use the hand lens to closely examine the quill. Answer question 1 in Observations. You may want to cut off the bottoms of the quills before the investigation begins.
3. Use the hand lens to examine the feather's vane. Gently ruffle the edge of the feather, and find the barbules on the barbs. Smooth the feather with your finger. Notice how easily the barbs can be smoothed back into place.

4. Obtain a down feather. Identify the quill, rachis, and barbs of this feather. In the space provided in Observations, draw the down feather. Label the quill, rachis, and barbs.

5. Notice the length, width, and flexibility of the shaft of the down feather. Answer question 2 in Observations.

6. Examine the down feather with a hand lens. Try to smooth the down feather as you did the contour feather. Answer question 3 in Observations.

7. Obtain a pinfeather, or filoplume. Examine the pinfeather with a hand lens. The pinfeather consists of a single, hairlike shaft that ends in a few barbs. In the space provided in Observations, draw a pinfeather. Label the shaft and barbs.

Part B. Examining a Chicken Bone

1. Observe the relative weight of a chicken leg bone (femur). Note its flexibility.

2. Using a scalpel or single-edged razor blade, carefully cut the chicken femur in half. **CAUTION:** *Be very careful when using a scalpel or razor blade. To avoid injury, cut in a direction away from your hands and body.* Observe the internal structure of the bone. Answer question 4 in Observations.

3. Follow your teacher's instructions for the proper disposal or storage of the chicken bone.

Part C. Examining Adaptations of Bird Feet

1. Observe the drawings of the birds in Figure 2 on this page and on the following page. Examine the toes of each bird. Count the number of toes on the foot of each bird and record this information in Data Table 1. Answer question 5 in Observations.

Osprey

Woodpecker

Jaçana

Heron

Mallard duck

Figure 2

Quail

Hummingbird

Rhea

Pelican

Whippoorwill

Figure 2 (continued)

2. Examine the foot of each bird in Figure 2 and indicate the position (front or back of foot) of the toes. Record this information in Data Table 1. Also examine the relative size of the talons, or nails. Describe them as large, medium, small, long, thin, etc. Record this information in Data Table 1.

3. Determine the structure and function of each foot from the following list. Record this information in Data Table 1.

- Scratching foot: rakelike toes for finding food in soil

- Perching foot: long back toe that can hold on to a perch tightly

- Swimming foot: webbed, paddlelike

- Running foot: three toes rather than four

- Wading foot: large foot and long leg for wading in shallow water

- Specialized foot: long talons and toes for running over leaves of large water plants

- Climbing foot: two hind toes for support when climbing upward to prevent falling backward

- Grasping foot: large curved claws to grab and hold such prey as fish, mice, and other small animals

Part D. Examining Adaptations of Bird Beaks

1. Examine the relative shape and size of the beak of each bird in Figure 2. Determine the structure and function of each beak from the following list. Record this information in Data Table 2.

- Chisel: used for drilling into trees

- Short and stout: used to eat insects, seeds, small crustaceans; multipurpose

- Tubular: used to obtain nectar from flowers

- Hooked: used to tear flesh

- Flat, broad, and slightly hooked: used to strain algae and small organisms from water

- Cracker: used to crack seeds; short and stout; sometimes curved upper portion

- Scoop: used to scoop fish from water; long and stout

- Spear-shaped and stout: used to spear fish

- Trap: used to trap insects in midair

Observations

Down Feather

Pinfeather

Data Table 1

Bird	Number of Toes	Toe Positions	Size of Talons	Type or Function
Heron	4	3 in front 1 in back	Short	Wading
Osprey	4	3 in front 1 in back	Large	Grasping
Woodpecker	4	2 in front 2 in back	Medium	Climbing
Duck	4	3 in front 1 in back	Small	Swimming
Jaçana	4	3 in front 1 in back	Long and thin	Specialized
Quail	4	3 in front 1 in back	Short	Scratching
Pelican	4	3 in front 1 in back	Short	Swimming
Hummingbird	4	3 in front 1 in back	Short	Perching
Rhea	3	3 in front	Medium	Running
Whippoorwill	4	3 in front 1 in back	Small	Perching

Data Table 2

Bird	Structure of Beak	Function of Beak
Heron	Spear-shaped	Spearing fish
Osprey	Hooked	Tearing flesh
Woodpecker	Chisel	Drilling into trees
Duck	Flat, broad, slightly hooked	Straining food from water
Jaçana	Short and stout	Eating insects
Quail	Cracker	Cracking seeds
Pelican	Scoop	Scooping up fish
Hummingbird	Tubular	Sucking nectar
Rhea	Short and stout	Eating insects
Whippoorwill	Trap	Trapping insects

1. Is the quill of the contour feather solid or hollow? The quill is hollow.

2. How does the down feather shaft compare to the contour feather shaft?

The shaft of the down feather is shorter, thinner, and more flexible than the shaft of the contour feather.

3. Do the barbs of the down feather stick together when you smooth it?

No. The barbules of the down feather lack hooks to lock them together.

4. Describe the external and internal features of the chicken femur. The bone is not very thick and is hollow. It is extremely lightweight. The ends of the bone appear to be thicker than the center. In some places, the inside of the bone resembles lace or a sponge; it has many open spaces separated by thin walls of bone.

5. How many toes do most birds have? Most birds have 4 toes.

Analysis and Conclusions

1. How does the structure of a contour feather shaft make it well adapted for flight?

The contour feather shaft is both hollow and rigid. This makes the feather lightweight but strong enough to stand firm against wind resistance.

2. How do hooks increase the strength of a contour feather? The hooks on one set of barbules latch onto another set of crossing barbules, thus locking the barbs together.

3. Down feathers are found underneath a bird's contour feathers. What is the function of this type of feather? The fluffiness of down feathers allows a layer of air to be trapped next to the bird's body. This air acts as insulation to keep the bird warm.

4. Why is the filoplume also called a pinfeather? The long, thin shape of the filoplume looks pinlike.

5. How are a bird's bones well adapted for flight? The light, hollow bones are easy to lift into the air. Also, the flexibility of the bones keeps them from breaking when they work against air resistance.

6. In what way are the feet of the woodpecker adapted to its feeding position?

The woodpecker stands vertically in trees while feeding. The position of its toes keeps the bird from falling

backward.

Critical Thinking and Application

1. What characteristics of the down feather make it useful as a stuffing for pillows and sleeping

bags? The flexible shaft and lack of hooks on the barbules make the down feather fluffy. This fluffiness

makes down a soft, comfortable stuffing and helps it trap air, making it a good insulator.

2. The skeleton and feathers of a bird are found. The bones are solid and heavy, and the forelimbs are short. Do you think that this bird was able to fly well when it was alive? Explain

your answer. It is very unlikely that this bird was an able flier. Solid, heavy bones would be difficult to lift

off the ground, especially if the bird had poorly developed forelimbs, or wings.

3. Write a description of the beak and feet of each of the following:

a. An aquatic bird that strains plankton from the water for food This type of bird might have a

webbed, paddlelike foot for easy movement through the water. It would also need a flat, wide, slightly

hooked beak to scoop up the plankton.

b. A bird that eats insects out of the cracks in trees This type of bird would need a climbing foot

with two toes facing backward to keep it from falling from the tree. It would need a long, pointed,

chisellike beak to remove insects from the tree cracks.

Going Further

1. Complete a nature study of birds. Obtain a field guide to birds. Use the guide to help identify the birds in your area. A pair of binoculars will also be helpful. Observe the movements, feeding behavior, coloration, nest shape, and location of the birds.

2. Many bird species have become extinct in recent years. Find out about the extinction of the passenger pigeon, dusky seaside sparrow, Hawaiian o'o, Carolina parakeet, and moa.

65

The Most Intelligent Mammal

You may want to refer students to pages 737–751 in the textbook for a discussion of mammals.

Time required: 45 minutes.

Pre-Lab Discussion

Mammals have the most highly developed brain of all animals. This enables them to perform a wide range of complicated behaviors.

Some of a mammal's behaviors are unlearned. This means that the mammal is capable of performing the behavior without being taught. Unlearned behaviors include reflexes and instincts. Reflexes are simple, quick, automatic responses—jerking away from contact with a hot object, for example. Instincts are inborn behavioral patterns that can be modified very little, if at all. A spider's web-building, a crane's courtship dance, and a newborn mammal's suckling are examples of instincts.

Many of a mammal's behaviors are learned, or acquired through experience. Because mammals have a large, highly sophisticated cerebrum—the part of the brain involved with learning, memory, and thinking—they are capable of performing a wide array of learned behaviors. Some examples of learned behaviors in humans include habits and solving visual or word problems. The most advanced type of learned behavior is known as insight learning, or reasoning. Reasoning is the ability to apply previous learning to a totally new situation. Reasoning is rare in animals other than primates and is found most often in humans, which are the most intelligent of all mammals.

In this investigation, you will study learned and unlearned human behavior.

Problem

Which types of human behaviors are unlearned and which are learned? What roles do reflexes, conditioned responses, habits, trial-and-error learning, and reasoning play in human behavior?

Materials *(per pair of students)*

Paper
Pencil
Clock or watch with second hand

Procedure
Part A. Reflexes

1. A reflex is a simple, automatic response to a stimulus. A reflex usually involves only part of the body. Working with a partner, you will alternate as subject and helper while you test two human reflexes. You will record the responses in Data Table 1.

2. Close your eyes and cover them with your hands. At the end of one minute, remove your hands and open your eyes while your partner watches your eyes closely. Record the response in Data Table 1.

3. Stand with your side to a wall. Hold your arm down at your side and slightly away from your body. Tightly press the back of your hand against the wall until your shoulder begins to ache. After one minute, step away from the wall while still holding your arm stiff. Record the response in Data Table 1.

Part B. Conditioned Responses

1. Read the following instructions to your partner: "Each time I say 'Write,' I want you to make a tally mark on a sheet of paper. Then place your pencil in position to make the next mark."

2. Give the command to write several times in succession. For most of the commands, hit your pencil on the desk at the same time that you say the word "Write."

3. Occasionally, hit your pencil on the desk but do not give the command to write. Try this several times. Answer question 1 in Observations.

Part C. Habits

1. Divide a sheet of lined paper in half lengthwise. Label one column "Normal Hand." Label the other column "Other Hand." Now use your normal writing hand to write your name as many times as you can in 30 seconds. Follow the same procedure in the second column using your other hand. Answer questions 2 and 3 in Observations.

2. Dictate the following passage to your partner while he or she writes it down. Dictate at a fairly rapid pace. "Habits are often useful in allowing routine activities to be carried out quickly. But most of us have some habits that we would like to break. Breaking a habit is not a simple thing to do."

3. Dictate the same passage again, but this time instruct your partner not to cross any *t*'s or dot any *i*'s. Answer question 4 in Observations.

Part D. Trial-and-Error Learning

1. Trial-and-error learning begins when an animal associates certain responses with favorable or unfavorable consequences. The animal then tries to repeat those behaviors that led to favorable results.

2. Find out how quickly you can successfully complete a path through Maze 1 in Figure 1 in Observations. Use a pencil to mark your path and have your partner time you. Record the time needed to complete Maze 1 in Data Table 2.

3. Complete the rest of the mazes in succession, timing each one as you go. Cover each completed maze as you finish so that you cannot look back at the completed mazes. Record your results in Data Table 2. Graph your results on the graph in Observations.

Part E. Reasoning

1. Reasoning is a type of learning that involves thinking, judgment, and memory. Reasoning enables humans to solve new problems without resorting to trial and error.

2. Use your ability to reason to solve the following problems.

   a. There are four separate, equal-sized boxes. Inside each box there are two separate small boxes. Inside each of the small boxes there are three even smaller boxes. Answer question 5 in Observations.

b. Figure 2 in Observations represents nine bears in a square enclosure at the zoo. Build two more square enclosures within this one so that each bear is in a pen by itself. Draw the borders of the two new enclosures directly on Figure 2.

c. There are five girls: Maureen, Sue, Jill, Robin, and Pam. They are standing in a row, but not necessarily in the order named. Neither Maureen nor Sue is next to Robin. Neither Sue nor Maureen is next to Pam. Neither Robin nor Sue is next to Jill. Pam is just to the right of Jill. Name the girls from left to right. Answer question 6 in Observations.

Observations

Data Table 1

Stimulus	Response
Light	Pupils get smaller
Pressure on arm muscle	Arm rises

1. What happened when you hit the pencil on the desk but did not give the command to write?

Answers will vary, but most students will report that their partner made a mark at least some of the time.

2. How many times did you write your name with your normal writing hand?

Answers will vary.

3. How many times did you write your name with your other hand?

Most students will write their name with their other hand fewer times than with their normal writing hand.

4. How many times did you cross *t*'s or dot *i*'s in the second passage?

Answers will vary, but students will probably cross some *t*'s and dot some *i*'s.

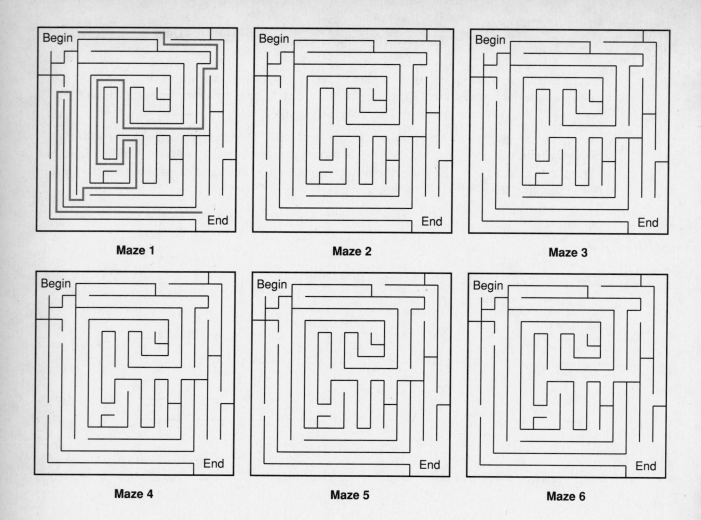

Figure 1

Data Table 2

Maze Number	Time (sec)
1	
2	
3	Answers will vary.
4	
5	
6	

Graph

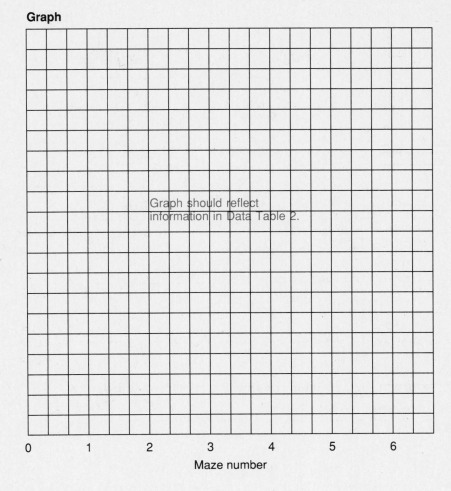

Graph should reflect
information in Data Table 2.

Time (sec)

0   1   2   3   4   5   6

Maze number

5. What is the total number of boxes? 36. _____

Figure 2

6. Name the girls from left to right: Sue, Maureen, Jill, Pam, Robin. _____

Analysis and Conclusions

1. Name three other reflexes in humans. Blinking, coughing, sneezing, breathing, vomiting, hiccuping, jerking hand back from a hot object, heartbeat.

2. How are reflexes useful to humans? Reflexes can protect us from injury and keep the body functioning normally.

3. Is a reflex a learned or an unlearned behavior? A reflex is an unlearned behavior.

4. Were you able to condition or "fool" your partner into always making a mark on the paper when you hit your pencil on the desk but did not give the command to write? Explain why you think you were or were not able to do so. Most students will not make the mark every time. The conditioning period was very short, so some students may have been fooled. Once they know what to expect, they will be more cautious.

5. Is the response to the pencil tap a learned or an unlearned behavior? It is a leaned behavior.

6. Why did a difference exist in the number of times you could write your name with your normal writing hand and with your other hand? You are not used to writing with your other hand and do not have as much practice writing with it.

7. What would you have to do to make your signature written by both hands the same? You would have to practice writing with your other hand.

8. Is a habit a learned or an unlearned behavior? A habit is a learned behavior.

9. Did any learning take place in Part D of this investigation? Give evidence to support your answer. Yes, learning did take place. This is shown by the fact that performance improved from Maze 1 to Maze 6.

Critical Thinking and Application

1. **How is the blinking response a protective reflex?** Blinking protects the eye by keeping unwanted objects out of it. You blink without thinking about it.

2. **Describe three conditioned reflexes that you exhibit while at school.**

   Answers will vary, but may include getting up when the bell rings, sitting down when the bell rings, raising your hand to ask a question or give an answer, walking a certain path, putting a heading on your paper, etc.

3. **How might you go about breaking yourself of a particular habit?** Answers will vary. Thinking consciously every time you exhibit the behavior, changing your routine, getting a hobby to occupy yourself—all of these behaviors can be helpful in breaking a habit.

4. **Describe three situations in which you learned through trial and error.**

   Answers will vary but might include tying shoelaces, learning to walk, learning to rollerskate, riding a bicycle, driving, playing a musical instrument, and skiing.

5. **Describe two situations in which the ability to reason was useful to you.**

   Answers will vary.

Going Further

1. Design and conduct an experiment to show how distractions, such as noise, television, or music, affect the time it takes to learn a short poem or solve an arithmetic problem. Construct a data table to record your results.

2. Cover Columns B, C, and D of the table on page 430 with a piece of paper. Study the words in Column A for one minute. Then write down as many words as you can remember. Record your score. Follow the same procedure for Column B, then C, and then D.

A	B	C	D
Zop	House	Purple	Sally
Wab	Tree	Gold	and
Dod	Shoe	Red	Bob
Jav	Sock	Blue	went
Cug	Dog	Yellow	to
Sor	Floor	Green	the
Duz	Rock	Orange	football
Tig	Father	Black	game
Wek	Candy	White	last
Foy	Picture	Pink	night

Which column was easiest to remember? How do you explain the difference in your ability to learn the words in each column? How can this experiment help you in studying?

The last column is the easiest to remember. Column A contains nonsense words; Column B unrelated, real words; Column C related words; and Column D words that form a sentence. Thus, as words become more meaningful they are easier to remember. That is why associations can aid studying.

66

Comparing Primates

You may want to refer students to pages 757–759 in the textbook for a discussion of primates.

Time required: 35 minutes.

Pre-Lab Discussion

In *The Descent of Man*, the English naturalist Charles Darwin formulated the hypothesis that human beings and other primates have a common ancestor. A hypothesis is a suggested explanation for observed facts. All scientific hypotheses, including that of Darwin, are based on observations.

Darwin observed that human beings and other primates differ in many important ways. Although all primates have opposable thumbs, the human hand is capable of more refined and exact movements than those of other primates. The human braincase, or cranium, has more volume and more mass than those of other primates. In addition, human beings are bipedal, or able to walk on two limbs. Other primates use all four limbs for locomotion. Being bipedal frees the arms and hands for other tasks, such as toolmaking. Darwin regarded these human traits as adaptations, resulting from natural selection. The adaptations of other primates, he suggested, evolved differently.

More recently, biochemists have determined that certain proteins found in different primates contain many of the same amino acid sequences. Scientists reason that because proteins are produced by DNA, human beings and other primates must have a similar genetic makeup. Paleontologists have also found fossil remains that provide evidence that all primates came from a common ancestor. These and other observations lend support to Darwin's hypothesis of human origins.

In this investigation, you will develop skill in observing and interpreting data provided by biochemists, paleontologists, and other scientists.

Problem

How are human beings similar to and different from other primates?

Materials *(per student)*

Metric ruler
Pencil
Protractor

Procedure

Part A. Comparing Amino Acid Sequences in Vertebrate Proteins

1. Figure 1 shows the amino acids found in selected sites in the hemoglobin of different vertebrates.

Amino Acid Positions in the Hemoglobin of Some Vertebrates

Primate	Human being	SER	THR	ALA	GLY	ASP	GLU	VAL	GLU	ASP	THR
	Chimpanzee	SER	THR	ALA	GLY	ASP	GLU	VAL	GLU	ASP	THR
	Gorilla	SER	THR	ALA	GLY	ASP	GLU	VAL	GLU	ASP	THR
	Baboon	ASN	THR	THR	GLY	ASP	GLU	VAL	ASP	ASP	SER
	Lemur	ALA	THR	SER	GLY	GLU	LYS	VAL	GLU	ASP	SER
Nonprimate	Dog	SER	SER	GLY	GLY	ASP	GLU	ILU	ASP	ASP	THR
	Chicken	GLN	THR	GLY	GLY	ALA	GLU	ILU	ALA	ASN	SER
	Frog	ASP	SER	GLY	GLY	LYS	HIS	VAL	THR	ASN	SER
Primate	Human being	PRO	GLY	GLY	ALA	ASN	ALA	THR	ARG	HIS	
	Chimpanzee	PRO	GLY	GLY	ALA	ASN	ALA	THR	ARG	HIS	
	Gorilla	PRO	GLY	GLY	ALA	ASN	ALA	THR	LYS	HIS	
	Baboon	PRO	GLY	GLY	ASN	ASN	ALA	GLN	LYS	HIS	
	Lemur	PRO	GLY	SER	HIS	ASN	ALA	GLN	LYS	HIS	
Nonprimate	Dog	PRO	SER	ASN	LYS	ASN	ALA	ALA	LYS	LYS	
	Chicken	PRO	GLU	THR	LYS	ASN	SER	GLN	ARG	ALA	
	Frog	ALA	HIS	ALA	LYS	ASN	ALA	LYS	ARG	ARG	

Figure 1

2. Count the number of molecules of each amino acid in human hemoglobin. **Note:** *Be sure to count the molecules of amino acid in human hemoglobin in the second section titled Primate as well as in the first section.* Record these totals in the appropriate column in Data Table 1.

3. Count the number of molecules of each amino acid in the hemoglobin of other vertebrates in Figure 1. (Remember to count both sections.) Record these totals in the appropriate columns in Data Table 1.

4. Going from left to right, note the position of each amino acid. Count the number of similarities in the amino acid positions in human hemoglobin as compared with the hemoglobin of each of the other vertebrates in Figure 1. Record your observations in Data Table 2.

5. Reexamine Figure 1 and count the number of differences in the amino acid positions in human hemoglobin as compared with the hemoglobin of each of the other vertebrates in Figure 1. Record your observations in Data Table 2.

Part B. Comparing Primate Features

1. Determine the relative size of the lower jaw of each primate by measuring the length in millimeters of lines *ab* and *bc* in Figure 2. Record these lengths in Data Table 3. Record the product of these lengths in Data Table 3.

2. Determine the angle of the jaw by using a protractor to measure the angle *xy* in each primate skull in Figure 2. Record your observations in Data Table 3.

Primate Skulls

Figure 2   Stress that the methods used here are not those used by anthropologists and paleontologists in comparing the bones of primates. These measurements serve only to give students relative differences in primate anatomy.

3. Examine the teeth of each of the three primates in Figure 3.

Teeth of Three Primates

Figure 3

4. Count the number of incisors, canines, premolars, and molars of each primate in Figure 3. Record your observations in the appropriate columns in Data Table 4.

5. Examine the two skeletons in Figure 4.

Two Primate Skeletons

Figure 4

6. Compare both views of skeleton A with those of skeleton B. Answer questions 1 and 2 in Observations.

Observations

Data Table 1

Number of Molecules of Different Amino Acids in Some Vertebrates									
Amino Acid	**Abbreviation**	**Human**	**Chimpanzee**	**Gorilla**	**Baboon**	**Lemur**	**Dog**	**Chicken**	**Frog**
Alanine	ALA	3	3	3	1	2	2	3	3
Arginine	ARG	1	1	0	0	0	0	1	2
Asparagine	ASN	1	1	1	3	1	2	2	2
Aspartic acid	ASP	2	2	2	3	1	3	0	1
Glutamine	GLN	0	0	0	1	1	0	2	0
Glutamic acid	GLU	2	2	2	1	2	1	2	0
Glycine	GLY	3	3	3	3	2	2	2	2
Histidine	HIS	1	1	1	1	1	0	0	2
Isoleucine	ILU	0	0	0	0	0	1	1	0
Leucine	LEU	0	0	0	0	1	0	0	0
Lysine	LYS	0	0	1	1	2	3	1	3
Proline	PRO	1	1	1	1	1	1	1	0
Serine	SER	1	1	1	1	3	3	2	2
Threonine	THR	3	3	3	2	1	1	2	1
Valine	VAL	1	1	1	1	1	0	0	1

Data Table 2

Similarities and Differences in Amino Acid Positions in Hemoglobin		
Organisms	**Number of Amino Acid Position Similarities**	**Number of Amino Acid Position Differences**
Human and chimpanzee	19	0
Human and gorilla	18	1
Human and baboon	12	7
Human and lemur	9	10
Human and dog	11	8
Human and chicken	7	12
Human and frog	6	13

Data Table 3

Comparison of Three Primate Skulls				
Skull	Length of Lower Jaw (mm) (ab)	Depth of Lower Jaw (mm) (bc)	Area of Lower Jaw (mm²) (ab x bc)	Angle of Jaw
A	60	25	1500	127°
B	42	20	840	124°
C	29	13	377	90°

Data Table 4

Comparison of Primate Teeth			
Type of Teeth	Number of Teeth		
	A	B	C
Incisors	4	4	4
Canines	2	2	2
Premolars	4	4	4
Molars	6	6	6

1. Describe three differences between skeleton A and skeleton B. Skeleton A has a curved vertebral column, a broad and bowl-shaped pelvis, and a skull that is centered over the vertebral column. Skeleton B has a straighter vertebral column, a longer pelvis, and a skull that is not centered over the vertebral column.

2. Which type of primate skeleton is considered bipedal? Skeleton A is bipedal.

Analysis and Conclusions

1. a. From your observations in Data Table 2, which primate is most closely related to the human being? The chimpanzee is most closely related to the human being. There are no amino acid position differences in the hemoglobin studied.

   b. Which primate is least closely related? The lemur is least closely related to the human being. There are 10 amino acid position differences in the hemoglobin studied.

436

2. a. Which nonprimate vertebrate listed in Data Table 2 is most closely related to the human being? The dog is most closely related to the human being. There are 8 amino acid position differences in the hemoglobin studied.

b. Which nonprimate is least closely related? The frog is least closely related to the human being. There are 13 amino acid position differences in the hemoglobin studied.

3. a. Which of the three primates shown in Figure 2 has the largest brain? What do you think is the name of this primate? Primate C has the largest brain. It is a human being.

b. Which of the three primates shown in Figure 2 has the smallest brain? What do you think is the name of this primate? Primate A has the smallest brain. It is a gorilla.

4. What is the relationship between jaw size and brain size in these three primates? In these three primates, the larger the jaw size, the smaller the brain size and vice versa.

5. From your observations in Data Table 4, what dental characteristics do the primates have in common? They all have the same types of teeth and the same number of each type of tooth.

6. Reexamine Figure 3. How would the diet of primate A differ from the diet of primate C? The large canine teeth of primate A are adapted for cutting and slashing tough materials. The teeth of primate C are small and less specialized, an adaptation to its varied diet.

7. What is an advantage of being bipedal? A bipedal animal has free use of its hands. It is also better able to see a wider range of its environment.

Critical Thinking and Application

1. Many primates use tools. For example, chimpanzees often use sticks to probe ant hills when searching for food. They also use leaves as sponges to collect drinking water. How is the use of tools by humans different from that of other primates? Primates use very primitive tools to aid in their survival. Humans generally use tools to improve their way of life, not as a means of survival. Humans make tools. The tools made and used by humans can be extremely complex.

2. The brain of the human being is larger than that of other primates. How would this relate to the different methods of communication displayed by humans and other primates? A larger brain allows humans to communicate through oral and written language, as well as through sounds and gestures. The communication methods of other primates are much less sophisticated.

3. Certain fossil evidence indicates that the primate ancestors of humans lived in areas where trees were scattered instead of clustered together. How might this type of environment have affected the development of bipedalism in humans? Animals living in areas of few trees would be unable to use their physical adaptations for climbing and swinging. This would allow for the evolution of bipedalism as a means of locomotion.

4. Describe three physical characteristics that are unique to human beings. Answers may include bipedalism, small unspecialized teeth, curving vertebral column, larger brain, head balanced on top of the backbone, and more flexible digits on the hand.

Going Further

Visit a local zoo to observe the behavior of gorillas, chimpanzees, baboons, and other primates. Observe the ways in which the animals communicate and interact with one another. What similarities and differences do you observe between the behaviors of the primates you studied and those of human beings? Use a notebook to record your observations.

67

The Hands of Primates

You may want to refer students to pages 757–760 in the textbook for a discussion of primates.

Time required: 45 minutes.

Pre-Lab Discussion

One of the differences between human beings and other primates is the structure of the hand. Being bipedal, or able to walk on two limbs, has freed the arms and hands of human beings for other tasks, such as making and using sophisticated tools. The human hand has a totally opposable thumb adapted for refined movements. In addition, the human hand can be rotated. The opposable thumb and the rotation of the hands enable humans to grasp and hold a variety of objects in many different ways.

In this investigation, you will compare the hands of several different primates. You will also examine the usefulness of a totally opposable thumb.

Problem

What are the similarities and differences between the hands of different primates? How is a totally opposable thumb useful to a human being?

Materials *(per pair of students)*

If it is not jacket or sweater season, you may wish to provide them for the students.

Masking tape
Comb
Bottle with screw-on cap
Jacket or sweater
Sewing needle
15-cm long piece of sewing thread
Clock or watch with second hand

Safety ⚗ ▩

Handle all glassware carefully. Be careful when handling sharp instruments. Note all safety alert symbols next to the steps in the Procedure and review the meanings of each symbol by referring to the symbol guide on page 10.

Procedure
Part A. Comparing the Hands of Different Primates

Caution students to be very careful, because they will have difficulty grasping and holding objects during this investigation.

1. Study the six different primate hands shown in Figure 1.

Tree shrew   Tarsier   Baboon   Orangutan   Gorilla   Human

Figure 1

2. After you have carefully examined the diagrams in Figure 1, answer questions 1 and 2 in Observations.

Part B. Examining the Usefulness of the Totally Opposable Thumb

1. Working with a partner, you will alternate as subject and helper throughout this part of the investigation.

2. Do each of the following activities and have your partner time how long it takes you to do each of them. Record this information in the appropriate column of the Data Table.

   a. Remove one shoe

   b. Put your shoe on again, and tie the shoelace

   c. Put on a jacket or sweater

   d. Unbutton a button and button it again

   e. Unscrew a bottle cap

   f. Open a door

   g. Write your name and address

   h. Comb your hair

   i. Take off your wristwatch and put it back on again

   j. Thread a sewing needle

3. Using masking tape, have your partner tape each of your thumbs to its adjacent index finger.

4. After your thumbs are securely taped, try each of the activities listed in step 2 again. Have your partner time how long it takes you to do each without the use of your thumbs. Record this information in the appropriate column of the Data Table. If an activity takes longer than 5 minutes, record the word "Unsuccessful."

Observations

Data Table

Activity	Time Needed with Thumbs	Time Needed without Thumbs
Remove one shoe		
Put shoe on again and tie shoelace		
Put on a jacket or sweater		
Unbutton a button and button it again		
Unscrew a bottle cap	Answers will vary.	
Open a door		
Write your name and address		
Comb your hair		
Take off wristwatch and put it back on		
Thread a sewing needle		

1. List two features that all of the hands in Figure 1 have in common.

All hands have 5 digits with claws or nails on each digit. Each hand has an opposable thumb.

2. List one feature that is unique to each of the hands. Tree shrew: claws; tarsier: enlarged pads on the tips of the digits; baboon: nails on the ends of the digits and hands adapted for walking; orangutan: elongated fingers and palm for climbing, as well as a short thumb; gorilla: a short thumb and broad hand; human: a long, opposable thumb with short fingers.

Analysis and Conclusions

1. List two features of the tree shrew's hand that make it well adapted for the environment in which it lives. The tree shrew's long, thin digits with sharp nails on their tips make this animal well adapted for climbing trees.

2. Based on the structure of its hand, in what type of environment would you expect the tarsier to live? Explain your answer. The tarsier lives in trees, as evidenced by its long, thin digits, which have enlarged pads on their tips for grasping and climbing.

3. The amino acid sequence of the hemoglobin molecules in humans and gorillas is very similar, indicating an evolutionary closeness. Do the structures of the gorilla and human hands support this idea? Explain your answer. The structures of gorilla and human hands are similar. Both have short fingers, greater width, and similar positioning of the thumb. Hand structure can be used to support evolutionary closeness.

4. Based on the activities that you tried and timed with your thumbs free and taped down, summarize your conclusions about the usefulness of your opposable thumb. Generally, students should find that without opposable thumbs, many ordinary tasks become impossible or at least extremely difficult and time-consuming.

Critical Thinking and Application

1. Many primates also have an opposable toe on each foot. How is this a useful adaptation? An opposable big toe allows the primate to better grasp objects and climb trees.

2. The hands of many primates are connected to very long arms. For what type of environment are these primates well adapted? Primates with long arms are well adapted for climbing and for swinging from tree branches.

3. Besides the activities conducted in this investigation, list three other activities that would be difficult for you to accomplish without opposable thumbs. Answers will vary, but may include eating, cooking, driving, playing a musical instrument, applying makeup, and working with various tools.

Going Further

Using wildlife magazines and other reference materials, observe the structure of the hands of other species of primates not shown in this investigation. How are the hands of each type of primate adapted for life in its particular environment?

68

Animal Behavior

You may want to refer students to pages 771–779 in the textbook for a discussion of animal behavior.

Time required: 45 minutes.

Pre-Lab Discussion

The way in which an organism responds in its environment is called *behavior*. Behaviors can be classified as either *inborn* or *learned*. Inborn behavior is also referred to as involuntary, unlearned, or instinctive behavior. Inborn behaviors are predictable, automatic responses to physical or psychological stimuli. The simplest inborn behaviors are known as reflexes. Some reflexes coordinate internal body processes, such as the slowing or quickening of the heartbeat. Other reflexes protect the organism. For example, when a cat is frightened by another animal, it will arch its back and fluff up its fur. This response makes the cat appear larger in an attempt to scare away the other animal. More complex inborn behaviors are known as instincts. Instincts control nest-building in birds, migrations in animals such as wildebeest and caribou, courtship "dances" in stickleback fish, and many other complicated animal behaviors.

Learned behavior is also referred to as acquired, voluntary, or conditioned behavior. This type of behavior depends on memory and repetition. When a conditioned behavior pattern is repeated so often that it becomes almost automatic, it becomes a habit. Habits permit organisms to perform familiar activities without consciously thinking about them. For this reason, habits are often confused with reflexes.

In this investigation, you will be observing both inborn and learned behaviors of a small mammal—a rodent.

Problem

What is a behavior? How do inborn and learned behaviors differ?

Materials *(per group)*

Rodent   Mice, rats, hamsters, gerbils, and guinea pigs are small and can be handled easily. Any of
Thick gloves   these animals can be purchased from local pet stores. If possible, you may ask students
to bring rodents to class if they have them as pets at home.

Small animal cage or cardboard box

Clay flower pot or glass container, 10 cm high

Animal maze   See annotations after Going Further.

Clock or watch with second hand

Safety 🔥 🐾

Caution students to wear thick leather gloves whenever handling a rodent. Tell students if rodents are handled gently and calmly, they are much less likely to become frightened or excited.

Put on a laboratory apron if one is available. Handle all glassware carefully. Follow your teacher's directions and all appropriate safety procedures when handling live animals. Note all safety alert symbols next to the steps in the Procedure and review the meanings of each symbol by referring to the symbol guide on page 10.

Procedure

Part A. Observing Inborn Behaviors

1. Obtain a rodent from your teacher. Observe the physical characteristics of your rodent and answer questions 1 and 2 in Observations.

2. Observe any behavioral responses of the rodent as it moves around the cage or box. Record your observations in Data Table 1.

3. Working with another group of students, carefully pick up your rodent and place it in the box of another rodent of the same species. Observe the two rodents' behaviors as they interact with each other. Record your observations in Data Table 1. **CAUTION:** *Handle the animals carefully and gently, without frightening them. Mice and rats may by picked up gently by their tails. Do not pick up gerbils or hamsters by their tails because the tips of their tails will break off. Wear leather gloves when handling rodents. Separate the animals immediately if one attacks the other.*

4. Return your rodent to its cage or box and allow it to readjust to its surroundings for several minutes.

5. Gently pick up your rodent and place it in an empty clay flower pot or glass container with slanted sides, as shown in Figure 1. Observe the rodent as it explores the flower pot and record your observations in Data Table 1. Record the time it takes the rodent to explore the flower pot, seek a way out and escape. Record the number of times it attempts to escape before succeeding.

Figure 1

6. Return the rodent to its original cage or box and allow it to readjust to its surroundings for several minutes before beginning Part B.

Part B. Observing Acquired Behaviors

1. Obtain a maze from your teacher. Place a piece of rodent food at the end of the maze. Carefully place the rodent at the beginning of the maze, as shown in Figure 2.

Top View of Animal Maze

Figure 2

444

2. In Data Table 2, record the time it takes the rodent to successfully complete the maze the first time.

3. Repeat steps 1 and 2 four more times and record the times in Data Table 2.

4. Return the rodent to its original cage or box. Return the rodent to your teacher.

Observations

Data Table 1

Type of Environment	Animal Behaviors
Alone in large area	
In an area with another member of the same species	Answers will vary.
Alone in small, confining area	

Data Table 2

Trial	Time Needed to Complete Maze
1	
2	Answers will vary.
3	
4	
5	

1. What type of rodent are you using to conduct this investigation? Answers will vary.

_____

2. List the physical characteristics of the rodent you are using in this investigation.

Answers will vary depending on the type of rodent used.

_____

_____

Analysis and Conclusions

1. In what ways did your rodent's behavior change when it came in contact with another rodent after having been alone? Answers will vary.

_____

_____

2. Why might an animal's behavior change when it comes in contact with another animal of its own species? The animal may become frightened, excited, or aggressive when it is in contact with another member of its species. Behaviors of groups of animals are often different from the behaviors shown by individual animals.

3. In what ways did your rodent's behavior change when it was placed in a small, confining place? Answers will vary.

_____

_____

4. Why might an animal respond differently to a small confining area than to a large nonconfining area? The animal may feel threatened, physically uncomfortable, or claustrophobic in its new smaller environment. Many species of animals will try to escape when placed in a smaller environment.

_____

5. Why is the information you collected in Data Table 1 considered to be inborn behavior?

The information in Data Table 1 describes inborn behaviors because these responses have not been taught to the animal.

6. How did the time it took the rodent to run the maze the first time compare with the time it took the rodent to run it the fifth time? Why might a change in time have occurred?

Students should notice a decrease in the time it takes the rodent to run the maze the fifth time in

comparison with the first time. Through repeated performance and trial-and-error, the rodent learned how to

successfully maneuver through the maze.

7. Why is the information you collected in Data Table 2 an example of acquired behavior?

The information in Data Table 2 describes a change in response to stimuli as a result of learning how to run

the maze.

Critical Thinking and Application

1. Why is the study of animal behavior an important part of biology?

In studying animal behavior, scientists may learn new ways to study and learn about human behavior. Also,

by studying the behaviors of insects and other animals that cause disease in humans, scientists may learn

how to effectively control these diseases.

2. How are behavioral responses to a stimulus of benefit to both the individual organism and the species? Behavioral responses to a stimulus enable an individual and a species to survive because the

animal takes the appropriate protective action in response to an environmental change.

3. How is inborn behavior important to an organism? Inborn behavior aids in the survival of an

organism by allowing it to respond to stimuli without having to learn the proper responses.

4. You enter the house of a new friend for the first time. You notice that your friend has a dog. What behaviors would you look for to determine if the dog was acting friendly or aggressively toward you? Friendly behaviors include tail wagging, jumping, or sitting. Aggressive behaviors include

barking or growling, bared teeth, crouching position, nonwagging tail, or erect ears.

Going Further

Due to the incredible variety of physical and behavioral adaptations they possess, insects have been successful in inhabiting even the harshest and remotest places on Earth. To observe the complex behaviors of ants, cut off the top of a 2-liter clear plastic soft drink bottle. Fill an individual-sized soft drink bottle with water and place it inside the 2-liter bottle. Fill the space between the two bottles with moistened sandy soil. Place a 10-centimeter-long piece of cotton in the small bottle to serve as a wick to provide water for the ants. Obtain about a dozen ants from your teacher and place them on the sand. To cover the outside of the 2-liter soft drink bottle, wrap a piece of plastic wrap over the opening and tape it to the sides of the bottle. Use a straight pin to make about 10 small holes in the plastic wrap. Place the entire setup in a pan of shallow water to keep the ants from escaping. Place food on the surface of the soil three times a week. Small pieces of lettuce and hard-boiled egg yolks make good ant food. Using a hand lens, observe the ants twice a week for one month. Use a notebook to record any social behaviors you observe among members of the ant colony.

Construction of an Animal Maze:

Simple mazes can be constructed out of balsa wood or sturdy cardboard boxes. Care should be taken to construct a maze that is challenging to the rodent but that can be completed within a reasonable amount of time. You may have to experiment with several different designs to find one that is appropriate for your needs. The wood-shop teacher in your school may be able to assist you in the construction of mazes.

69

Competition or Cooperation?

You may want to refer students to pages 771–779 in the textbook for a discussion of animal behavior.

Time required: 40 minutes.

Pre-Lab Discussion

You might want to read the essay on Cooperative Learning in the front of the Annotated Teacher's Edition of the textbook for ideas on structuring this investigation as a cooperative learning assignment for your students.

A task can be completed or a problem solved using several different organizational strategies. A task can be completed by working alone or as part of a team. An animal might live, hunt, and raise and care for its young alone, or it might live with others of its kind to carry out these same tasks using cooperation.

Humans depend to a large extent on learned behaviors in order to process information, complete tasks, and solve problems. A person can complete a task or solve a problem by working independently or a group of people can cooperate to complete the assigned task.

In this investigation, you will examine different ways to complete an assigned task.

Problem

Is competition between individuals or cooperation among team members a more efficient means of completing a task?

Materials *(per group)*

Clock or watch with second hand.

Procedure

See the frontmatter essay in the Annotated Teacher's Edition of the textbook for information on cooperative learning as an instructional technique. You might want to use one of the grouping strategies described to randomly group students for this investigation.

1. Decide which members of your group should play the following roles:

   a. Timekeeper   Allow the group to make the initial role assignments and to determine the rotation order.

   b. Independent worker

   c. Cooperative team (two or more students, depending on group size, who will work together to complete a task)

2. The student who is working independently will complete each task with no outside assistance, whereas the cooperative team will complete each task by working together. The timekeeper is responsible for allowing only the designated amount of time to be used for a task and for recording the groups' observations in the Data Table. Each student will have the opportunity to be the timekeeper, the independent worker, and part of the cooperative team.

3. The independent worker should perform the task first. The cooperative team should neither observe the task being performed nor see the final product until they have completed the same task. Remember to change assignments following the completion of each task.

The diagrams have been left out of the student's edition and blanks have been left in Tasks C and D to prevent students from thinking about their responses before officially beginning each task.

4. **Task A:** In 2 minutes count the number of triangles in the diagram provided by your teacher. The timekeeper should check the correctness of each count using the key provided by your teacher. Record your observations in the Data Table. _Provide each group with a diagram of Figure 1, which is found on the page following Going Further._

5. **Task B:** In 2 minutes count the number of boxes in the diagram provided by your teacher. Record the number of responses in the Data Table. _Provide each group with a diagram of Figure 2, which is found on the page following Going Further._

6. **Task C:** In 1 minute name and record as many words as you can that begin with the letter _____. Record the number of responses in the Data Table. _Allow the timekeeper for Task C to select the that will complete the sentence for his or her_

7. **Task D:** In 1 minute name and record as many _____ as you can. Record the number of responses in the Data Table. _This sentence can be completed by the group's timekeeper or you might assign each group one of the following: states and their capitals, countries in Africa/Europe/Asia, orders of mammals, classes of invertebrates._

Observations

Data Table

Task	Number of Responses	
	Independent Worker	**Cooperative Team**
A		
B	Answers will vary, but the cooperative team should have more responses.	
C		
D		

1. Which organizational strategy resulted in the greater number of correct responses?

   Answers will vary, but should be supported by information recorded in the Data Table.

2. What kinds of behaviors were observed as the cooperative team completed each task?

   Answers will vary, but may include sharing information, talking, explaining to each other reasons for answers, and encouraging each other.

3. What cooperative efforts have you observed or participated in at school?

   Answers will vary, but might include band, choir, drama, sports, cheerleading, debate club, and homework completion.

Analysis and Conclusions

1. Why is communication important during cooperative work? _Communication contributes to efficiency by enabling everyone involved in a task to understand their role and the outcome._

2. How are most of your at-school tasks structured—cooperatively or competitively? Explain your answer. Answers will vary. _____

_____

3. Is cooperation an appropriate strategy for completing all the tasks expected of you in a normal school day? Explain your answer. No. Some tasks, such as test taking, are individual in nature so that each individual's progress can be determined.

_____

_____

4. Does cooperation provide an advantage to animals in their natural habitats? Be sure to include an example as you explain your answer. Yes. Cooperation allows some animals to better feed and protect themselves. Examples may vary, but might include social insects, grazing herds, and hunting groups of lions.

_____

Critical Thinking and Application

1. Would there be an advantage to an animal of one species cooperating with an animal of another species? Explain your answer. Yes. Explanations may vary, but students should give examples of mutualistic relationships.

_____

_____

2. In what situations do you think cooperation would be more productive than competition? Answers will vary, but students may include various aspects of business planning and manufacturing as part of their answer.

_____

_____

Going Further

Design an experiment to illustrate the role of communication in completing a task where two or more people are cooperating. You might want to consider the role of both verbal and nonverbal communication as you design your experiment.

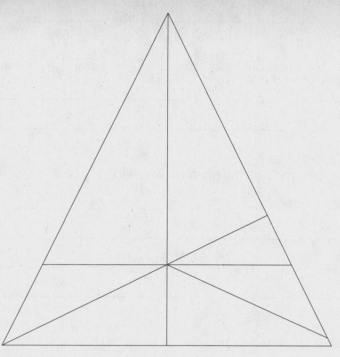

Figure 1

Sixteen triangles can be identified.

To identify each triangle, label each point of intersection and name each triangle using the letters at its vertices.

You may wish to make a photocopy master of this diagram by tracing or drawing it on an unlined sheet of paper. You may also wish to redraw the diagram to make it larger or smaller. Note that the three lines in the lower right-hand corner do not intersect at a common point. This eliminates many possible triangles.

If you choose to photocopy this diagram directly, make sure that the answer and teacher's notes are covered so that they do not appear on the students' copies.

Figure 2

Twenty-six boxes can be identified. Follow the same procedure for identification that is described in the copy accompanying Figure 1.

You may wish to make a photocopy master of this diagram by tracing or drawing it on an unlined sheet of paper. You may also wish to redraw the diagram to make it larger or smaller. If you choose to photocopy this diagram directly, make sure that the answer and teacher's notes are covered so that they do not appear on the students' copies.

70

Vertebrate Skeletons

You may want to refer students to pages 785–799 in the textbook for a discussion of comparative vertebrate anatomy.

Time required: 45 minutes.

Pre-Lab Discussion

The body plans of all vertebrates are similar in some ways. One characteristic common to all vertebrates is the presence of a skeleton. The skeleton of a vertebrate is an *endoskeleton*, or internal skeleton. It is made up, in part, of living cells and thus is able to grow. It is not shed as are many exoskeletons. The endoskeleton provides support, protects the internal organs, and is a site for the attachment of muscles. In jawless fishes—lampreys and hagfishes—and in sharks and rays, the endoskeleton is made of cartilage. Bony fishes, amphibians, reptiles, birds, and mammals have endoskeletons of bone with small amounts of cartilage present.

The examination of similar skeletal features in different types of vertebrates reveals important evolutionary links among members of this diverse group. Many biologists consider skeletal similarities to be evidence that these different animals have evolved from a common ancestor. Structures such as bones that have a common origin but different function are called *homologous structures*.

In this investigation, you will compare the skeletons of several different vertebrates and look for evidence of homologous structures. You will also classify unknown bone specimens based on their similarities to and differences from known vertebrates.

Problem

What are the similarities and differences among certain vertebrate skeletons? What homologous structures can be identified on these skeletons?

Materials *(per group)*

If actual skeletons or models are available, they should be used in conjunction with this investigation.

Set of "mystery" bones. The "mystery" bones can be made by boiling a chicken and removing the meat from the bones. For a more challenging problem you can obtain pig, lamb, or cattle bones from a butcher or grocery store. Each group should be given several bones from the same type of animal to identify.

Procedure

1. Carefully examine the labeled human skeleton in Figure 1. The human skeleton contains more than 200 bones. Become familiar with the names and structures of the bones in Figure 1.

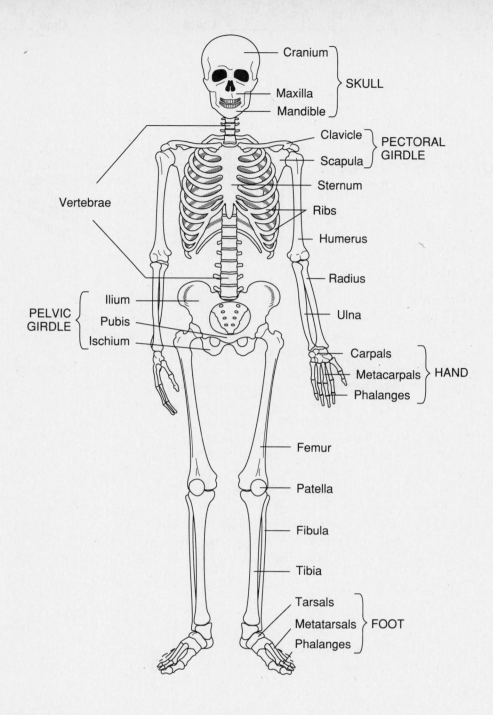

Human Skeleton

Figure 1

2. Look at the frog skeleton in Figure 2. As you examine the skeleton, compare it to the human skeleton in Figure 1. Label the bones of the frog skeleton using the names from Figure 1.

3. Repeat step 2 with the skeletons of the crocodile, pigeon, and cat in Figures 3, 4, and 5.

4. Obtain a set of "mystery" bones from your teacher. Identify the bones by comparing them to the bones of each skeleton observed in this investigation. Answer questions 9 and 10 in Observations.

Observations

Figure 2   **Frog Skeleton**

Figure 3   **Crocodile Skeleton**

Figure 4   **Pigeon Skeleton**

Figure 5   **Cat Skeleton**

1. **What are three characteristics that all of the skeletons share?** Answers will vary, but may include

   a bony skeleton, 4 limbs, a skull, presence of vertebrae in the backbone, jaws, and an internal skeleton.

2. **What are three differences that exist among the skeletons?** Answers will vary, but may include

   number of bones, presence of a tail, shape of bones, overall size, and type of teeth.

3. **How do the forelimbs differ from the hindlimbs in terms of the way they bend?**

   The forelimbs bend backward at the elbow joint. The hindlimbs bend forward at the knee joint.

4. **How are the vertebral columns of the skeletons similar?** All of the skeletons have vertebral columns

   that consist of a series of individual vertebrae in a chain.

5. **How are the vertebral columns of the skeletons different?** The vertebral columns have different

   numbers and sizes of vertebrae.

6. **How are the hindlimbs similar?** Each of the skeletons has one bone (femur) in the upper portion of

   the leg.

7. **How are the hindlimbs different?** Each of the skeletons has a different number of bones in the power

   portion of the leg, the ankle, and the foot.

8. **How do the foot bones of these vertebrates differ from one another?**

   The pigeon has one of its toes pointing backward; the frog has long feet for swimming; the cat has 4

   elongated metatarsals (one is lost) in its foot; the crocodile has a relatively small foot.

9. How do the bones in the limbs of the frog differ from those in the other four skeletons?

The frog has only one bone in the forearm (radio-ulna) and one bone in the lower leg (tibia-fibula).

10. Describe the "mystery" bones in your collection. Answers will vary.

11. To what parts of the skeleton do your "mystery" bones belong? Answers will vary.

Analysis and Conclusions

1. How do the functions of the forelimbs differ among the five vertebrates you have examined?

The forelimbs of humans are used for grasping objects, the forelimbs of a frog are used in landing after a jump, the forelimbs of a pigeon are used for flying, and the forelimbs of the crocodile and the cat are used for walking.

2. What type of evidence would indicate that the human hand, pigeon wing, and cat paw are homologous structures? These structures contain bones of similar shape, number, and arrangement, but of different function.

3. Which two animals have backbones that are most alike? Explain your answer.

With the exception of the tail, the backbones of the human and the cat are most alike in the number and arrangement of vertebrae.

4. Which two animals have backbones that are least alike? Explain your answer.

The backbones of the human and the frog are least alike. The number and shape of the vertebrae are very different.

5. Which two animals have forelimbs that are most alike? Explain your answer.

The forelimbs of humans and cats are most alike. The proportions and number of bones in the forearm and hand are similar.

6. Which two animals have forelimbs that are least alike? Explain your answer.

The forelimbs of humans and birds are least alike. The proportions and number of bones in the forearm and hand are very different.

7. Which two animals have hindlimbs that are most alike? Explain your answer.

Although the cat has elongated metatarsals, its hindlimb is most similar to the human hindlimb in the proportions and number of bones.

8. Which two animals have hindlimbs that are least alike? Explain your answer.

Both the bird and the frog have foot structures that are very dissimilar to that of the human. The frog also has only one bone in its lower leg.

9. To what type of animal do you think your "mystery" bones belong? On what evidence do you base your conclusion? Answers will vary.

Critical Thinking and Application

1. Are bones that are similar in structure always similar in function? Give an example to defend your answer. No. While the forearms of the cat and human are similar in structure, the cat generally uses its forearms for walking and the human uses its forearms for grasping objects.

2. What evidence have you obtained in this investigation to support the theory that vertebrates evolved from a common ancestor? All of the vertebrates examined in this investigation had homologous structures within their skeletons.

3. Do you think bones should be named according to their structure or their function? Defend your answer. Answers may vary, but students will probably suggest that the comparison of bones is more consistent and less complicated when they are named by structure. How would you go about locating a human's "wing"?

4. In terms of classification, why should the human and cat skeletons be most closely related? Do your observations in this investigation support this idea? Both humans and cats are classified as mammals. Student observations in this investigation should support this idea because many similarities between human and cat skeletons were found.

Going Further

Using reference materials, find examples of other vertebrate skeletons. How are these skeletons similar to and different from those you have studied in this investigation? How are the skeletons of these other vertebrates adapted to the environments in which they live?

71

Constructing a Model
of a Nerve Cell

You may want to refer students to
pages 810–815 in the textbook for
a discussion of nerve cells and
nerve impulses.

Time required: 35 minutes.

Pre-Lab Discussion

Nerve cells communicate with each other by sending electrical signals. The electrical
activity of nerve cells was discovered more than 150 years ago by the Italian scientist
Luigi Galvani. The electricity in nerve cells comes from the movements of charged
particles into and out of the cells. These charged particles are supplied by minerals in
the diet such as table salt. Even nerve cells that are not sending signals have a voltage, or
difference in positively charged and negatively charged ions on each side of the cell
membrane. If they did not, the nerve cells—like dead batteries—would not function. This
voltage is called a *resting potential*.

In this investigation, you will construct a model of a nerve cell. You will also
observe how the distribution of ions around the membrane generates a resting potential.

Problem

How do nerve cells develop a resting potential?

Materials *(per group)*

2 alligator clips
2 150-mL beakers
2 40-cm pieces of copper wire
DC millivolt meter A voltmeter that measures in a range from 0 to 0.01 volts can be used in place of a millivolt
Dialysis membrane meter. The voltage being measured, however, is about 8 to 10 millivolts, so the deflection
2 glass stirring rods will be small. The meter used should be able to deflect both positive and negative charges.
2 15-cm pieces of nickel-chromium alloy wire
3 M potassium chloride solution For 1L of 3 M potassium chloride solution, add 223.7g potassium
String   chloride to a 1-L graduated cylinder or beaker. Add distilled water
Rubber band   until the total volume of the solution is 1 L.
Scissors
Screwdriver
3 M sodium chloride solution For 1L of 3 M sodium chloride solution, add 175.3 g sodium chloride to a
                            1-L graduated cylinder or beaker. Add distilled water until the total
                            volume of the solution is 1 L.

Safety 🧪 ⬛ 👁 ▰ ◀▮

Put on a laboratory apron if one is available. Put on safety goggles. Handle all glassware carefully. Always use special caution when working with laboratory chemicals, as they may irritate the skin or cause staining of the skin or clothing. Never touch or taste any chemical unless instructed to do so. Be careful when handling sharp instruments. Observe proper laboratory procedures when using electrical appliances. Note all safety alert symbols next to the steps in the Procedure and review the meanings of each symbol by referring to the symbol guide on page 10.

Procedure

▰ 1. Using scissors, cut a 20-cm strip of dialysis membrane. **CAUTION:** *Be careful when using sharp instruments.* Place the dialysis membrane in a beaker of water. Put the beaker aside for now.

🧪 2. Tightly coil a 15-cm strip of nickel-chromium alloy wire around one end of a glass stirring rod. Allow 3 cm of the nickel-chromium alloy wire to remain uncoiled and parallel to the length of the stirring rod. See Figure 1. Repeat this procedure using the other piece of nickel-chromium alloy wire and stirring rod.

Copper wire   Stirring rod

Nickel-chromium alloy wire   Alligator clip

Figure 1

3. Attach an alligator clip to one end of a 40-cm length of copper wire by pulling the wire through the hollow end of the clip and looping it around the screw. Tighten the screw with a screwdriver. Repeat this procedure using the other alligator clip and piece of copper wire.

4. To construct an electrode, clamp each alligator clip to a stirring rod so that the jaws of the alligator clip make contact with the uncoiled portion of the nickel-chromium alloy wire. See Figure 1.

5. Attach one electrode to the positive terminal of the millivolt meter by looping the free end of the copper wire around the post and tightening the nut. Attach the other electrode to the negative terminal of the millivolt meter.

⬛ 👁 6. Half fill a clean 150-mL beaker with 3 M sodium chloride solution. **CAUTION:** *Be careful when using chemicals.* Place the electrode attached to the positive terminal of the millivolt meter in the beaker. Tell students not to allow the alligator clip to touch the sodium chloride solution while making their observations. If necessary, have students slide the glass stirring rod down farther through the nickel-chromium alloy wire to support the electrode.

If the dialysis membrane does not open completely by rubbing it between the fingers, it is possible to open it by blowing into it or running water through the partially open end.

7. Remove the dialysis membrane from the beaker. To open it, rub both ends between your fingers. Tie off one end of the dialysis membrane with the string to make a sac.

8. Half fill the dialysis membrane with 3 M potassium chloride solution. **CAUTION:** *Be careful when using chemicals.* The dialysis membrane sac represents a model of a nerve cell.

9. Insert the electrode attached to the negative terminal of the millivolt meter into the potassium chloride solution in the sac.

10. Use a rubber band to close the open end of the dialysis membrane and to hold the dialysis membrane around the stirring rod.

11. Place the dialysis membrane sac into the beaker containing sodium chloride. The beaker of sodium chloride represents the fluid surrounding the nerve cell. Make sure the sac does not touch the other electrode and the wires do not touch each other. See Figure 2.   Tell students not to allow the alligator clip or the rubber band to touch the sodium chloride solution while making their observations. If necessary, have students slide the glass stirring rod down farther through the nickel-chromium alloy wire to support the electrode.

Figure 2

12. Observe the direction in which the indicator on the millivolt meter moves. Note the number of millivolts registered on the meter. Record this information in the appropriate place in Observations.   Tell students to allow the dialysis membrane sac to sit in the sodium chloride for one minute or more to build up a potential. As the potassium chloride diffuses out of the sac, a potential will build until it reaches about 8 millivolts.

Observations

1. In which direction does the indicator on the millivolt meter move?

   The indicator moves to the right (toward the positive electrode or away from the potassium chloride solution).

2. How many millivolts are registered on the millivolt meter? The meter should register about 8 to 10 millivolts.

Analysis and Conclusions

1. Assuming that the indicator on the millivolt meter moves in the same direction the electrons are flowing, do electrons flow toward or away from the potassium chloride solution?

   Electrons flow away from the potassium chloride solution.

2. Because electrons are negatively charged, they are repelled by other negative charges and tend to move away from them. Based on your observations, what is the charge inside the nerve cell model? How does this compare to the charge inside an actual nerve cell?

   The charge inside the nerve cell model is negative. It is the same as an actual nerve cell.

3. How does the distribution of sodium and potassium ions in the model compare to the distribution of ions in an actual nerve cell? The distribution of ions is the same in the model as in an actual nerve cell.

4. Both sodium ions and potassium ions are positively charged. Chloride ions, however, are negatively charged. Based on your observations, do potassium ions or sodium ions move more easily through the membrane of the nerve cell model? Explain your answer.

   Potassium ions must move through the membrane more easily than sodium ions. As a result, more positive ions leave the sac than enter, leaving a net negative charge inside the sac.

5. How do nerve cells develop a resting potential? Nerve cells develop a resting potential by maintaining a high concentration of potassium ions inside and a high concentration of sodium ions outside. The potassium ions diffuse out through the membrane faster than sodium ions diffuse in, causing a net loss of positive charges inside and making the inside negatively charged.

Critical Thinking and Application

1. Unlike an actual nerve cell, the model does not have a sodium-potassium pump to maintain the distribution of ions. How would this affect the functioning of the model over time? Explain your answer. Eventually, as a result of diffusion, the concentration of ions will become equal on both sides of the membrane, causing the resting potential to disappear.

2. The data below show how the speed of an action potential is affected by the diameter of the axon.

Diameter (μm)	Speed (m/sec)
2	10
4	20
7	30
9	40
20	90

Using the grid below, construct a line graph of the data. Plot the diameter of the axon on the horizontal axis and the speed of the action potential on the vertical axis. How does the diameter of the axon affect the speed of conduction of the action potential? Based on your graph, how fast would an action potential be propagated through an axon with a diameter of 14 μm? As the diameter of the axon increases, so does the speed of conduction of the action potential. Based on the graph, a nerve cell with a diameter of 14 μm would conduct at a rate of approximately 63 m/sec.

3. Too much sodium in the diet can cause high blood pressure in some individuals. What would happen to the functioning of the nervous system if there were no sodium in the diet? Explain your answer. Without sodium in the diet, the nervous system would cease to function. Sodium is

necessary in order for the nerve cell to develop a resting potential.

4. In the model nerve cell you constructed, how can you tell that the movements of potassium and sodium ions caused the voltage rather than the movement of chloride ions?

Because the concentration of chloride ions was the same on both sides of the membrane, no net movement

of chloride ions was expected, especially because the membrane would affect the movement of chloride ions

in the same way in either direction.

5. How is a resting nerve cell similar to a battery that is in use? Even where there is no action

potential, a resting nerve cell has a resting potential much as an unused battery has a voltage. If this were

not the case, the nerve cell could not transmit impulses, just as a battery without a voltage could not run

equipment.

Going Further

Repeat this investigation using potassium chloride and sodium chloride solutions of varying concentrations. How does the concentration of the solutions affect the amount of voltage produced by the model nerve cell? How might this information be important to the study of an actual nerve cell?

Skin Sensitivity

You may want to refer students to pages 827–831 in the textbook for a discussion of the senses.

Time required: 50 minutes.

Pre-Lab Discussion

The senses receive information about the environment and relay it to the central nervous system, where the information is interpreted. The sense organs contain specialized neurons called *receptors,* each of which is adapted to receive a particular kind of stimulus. Like all neurons, receptors follow the *all-or-none principle.* That is, any stimulus that is weaker than the *threshold* will produce no impulse; any stimulus that is as strong as or stronger than the threshold will produce an impulse. The threshold is the minimum level of a stimulus that is required to activate a neuron.

The receptors for the sense of touch are scattered over the surface of the entire body. The receptors, however, are more closely grouped together in some areas of the body than in others. In addition, the receptors in one area may respond to a weaker threshold than receptors in another area.

In this investigation, you will study the distribution and sensitivity of the touch receptors of the human body.

Problem

How sensitive is the skin?

Materials *(per pair of students)*

3 bristles of various thickness   Natural horsehair or boar bristles work best. Bristles may be removed
Blindfold   from paintbrushes or other types of brushes. Have three distinctly
                                   different thicknesses available.
9 toothpicks
Masking tape
Metric ruler
Pencil   The pencil should be a number 1 or 2 pencil. The tip should not be sharply pointed.
Blunt probe Sharp points should be rounded off to match the shape of a blunt probe.

Safety ▨

Be careful when handling sharp instruments. Note all safety alert symbols next to the steps in the Procedure and review the meanings of each symbol by referring to the symbol guide on page 10.

Procedure

Part A. Determining Threshold

1. Blindfold your partner.

2. Gently touch your partner on the fingertip with one of the three bristles just until the bristle bends. Your partner should tell you whether he or she feels the touch of the bristle. **Note:** *Avoid parts of the fingertip that have calluses.*

3. Touch each of the three bristles to the fingertip five times. Try to alternate the bristles so that your partner will not know which bristle is being used. In Data Table 1, record the bristles that are felt by placing a check mark in the appropriate place. If the bristles are not felt, leave the space blank.

4. Repeat steps 2 and 3 for the palm, back of the hand, inside of the forearm, and back of the neck. Record the information in the appropriate places in Data Table 1.

5. Switch roles with your partner and repeat steps 2 through 4.

Part B. Distinguishing Between Two Stimuli

1. Obtain nine toothpicks. Tape two toothpicks together so that their tips are 5 millimeters apart. Use the metric ruler to ensure that the spacing between the toothpicks is accurate. Make sure that the tips of the toothpicks are even with each other. See Figure 1. Using the same procedure, tape three pairs of toothpicks together so that the tips of the first pair are 10 millimeters apart, the tips of the second pair are 15 millimeters apart, and the tips of the last pair are 20 millimeters apart. Allow the last toothpick to remain unpaired and untaped.

Masking tape

Toothpicks

5 mm

Figure 1

2. Blindfold your partner. Gently touch your partner's fingertip with any of the sets of toothpicks. **CAUTION:** *Be very careful when touching your partner's skin. Apply only a small amount of pressure.* Have your partner identify whether you are using one or two toothpicks. Record this information in the appropriate place in Data Table 2.

3. Repeat step 2 with the remaining sets of toothpicks. Use the sets of toothpicks in random order so that your partner will not know the pattern in the testing. **Note:** *Use the same pressure on the toothpicks in all trials.*

4. Repeat steps 2 and 3 using the palm, back of the hand, inside of the forearm, and back of the neck. Record the information in the appropriate places in Data Table 2.

5. Switch roles and repeat steps 2 through 4.

Part C. Locating a Stimulus

1. Blindfold your partner and give him or her a blunt probe to use as a pointer.

2. With a pencil, touch your partner's fingertip so as to make a visible mark on the skin. **CAUTION:** *Do not press so hard as to break the skin. Make sure that the pencil has a rounded, blunt tip.*

3. Have your partner try to touch the same point on his or her skin with the blunt probe that you touched with the pencil.

4. With the metric ruler, measure the distance between your mark and the point of the probe. Record this measurement in the appropriate place in Data Table 3.

5. Repeat steps 2 through 4 two more times using points near, but not the same as, the first point. Record the information in the appropriate place in Data Table 3.

6. Repeat steps 2 through 5 on the palm, back of the hand, inside of the forearm, and back of the neck. Record the information in the appropriate places in Data Table 3.

7. Switch roles and repeat steps 1 through 6.

8. Calculate the average distance between the pencil mark and the probe for each of the five sets of data. Record the averages.

Observations

Data Table 1

Skin Surface	Small Bristle	Medium Bristle	Large Bristle	Trial
Fingertip				1
				2
				3
				4
				5
Palm of hand				1
				2
				3
				4
		Answers will vary.		5
Back of hand				1
				2
				3
				4
				5
Inside of forearm				1
				2
				3
				4
				5
Back of neck				1
				2
				3
				4
				5

Table 2

Body Part	Number of Stimuli Felt				
	One Toothpick	Toothpicks 5 mm Apart	Toothpicks 10 mm Apart	Toothpicks 15 mm Apart	Toothpicks 20 mm Apart
Fingertip					
Palm of hand			Answers will vary.		
Back of hand					
Inside of forearm					
Back of neck					

Data Table 3

	Distance Between Pencil Mark and Probe (mm)				
Trial	Fingertip	Palm of Hand	Back of Hand	Inside of Forearm	Back of Neck
1					
2			Answers will vary.		
3					
Average					

Analysis and Conclusions

1. Of the parts of the body you tested, which part had the lowest threshold? Which part had the highest threshold? Answers may vary, but generally the fingertip has the lowest threshold, and the back of the hand or the back of the neck has the highest threshold.

2. Of the parts of the body you tested, which part was best able to distinguish between the closest stimuli? Which part was least able to distinguish between the closest stimuli? Generally the fingertip was best able to distinguish between the closest stimuli. The inside of the forearm was least able to distinguish between the closest stimuli.

3. What does your answer to question 2 indicate about the distribution of touch receptors in the skin? Students should conclude that receptors are most closely arranged in the skin of the fingertips and that they are farther apart in the skin of the forearm. The palm of the hand, back of the hand, and back of the neck are somewhere in between.

4. On which part of the body you tested were you best able to locate a stimulus? On which part were you least able to locate a stimulus? Generally students will be best able to locate a stimulus on the fingertip and least able to locate a stimulus on the back of the hand or inside of the forearm.

5. How are the results of Part C related to the results of Parts A and B? The areas of the body that have the most receptors are best able to distinguish between two stimuli that are very closely located. The density of these receptors is also responsible for the body's ability to determine the presence and origin of a stimulus. Areas in which the receptors for touch are more widely distributed are less apt to distinguish between two stimuli and are less able to locate the exact location of a stimulus.

6. Were there any differences between your results and those of your partner? If so, what might account for these differences? Answers will vary. Differences in individual body structure might account for differences in the number and efficiency of touch receptors in the various parts of the body.

Critical Thinking and Application

1. Braille is a special system of writing with raised dots. Blind people read Braille by touching these dots and recognizing patterns for each letter. The Braille pattern below is for the word *biology.*

How does the body's arrangement of nerve receptors for touch make the Braille system possible? There are so many closely arranged touch receptors on the fingertips that the dots can be distinguished readily.

2. In addition to touch receptors, the skin contains receptors for pain. How are pain receptors helpful to us? Pain receptors give a warning that damage may be occurring to a part of the body. For example, the pain receptors in your hand will activate your body to respond and pull away when you touch a hot stove, thus minimizing the damage done by the burn.

3. In what way is the concentration of touch receptors in the human hand related to its functions? The high concentration of touch receptors makes the human hand efficient in grasping, holding, and touching objects. The receptors also help the hand in sophisticated tasks such as toolmaking and playing a musical instrument.

4. When you put on a wristwatch, you become aware of the pressure it applies to the touch receptors in your wrist. Why do you think that you will not be aware of the presence of the watch after a period of time? The human brain is able to ignore certain constant stimuli. When a stimulus is constant, many receptors stop sending impulses to the brain. These receptors will start sending messages again when the stimulus changes in some way.

Going Further

1. To determine the sensitivity of other areas of the body, such as the upper arm, the knee, the foot, or various parts of the face, repeat the procedures in Parts A, B, and C of this investigation. Record your observations and compare them with those in this investigation.

2. Use blunt probes warmed in warm water to determine the distribution of heat receptors in the skin. **CAUTION:** *Do not heat the probes to a temperature above 40°C.* Record your observations.

3. Use blunt probes cooled in ice water or in a refrigerator to determine the distribution of cold receptors in the skin. Record your observations.

73

Bone Composition and Structure

You may want to refer students to pages 837–840 in the textbook for a discussion of the structure of bones.

Time required: 50 minutes plus a 5-minute observation period after 3 days.

Pre-Lab Discussion

Human bone contains living tissue and nonliving materials. The living tissue includes bone cells, blood vessels, fat cells, nerve cells, and cartilage. The nonliving materials include water, and minerals such as calcium and phosphorus. In fact, bones are hard and strong because they contain a great amount of calcium. Bone is composed of *compact bone* and *spongy bone*. Unlike compact bone, which is very hard and dense, spongy bone is soft and has many spaces in it.

In this investigation, you will examine the internal structure of compact bone. You will also determine the percentage of water in bone and observe how calcium gives strength to bone.

Problem

What is the internal composition and structure of bone?

Materials *(per group)*

Prepared slide of compact bone
  with Haversian system [1]
Microscope
2 uncooked pork bones [2]
Triple-beam balance
Felt-tip marking pen
Heat-resistant gloves
Heat-resistant pad

Large metal cookie sheet or cooking tray
100 mL of 20% hydrochloric acid solution [3]
250-mL beaker
Oven [4]
Tongs
Paper towels
100-mL graduated cylinder [4]
Masking tape

[1] Prepared slides are available from a biological supply house.

[2] Fresh pork bones are available from a local butcher or grocery store. The bones should be fresh to ensure that they contain water.

[3] To make 1 L of 20% hydrochloric acid solution, slowly and carefully add 200 mL concentrated hydrochloric acid to 800 mL distilled water. Stir constantly while mixing.

Use the school oven in the cafeteria or home economics department.

Safety

Put on a laboratory apron if one is available. Put on safety goggles. Handle all glassware carefully. Use extreme care when working with heated equipment or materials to avoid burns. Always use special caution when working with laboratory chemicals, as they may irritate the skin or cause staining of the skin or clothing. Never touch or taste any chemical unless instructed to do so. Always handle the microscope with extreme care. You are responsible for its proper care and use. Use caution when handling glass slides as they can break easily and cut you. Note all safety alert symbols next to the steps in the Procedure and review the meanings of each symbol by referring to the symbol guide on page 10.

Procedure
Part A. Calculating the Percentage of Water in a Bone

1. Place a small piece of paper towel on the pan of a triple-beam balance. Move the rider on the front beam of the balance until the pointer of the balance points to zero. Find the mass of the paper towel to the nearest tenth of a gram.

2. Place an uncooked pork bone on the balance and find the mass of the bone and paper towel to the nearest tenth of a gram. To determine the mass of the pork bone, subtract the mass of the paper towel from the mass of the bone and paper towel. Record this information in Data Table 1.

3. Using the felt-tip marking pen, write the last name of one of your group members on the surface of the bone.

4. Place the bone, along with bones of the other groups, on a large metal cooking tray. Place the cooking tray in an oven that has been preheated to 149°C (300°F) for 25 minutes. **CAUTION:** *To avoid burns, place the tray in the hot oven carefully.*

5. Using heat-resistant gloves, remove the tray from the oven and place it on a heat-resistant pad to cool. **CAUTION:** *To avoid burns, use heat-resistant gloves to remove the hot tray from the oven slowly and carefully.*

6. After the bone has cooled for 10 minutes, place it on the piece of paper towel on the triple-beam balance and again determine its mass to the nearest tenth of a gram. Record this information in Data Table 1.

7. The loss in mass of the bone is due primarily to the evaporation of water and to some oxidation of the minerals in the bone. Calculate the percentage of water in the pork bone by using the following formula:

$$\frac{\text{mass before heating} - \text{mass after heating}}{\text{mass before heating}} \times 100 = \text{percentage of water}$$

8. Record the percentage of water in the bone in the appropriate place in Observations.

9. Follow your teacher's instructions for proper disposal of the bone.

Part B. Observing Bone Cells
Students should perform Part B of the investigation while waiting for their pork bones to heat.

1. Observe a prepared slide of compact bone under the low-power objective of a microscope. Notice the circular-patterned units in the cross section of the bone. Each of these circular units is a Haversian system.

2. Switch to high-power to observe the structures that make up each Haversian system. **CAUTION:** *When switching to the high-power objective, always look at the objective from the side of the microscope so that the objective does not hit or damage the slide.*

3. Focus on a group of concentric circles. The central, hollow core of these circles is called the Haversian canal. The Haversian canal contains nerves and blood vessels. The rings around the Haversian canal are called lamellae (singular, lamella). The small dark cavities between adjacent lamellae are called lacunae (singular, lacuna). Lacunae appear as long, dark areas between lamellae.

4. Within each Haversian system, the lacunae are interconnected by small, branching canals called canaliculi (singular, canaliculus). Canaliculi appear as thin, dark lines that resemble the spokes of a wheel. Fluids pass from one part of the bone to another through the canaliculi.

5. Look for darkly stained bodies within the lacunae. These are the osteocytes, or living bone cells. See Figure 1. Notice that osteocytes have fine branches that extend into the canaliculi. The osteocytes are responsible for controlling the life functions of the bone.

6. In the appropriate place in Observations, draw a section of bone tissue as seen through the high-power objective of the microscope. Label the following parts of the Haversian system: Haversian canal, lamella, lacuna, canaliculus, and osteocyte. Record the magnification of the microscope.

Figure 1

474

Part C. Observing the Role of Calcium in a Bone

Students should complete steps 1–3 in Part C while waiting for their pork bones to heat.

1. Obtain another uncooked pork bone. Observe the flexibility of the bone by trying to bend and twist it. Record your observations in Data Table 2.

2. Place the bone in a 250-mL beaker. Use masking tape to label the beaker with the name of one member of your group.

3. Carefully add 100 mL of a 20% hydrochloric acid solution to the beaker. **CAUTION:** *Wear safety goggles when using hydrochloric acid. Hydrochloric acid can burn the skin or clothing. If any acid spills on your skin or clothing, wash the affected area with water immediately. Notify your teacher.*

4. Put the beaker in a place where it will remain undisturbed for 3 days.

5. Using tongs, carefully remove the bone from the acid. Rinse the bone under running tap water to remove any acid solution.

6. Dry the bone with a paper towel. Again test the flexibility of the bone. Record your observations in Data Table 2.

7. Follow your teacher's instructions for the proper disposal of the bone and the acid solution.

Observations

Data Table 1

Object	Mass Before Heating (g)	Mass After Heating (g)
Pork bone	Answers will vary.	

Percentage of water in pork bone = Answers will vary, but should be approximately 10–15%.

Magnification _____

Haversian System of a Human Bone

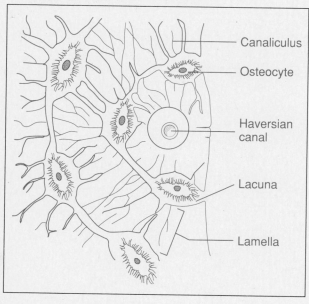

Canaliculus

Osteocyte

Haversian canal

Lacuna

Lamella

Data Table 2

Object	Description of Flexibility
Pork bone before being soaked in acid	The pork bone is hard, rigid, and inflexible. It cannot be bent.
Pork bone after being soaked in acid	The pork bone is soft and easy to twist and bend.

1. Is the percentage of water loss in your group's bone exactly the same as that of other groups? If not, why might the percentages vary? Students should find that their percentages are not exactly the same. Some bones may contain more water than others.

2. Why is water a necessary substance in a bone? Water is necessary to carry materials into and out of the living bone cells. Without water the bone cells would die.

3. Many people incorrectly think of bone as nonliving tissue. How is a bone similar to other living tissues? Both bones and other tissues are made up of cells that have specialized functions within the organism in which they are found. Bone cells have nuclei and cell membranes, as do other types of animal cells.

4. What materials are removed from a bone when it is soaked in a hydrochloric acid solution for several days? What evidence do you have to support your answer? Calcium and other minerals are removed from a bone. The absence of calcium causes bone to lose its rigid structure.

Critical Thinking and Application

1. Suppose a person's diet lacks the mineral calcium. How would this deficiency affect the skeletal system? Because bones are made of calcium, an absence of calcium would cause the bones to become weak. Therefore, the bones could be broken more easily.

2. Bone ash is a white, powdery material obtained from charred bones. Why do you think bone ash is used in fertilizers? The calcium and phosphorus found in bone ash are excellent nutrients for plants.

3. What is the function of the osteocytes when a bone is broken? When a bone is broken, the osteocytes become active, producing new bone tissue to heal the broken bone.

Going Further

1. Determine the percentage of water in other types of bones, such as cattle bones or chicken bones.

2. Use reference materials to research the degenerative bone disease known as osteoporosis. What is the cause of this disease? What are its symptoms? What age group does it normally affect? What preventive measures can be taken to combat osteoporosis?

74

The Skeletal System

You may want to refer students to pages 837–842 in the textbook for a discussion of the skeletal system.

Time required: 45 minutes.

Pre-Lab Discussion

The skeleton is not just a framework of bones. It serves as an attachment for muscles, as support for the body, and as protection for vital organs. Bones also store certain minerals and contain special cells that form red and white blood cells. The human body contains 206 bones.

The bones of the human skeleton are grouped into two divisions: the *axial skeleton* and the *appendicular skeleton*. The axial skeleton includes the skull, vertebrae, and rib cage. The appendicular skeleton includes the rest of the skeleton: the arms, legs, shoulder girdle, and pelvic girdle.

In addition to bone, human skeletons also contain *cartilage*. In fact, the human skeleton is initially formed from cartilage, which is gradually replaced by bone. Cartilage is found in adult humans between the vertebrae of the spinal column, at the tips of ribs and other bones, and in the nose, ears, and larynx. Some lower vertebrates, such as the shark and the lamprey, have skeletons composed entirely of cartilage. Of the three types of cartilage found in the human body—hyaline, fibrous, and elastic—*hyaline cartilage* is the most common. It is pearly white and glassy or translucent in appearance. Hyaline cartilage is found at the ends of bones in movable joints.

In this investigation, you will observe the structure of bone and cartilage. You will also identify the main parts of the human skeleton.

Problem

How is the human skeleton organized?

Materials *(per group)*

Prepared slide of a cross section of hyaline cartilage   Available from a biological supply house.
Microscope
Long bone from chicken leg   Begin saving chicken bones (drumsticks are fine). Boiling them will cause
Dissecting tray   excess meat and cartilage to fall off and will disinfect them. Let them dry
Scalpel   out. If you prefer, you may assign students to bring in their own chicken
2 colored pencils   bones. Make certain that these bones are cleaned properly.

Safety 🔥 ▒

Put on a laboratory apron if one is available. Handle all glassware carefully. Be careful when handling sharp instruments. Always handle the microscope with extreme care. You are responsible for its proper care and use. Use caution when handling glass slides as they can break easily and cut you. Note all safety alert symbols next to the steps in the Procedure and review the meanings of each symbol by referring to the symbol guide on page 10.

Procedure
Part A. Observing the Structure of a Long Bone

1. Obtain a long bone of a chicken leg. Observe the outside covering and features of the bone. Note the smooth covering at both ends of the bone. Also notice the presence of small holes along the surface of the bone. In the appropriate place in Observations, describe the outside surface of the chicken leg bone.

2. With a scalpel, cut one end of the bone to expose the fine structure of the spongy bone and some bone marrow. **CAUTION:** *Be careful when handling a scalpel. Carefully cut in a direction away from your hands and body.*

3. Use Figure 1 as you observe the chicken bone. Observe the periosteum, which covers and protects the bone. Beneath the periosteum is a hard dense layer called compact bone. Notice the softer spongy bone near the ends of the bone. Spongy bone contains many small spaces. In long bones, the spongy bone also contains red marrow, which produces red and white blood cells. Note the internal cavity of the bone, which may contain some fat-storing yellow marrow. On the outer edge of the end of the bone, find the plate of protective cartilage. Each of the wide ends of a long bone is called the epiphysis, whereas the long shaft of the bone is called the diaphysis.

Figure 1

4. In the appropriate place in Observations, sketch the internal structure of the chicken leg bone. Label the periosteum, compact bone, spongy bone, red marrow, yellow marrow, cartilage, epiphysis, and diaphysis.

5. Follow your teacher's instructions on proper disposal of the chicken bone.

478

Part B. Examining Cartilage

1. Cartilage is more flexible than bone; thus it can take a great deal of stress. Live cartilage cells, called chondrocytes, are found in cavities called lacunae. Unlike bone, cartilage contains no blood vessels. Materials enter and leave chondrocytes by diffusion to and from the blood vessels in adjacent layers of tissue.

2. Observe a prepared slide of the cross section of hyaline cartilage under the low-power objective of a microscope. Locate some chondrocytes. In the appropriate place in Observations, sketch the cartilage tissue under low power. Label the chondrocytes. Record the magnification of the microscope.   Explain to students that the cartilage appears red on the side because it has been stained. This makes the structures more easily seen.

3. Switch to high power. **CAUTION:** *When switching to the high-power objective, always look at the objective from the side of the microscope so that the objective does not hit or damage the slide.* Observe the chondrocytes under high power. Notice that the chondrocytes usually occur in groups of two or four cells. In the appropriate place in Observations, sketch and label some chondrocytes as seen under high power. Record the magnification of the microscope.

Part C. Examining the Human Skeleton

1. With a colored pencil, color the axial skeleton in Figure 2 in Observations.

2. With the other colored pencil, color the appendicular skeleton.

3. In the appropriate place in Observations, match the names of the bones of the skeleton with their corresponding numbers as shown in Figure 2.

Observations

1. Describe the outside surface of the chicken leg bone. ____ Smooth, whitish-pinkish in color, narrower in ____

   the center, wider at the joint, pores on outer surface.

Internal Structure of Chicken Leg Bone

Low-power objective

Magnification _____

High-power objective

Magnification _____

Cartilage

Chondrocytes

Cartilage

2. What color did you color the axial skeleton? Answers will vary. _____

The appendicular skeleton? Answers will vary. _____

3. Write the numbers of the bones in Figure 2 that correspond to the names of the bones given below.

Carpals	11
Scapula	3
Fibula	17
Clavicle	2
Radius	9
Tibia	16
Ribs	5
Metacarpals	12
Cranium	1
Tarsals	18
Phalanges	13
Ulna	10
Humerus	6
Sternum	4
Femur	14
Pelvis	8
Metatarsals	19
Vertebral column	7
Patella	15

Figure 2   **Human Skeleton**

Analysis and Conclusions

1. Why is it necessary that the ends of bones be smooth? Bones must be smooth at the ends so they can move freely at the joint.

2. What is the function of the small holes in the bone surface? The small holes in the bone surface allow blood vessels to enter the bones.

3. What is the importance of red bone marrow? Red bone marrow produces red and white blood cells.

4. How is cartilage similar to bone? Both cartilage and bone contain living cells and provide protection and support for other parts of the body.

5. How do cartilage and bone differ? Cartilage is more flexible than bone. Cartilage, unlike bone, contains no blood vessels and must transport materials through diffusion to and from adjacent tissues.

6. Which part of the human skeleton, axial or appendicular, appears to have the greater number of bones? On what observations do you base this conclusion? Of the 206 human skeletal bones, 126 are appendicular and 80 are axial. The large number of bones in the hands and feet contributes to this difference in number.

Critical Thinking and Application

1. The skeleton of an unborn baby consists of a large amount of cartilage, which will later change to bone. Of what advantage to the unborn child is a skeleton made of cartilage?

Cartilage is more flexible and can handle more stress than bone. The flexible cartilage of the baby's skeleton is better able to conform to the confined space the baby must occupy during its prenatal development.

2. Leukemia is a disease in which white blood cells grow in an uncontrolled manner. Explain why a bone-marrow transplant is sometimes used as a treatment for this disease.

Red bone marrow is the site of blood cell production. In leukemia, the bone marrow loses its ability to produce red blood cells because of the uncontrolled growth of white blood cells. As a result, the production of blood cells is affected. A transplant from an unaffected close relative or twin will enable normal blood cells to be produced.

3. Of what advantage is the layer of spongy bone found on the inside of a long bone?

While adding to the strength of the bone, the spongy bone does not add significantly to its mass. Lighter bones enable the human being to move more quickly and with greater agility.

4. How is the large number of bones found in the feet and hands of human beings both an advantage and a disadvantage? The large number of bones in the feet and hands allows humans to walk and grasp objects with more agility. However, this complex, interconnecting network of small bones is more likely to sustain an injury.

Going Further

1. Electricity can be used to speed up the healing of broken bones. Use reference materials to do research on this topic. Report your findings to the class.

2. Using reference materials, research the so-called soft spots, or fontanels, of a newborn baby's skull. What are fontanels and what is their function?

75

The Muscular System

You may want to refer students to pages 842–846 in the textbook for a discussion of the muscular system.

Time required: 45 minutes.

Pre-Lab Discussion

Muscle tissue consists of groups of cells that are specialized for contraction. In the body, muscle tissue is usually organized into organs called muscles. Muscles contain connective tissue, nerves, and blood vessels in addition to muscle tissue. Although the term muscle often refers to an entire organ, it is also frequently used to refer to muscle tissue alone. There are three different types of muscle tissue in the bodies of humans and other vertebrates: skeletal, smooth, and cardiac.

Skeletal muscles are attached to the bones, cover the skeleton, give shape to the body, and make movement possible. The individual cells in skeletal muscle are often called fibers rather than cells because they are long and thin and quite different in structure from typical cells. Skeletal muscle fibers are larger than most cells (as much as 40 centimeters in length!), contain many nuclei, and have many transverse stripes that are visible when the fibers are viewed under a microscope. Because of these stripes, or striations, skeletal muscle is called striated muscle. Skeletal muscle is also known as voluntary muscle because it is under conscious control.

Smooth muscle is very prominent in the walls of the stomach, intestine, and urinary bladder. Smooth muscle also occurs in the walls of blood vessels, in glands, and in the skin. The cells of smooth muscle are spindle-shaped, have individual nuclei, and are not striated. Smooth muscle is also called involuntary muscle because it is not under conscious control.

Cardiac muscle is found only within the walls of the heart. Like smooth muscle, cardiac muscle is not under conscious control—it is a type of involuntary muscle. Like skeletal muscle, cardiac muscle is striated—the cells in cardiac muscle are striped. Cardiac muscle cells contain one nucleus and form branching fibers with adjacent cardiac muscle cells.

In this investigation, you will observe prepared slides of three types of muscle cells. You will also examine a chicken wing to observe its muscle structure.

Problem

How is the human muscular system organized?

Materials *(per group)*

Prepared slides of skeletal, smooth, and cardiac muscle [1]	Scalpel
	Scissors
Microscope	Probe
Whole chicken wing [2]	Forceps
Hand lens	Paper towels
Dissecting tray	

[1] Prepared slides are available from a biological supply house.

[2] Whole chicken wings are available from butcher shops and local grocery stores. Many butchers will sell the chicken wings at a reduced cost for use in the classroom.

Put on a laboratory apron if one is available. Handle all glassware carefully. Be careful when handling sharp instruments. Always handle the microscope with extreme care. You are responsible for its proper care and use. Use caution when handling glass slides as they can break easily and cut you. Note all safety alert symbols next to the steps in the Procedure and review the meanings of each symbol by referring to the symbol guide on page 10.

Procedure
Part A. Examining Three Types of Muscle Cells

🔬 1. Observe a prepared slide of skeletal muscle under the low-power objective of the microscope.

2. Switch to high power. **CAUTION:** *When switching to the high-power objective, always look at the objective from the side of the microscope so that the objective does not hit or damage the slide.*

3. Count the number of nuclei that are contained within one skeletal muscle fiber. Note whether this cell has striations (stripes). Observe the cell shape. Classify skeletal muscle as voluntary or involuntary. Record the information in the appropriate place in the Data Table.

4. In the appropriate place in Observations, sketch a few of the skeletal muscle fibers that you observed under high power. Label the nucleus, cell membrane, cytoplasm, and striations. Record the magnification of the microscope.

5. Observe a prepared slide of smooth muscle under low power. Switch to high power and observe the number of nuclei within one cell, the cell shape, and the presence or absence of striations. Classify smooth muscle as voluntary or involuntary. Record the information in the appropriate place in the Data Table.

6. In the appropriate place in Observations, sketch a few of the smooth muscle cells that you observed under high power. Label the nucleus, cell membrane, and cytoplasm. Record the magnification of the microscope.

7. Observe a prepared slide of cardiac muscle under low power. Switch to high power and observe the number of nuclei within one cell, the cell shape, and the presence or absence of striations. Classify smooth muscle as voluntary or involuntary. Record the information in the appropriate place in the Data Table.

8. In the appropriate place in Observations, sketch a few of the smooth muscle cells that you observed under high power. Label the nucleus, cell membrane, cytoplasm, and striations. Record the magnification of the microscope.

Part B. Examining the Muscles in a Chicken Wing

1. Rinse the chicken wing under running water. Dry it thoroughly with paper towels and place it in the dissecting tray.

▦ 2. Remove the skin from the chicken wing. With the forceps, grasp the skin near the shoulder and pull the skin away from the underlying muscles. Use scissors to cut the skin along the entire length of the chicken wing. **CAUTION:** *Be careful when handling sharp instruments. Cut in a direction away from your hands and body.* Make sure you cut the skin exactly as shown in Figure 1. **Note:** *Be careful not to cut through the underlying muscles with the scissors.*

Figure 1

3. Carefully pull off the skin. Observe the fascia, the transparent connective tissue that surrounds the muscles and holds the muscles to the skin. With a probe or scalpel, gently separate the fascia from the skin. **Note:** *The skin covering the joints is difficult to remove. Work carefully, using scissors or a scalpel to remove this skin.* Remove the skin up to the second joint. It is not necessary to remove the skin from the wing tip. Cut away the excess skin around the second joint. Discard the skin according to your teacher's instructions. **Note:** *You may want to wash your hands and rinse the chicken wing at this time.*

4. Observe the muscles in the chicken wing. Observe the tendons, the shiny white cords of connective tissue at the ends of the muscles. Tendons attach muscles to bones.

5. Grasp the wing by the shoulder and the wing tip. As you bend and straighten the wing, notice how the muscles contract as they move. Locate and identify the antagonistic muscles, which are pairs of muscles that work in opposition to each other. Thoroughly wash your hands with soap and water.

6. In the appropriate place in Observations, sketch the muscles and bones of the chicken wing. Label the bones, the muscles, the tendons, and an antagonistic muscle pair.

7. Examine Figure 2, which shows the muscles and bones of the human arm. The elbow joint, which is a hinge joint, is similar to the joint in the chicken wing. On Figure 2, locate the tendons that attach the muscles to the bones. As a muscle contracts, the attachments either remain stationary or move. The attachment end that moves a bone is called the insertion. The attachment end that remains stationary, anchoring the muscle, is called the origin. Locate the origins and insertions in the chicken wing.

Figure 2

8. Dispose of the dissected chicken wing according to your teacher's instructions. Wash, dry, and put away the dissecting tools you used in this part of the investigation.

Observations

Data Table

Type of Muscle Cell	Number of Nuclei per Cell	Striations	Cell Shape	Voluntary or Involuntary?
Skeletal	Many	Present	Long, tapered ends	Voluntary
Smooth	One	Absent	Long, spindle-shaped	Involuntary
Cardiac	One	Present	Branched	Involuntary

Magnification _____   Magnification _____   Magnification _____

Skeletal Muscle   **Smooth Muscle**   **Cardiac Muscle**

Chicken Wing

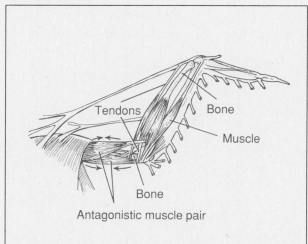

Analysis and Conclusions

1. a. How are skeletal muscle tissue and cardiac muscle tissue similar?

Both skeletal muscle tissue and cardiac muscle tissue have striations.

_____

b. How are they different? Skeletal muscle tissue consists of long fibers that contain many nuclei.

Cardiac muscle tissue has many branched cells with one nucleus. Whereas skeletal muscles are

voluntary, cardiac muscles are involuntary.

_____

2. How does smooth muscle tissue differ from the other two types of muscle tissue?

Smooth muscle tissue consists of small, spindle-shaped cells, each containing a nucleus. There are no

striations in smooth muscle tissue.

3. Where in the body is each of the three types of muscle tissue found?

Skeletal muscle tissue Any part of the body that requires voluntary movement.

Smooth muscle tissue The digestive tract, urinary bladder, blood vessels, glands, skin.

Cardiac muscle tissue The heart only.

4. What enables the chicken to move its wing? The muscle tissue in the chicken's wing enables it

to move.

5. How might injury to one of the muscles in an antagonistic muscle pair affect movement?

Because antagonistic muscles work together in pairs to cause movement, injury to one of the muscles might

keep any movement from occurring.

Critical Thinking and Application

1. What effect will the tearing of a tendon have on its corresponding muscle? How could this

situation be repaired? A tendon attaches skeletal muscle to bone. If an entire tendon is severed,

movement of the bone is lost. This occurs because the tendon, which is pulled by the muscle, is no longer

attached to the bone that the tendon pulls on. The only way to reattach the tendon is through surgery.

This often involves microsurgery, or surgery through a microscope, because of the small size of some

tendons.

2. Suppose smooth muscles rather than skeletal muscles could be attached to the skeleton and given voluntary control. How might the movement of the skeleton be affected?

Smooth muscles move much more slowly than skeletal muscles. If smooth muscles were attached to the

skeleton, the skeleton would be unable to move with its normal speed and power.

3. Why would a bird be unable to fly if there was some damage to the nerve in the wing?

Nerves carry messages from the brain to the muscles. If a nerve in the wing is damaged, messages cannot

be sent to the wing muscles. As a result, the wing cannot move.

Going Further

1. To prepare your own slide of muscle tissue, place a small piece of raw pork or raw beef in a solution containing 35 g of potassium hydroxide and 100 mL of distilled water. Allow the meat to soak in the solution for about 30 minutes. Remove the meat from the solution. Place the meat on a clean glass slide and with a dissecting needle tease the muscle fibers apart. Add a coverslip and observe the muscle fibers under a microscope.

2. Using reference materials, learn how muscles, tendons, ligaments, cartilage, and bones are arranged to allow movement in a knee joint. Why are knee injuries common in athletes?

76

Mechanical and Chemical Digestion

You may want to refer students to pages 867–875 in the textbook for a discussion of digestion.

Time required: 45 minutes.

Pre-Lab Discussion

When an animal eats, the food must be digested, or broken down into nutrients that the animal's cells can use. In vertebrates, unlike some other animals, digestion is extracellular and takes place in a digestive tube. Within this tube, food is mechanically and chemically digested. *Mechanical digestion* involves mixing, grinding, or crushing large pieces of food into small pieces. *Chemical digestion* occurs when digestive enzymes break down complex molecules, such as carbohydrates, into simple molecules, such as glucose. Although chemical digestion can occur without digestive enzymes, these enzymes catalyze, or speed up, the reaction. For this reason, digestive enzymes are called *catalysts*.

In this investigation, you will examine the processes of mechanical and chemical digestion. You will also observe how enzymes affect the rate of chemical digestion.

Problem

How are foods mechanically and chemically digested? What effect do digestive enzymes have on the rate of digestion?

Materials *(per group)*

Egg white from half of a boiled egg
6 test tubes
Test tube rack
5% hydrochloric acid solution
Mixture of 5% hydrochloric acid solution and 1% pepsin solution [1]
Triple-beam balance
Scalpel
Dissecting tray
10-mL graduated cylinder
Glass-marking pencil
Olive oil
1% pancreatin solution [2]
5% soap or bile salt solution [3]
pH paper [4]
Medicine dropper

Before class, boil eggs and cut them in half lengthwise. Discard the yolks and give each student group an egg white half.

Carefully add 50 mL concentrated hydrochloric acid to 1 L distilled water while constantly stirring the solution.

[1] Pepsin can be obtained from a biological supply house. To make 1% pepsin solution, add 1 g pepsin to a 100-mL graduated cylinder. Fill the graduated cylinder with distilled water to the 100-mL mark. Stir until completely dissolved. To make a hydrochloric acid and pepsin mixture, mix equal parts of 5% hydrochloric acid solution and 1% pepsin solution. Stir until completely mixed.

[2] Pancreatin is available from a biological supply house. Add 1 g pancreatin powder to a 100-mL graduated cylinder. Fill cylinder to the 100-mL mark with distilled water. Mix until completely dissolved.

[3] Bile salt is available from a biological supply house. Add 5 mL liquid soap or 5 g bile salt to a 100-mL graduated cylinder. Fill cylinder to the 100-mL mark with distilled water. Mix until completely dissolved.

[4] Available from a biological supply house.

Safety 🔥 ⚗ 👁 ▦

Put on a laboratory apron if one is available. Put on safety goggles. Handle all glassware carefully. Always use special caution when working with laboratory chemicals, as they may irritate the skin or cause staining of the skin or clothing. Never touch or taste any chemical unless instructed to do so. Be careful when handling sharp instruments. Note all safety alert symbols next to the steps in the Procedure and review the meanings of each symbol by referring to the symbol guide on page 10.

Procedure

Part A. Chemical Digestion of Fat

1. Place three test tubes in the test tube rack. With the glass-marking pencil, label the test tubes 1, 2, and 3.

2. Add 10 mL of water and 2 drops of olive oil to each test tube. Gently swirl the test tubes to mix the contents of each.

3. Dip a piece of pH paper into each mixture. Record the pH for each mixture in the appropriate place in Data Table 1.

4. Add 5 mL of pancreatin solution to test tube 2. Add 5 mL of pancreatin solution and 3 mL of soap or bile salt solution to test tube 3. Gently swirl the test tubes to mix the contents. **CAUTION:** *Wear safety goggles when working with laboratory chemicals. Be careful not to get the solutions in your eyes or spill them on your hands or clothing.*

5. After 5 minutes, measure the pH of each mixture. Record this information in the appropriate places in Data Table 1.

6. After 5 more minutes, repeat step 5.

Part B. Mechanical and Chemical Digestion of Protein

1. Place three test tubes in a test tube rack. With a glass-marking pencil, label the test tubes 1, 2, and 3.

2. Using a scalpel, cut the egg white into three equal pieces. **CAUTION:** *Be careful when handling sharp instruments. Cut in a direction away from your hands and body.*

3. Find the mass of each piece of egg white. **Note:** *Try to make each piece have approximately the same mass.*

4. Place one piece of egg white in test tube 1.

5. Use a scalpel to chop the second piece of egg white into small pieces. Place the small pieces of egg white in test tube 2.

6. Use a scalpel to chop the third piece of egg white into small pieces. Place the small pieces of egg white in test tube 3.

7. To test tube 1, add 10 mL of hydrochloric acid solution. To test tube 2, add 10 mL of hydrochloric acid solution. To test tube 3, add 10 mL of the mixture of hydrochloric acid solution and pepsin solution. See Figure 1. Gently swirl each test tube so that the liquids mix well with the egg white.

Mixture of 5% hydrochloric solution and 1% pepsin sol

5% hydrochloric acid sol

Small pieces of egg white

Large piece of egg white

Figure 1

8. Set the test tubes aside and allow them to remain undisturbed for 24 hours. After 24 hours, observe each test tube. Record your observations in the appropriate places in Data Table 2.

Observations

Data Table 1

Time	pH of Substances		
	Test Tube 1 **(water + oil)**	**Test Tube 2** **(water + oil +** **pancreatin)**	**Test Tube 3** **(water + oil +** **pancreatin + soap)**
Start	Neutral (7)	Neutral (7)	Neutral (7)
After 5 minutes	Neutral (7)	Slightly acidic	Acidic
After 10 minutes	Neutral (7)	Slightly acidic	Acidic

Data Table 2

Substance	Observations
Test tube 1 (large egg white + hydrochloric acid)	Little digestion occurs. Egg white has been broken down only slightly.
Test tube 2 (small egg white + hydrochloric acid)	Small pieces of egg white will show more digestion than piece in test tube 1.
Test tube 3 (small egg white + hydrochloric acid + pepsin)	Greatest amount of chemical breakdown has occurred. The least egg white remains.

Analysis and Conclusions

1. Which test tube showed the greatest degree of fat digestion? _Test tube 3._ _____

2. How were you able to determine experimentally that fat digestion had occurred?

   The digestion of fats results in the formation of fatty acids, which cause the solution to become acidic. This

   acidity can be determined by using an indicator such as pH paper.

3. In which test tube did the smallest degree of protein digestion occur? How do you explain this?

   Test tube 1 shows the smallest degree of digestion. The one large piece of egg white has a small surface

   area, so little of the protein is exposed to the hydrochloric acid. Also, test tube 1 contains no enzymes to

   speed up the reaction.

4. In which test tube did the greatest degree of protein digestion occur? How do you explain this? Test tube 3 shows the greatest degree of digestion. The small pieces of egg white increase the surface area of the protein and expose much of it to the acid and pepsin. The hydrochloric acid produces an acid pH, which increases the effectiveness of the enzyme pepsin.

Critical Thinking and Application

1. What roles do the teeth and tongue play in the process of digestion?

The teeth and tongue aid in mechanical digestion by tearing and grinding food into smaller pieces. This process increases the surface area of the food, making it more accessible to digestive enzymes.

2. Bile is produced in the liver but stored in the gallbladder, where it becomes concentrated before being released into the digestive tract. How would surgery involving the removal of the gallbladder affect the process of digestion? Bile aids in the digestion of fats. Although the liver produces bile and can release it directly into the digestive tract, this unconcentrated bile is less effective in fat digestion. A person lacking a gallbladder would have to limit his or her intake of fats.

3. A person who has had a small section of small intestine removed surgically loses weight. Explain why weight loss might follow such surgery. The small intestine is the site of nutrient absorption in the body. If part of the small intestine is surgically removed, there is less area where absorption can occur. As fewer nutrients are absorbed, the person might experience a loss of weight.

4. Bulimia is an eating disorder in which a person forces the body to eject the contents of the stomach, usually through the mouth. Explain why most bulimics eventually develop dental problems. The liquid material that is ejected contains partially digested food, hydrochloric acid, and enzymes. When these substances come into contact with the enamel of the teeth, they cause the enamel to dissolve. Thus decay can more readily occur.

Going Further

Label eight test tubes 1 through 8. In each tube, place 10 mL of the mixture of 1% pepsin solution and 5% hydrochloric acid solution. Immerse test tubes 1 and 2 in ice water, keep test tubes 3 and 4 at room temperature, and place test tubes 5 and 6 in a water bath at 40°C. Boil test tubes 7 and 8 for a few minutes, allow them to cool, and then place them in the water bath. Add equal amounts of finely chopped, hard-boiled egg white to each test tube. What influence does temperature have on the effectiveness of pepsin in protein digestion? Construct a data table showing your observations.

77

Measuring Food Energy

You may want to refer students to pages 855–866 in the textbook for a discussion of food and nutrition.

Time required: 50 minutes.

Pre-Lab Discussion

All living things need energy to carry out metabolic activities. Animals—unlike many plants, protists, and bacteria—do not have the means to get energy directly from sunlight or simple inorganic chemicals. The energy requirements of animals must be met by taking in food.

The energy content of food can be determined by burning a sample of food in a device called a calorimeter. Heat energy released by combustion is absorbed by a container of water. Any rise in water temperature is measured and then used to determine the value of the heat energy released by the burning food sample. Heat energy is expressed in units called calories. One calorie is the amount of heat needed to raise the temperature of 1 gram of water by 1 degree Celsius. This unit, however, is too small for evaluating food energy. A Calorie, which is equal to 1000 calories, is used to measure food energy.

In this investigation, you will construct a simple calorimeter and use it to measure the amount of heat energy contained in certain foods.

Problem

How is the energy in food measured?

Materials *(per group)*

Ring stand	Four food samples	Food samples can include nuts, dried beans and cereals, dry snack foods, and hard cheeses.
Test tube clamp	Heat-resistant gloves	
Test tube	Triple-beam balance	
Paper clip	100-mL graduated cylinder	
Cork stopper [1]	Matches	
Fireproof pad	Thermometer	
Metric ruler		

[1] Use cork stoppers with a base diameter of at least 4 cm. Test tube stoppers are too small.

Safety ⚗ 🕶 🧤 👁

Put on a laboratory apron if one is available. Put on safety goggles. Handle all glassware carefully. Use extreme care when working with heated equipment or materials to avoid burns. Note all safety alert symbols next to the steps in the Procedure and review the meanings of each symbol by referring to the symbol guide on page 10.

Procedure

🔺 1. To assemble a calorimeter, set up a ring stand, test tube clamp, test tube, and fireproof pad as shown in Figure 1.

Figure 1

2. To make a food platform for the calorimeter, bend the outer end of a paper clip straight down so that it is at a right angle to the rest of the clip. Insert the free end of the clip into the middle of the narrow end of the cork stopper. See Figure 2.

3. Place the food platform on the fireproof pad. Adjust the height of the test tube so that the space between the food platform and the bottom of the test tube is 2 cm.

4. Use a graduated cylinder to measure exactly 15 mL of water into the test tube. Record the mass of the water in the appropriate place in the Data Table. **Note:** *Remember that 1 mL of water has a mass of 1 g.*

5. Measure the temperature of the water in the test tube. Record this number in the appropriate place in the Data Table. **Note:** *Be sure to remove the thermometer from the test tube after you record the temperature.*

Figure 2

6. Select a food sample and find its mass using the triple-beam balance. Record the mass in the appropriate place in the Data Table. Also record the name of the food sample used in the appropriate place in the Data Table. Tell students to measure food mass and water temperature carefully to ensure accuracy.

☚
👁 7. Place the food sample on the paper clip platform. Ignite the food sample with a match, and quickly place the platform under the test tube. **CAUTION:** *Wear safety goggles when doing this part of the investigation. Be careful when using matches.* Allow the food to burn completely. Reignite the sample if necessary. You may wish to provide extra ventilation while completing step 7.

8. After the sample has burned completely, measure the temperature of the water in the test tube. **CAUTION:** *Do not touch the test tube; it may be hot.* Record the temperature of the water.

9. Find the mass of the remainder of the burned food sample. Record the mass.

10. Determine the change in mass of the food sample. Record the result.

11. Determine the change in the temperature of the water in the test tube. Record the result.

12. Repeat steps 3 through 11 using three other food samples. **Note:** *Remember to empty the water out of the test tube and to use cool water for each sample.*

13. Use the formula below to find the energy value, or Calories, per food sample. Record the results in the appropriate place in the Data Table. **Note:** *The specific heat of water is 1 Calorie per kilogram degree Celsius.*

$$\text{Calories per food sample} = \text{Change in water temperature} \times \text{Mass of water} \times \text{Specific heat of water} \times \frac{1 \text{ kg}}{1000 \text{ g}}$$

14. Use the formula below to find the Calories per gram of food sample. Record the results in the appropriate place in the Data Table.

Calories per gram = Calories per food sample/Change in mass of food sample

Observations

Data Table

Variable	Food Sample			
Mass of food sample before burning (g)		Answers will vary.		
Mass of food sample after burning (g)				
Change in mass of food sample (g)				
Mass of water (g) (1 mL = 1 g)	15	15	15	15
Temperature of water before heating (°C)				
Temperature of water after heating (°C)				
Change in water temperature (°C)				
Calories per food sample				
Calories per gram				

Analysis and Conclusions

1. What is the difference between a calorie and a Calorie? _A calorie is the amount of energy needed_
to raise the temperature of 1 g water 1°C. A Calorie equals 1000 calories.

2. Why must the food sample be ignited before placing the platform under the test tube?
Heat from the lighted match might raise the temperature of the water in the test tube and alter the data.

3. Why must the thermometer be removed from the test tube when the food sample is burning?
Heat from the burning food sample may directly affect the thermometer, causing the reading to be
inaccurate or the thermometer to explode.

4. How do your results compare to those of other student groups in your class? Give reasons for any variations. Answers will vary. Heat was lost to the air and to the test tube; food was not burned completely; food was ignited before it was placed under the test tube.

5. Fats yield more food energy than proteins or carbohydrates. Which of your food samples most likely contained the greatest amount of fat? The sample that produced the most Calories when burned most likely contained the most fat.

Critical Thinking and Application

1. Swimming for one hour burns up 600 Calories. For each food sample you tested, calculate how many grams of food you would have to eat to get this energy. Answers will vary.
Grams of food = 600 Calories/number of Calories per gram.

2. Fad diets, which have become popular in the past two decades, involve the consumption of large amounts of a limited variety of foods. Explain why some fad diets may be an unhealthful way to lose weight. Due to the limited food menu, fad diets may not provide the person with the proper amounts of nutrients. As a consequence, the person may lose weight but become malnourished. This malnourishment may cause disorders or diseases.

3. Although fiber is not officially classified as a nutrient, it is an important component of the American diet today. What is the role of fiber in the human body?
Fiber helps to increase peristalsis in the digestive system. Peristalsis moves food through the digestive system rapidly. Because fiber adds bulk to the diet, it pushes food material through the system, thereby aiding in digestion and elimination.

4. Contrast the snacks for a person who is trying to lose weight with those for a person who is growing very rapidly. The person who is dieting might avoid snacks entirely, but low-Calorie raw vegetables, fresh fruits, or vegetable juices are suitable. The person trying to keep up with rapid growth many choose these foods, plus other foods such as sandwiches and occasionally cakes, cookies, or pies to increase Caloric and nutrient intake.

Going Further

Using the procedure from this investigation, determine the Caloric value of various diet foods and their counterparts. Is there a difference in their Caloric values?

78

Measuring Lung Capacity

You may want to refer students to pages 882–891 in the textbook for a discussion of the human respiratory system.

Time required: 40 minutes.

Pre-Lab Discussion

The amount of air that you move in and out of your lungs depends on how quickly you are breathing. The amount of air that is moved in and out of the lungs when a person is breathing normally is called the *tidal volume*. This amount of air provides enough oxygen for the body when the person is resting. It is possible to inhale more deeply and exhale more forcefully than usual. The maximum amount of air moved in and out of the lungs when the deepest possible inspiration is followed by the strongest possible expiration is called the *vital capacity*.

In this investigation, you will determine the tidal volume and vital capacity of your lungs.

Problem

How are the tidal volume and vital capacity of the human lungs measured?

Materials *(per pair of students)*

2 round balloons (1 for each student in the pair)
Metric ruler
Meterstick
Bathroom scale (1 per class is adequate)

Safety

Do not participate in this investigation if you have any breathing difficulties.
Students should be allowed to participate in this investigation on a voluntary basis. Students with respiratory illnesses should not be required to participate. You may wish to consult the school nurse for information about students who should not be allowed to conduct this investigation.

Procedure
Part A. Measuring Tidal Volume

You may wish to tell students to pinch their nostrils shut while exhaling into the balloon to prevent air from escaping through the nose.

1. Stretch a round balloon lengthwise several times.

2. Inhale normally and then exhale normally into the balloon. **Note:** *Do not force your breathing.*

3. Immediately pinch the end of the balloon shut so that no air escapes. Place the balloon on a flat surface. Have your partner use the metric ruler to measure the diameter of the balloon at its widest point. See Figure 1. Record this measurement in Data Table 1.

4. Deflate the balloon and repeat steps 2 and 3 two more times. Use your three measurements to calculate an average tidal volume. Record this measurement in Data Table 1.

Figure 1

Part B. Measuring Vital Capacity

1. After breathing normally, inhale as much air into your lungs as possible. Exhale as much air as you can from your lungs into the balloon.

2. Immediately pinch the end of the balloon shut so that no air escapes. Place the balloon on a flat surface. Have your partner use the metric ruler to measure the diameter of the balloon at its widest point. Record this measurement in Data Table 1.

3. Deflate the balloon and repeat steps 1 and 2 two more times. Use your three measurements to calculate an average vital capacity. Record this measurement in Data Table 1.

4. Use Figure 2 to convert the balloon diameters in Data Table 1 into lung volumes. On the horizontal (x) axis, locate the diameter of the balloon in centimeters and follow the number up until it meets the curved line. Then move across in a straight line to the vertical (y) axis and approximate the lung volume. Record this measurement in Data Table 2. Repeat this procedure for all of the balloon diameters in Data Table 1.

Figure 2

Part C. Calculating Estimated Vital Capacity

1. Research has shown that the capacity of a person's lungs is proportional to the surface area of his or her body. To find the surface area of your body, you will need to know your height in centimeters and your mass in kilograms. Use a meterstick to find your height and the bathroom scale to find your mass. Record these measurements in Data Table 3.

2. Use Figure 3 to estimate the surface area of your body. Find your height in centimeters on the left scale. Mark this point. Find your mass in kilograms on the right scale. Mark this point. Use a metric ruler to draw a straight line connecting these two points. Now look at the center scale. The point at which your line crosses this scale gives your surface area in square meters. Record this number in Data Table 3.

Figure 3

3. To calculate the estimated vital capacity of your lungs, multiply your surface area by the ratio of vital capacity to surface area. For females this ratio is 2000 mL per square meter. For males this ratio is 2500 mL per square meter. Record the estimated vital capacity of your lungs in Data Table 3.

Observations

Data Table 1

Balloon Diameter (cm)		
Trial	Tidal Volume	Vital Capacity
1		
2	Answers	will vary.
3		
Average		

Data Table 2

Lung Volume (cm³)		
Trial	Tidal Volume	Vital Capacity
1		
2	Answers	will vary.
3		
Average		

Data Table 3

Body Component	Data
Height (cm)	
Mass (kg)	Answers will vary.
Surface area (m²)	
Vital capacity (cm³)	

Analysis and Conclusions

1. Why is it important to measure tidal volume and vital capacity three times and calculate averages for these measurements? Making more measurements provides better data. Averaging several trials should help to compensate for errors in measuring.

2. How do your tidal volume and vital capacity compare with those of other class members? Why might there be some variation in the measurements of different people? Answers will vary. Students may mention body size, sex, illness, athletic training, or inaccuracy of measurement as reasons for the differences.

3. How does your estimated vital capacity compare to your measured vital capacity? Answers will vary.

4. If there is a difference, suggest a reason for this. Answers will vary, depending on the answer to question 3. Students may suggest that they are more or less athletic than the average person. Students may also mention technical sources of inaccuracy, such as the rough method of calibration.

5. Why might it be important to know a person's tidal volume or vital capacity? Answers will vary. Vital capacity could be monitored to determine the physiological effects of exercise on the body. A low tidal volume or vital capacity might help to diagnose a respiratory illness such as asthma, pneumonia, or emphysema.

Name _____ Class _____ Date _____

6. Even when you exhale as forcefully as possible, some air remains in the lungs. Why is this an important occurrence? About 1 L of air remains in the lungs at all times. This air helps the lungs to

retain some shape within the chest cavity, making the inhalation of new air possible. A completely collapsed

lung can cause extensive physiological damage.

Critical Thinking and Application

1. Figure 4 shows measurements of a jogger's vital capacity. The measurements were taken using a method similar to the one you used in this investigation. The vital capacity was measured at the beginning of the jogger's training period and then every five days after that. Use the data in Figure 4 to construct a line graph on the graph provided.

Day of Training Period	Vital Capacity (cm³)
0	4800
5	4830
10	4890
15	4910
20	4960
25	5040
30	5130

Figure 4

2. What happened to the jogger's vital capacity as the training period progressed?

The vital capacity increased. The greatest increases occurred at the end of the training period.

3. What probably caused the change in the jogger's vital capacity? The exercise probably caused the

increase in vital capacity. The body responded to the greater demand for oxygen.

4. How might vital capacity be important to some musicians? Increased vital capacity would be helpful

to players of woodwind or brass instruments and to singers because they could hold notes for a longer

period of time.

5. How do you think smoking would affect vital capacity? Smoking would act to decrease vital

capacity. Cigarette smoke can cause extensive damage to the human respiratory system.

Going Further

1. The vital capacity of the lungs is affected by the anatomical build of a person, the position of the person during the vital capacity measurement, and the stretching capability of the lungs and chest cavity. Measure the vital capacity of your lungs while sitting up and then while lying down. In each position, inhale as much air into your lungs as possible and exhale as much air as you can into a balloon. Measure the diameter of the balloon each time. Compare your vital capacity in each position.

2. If a bell jar is available, construct a model of human lungs as shown in Figure 5. To make the model "breathe," pull down and then push up on the rubber sheet. Describe what happens. How does the working of this model relate to the working of your diaphragm and lungs?

Figure 5

79

The Effect of Exercise on Respiration

You may want to refer students to pages 882–891 in the textbook for a discussion of the human respiratory system.

Time required: 45 minutes.

Pre-Lab Discussion

In multicellular organisms, specialized organs and organ systems are used to exchange the gases involved in cellular respiration with the external environment. The function of the human respiratory system is to take oxygen into the body and to release carbon dioxide from the body. As a result of changes in the environment or the amount of physical activity, levels of carbon dioxide and oxygen in the blood change. The body attempts to maintain the proper balance of carbon dioxide and oxygen levels in the blood by increasing or decreasing the rate of breathing. The presence of carbon dioxide can be detected with the testing solution bromthymol blue. A change of color in this solution indicates the presence of carbon dioxide.

In this investigation, you will determine the effect of exercise on the breathing rate. You will also use bromthymol blue to determine the presence of carbon dioxide in exhaled air, and the effect of exercise on the amount of carbon dioxide produced.

Problem

How are breathing rate and production of carbon dioxide affected by exercise?

Materials *(per group)*

200 mL of bromthymol blue solution
2 500-mL jars or flasks
Glass stirring rod
8 drinking straws
100-mL graduated cylinder
65 mL of 4% ammonia solution
Medicine dropper
Clock or watch with second hand

Dissolve 0.4 g bromthymol blue powder in 1 L distilled water. If solution appears green, add 4% sodium hydroxide solution to bromthymol blue drop by drop until color is blue. Bromthymol blue may also be purchased premixed from a biological supply house.

Add 40 mL ammonia to a 1-L graduated cylinder or volumetric flask. Fill to the 1-L mark with distilled water. Pour into dropper bottles for student use.

Safety

Students should be allowed to participate in this investigation on a voluntary basis. Students with respiratory illnesses should not be required to participate. You may wish to consult the school nurse for information about students who should not be allowed to conduct this investigation.

Put on a laboratory apron if one is available. Put on safety goggles. Handle all glassware carefully. Always use special caution when working with laboratory chemicals, as they may irritate the skin or cause staining of the skin or clothing. You will be exercising during this investigation. If at any time you feel faint or dizzy, sit down and immediately call your teacher. Note all safety alert symbols next to the steps in the Procedure and review the meanings of each symbol by referring to the symbol guide on page 10.

Procedure
Part A. Breathing Rate at Rest

After each part of this investigation, rest and allow your heart rate and breathing rate to return to normal. **CAUTION:** *If at any time during this investigation you feel faint or dizzy, sit down and immediately call your teacher.*

1. Sit down and relax for several minutes before doing this part of the investigation. Remain seated throughout this part of the investigation.

2. Count the number of times you inhale at rest in one minute. You may wish to have one of your group members watch the clock as you count your number of breaths. Record this measurement in Data Table 1.

3. Repeat step 2 two more times and calculate your average breathing rate at rest. Record this number in Data Table 1.

Part B. Breathing Rate After Exercise

1. Run in place for one minute.

2. Return to your chair and record the number of times you inhale in one minute. Record this measurement in Data Table 1.

3. Repeat steps 1 and 2 two more times and calculate your average breathing rate after exercise. Record this number in Data Table 1.

Part C. Amount of Carbon Dioxide Exhaled at Rest

1. Pour 100 mL of bromthymol blue solution into a jar or flask.

2. Have one member of your group use a drinking straw to breathe out normally into the bromthymol blue solution for exactly one minute. **CAUTION:** *Be careful not to suck the solution into your mouth.* The bromthymol blue solution should turn a pale yellow color at the end of one minute.

3. With a medicine dropper, add 1 drop of ammonia to the jar and stir once with a glass stirring rod.

4. Continue to add ammonia one drop at a time. Count each drop and stir once between drops until the solution turns blue. In Data Table 2, record the total number of drops of ammonia needed to turn the solution blue.

5. Repeat steps 2 through 4 two more times using the same bromthymol blue solution. Find the average number of ammonia drops needed for the three trials and record this number in Data Table 2.

Part D. Amount of Carbon Dioxide Exhaled After Exercise

1. Pour 100 mL of bromthymol blue solution into a second jar or flask.

2. Have the same group member who was the test subject in Part C stand up and run in place for one minute.

3. Have the group member use another drinking straw to exhale into the bromthymol blue solution for exactly one minute. **CAUTION:** *Be careful not to suck the solution into your mouth.*

4. With a medicine dropper, add 1 drop of ammonia to the jar and stir once with a glass stirring rod.

5. Continue to add ammonia one drop at a time. Count each drop and stir once between drops until the solution turns blue. In Data Table 2, record the total number of drops of ammonia needed to turn the solution blue.

6. Repeat steps 2 through 5 two more times using the same bromthymol blue solution. Find the average number of ammonia drops needed for the three trials and record this number in Data Table 2.

Observations

Data Table 1

Breathing Rate (times per minute)		
Trial	At Rest	After Exercise
1		
2	Answers will vary.	
3		
Average		

Data Table 2

Number of Ammonia Drops		
Trial	At Rest	After Exercise
1		
2	Answers will vary.	
3		
Average		

Analysis and Conclusion

1. Compared with your normal breathing rate at rest, what happened to your breathing rate after exercise? The breathing rate should be higher after exercise.

_____

2. Why would your breathing rate change after exercise? Exercise produces a greater demand for oxygen by the body, thus increasing the breathing rate.

3. Were your results the same as the results of all of your classmates? What might account for any differences? Variables include differences in lung size, body structure, physical condition, and the intensity of exercise within the one-minute period.

4. In Parts C and D, what does the number of ammonia drops represent?
The number of ammonia drops represents the amount of chemical needed to neutralize the effect of the carbon dioxide in the bromthymol blue solution.

5. Are the average numbers of ammonia drops needed to restore the blue color to the solutions in Parts C and D the same? If not, why are they different? No. After exercise, students exhaled more carbon dioxide into the bromthymol blue. Thus more ammonia drops were needed to return the solution to a blue color.

6. What effect does exercise have on the amount of carbon dioxide released from the lungs? During exercise, cellular respiration is increased, releasing more carbon dioxide into the bloodstream, which carries the carbon dioxide to the lungs to be exhaled.

Critical Thinking and Application

1. What factors would an athlete have to consider if he or she were training or competing at a high-altitude location such as Denver, Colorado? Atmosphere at high altitudes contains less oxygen than at sea level. Training and conditioning would have to compensate for this decreased oxygen level.

2. Why do some athletes inhale pure oxygen after strenuous activity? Inhaling pure oxygen will supply the body with an immediate concentrated supply of oxygen to compensate for the oxygen that has been depleted from the body through exercise.

3. List three benefits of exercise to your body. Answers may include weight loss, maintenance of ideal body weight, increased energy, more resistance to disease, better muscle tone, and better vital capacity.

4. The nicotine in cigarette tobacco enters the bloodstream, where it constricts the blood vessels. How would this affect the breathing rate? The breathing rate will increase due to the decreased ability of the smaller blood vessels to move oxygen into the blood and remove carbon dioxide from it.

Going Further

1. Find out if germinating seeds give off carbon dioxide during respiration. Obtain about 10 to 15 germinating lima bean seeds. Place them in a flask, or small jar, and add enough bromothymol blue solution to cover about half of the seeds. Stopper the flask or, if a jar is used, place a lid on it. Place the jar aside for 30 minutes and then observe the results. What color should the bromthymol blue solution turn if carbon dioxide is given off by the seeds?

2. Collect breathing rates for members of your family and other people of different ages. Categorize the data by 10-year increments and illustrate the results with a bar graph.

80

Simulating Blood Typing

You may want to refer students to pages 230–231 and 905–907 in the textbook for a discussion of blood type and blood components, respectively.

Time required: 30 minutes.

Pre-Lab Discussion

Human blood may be classified according to the presence or absence of certain *antigens,* or factors, that are attached to the surface of the red blood cells, or erythrocytes. Two of the antigens used in blood typing are known as A and B. A person whose red blood cells have only antigen A has type A blood, whereas a person whose red blood cells have only antigen B has type B blood. People who have both A and B antigens on their red blood cells have type AB blood. Those whose blood cells have neither A nor B antigens have type O blood.

The plasma of each blood group contains a certain type or combination of *antibodies*. Antibodies are substances that attack antigens. Blood type A plasma contains anti-B antibodies, whereas blood type B plasma has anti-A antibodies. Anti-A antibodies attack red blood cells that have A antigens; anti-B antibodies attack those that have B antigens. The attacking antibodies bind to the red blood cells, causing them to *agglutinate,* or clump together. Type AB plasma has both A and B antigens and has neither type of antibody. Type O blood has neither A nor B antigens and contains both anti-A and anti-B antibodies. In transfusions, the blood types of the donor and recipient must be carefully matched because transfusion of the wrong type of blood can be fatal to the recipient.

In this investigation, you will simulate human blood typing.

To prepare the simulated anti-A and anti-B sera and blood:

Add 3 g sodium iodide to 100 mL distilled water and stir until dissolved. Pour the solution into dropper bottles labeled anti-A serum.

Problem

How is a person's blood type determined?

Add 3.4 g silver nitrate to 100 mL distilled water and stir until dissolved. Pour the solution into dropper bottles labeled anti-B serum.

Materials *(per group)*

Glass slide with two depressions
Simulated anti-A serum
Simulated anti-B serum
Simulated blood—types A, B, AB, O

Add 6.6 g lead nitrate to 100 mL distilled water and stir until dissolved. Pour the solution into dropper bottles labeled Bottle 3. This will represent type A blood.

Add 4.2 g barium chloride to 100 mL distilled water and stir until dissolved. Pour the solution into dropper bottles labeled Bottle 1. This will represent type B blood.

Add equal amounts of lead nitrate and barium chloride solutions to dropper bottles labeled Bottle 4. This will represent type AB blood.

Pour 100 mL distilled water into dropper bottles labeled Bottle 2. This will represent type O blood.

Safety ⚗ 🔥 👁

Put on a laboratory apron if one is available. Put on safety goggles. Handle all glassware carefully. Always use special caution when working with laboratory chemicals, as they may irritate the skin or cause staining of the skin or clothing. Never touch or taste any chemical unless instructed to do so. Note all safety alert symbols next to the steps in the Procedure and review the meanings of each symbol by referring to the symbol guide on page 10.

Procedure

1. Put on safety goggles. Place 2 drops of the solution in the dropper bottle labeled Bottle 1 in each of the two depressions in the glass slide. To the left depression, add 2 drops of the solution in the bottle labeled anti-A serum. To the right depression, add 2 drops of the solution in the bottle labeled anti-B serum. **CAUTION:** *Use caution when working with laboratory chemicals. If a laboratory chemical comes into contact with your skin, wash the area with water immediately.*

2. Examine the substances in the two depressions for signs of clumping. If clumping occurs only on the left side of the depression slide, this simulates the presence of type A blood. If clumping occurs only on the right side of the depression slide, this simulates the presence of type B blood. If clumping occurs on both sides of the depression slide, this simulates the presence of type AB blood. If no clumping occurs on either side of the depression slide, this simulates the presence of type O blood. See Figure 1. Record your observations in the appropriate places in the Data Table.

Simulated Type A Blood

Simulated Type B Blood

Simulated Type AB Blood

Simulated Type O Blood

Figure 1

3. Based on your results, determine the type of simulated blood that is contained in Bottle 1. Record this information in the appropriate place in the Data Table.

4. Carefully wash and dry the glass slide thoroughly.

5. Repeat steps 1 through 4 using the solutions in Bottles 2, 3, and 4.

Observations

Data Table

Bottle	Clumping in the Left Side of the Depression Slide?	Clumping in the Right Side of the Depression Slide?	Simulated Blood Type
1	no	yes	B
2	no	no	O
3	yes	no	A
4	yes	yes	AB

Analysis and Conclusions

1. **a.** Which simulated blood type(s) showed clumping when simulated anti-A serum was added?

   Simulated blood types A and AB.

   b. Which simulated blood type(s) showed clumping when simulated anti-B serum was added?

   Simulated blood types B and AB.

2. **a.** If clumping occurs when both anti-A serum and anti-B serum are added, what is the blood

   type? Blood type AB.

   b. If clumping does not occur when either anti-A serum or anti-B serum is added, what is the

   blood type? Blood type O.

3. Which blood type(s) must people have in order to safely receive a transfusion of type A

   blood? A, AB.

4. Which blood type(s) must people have in order to safely receive a transfusion of type B blood?

   B, AB.

5. Which blood type(s) must people have in order to safely receive a transfusion of type AB

   blood? AB.

6. How is this simulation similar to actual human blood typing? This simulation is based on the fact

   that certain solutions will chemically react and either form or not form precipitates. The presence or absence

   of a precipitate can be compared to the agglutination that either does or does not occur when different blood

   types are mixed together. Both the formation of a precipitate and the agglutination of blood cells can be

   thought of as a "positive" test.

Critical Thinking and Application

1. Why is it advisable for you to know your own blood type? By knowing your own blood type you

   can better avoid an emergency transfusion of an incompatible blood type. You would also know whether or

   not you were a compatible donor for an emergency transfusion.

2. How could you tell whether two blood samples are compatible for a transfusion if no typing serum were available? If no blood typing serum were available, a small amount of the two samples could be mixed and examined for agglutination.

3. Why is a person with type AB blood sometimes called a "universal recipient"?

There are no antibodies in the plasma of type AB blood. Because of this, people with type AB blood can receive blood of any type without stimulating an immune response.

4. Why is a person with type O blood sometimes called a "universal donor"?

There are no antigens on the red blood cells found in type O blood. Because of this, type O blood can be given to people with any of the four blood types without stimulating an immune response in the recipients.

5. Why is a person with type O blood unable to receive blood from any type other than O?

Type O blood plasma contains both anti-A and anti-B antibodies. Transfusion of any blood type other than type O will result in the activation of these antibodies and the agglutination of the red blood cells.

Going Further

1. Successful organ transplant surgery depends on advances made in the area of tissue typing and compatibility. Using reference materials, write a report comparing blood typing with the relatively new science of tissue typing.

2. Use reference materials to research the topic of Rh factors. How were they discovered? How is a person's blood tested for Rh factor? Why is this knowledge important?

81

Simulating Urinalysis

You may want to refer students to pages 908–911 in the textbook for a discussion of the excretory system.

Time required: 60 minutes.

Pre-Lab Discussion

All organisms produce wastes. These waste materials must be removed so that the organism is not poisoned by its own metabolism. In humans, *urine* is the fluid produced by the kidneys as they remove waste chemicals from the blood. Urine is made up primarily of water, with some salts and organic materials dissolved in it. The concentration of each of these substances varies with a person's health, diet, and degree of activity.

By testing the chemical composition of urine, doctors can learn much about the general health of an individual. Urinary tract infections, kidney malfunction, diabetes, and liver disease are just some of the medical problems that can be diagnosed through *urinalysis*. Urinalysis involves the physical, chemical, and visual examination of a urine sample.

In this investigation, you will perform several tests to detect substances in a sample of artificial urine. You will also determine the contents of an artificial urine sample of unknown composition.

Problem

What chemical substances are found in a sample of artificial urine?

Materials *(per group)*

12 test tubes	Urine sample without glucose [5]
Glass-marking pencil	Urine sample with phosphate [2]
Test tube rack	Urine sample without phosphate [5]
Test tube holder	Urine sample with albumin [3]
10-mL graduated cylinder	Urine sample without albumin [5]
Hot plate	Urine sample with chloride [4]
Bunsen burner	Urine sample without chloride [5]
400-mL beaker	Benedict's solution [6]
Matches	Silver nitrate solution [7]
Urine sample with glucose [1]	10% acetic acid solution [8]

Prepare 1 L of each urine sample as follows:

[1] Urine with glucose—add 10 drops yellow food coloring and 1 tablespoon glucose to 1 L distilled water.

[2] Urine with phosphate—add 10 drops yellow food coloring and 1 tablespoon sodium phosphate dibasic anhydride (Na_2PO_4) to 1 L distilled water.

[3] Urine with albumin—add 10 drops yellow food coloring and 1 egg white to 1 L distilled water.

[4] Urine with chloride—add 10 drops yellow food coloring and 1 tablespoon sodium chloride (table salt) to 1 L distilled water.

[5] Urine without glucose, phosphate, albumin, or chloride can be made by adding 10 drops yellow food coloring to 1 L distilled water.

[6] To make Benedict's solution dissolve 173 g sodium citrate and 100 g sodium carbonate in 700 mL distilled water. Heat until chemicals are dissolved. Filter. Dissolve 17.3 g copper sulfate in 100 mL distilled water. Slowly add to the first solution, stirring constantly. Add distilled water to a total volume of 1 L. Benedict's solution can also be purchased premixed from a biological supply house.

[7] To make a silver nitrate solution, add 2 g silver nitrate to 125 mL distilled water. Stir until dissolved. Pour into dropper bottles.

[8] To make a 10% acetic acid solution, add 10 mL acetic acid to 90 mL distilled water while stirring. Pour solution into dropper bottles.

Safety ⚗ 🥽 🧤 ☐ 👁 🔌

Put on a laboratory apron if one is available. Put on safety goggles. Handle all glassware carefully. Use extreme care when working with heated equipment or materials to avoid burns. Always use special caution when working with laboratory chemicals, as they may irritate the skin or cause staining of the skin or clothing. Never touch or taste any chemical unless instructed to do so. Observe proper laboratory procedures when using electrical appliances. Note all safety alert symbols next to the steps in the Procedure and review the meanings of each symbol by referring to the symbol guide on page 10.

Procedure
Part A. Test for Glucose

Commercial glucose testing papers can also be used for this part of the investigation. They are available at a local drugstore and no heat is required for the test.

⚗ **1.** Place two test tubes in a test tube rack. With a glass-marking pencil, label one test tube "G" for glucose. Allow the other test tube to remain unlabeled as it will act as the control.

🥽 🧤 **2.** Use the 400-mL beaker to prepare a hot water bath. **CAUTION:** *Use extreme care when working*
👁 🔌 *with hot water. Do not let the water splash onto your body.*

☐ **3.** Add 3 mL of Benedict's solution to both test tubes. **CAUTION:** *Use extreme care when handling Benedict's solution to avoid staining of the skin and clothing.*

4. Add 3 mL of the urine sample with glucose to the test tube labeled "G." Add 3 mL of the urine sample without glucose to the unlabeled test tube. Note the appearance of the substance in each test tube. Record this information in Data Table 1.

5. Place both test tubes in the hot water bath for 2 minutes.

6. After 2 minutes, remove the test tubes from the hot water bath with a test tube holder. Place the test tubes in the test tube rack. **CAUTION:** *Be careful when working with heated equipment or materials to avoid burns.* Note any color changes in the test tubes. Record your observations in Data Table 1.

Part B. Test for Chloride

⚗ **1.** Place two test tubes in a test tube rack. With a glass-marking pencil, label one test tube "C" for chloride. Allow the other test tube to remain unlabeled as it will act as the control.

2. Add 5 mL of the urine sample with chloride to the test tube labeled "C." Add 5 mL of the urine sample without chloride to the unlabeled test tube. Note the appearance of the substance in each test tube. Record this information in Data Table 2.

☐ **3.** Carefully add 3 drops of silver nitrate solution to each test tube. **CAUTION:** *Use caution when working with silver nitrate solution because it can stain the skin and clothing.* Observe the top surface of the liquid in each test tube. Record its appearance in Data Table 2.

Part C. Test for Albumin

⚗ **1.** Place two test tubes in a test tube rack. With a glass-marking pencil, label one test tube "A" for albumin. Allow the other test tube to remain unlabeled as it will act as the control.

2. Half fill the test tube labeled "A" with the urine sample with albumin. Half fill the unlabeled test tube with the urine sample without albumin.

🥽 **3.** Using a test tube holder, pass the top surface of each test tube over the flame of a Bunsen
🧤 burner for 15 to 20 seconds. See Figure 1. **CAUTION:** *Secure all loose clothing and hair when*
👁 *using a Bunsen burner. When heating a test tube, always point it away from yourself and other students.* After heating each test tube, place it in a test tube rack. Note the appearance of each substance. Record your observations in Data Table 3.

Test tube holder

Test tube

Bunsen burner

Figure 1

4. Add 5 drops of acetic acid to each test tube. **CAUTION:** *Be careful when using an acid.* Note the appearance of each substance. Record your observations in Data Table 3.

Part D. Test for Phosphate

1. Place two test tubes in a test tube rack. With a glass-marking pencil label one test tube "P" for phosphate. Allow the other test tube to remain unlabeled as it will act as the control.

2. Half fill the test tube labeled "P" with the urine sample with phosphate. Half fill the unlabeled test tube with the urine sample without phosphate.

3. Using a test tube holder, pass the top surface of each test tube over the flame of a Bunsen burner for 15 to 20 seconds. **CAUTION:** *Secure all loose clothing and hair when using a Bunsen burner. When heating a test tube, always point it away from yourself and other students.* After heating each test tube, place it in a test tube rack. Note the appearance of each substance. Record this information in Data Table 4.

4. Add 5 drops of acetic acid to each test tube. Record your observations in Data Table 4. **CAUTION:** *Be careful when using an acid.*

Part E. Testing an Unknown Urine Sample

To prepare the unknown urine samples, mix samples containing all, a few, one, or none of the previously tested substances. Number the samples and keep a record of their contents.

1. Obtain a sample of artificial urine marked "unknown." Record the identification number of the sample in Data Table 5.

2. Using four clean test tubes, perform the glucose, chloride, albumin, and phosphate tests on the unknown sample. Follow the Procedures in Parts A through D of this investigation.

3. Record your results in Data Table 5.

Observations

Data Table 1

Substance	Color Before Heating	Color After Heating
Urine sample with glucose	Blue	Orange-red
Urine sample without glucose	Blue	Blue

Data Table 2

Substance	Color Before Adding Silver Nitrate	Color After Adding Silver Nitrate
Urine sample with chloride	Clear yellow	White cloud forms
Urine sample without chloride	Clear yellow	Clear yellow

Data Table 3

Substance	Appearance After Heating	Appearance After Adding Acetic Acid
Urine sample with albumin	White haze forms at top	White haze remains, does not disappear with acetic acid
Urine sample without albumin	Clear yellow	Clear yellow

Data Table 4

Substance	Appearance After Heating	Appearance After Adding Acetic Acid
Urine sample with phosphate	White haze forms at top	White haze disappears with addition of acetic acid
Urine sample without phosphate	Clear yellow	Clear yellow

Data Table 5

Composition of Unknown Urine Sample # _____	
Test	**Present or Absent?**
Glucose	
Chloride	Answers will vary with unknown used.
Albumin	
Phosphate	

Analysis and Conclusions

1. Why is it necessary to perform tests on the urine samples that do not contain any chemical substances? The substances without added chemicals will act as controls in the experiment. These samples will show how artificial urine reacts with the test chemicals if certain substances are not present.

2. If the top portion of a urine sample is heated and no haze forms, what conclusion can be drawn about the sample? It can be determined that no phosphate or albumin is present in the sample.

3. If you add Benedict's solution to a urine sample from a person who has diabetes and heat it, what color would you expect the heated sample to be? Explain your answer.
Because the person with diabetes has a measurable amount of glucose in the urine, you would expect the sample to have an orange-red color after heating it.

4. Which substances did you find in your unknown urine sample? Do you think this sample might have come from a healthy person? Explain your answer. Answers will vary depending on the contents of the unknown sample. The urine of a healthy person should contain chloride and phosphate but not albumin and glucose.

Critical Thinking and Application

1. Why does the chemical content of urine change throughout the day?
Eating and physical activity can cause changes in the chemical content of urine.

2. If a doctor finds high levels of protein in a patient's urine sample, the doctor will probably test the patient's urine several times over a week before drawing any conclusions. What might be the reason for this? The presence of protein in the urine may be due to heavy exercise or other temporary chemical imbalances. After several days the protein may no longer be present in the person's urine.

3. If a white haze forms at the top of a heated urine sample, how can you determine whether it is

due to the presence of phosphate or albumin? Acetic acid can be added to the sample. If the haze

remains, albumin is present. If the haze disappears, phosphate is present.

_____

4. While a blood sample contains glucose, phosphate, albumin, and chloride molecules, a normal urine sample contains only phosphate and chloride molecules. What does this indicate about

one of the functions of the kidneys? One of the functions of the kidneys is to filter out glucose and

albumin from the waste material and return them to the body.

_____

_____

Going Further

1. People with diseased kidneys must frequently have waste products removed from their blood by a procedure called dialysis. Use reference materials to research this procedure. You may also wish to interview a hospital dialysis technician.

2. Aquatic animals get rid of waste products by continuously excreting them directly to the outside watery environment. Design an experiment to show this using a goldfish. How is pH an important factor in maintaining tropical fish?

A Shorter Lab Period

You may wish to omit Part E of this investigation.

82

Observing Human Growth

You may want to refer students to pages 923–925 in the textbook for a discussion of the pituitary gland.

Time required: 30 minutes.

Pre-Lab Discussion

The human *endocrine system* is made up of a number of ductless glands that secrete chemicals that control certain body activities. The chemicals released by endocrine glands are called *hormones*. A hormone is a chemical that is produced in one part of an organism and is transported to other parts of the organism where it controls certain activities of tissues and organs. The *pituitary gland,* found near the base of the brain, is a small gland that releases many hormones. One of these hormones is *growth hormone,* or GH. GH stimulates the growth of bone, muscle, and many other tissues.

Humans grow at varying rates from birth through adolescence. These rates include a growth spurt when the body grows at a rapid rate. Although both males and females go through a growth spurt, they do not grow at the same rates and they do not have their growth spurts at the same ages.

In this investigation, you will observe and interpret male and female growth statistics.

Problem

How do the growth rates of males and females compare?

Materials *(per pair of students)*

Tape measure or meterstick
2 colored pencils

Procedure

1. Have your partner use the tape measure or meterstick to measure your height in centimeters. Record this number and your age in the appropriate place in Observations. Also record this information in the data table provided by your teacher on the chalkboard.
   Provide a large data table on the chalkboard where students can record their heights and ages.
2. After all students in your class have recorded their heights and ages on the chalkboard, calculate the average height for males and the average height for females in each age group. Record these averages in the Data Table.

3. On Graph 1, construct line graphs of the information shown in the Data Table. Use one of the colored pencils to draw the line graph for females and the other colored pencil to draw the line graph for males.

4. Figure 1 shows the average heights for human females and males from birth to 18 years of age. On Graph 2, construct line graphs of the information shown in Figure 1. Use one of the colored pencils to draw the line graph for females and the other colored pencil to draw the line graph for males.

517

Average Height (cm)		
Age Group (yr)	Female	Male
At birth	50	51
2	87	88
4	103	104
6	117	118
8	128	128
10	139	139
12	152	149
14	160	162
16	163	172
18	163	174

Figure 1

Observations

Your height = _____ centimeters   Your age = _____ years

Data Table

Average Height (cm)		
Age Group (yr)	Female	Male
13		
14		
15	Answers will vary.	
16		
17		

Graph 1

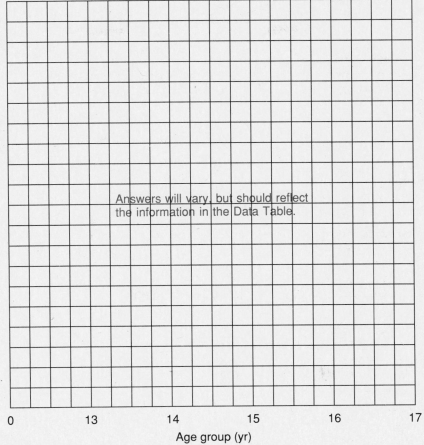

Answers will vary, but should reflect the information in the Data Table.

Average height (cm)

0   13   14   15   16   17

Age group (yr)

Graph 2

Average height (cm)

Male

Female

0   2   4   6   8   10   12   14   16   18   20

Age group (yr)

Analysis and Conclusions

1. Based on the information in Figure 1, at approximately what age does the height of males and females double from birth? Males and females have doubled in height by about age 4.

2. Based on the information in Figure 1, at what ages do females grow more rapidly than males? Females grow more rapidly than males between the ages of 10 and 12.

3. Based on the information in Figure 1, at what ages do males grow more rapidly than females? Males grow more rapidly than females between the ages of 14 and 16.

4. Based on your observations, how many students are above the average height for their age? Answers will vary.

5. Based on your observations, how many students are below the average height for their age? Answers will vary.

6. As a group, are the students in your class above or below the average height? Answers will vary.

7. If there are very few students in a particular age group, how might this affect the reliability of your graph? The fewer students in each age group, the less reliable the data will be.

Critical Thinking and Application

1. If a person has an inactive pituitary gland at birth, what effects would this condition have on the body? If the pituitary gland were inactive, growth hormone would not be secreted. Because growth hormone stimulates the growth of the body and helps control metabolism, pituitary dwarfism would occur.

2. Why might damage to the pituitary gland be far more serious than damage to other endocrine

glands? Because the pituitary gland secretes hormones that control body growth and regulate the activity

of other endocrine glands, its malfunctioning can cause serious widespread medical problems.

3. A condition known as acromegaly is the sudden growth of certain body parts, such as the hands and face, after normal body growth has been completed. How might this condition

occur? Sudden increases in pituitary gland activity might increase the production of growth hormone. This

would stimulate the growth of bone and cartilage, producing the condition of acromegaly.

4. Some hormones prescribed by doctors are taken orally while others are injected directly into the body. Why might these hormones be administered in different ways?

The digestive system can actually break down certain hormones, making them useless. These hormones

must be injected directly into the body.

Going Further

1. Collect and record the data from other classes that have completed this investigation. Calculate the average height for females and the average height for males in each age group for all classes. Construct a line graph for female heights and a line graph for male heights. Do these averages more closely resemble the averages reported in Figure 1 of this investigation?

2. Anabolic steroids are hormones that stimulate muscle tissue growth. Using reference materials, research the health hazards associated with the use of anabolic steroids by weight lifters and other athletes. How can it be determined whether an athlete is using anabolic steroids?

83

Ovaries and Testes

You may want to refer students to pages 935–939 in the textbook for a discussion of the human reproductive system.

Time required: 40 minutes.

Pre-Lab Discussion

Reproduction is the process by which offspring are produced. The most important function of reproduction is to continue the species. Reproduction may also serve to increase the number of individuals in a species.

Humans reproduce sexually. Gametes are produced in specialized sex organs, or *gonads*. The gonad of the human male is the *testis* (plural, *testes*). The two functions of this organ are the production of *sperm cells,* which are the male gametes, and the production of the male hormone *testosterone*. The gonad of the human female is the *ovary*. The two ovaries of the human female produce *egg cells,* which are the female gametes, and also secrete female sex hormones.

In this investigation, you will examine prepared slides of mammalian ovaries and testes. You will also investigate the process of egg and sperm production.

Problem

What structures are found in a mammalian ovary and testis? How are eggs and sperm produced?

Materials *(per group)*

Microscope
Prepared slides of:
 Cat ovary, transverse cross section   Prepared slides are available from biological supply houses.
 Rat testis, longitudinal cross section
 Rat epididymis, transverse cross section

Safety 🔬

Handle all glassware carefully. Always handle the microscope with extreme care. You are responsible for its proper care and use. Use caution when handling glass slides as they can break easily and cut you. Note all safety alert symbols next to the steps in the Procedure and review the meanings of each symbol by referring to the symbol guide on page 10.

Procedure
Part A. The Mammalian Ovary

⚠ 1. Obtain a stained slide of a transverse cross section of a mature ovary of a nonpregnant cat. Using the low-power objective of a microscope, focus on a part of the ovary where you can see both the outer edge and the interior of the ovary. The outermost layer of cells of the ovary consists of the germinal epithelium, a single layer of epithelial cells. Immediately below the germinal epithelium is the connective tissue called the stroma. Within the stroma you will observe numerous round structures of various sizes. These structures are the follicles, where the ovarian eggs develop and mature. In some of the follicles you can observe the developing egg, a large, circular cell with a darkly stained nucleus.

2. Examine different areas of the slide under low power to find follicles containing eggs in various stages of development. Using Figure 1 as a guide, trace the development of one developing egg cell. A developing egg is surrounded by a covering, or corona, of follicle cells. As the follicle matures, a cavity filled with the female hormone estrogen develops. Estrogen is essential to the growth and development of the maturing egg. The mature follicle gradually moves to the surface of the ovary, where it ruptures the surface and releases the egg into the Fallopian tube.

Figure 1

3. After a follicle ruptures and releases an egg from the ovary, the follicle undergoes a series of changes and becomes an endocrine structure called the corpus luteum. In this process, the follicle cells enlarge and a yellowish substance called lutein accumulates in their cytoplasm. The lutein cells secrete the hormones estrogen and progesterone, which are responsible for building up the lining of the uterus in preparation for pregnancy. Examine a corpus luteum on your slide. If pregnancy does not occur, the corpus luteum continues to grow for about 10 to 12 days and then shrinks, eventually becoming a small, white ovarian scar called a corpus albicans. Locate a corpus albicans on your slide.

Part B. The Mammalian Testis

🔺 1. Obtain a stained slide of the testis of a mature rat for examination under the low-power objective of a microscope. The thick outer covering of the testis is called the tunica albuginea. The testis is separated into several wedge-shaped compartments by partitions called septa (singular, *septum*). Within each compartment examine the cluster of small circles. These are the cut surfaces of the tiny, coiled seminiferous tubules, which are involved in the production of sperm. The seminiferous tubules lead into the epididymis, a long, narrow, flattened structure attached to the posterior surface of the testis. Sperm complete their maturation while passing through the epididymis. The lower portion of the epididymis uncoils and widens into a long duct called the vas deferens.

2. In the appropriate place in Observations, label the following structures of the testis: tunica albuginea, septa, seminiferous tubules, epididymis, and vas deferens.

3. Carefully switch to the high-power objective and adjust your slide so that you are focusing on one of the seminiferous tubules. **CAUTION:** *When turning to the high-power objective, always look at the objective from the side of the microscope so that the objective does not hit or damage the slide.*

4. Notice that the walls of the seminiferous tubule consists of many layers of cells. The cytoplasm of these cells will most likely be stained red and the chromosomes in the nuclei will most likely be stained blue. Closely examine these cells in order to trace the various stages of spermatogenesis, or sperm cell production. The cells nearest to the outer surface of the seminiferous tubule are called spermatogonia. These are the sperm-producing cells. The spermatogonia divide by mitosis. Half of the daughter cells remain as spermatogonia, while the other half undergo changes and become cells called primary spermatocytes. The primary spermatocytes make up the layer next to the spermatogonia. Try to observe the chromosome arrangement in the primary spermatocytes.

5. The diploid primary spermatocyte undergoes the first stage of meiosis, producing two haploid cells called secondary spermatocytes. The secondary spermatocytes are found in a layer next to the primary spermatocytes. The two secondary spermatocytes undergo the second meiotic division, producing four haploid spermatid cells. The spermatid cells make up the innermost layer of the seminiferous tubule. A spermatid cell develops into a sperm with an oval head and a long, whiplike tail.

6. Observe how the sperm cells are clustered around elongated cells that are evenly spaced around the circumference of the seminiferous tubule. These cells, called Sertoli cells, probably provide nutrients for the developing sperm cells. Observe how the sperm cells have their tails facing out into the central opening, or lumen, of the seminiferous tubule.

7. In the appropriate place in Observations, label the following parts of the seminiferous tubule: spermatogonia, primary spermatocytes, secondary spermatocytes, spermatids, sperm cells, Sertoli cells, and lumen.

🔺 8. Obtain a prepared slide of a cross section of the epididymis of a mature rat. Observe the epididymis under low and high power. Note the sperm cells clustered within the lumen of the epididymis. Observe that the cells lining the lumen are lined with cilia. These cilia help propel the sperm cells through the epididymis. Observe the smooth muscle cells in the walls of the epididymis. As these muscles contract, the sperm cells are pushed through the epididymis, toward the vas deferens.

9. In the appropriate place in Observations, label the following parts of the epididymis: lumen, sperm cells, cilia, and smooth muscle cells.

Observations

Rat Testis

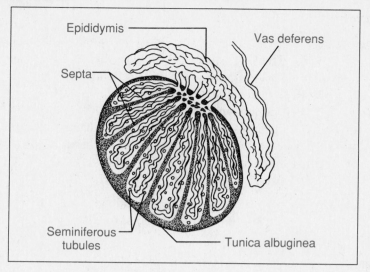

- Epididymis
- Vas deferens
- Septa
- Seminiferous tubules
- Tunica albuginea

Rat Seminiferous Tubule

- Spermatogonia
- Primary spermatocytes
- Secondary spermatocytes
- Lumen
- Spermatids
- Sperm cells
- Sertoli cells

Rat Epididymis

- Lumen
- Sperm cells
- Cilia
- Smooth muscle cells

Analysis and Conclusions

1. In what way are mature sperm and egg cells different from all other types of body cells?

   While all other body cells are diploid, sperm and egg cells are haploid.
   _____

   _____

2. What is the function of the corpus luteum in the ovary? Hormones secreted by the corpus luteum

   prepare the lining of the uterus for pregnancy.
   _____

3. What is the adaptive advantage of the tail on the sperm cell? The tail allows the sperm cell to be

   motile and swim upward through the female reproductive system.
   _____

4. What are two functions that are common to both ovaries and testes?

   Both the ovaries and the testes are responsible for the production of gametes. They also secrete important

   hormones.
   _____

5. Describe three ways in which sperm-cell development is different from egg-cell development.

   Sperm cells are much smaller than egg cells. While the male reproductive system releases countless sperm

   at one time, the female reproductive system releases only one egg. Egg production ceases at a certain point

   in a female's life, whereas males produce sperm throughout their lifetime.
   _____

   _____

Critical Thinking and Application

1. The middle section of a sperm cell is packed with mitochondria. Use your knowledge of cell organelle function to determine the purpose the mitochondria serve in the sperm cell.

   Mitochondria are the "powerhouses" of the cell. They supply most of the energy for the cell. Sperm need

   large amounts of energy to swim to the egg. The presence of mitochondria in the middle section of the

   sperm provides the energy needed by the tail as the sperm swims.
   _____

2. What might happen if more than one egg were released at the same time from the ovaries?

   If two eggs were simultaneously released from the ovaries and both eggs were fertilized by different sperm

   cells, two embryos would develop. These embryos, called fraternal twins, could be of different sexes and

   have many different physical characteristics.
   _____

3. A mature egg cell contains a great deal more cytoplasm than a mature sperm cell. What is the possible function of the added cytoplasm found within the egg cell?

The extra cytoplasm in the egg cell provides nourishment for the developing embryo.

Going Further

1. Examine prepared slides of the sperm cells of different animals. Compare their similarities and differences.

2. Infertility is a problem faced by some couples who desire to have children. Identify possible causes of this problem. Is it simply the inability to produce sperm or eggs? What corrective measures can be taken for males and females?

3. Do library research on *in vitro* fertilization. Be sure to include information on why the technique is used, what procedures are involved, and how successful the technique is.

84

The Human Menstrual Cycle

You may want to refer students to pages 939–942 in the textbook for a discussion of the menstrual cycle.

Time required: 45 minutes.

Pre-Lab Discussion

The *menstrual cycle* is the hormone-controlled reproductive cycle of human females. It involves the periodic development and release of an egg and the periodic shedding of the uterine lining. The menstrual cycle involves interactions of the hypothalamus, pituitary, ovary, and uterus. The cycles usually occur between puberty and menopause. The cycle may be interrupted by pregnancy, illness, or other factors. The menstrual cycle is about 28 days long, but it varies from one female to another.

Each egg produced by the female matures inside a *follicle,* or egg sac, near the surface of the ovary. When the egg is fully mature, the follicle bursts and the egg is released into a Fallopian tube, which leads to the uterus. An unfertilized egg will pass from the female's body within a short time. If this occurs, the lining of the uterus, which has been prepared for the implantation of a fertilized egg, deteriorates and also passes out of the body. The process by which blood and uterine cells are shed through the vagina is called *menstruation.* Menstruation is one phase of the four-phase menstrual cycle.

In this investigation, you will examine the changes that occur during the different phases of the menstrual cycle.

Problem

What changes occur within the body of a human female during the menstrual cycle?

Materials *(per student)*

Metric ruler
Colored pencils

Procedure
Part A. The Follicle Phase

1. Many egg cells are located within the ovary of a human female. Each egg is contained within a structure called a follicle. Under the influence of follicle-stimulating hormone, or FSH, the follicle matures within the ovary. The amount of FSH in the bloodstream influences the growth and development of the maturing follicle. Figure 1 shows the various stages of a follicle's maturation. Notice that an immature follicle is much smaller than a mature follicle.

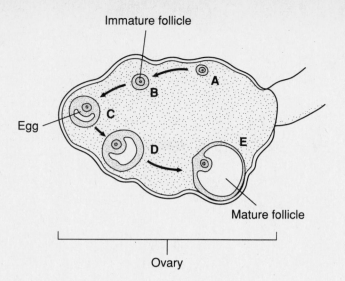

Immature follicle

A

B

Egg

C

D

E

Mature follicle

Ovary

Figure 1

2. Figure 2 shows the concentration of FSH in the bloodstream of an average human female throughout the 28-day menstrual cycle. On Graph 1, prepare a line graph of the data in Figure 2. In the boxes above Graph 1, make drawings of the various stages of follicle maturation. The drawings should match the lettered stages shown in Figure 1.

The actual units used to measure FSH levels in the blood are called milli-international units/milliliter of blood.

Amount of FSH in Bloodstream (units per milliliter)			
Day	**FSH**	**Day**	**FSH**
1	9	15	9
2	11	16	8
3	13	17	8
4	14	18	8
5	15	19	8
6	14	20	7
7	14	21	7
8	15	22	6
9	13	23	5
10	11	24	5
11	9	25	6
12	18	26	7
13	13	27	7
14	9	28	8

Figure 2

3. Answer questions 1 through 4 in Observations.

Part B. The Luteal Phase

1. Once a follicle is mature, it bursts open and the egg is released. This process is called ovulation. The egg passes into the Fallopian tube where it may or may not be fertilized. Once the mature follicle loses its egg, it forms a body within the ovary called the corpus luteum. Figure 3 shows the changes that occur within the corpus luteum during the menstrual cycle. After maturation, the corpus luteum begins to break apart and disappear. A hormone called luteinizing hormone, or LH, is responsible for causing changes in the corpus luteum.

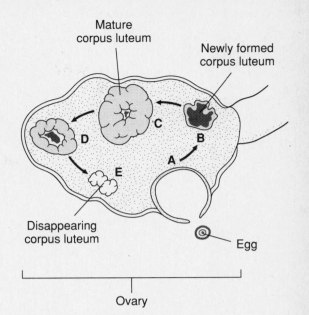

Figure 3

2. Figure 4 shows the concentration of LH in the bloodstream of an average human female during the 28-day menstrual cycle. On Graph 2, prepare a line graph of the data shown in Figure 4. In the boxes above Graph 2, make drawings of the various stages of corpus luteum maturation. The drawings should match the lettered stages shown in Figure 3.

The actual units used to measure LH levels in the blood are called milli-international units/milliliter of blood.

Amount of LH in Bloodstream (units per milliliter)			
Day	LH	Day	LH
1	9	15	30
2	12	16	14
3	16	17	10
4	18	18	9
5	19	19	7
6	16	20	5
7	12	21	3
8	19	22	3
9	15	23	2
10	16	24	3
11	20	25	3
12	30	26	4
13	75	27	4
14	58	28	4

Figure 4

3. Answer questions 5 through 8 in Observations.

Part C. Uterine Changes During the Menstrual Cycle

1. As the follicle and luteal phases of the menstrual cycle occur, a series of changes occurs in the uterus. Through rapid cell division, the lining of the uterine walls becomes very thick. At one point in the menstrual cycle, the uterus lining ceases to thicken and begins to break apart. This loss of the uterine lining through the vagina is called menstruation. See Figure 5.

A	B	C
Menstruation	Thin uterine lining	Thick uterine lining

Figure 5

2. Two hormones that are responsible for the building up of the uterine lining are estrogen and progesterone. Figure 6 shows the amounts of estrogen and progesterone found in the bloodstream of an average human female during the 28-day menstrual cycle. On Graph 3, prepare line graphs of the data in Figure 6. Use a different colored pencil to construct each of the line graphs. In the squares shown above Graph 3, make drawings of the various stages of uterine thickness. The drawings should match the lettered stages shown in Figure 5.

Estrogen is measured in picograms/milliliter of blood. Progesterone is measured in nanograms/milliliter of blood.

Amount of Estrogen and Progesterone in Bloodstream (units per milliliter)					
Day	Estrogen	Progesterone	Day	Estrogen	Progesterone
1	20	6	15	180	23
2	20	8	16	150	37
3	25	10	17	120	58
4	25	10	18	100	83
5	30	10	19	50	104
6	80	10	20	30	120
7	130	12	21	25	120
8	140	12	22	25	118
9	180	13	23	25	103
10	200	15	24	25	72
11	220	15	25	30	40
12	230	16	26	30	30
13	220	18	27	25	20
14	200	20	28	25	18

Figure 6

3. Answer questions 9 through 11 in Observations.

Observations

Graph 1

Graph 2

E   A   B   C   D

Graph 3

A

B

C

1. Between days 25 and 12 of the menstrual cycle, what happens to the amount of FSH produced by the body of an average human female? The amount of FSH produced by the body increases.

_____

2. What happens to the follicle between days 25 and 12 of the menstrual cycle?

The follicle matures, or increases in size.

_____

535

3. During which days of the menstrual cycle is the level of FSH at its lowest in the bloodstream?

Answers may vary, but should be approximately days 14 to 24.

4. About how long is the follicle phase of the menstrual cycle? About 18 days long.

5. On which day of the menstrual cycle is the production of LH the greatest?

On day 13.

6. What event occurs immediately after this increased production of LH?

Ovulation will occur.

7. What happens to the corpus luteum during days 15 through 24 of the menstrual cycle?

The corpus luteum matures during this time.

8. a. During which days of the menstrual cycle is the production of LH the lowest?

Answers may vary, but should be approximately days 23 to 28.

   b. What is happening to the corpus luteum at this time? The corpus luteum is breaking apart at this time.

9. a. What happens to the amount of estrogen produced by the body during days 6 to 12 of the menstrual cycle? The amount of estrogen produced during days 6 to 12 sharply increases.

   b. What is occurring to the uterus during this time? The walls of the uterus are beginning to thicken.

10. a. What happens to the amount of progesterone produced by the body during days 13 to 23 of the menstrual cycle? The amount of progesterone produced during days 13 to 23 increases.

   b. What is occurring to the uterus during this time? The walls of the uterus continue to thicken.

11. a. During which days of the menstrual cycle are the levels of both estrogen and progesterone

at their lowest? The levels of both estrogen and progesterone are lowest during days 1 to 5.

_____

b. What event is occurring at this time? Menstruation is occurring.

_____

Analysis and Conclusions

1. How is the name follicle-stimulating hormone appropriate for its function?

Follicle-stimulating hormone is responsible for the growth and development of the follicle. FSH stimulates the

follicle to mature.

2. How is the name luteinizing hormone appropriate for its function?

Luteinizing hormone is responsible for the growth and development of the corpus luteum.

3. Based on your observations, do you think estrogen and progesterone both cause similar

changes in the uterus? Explain your answer. Because the uterus continues to thicken as both

estrogen and progesterone are released into the bloodstream, it can be concluded that they have a similar

function in the menstrual cycle.

4. What events occur during the follicle phase of the menstrual cycle?

A follicle within the female's ovary begins to enlarge and mature due to the production and secretion of the

hormone FSH.

5. What events occur during the luteal phase of the menstrual cycle?

After the follicle releases its egg during ovulation, it develops into the corpus luteum due to the production

and secretion of the hormone LH.

Critical Thinking and Application

1. Why are the events described in this investigation referred to as a cycle?

   The events in the menstrual process occur over and over again in the same pattern from puberty through

   menopause; therefore they are considered to be cyclic.

2. The word "menstrual" comes from the Latin word *mensis,* meaning "month." How is the name appropriate for this cycle of the human female reproductive system?

   The menstrual cycle occurs approximately every 28 days, or monthly, in the average human female.

3. If a female did not produce sufficient quantities of FSH and LH, how would her ability to have children be affected? If a female was unable to produce sufficient quantities of FSH and LH, ovulation

   would not occur and the uterine lining would not be prepared for pregnancy. As a result, the woman would

   be infertile.

Going Further

1. A comparable cycle involving a periodic growth and loss of uterine cells occurs in mammals other than primates, but little or no blood is lost. The shedding of cells is called estrus, and the cycle is called the estrous cycle. Use reference materials to investigate the estrous cycles of common mammals such as dogs and cats.

2. Women commonly experience a variety of pains, discomforts, and/or emotional disturbances before or during menstruation. In some women, the premenstrual period may be characterized by irritability, sluggishness, or deep depression. Use reference materials to research other symptoms of Premenstrual Syndrome (PMS) and some of the ways in which these symptoms can be medically treated.

85

Examining an Unfertilized Chicken Egg

You may want to refer students to pages 943–947 in the textbook for a discussion of human development.

Time required: 30 minutes.

Pre-Lab Discussion

The embryonic development of an organism begins soon after the fertilization of an egg cell by a sperm. During this period of development, the embryo is protected and nourished by a set of surrounding membranes. As development proceeds, all of the complex organs and tissues appear in a definite order.

It is difficult to study human embryological development because the embryo develops internally in a placenta. For this reason embryos that develop externally have been widely used in developmental studies. Because of their availability, easily observed features, and similarity to mammalian embryo development, chick embryos are used extensively.

In order for a chick egg to develop, the egg must first be fertilized by a sperm from a male chicken. The egg must then be kept warm by the female chicken or placed in an incubator for 21 days. Eggs purchased in the grocery store usually have not been fertilized or incubated.

In this investigation, you will examine the internal structures of an unfertilized chicken egg.

Problem

How is the chicken egg adapted to support an embryo?

Materials (per group)

Unfertilized chicken egg   Unfertilized chicken eggs are available from a grocery store.
Hand lens
Petri dish   Prepared slides or 35-mm slides of developing chick embryos are available
Metric ruler   from a biological supply house. These slides allow students to observe the
                        various stages of embryonic development without having to work with living
Forceps   specimens.

Safety ⚗

Put on a laboratory apron if one is available. Handle all glassware carefully. Note all safety alert symbols next to the steps in the Procedure and review the meanings of each symbol by referring to the symbol guide on page 10.

Procedure

1. Obtain an unfertilized chicken egg from your teacher. Gently crack the egg crosswise on the side of a petri dish. Separate the two halves of the egg shell as you would to put an egg in a frying pan. Allow the contents of the egg to drop into the petri dish. **Note:** *Be careful not to break the yolk.*

2. Examine the outside of the egg shell with a hand lens. Place the egg shell to the side for later examination. Answer question 1 in Observations.

3. Using Figure 1 as a guide, examine the internal structures of the chicken egg. On the surface of the yolk locate a small, white, round dot. This dot is the germinal disk, from which an embryo would form after fertilization. Use a metric ruler to find the diameter of the germinal disk in millimeters. Answer question 2 in Observations.

Figure 1

4. Find two dense, white, cordlike structures. These structures are called the chalazae (singular, chalaza). Using forceps, gently pull on one of the chalazae. Answer question 3 in Observations.

5. The white of the egg contains water and a protein called albumen. Notice that the egg white surrounds the yolk and is fairly thick.

6. Observe the yolk. The yolk of the egg contains fats, minerals, and vitamins. These materials, which come from the liver of the hen, pass to the ovary and become part of the egg. Touch the yolk gently with the forceps. Note that it is surrounded by a membrane called the vitelline membrane.

7. Examine the inside of the shell and the membranes attached to it. Try to locate an air space between the membranes and shell. The chick uses the air in the air space only when it is ready to hatch. Answer question 4 in Observations.

8. In the space provided in Observations, draw the egg you have examined. Label the albumen, yolk, chalazae, germinal disk, air space, shell membrane, vitelline membrane, and shell.

9. Follow your teacher's instructions for the proper disposal of the chicken egg and shell.

Observations

Chicken Egg

Name _____ Class _____ Date _____

1. Describe the texture of the chicken egg shell. The egg shell has a hard, porous texture.
_____

2. What is the approximate diameter of the germinal disk? The diameter of the germinal disk will

probably be 1 to 2 mm.
_____

3. To what are the chalazae attached? The chalazae are attached to the yolk of the egg.
_____

4. At which end of the egg, the blunt or the pointed end, is the air space located?
The air space is located at the blunt end of the egg shell.
_____

Analysis and Conclusions

1. What functions does the shell provide for the embryo? The shell protects the embryo from injury,

permits gas exchange, and provides calcium for the developing embryo.
_____

2. If the shell membranes are removed from the shell and water is added, the water will seep out

of the shell. What feature of the shell would allow this to occur? The shell is porous, allowing for

the passage of oxygen into the egg.
_____

_____

3. If the membranes remain in a shell, very little water will seep out. What function do the

membranes probably perform for the developing embryo? The membranes protect the embryo and

prevent the egg from losing water that is necessary for the survival of the embryo.
_____

_____

4. What is the likely function of the chalazae? The chalazae help to anchor the yolk in the center of the

egg.
_____

5. What might the egg white provide for the developing embryo? The egg white cushions the embryo

within the egg and provides it with water and protein.
_____

_____

6. What might the egg yolk provide for the developing embryo? The egg yolk contains stored food for the developing embryo.

Critical Thinking and Application

1. In the developing human, there is no albumen or yolk serving as a source of nutrients. How does the human embryo obtain nutrients for growth and development?
   The human embryo obtains nutrients and oxygen through a structure called the placenta. The placenta also acts to remove waste products from the area around the embryo.

2. A chick embryo develops in 21 days, but a human embryo develops in about 266 days. Why are longer periods of development possible in humans and other mammals?
   A human embryo receives its nourishment by way of the placenta. The human embryo and the embryos of other mammals are not dependent on food stored in a yolk, which is rapidly depleted.

3. "Candling" is a process by which egg processors look at an egg through a light source to determine whether or not it has been fertilized. Why is the "candling" of chicken eggs important to egg processors? "Candling" allows egg processors to quickly separate fertilized eggs from unfertilized eggs without damaging the eggs. The fertilized eggs can be kept by the processors to increase the chicken population. The unfertilized eggs can be sold to grocery stores, restaurants, and other food suppliers.

Going Further

1. Examine prepared glass slides of developing chicken embryos. Identify and describe the different stages of development. Compare the development of a chick embryo to the development of a human embryo. What similarities do you find? What differences?

2. Construct your own chicken egg incubator, obtain some fertilized eggs, and care for the eggs for 20 days. On day 21, watch as the chicks hatch from their eggs.

A Model for Disease Transmission

You may want to refer students to pages 953–960 in the textbook for a discussion of the nature of disease.

Time required: 40 minutes plus observations after 2 days.

Pre-Lab Discussion

A *disease* is a condition that interferes with the normal functioning of a living thing but is not the result of an injury. Generally, a disease has certain symptoms. The disease can affect the entire body or only parts of the body. People can be born with certain diseases, such as genetic disorders. Other diseases can develop during a person's lifetime.

An *infectious disease* is one that is caused by an organism or virus that enters the body. Most disease-causing microorganisms do not move from one person to another on their own. Instead, the microorganisms are transmitted through contact with an infected person or a contaminated object or substance.

In this investigation, you will observe how easily a harmless microorganism is transmitted from person to person.

Problem

How easily can infectious disease be spread?

Materials *(per group of four students)*

4 petri dishes containing sterile nutrient agar
Glass-marking pencil
Sterile cotton swabs
Sterile distilled water [1]
Yeast culture [2]
Wire inoculating loop
Bunsen burner
Flint striker or matches

Dissolve 3 g beef extract, 5 g peptone, and 15 g agar in 1 L distilled water. Heat at low temperature until dissolved. Pour into petri dishes and cover the dishes. Sterilize petri dishes in autoclave or pressure cooker for 15 minutes at 15 pounds pressure.

[1] Boil distilled water for 15 minutes and allow to cool.

[2] Dissolve 20 g glucose in 200 mL distilled water. Add a package of dry yeast. Stir until yeast cells are suspended.

Safety 🔺 🥽 👁

Put on a laboratory apron if one is available. Put on safety goggles. Handle all glassware carefully. Note all safety alert symbols next to the steps in the Procedure and review the meanings of each symbol by referring to the symbol guide on page 10.

Procedure

1. Assign a number from 1 to 4 to each member of your group.

2. Using a glass-marking pencil, draw a line on the bottom of an agar plate to divide it in half. Label one side of the plate "Control" and the other side "Experimental." Also write your assigned number on the bottom of the plate.

3. Swab your left hand with a sterile cotton swab moistened in sterile distilled water. Then swab one corner of the control side of the agar with the same swab.

4. Sterilize a wire loop by passing it through the flame of a Bunsen burner until the entire length of the wire has been heated to a red glow. **CAUTION:** *Put on safety goggles whenever you use a Bunsen burner.*

5. Streak your plate with the sterilized wire loop as shown in Figure 1. The streak should begin from the point at which the plate was touched with the swab. **Note:** *The wire loop should be sterilized after each use by heating as before.*

Figure 1

6. Your teacher should swab the right hand of group member 1 with a culture of yeast. Group member 1 should then shake hands with group member 2. Group member 2 should then shake hands with group member 3. Finally, group member 3 should shake hands with group member 4.

7. You and your group members should swab the right hand with sterile cotton swabs moistened with sterile distilled water. Then using the same swab, you all should swab one corner of the experimental side of your individual agar plate and repeat steps 4 and 5 of the Procedure.

8. Wash your hands thoroughly with soap and water after swabbing.

9. You and your group members should cover all the agar plates and incubate them in an inverted position for 48 hours, after which they should be examined.

Observations

1. Compare the control and experimental sides of the plates. Describe the differences between them. Both the control and the experimental side should have bacterial colonies. On the experimental side, the yeast colonies appear grayish, slightly oval, and slightly raised. They grow faster and take up more space than do the bacterial colonies of the same age on the control side.

2. Why is it necessary to compare your control plates with the yeast culture?

The comparison enables the students to differentiate the yeast colonies from other microbes that are

present on the plates.

Analysis and Conclusions

1. How are most disease-causing microorganisms transmitted? They are transmitted through contact

with an infected person or a contaminated object or substance.

2. How were the yeast colonies transmitted from plate 1 to plates 2, 3, and 4?

The method of transmission is direct contact (handshaking).

3. Which plate should have contained the greatest number of yeast? Which plate should have

contained the least? Explain your answer. Plate 1 should show the greatest number of yeast and plate

4 should show the least. The number of transmitted yeast colonies decreases with each physical contact.

Critical Thinking and Application

1. What do you think is the best way to prevent the transmission of infectious diseases?

The transmission of infectious diseases can best be prevented by avoiding contact with infected people or

contaminated substances. Antibiotics can also be used to kill bacteria.

2. How would population density influence the transmission of diseases?

A dense and crowded human population greatly increases the likelihood of infectious disease transmission.

3. List three infectious diseases that are commonly spread among human populations.

Answers will vary but may include flu, colds, chicken pox, measles, mumps, ringworm, and athlete's foot.

4. List three ways in which diseases can be directly and indirectly spread.

Answers will vary but may include sneezing, coughing, physical contact, blood transfusion, animal bites, and contaminated food and water.

5. Children must be immunized for certain diseases before they enter school. Why is immunization required by law? Immunizations prevent infants and children from contracting certain infectious diseases and starting an epidemic within the school population.

Going Further

1. Test the sensitivity of the bacteria in your plates to antibiotics. Using forceps, place a pretreated antibiotic disk in the center of each of your petri dishes. Turn the petri dishes upside down and incubate them at 37°C for 24 to 48 hours. When incubation is complete, some areas on the surface of the agar should look cloudy or white. These areas have bacteria growing on them. Check for clear or less dense circular regions around each disk. A clear region around the disk indicates that the antibiotic has either killed bacteria or inhibited their growth.

2. Carry out an experiment to show that microbes are sprayed into the air by talking and laughing. Talk for 30 seconds facing a sterile nutrient agar plate held 15 cm from your mouth. Repeat this procedure with a second agar plate held at arm's length from your mouth. Repeat the same procedure for two more agar plates, but this time cough onto each. Repeat the procedure for two more agar plates, but this time laugh in the direction of each plate. Cover each plate and incubate them at room temperature for 24 to 48 hours. Observe the amount of microbial growth on each plate. Write a brief report explaining your results.

87

Relating Chronic Diseases and Nutrition

You may want to refer students to pages 953–963 in the textbook for a discussion of diseases.

Time required: 30 minutes.

Pre-Lab Discussion

During your teens, you will grow at a faster rate than at any other time in your life except infancy. This growth involves more than just height and weight. Your bones increase in density, and your muscles develop in size and strength. Your endocrine glands also grow and develop. Good eating habits are especially important during this period of rapid growth.

A well-balanced diet definitely contributes to a healthy body. Yet many teenagers do not have good eating habits. They may skip breakfast, choose snacks that are rich in fats and sugars, go on crash diets, and neglect foods that contain important nutrients. For most Americans, improper nutritional habits cause health problems.

Good eating habits during the teenage years usually mean fewer problems during later years. Scientists have begun to take a closer look at the relationship between nutrient intake and chronic, life-threatening diseases. Heart disease, diabetes, high blood pressure, kidney disease, various digestive disorders, and even certain types of cancer have all been found to be connected with nutrition. It is becoming more and more evident that "you are what you eat."

In this investigation, you will plan nutritionally balanced menus and calculate the number of Calories you consume and burn in an average day.

Problem

Can you plan a menu that meets the Recommended Dietary Allowances (RDA) published by the Food and Nutrition Board of the National Academy of Sciences? How closely does your Calorie consumption equal the Calories you burn?

Materials *(per group)*

Calculator (optional)
Pencil
Additional tables of nutrition information (optional)

Procedure

1. From the foods listed in the Table of Nutrition Information, plan a day's menu. Choose those items you would like to eat for breakfast, lunch, dinner, and snacks. List them in the chart entitled "My Menu" in Observations. Also list the nutrition information for each item.

2. Total each column in your menu chart. Compare the totals with the data in the Recommended Dietary Allowances Table.

Recommended Dietary Allowances

Sex	Age	Calories	Protein (g)	Calcium (mg)	Iron (mg)	Vitamins A (i.u.)	B₁ (mg)	C (mg)
Males	12–16	2700–3000	46–54	1200	18	5000	1.4	50–60
Females	12–16	2100–2400	44–48	1200	18	4000	1.1	50–60

g = grams, mg = milligrams, i.u. = international units

Table of Nutrition Information

Food	Amount	Calories	Protein (g)	Calcium (mg)	Iron (mg)	Vitamins A (i.u.)	B₁ (mg)	C (mg)
Hamburger	113 g	300	20.2	11	3.1	40	.09	0
Hot dog or hamburger bun	1	90	2.5	22	0.6	trace	.08	trace
T-bone steak	227 g	800	30.0	16	4.4	150	.12	0
Fried chicken	¼	230	22.4	18	1.8	230	.07	0
Egg	11 g	80	6.5	27	1.2	590	.15	0
Flounder	100 g	70	14.9	61	0.8	—	.06	—
Bacon	1 slice	50	1.8	1	0.2	0	.04	0
Hot dog	1	125	7.0	3	0.6	0	.08	0
Shrimp	0.2 kg	145	28.3	26	1.8	—	—	—
American cheese	28 g	105	7.0	198	0.3	350	.01	0
Milk	1 cup	160	9.0	288	0.1	350	.07	2
Ice cream	1 cup	255	6.0	194	0.1	590	.05	1
Lima beans	½ cup	130	8.0	28	2.9	—	.12	—
Green beans	½ cup	15	1.0	31	0.4	340	.05	8
Broccoli	1 stalk	25	3.1	88	0.8	2500	.09	90
Corn	1 ear	70	3.0	2	0.5	310	.09	7
Blackeyed peas	½ cup	90	6.5	20	1.7	280	.02	14
Baked potato	1 med.	145	4.0	14	1.1	trace	.15	31
French fries	20	310	4.0	18	1.4	trace	.14	24
Potato chips	20	230	2.0	16	0.8	trace	.08	6
Apple	1 med.	80	0.3	10	0.4	120	.04	6
Banana	1 med.	100	1.0	10	0.8	230	.06	12
Fresh strawberries	½ cup	35	0.5	14	0.6	80	.02	16
Orange juice	1 cup	120	2.0	25	0.2	550	.22	124
White bread	1 slice	65	2.0	22	0.6	trace	.06	trace
Chocolate chip cookie	1	50	0.5	4	0.2	10	.01	trace
Chocolate cake	1 piece	235	3.0	41	0.6	100	.02	trace
Corn flakes	1 cup	95	2.0	6	0.5	0	.10	0
Pancake	1	105	3.2	27	0.6	.54	.08	trace
Syrup	1 Tbsp.	50	0	33	0.6	0	—	0

548

3. The number of Calories you burn depends in part on the activities you perform. Fill in the chart entitled "My Activities" with the time you spend during an average day on each activity listed.

4. To calculate the total Calories burned in each activity category, multiply A x B x C. Keep the time units the same within each category. For example, if time is spent in hours, use the figure for Calories burned per hour. Add the categories to find the total Calories burned in 24 hours.

Observations

My Menu

Meal	Calories	Protein (g)	Calcium (mg)	Iron (mg)	Vitamins A (i.u.)	B$_1$ (mg)	C (mg)
Breakfast							
Lunch			Answers will vary.				
Dinner							
Snacks							
TOTALS							

My Activities

Activity	A Calories Burned (per hr or min)	B Minutes or Hours Spent in Activity	C Your Mass	Total Calories
Sleeping Napping	.0075/min .45/hr			
Reading Watching TV Eating Sitting in class	.0108/min .64/hr			
Dressing Showering Driving car	.015/min .90/hr		Answers will vary.	
Light activity Walking Lab work	.0308/min 1.84/hr			
Moderate activity Gym class Bicycling Dancing Easy jogging	.0395/min 2.37/hr			
Heavy work Swimming Tennis Basketball Wrestling Climbing stairs	.0483/min 2.9/hr			

1. Compare your total Calories burned in 24 hours with the total Calories you would consume according to the menu you planned in step 2 of the Procedure.

   Calories burned: _____

   Calories consumed: _____

Analysis and Conclusions

1. **a.** How do the totals from your menu chart compare with the Recommended Dietary Allowances? Answers will vary. _____

   _____

   b. Does your menu provide too many, too few, or the right number of Calories?
   Answers will vary depending on the answer to question 1.
   _____

   c. In what areas, if any, is your menu deficient? Answers will vary. _____

_____

_____

2. Not all of the recommended nutrients have been included in the charts for this investigation. Name four other nutrients, including minerals and vitamins, that should be included in your diet. Answers will vary but might include vitamins D, E, B_6, B_{12}, niacin, riboflavin (B_2), phosphorus, iodine, zinc, magnesium, fiber, fats, and carbohydrates.

_____

3. What portion of a gram is 1 milligram? A milligram is 1/1000 g. _____

_____

4. Compare your total Calories burned in 24 hours with your total Calories consumed. If this is your normal pattern, what conclusion can you draw regarding your Calorie intake?
Answers will vary.

_____

_____

5. List three diseases and disorders that have been associated with poor nutrition.
Answers will vary but might include coronary heart disease, diabetes, high blood pressure, kidney disease, digestive disorders, some types of cancers, gout, arthritis, and scurvy.

_____

Critical Thinking and Application

   1. What two things can you do to safely lose weight? You can decrease your intake of Calories and increase the number of Calories you burn through exercise.

_____

   2. Of the two weight-loss methods you listed in question 1, which do you think is the better method and why? It is better to exercise than to diet. Dieting can cause you to miss some important nutrients.

_____

3. Many companies now advertise breakfast cereals that are lower in sugar. Why do you think it is better to eat a breakfast cereal that is lower in sugar? Sugar can promote tooth decay. Also, cereals lower in sugar usually contain fewer Calories.

4. Explain how it is possible for a person to appear overweight but suffer from malnutrition. Malnutrition occurs when the body does not take in the proper amounts of nutrients. A person may consume food that adds Calories but not nutrients to the system. As a result, the excess Calories can cause body fat to accumulate.

Going Further

1. Keep a record of all foods you eat every day for one week. Compute your Calorie intake each day. Compute your average daily Calorie intake for the week. How well does your list of foods eaten meet the Recommended Dietary Allowances? Is your daily food intake well balanced in terms of the four basic food groups? What conclusions can you draw regarding your eating habits?

2. Many food products have nutritional information listed on the package. Look at this information for some of your favorite foods. How well do these foods meet the requirements for Recommended Dietary Allowances?

3. Obtain nutrition information for the major items sold at your favorite fast-food restaurant. Make a chart or booklet of this information and share it with your classmates.

88

Lysis by a Bacteriophage

You may want to refer students to pages 969–976 and 979–981 in the textbook for a discussion of viruses.

Time required:
    Part A–50 minutes
    Part B–50 minutes plus observation period after 24 and 48 hours.

Pre-Lab Discussion

Some diseases that affect people are caused by viruses. Viruses also cause plant diseases and infect bacteria. A virus consists of a core of nucleic acid surrounded by a protein coat. Although unable to grow or independently carry out the processes characteristic of living things, a virus has the ability to reproduce inside living cells. Electron microscope examination shows that when a virus infects a cell, it first attaches itself to the wall or cell membrane of the cell. The virus then injects its nucleic acid into the interior of the cell through an opening it has made in the host-cell wall or membrane. Once inside, the nuclear material of the virus uses the ribosomes and enzymes of the cell to produce more viral nucleic acids and protein coats. The viral nucleic acids and protein coats are assembled into new viruses. By the action of enzymes produced by these new viruses, the host cell bursts, or *lyses*. The viruses leave the cell and infect other cells.

Lysis is an important tool used by virologists to detect the presence of viruses in a cell population. If a culture of bacteria is inoculated with bacteriophages, or viruses that infect bacteria, the lysis of the bacterial cells makes the culture appear clear. This clear area is called a *plaque*. The clearer a phage-infected culture of bacteria is, the greater the number of phages present in the culture.

The culturing of bacteria and bacteriophages requires the use of *aseptic,* or sterile, techniques. Aseptic techniques prevent contamination of existing cultures by other microorganisms. The heat produced by autoclaving or passing certain materials through the flame of a Bunsen burner is sufficient to destroy microorganisms and keep the environment sterile.

In this investigation, you will detect the presence of bacteriophages in a bacterial culture. You will also acquire skill in preparing viral and bacterial cultures using aseptic techniques.

Problem

How is the presence of bacteriophages in a culture of bacteria demonstrated?

Materials *(per group)*

Bunsen burner
Culture of T-4 bacteriophage   Available from a biological supply house.
Inoculating loop
6 sterile test tubes each containing   Dissolve 3 g beef extract and 5 g peptone in 1 L distilled water. Pour
    nutrient broth   1 mL broth into each test tube, and sterilize test tubes in an autoclave
     or pressure cooker set at 15 pounds pressure for 15 minutes.
Glass-marking pencil
Test tube rack
Nutrient agar plate[1]   [1] Add 3 g beef extract, 5 g peptone, and 15 g agar to 1 L distilled water.
Culture of *Escherichia coli*[2]   Heat the mixture until the agar dissolves. Pour the agar into petri dishes,
Sterile cotton swab   and sterilize them in an autoclave or pressure cooker set at 15 pounds
Incubator   pressure for 15 minutes.

[2] Available from a biological supply house.

Put on a laboratory apron if one is available. Handle all glassware carefully. Put on safety goggles. When using the Bunsen burner, be sure that hair or loose clothing does not come into contact with the flame. Follow your teacher's directions and all appropriate safety procedures when handling microorganisms. Wash your hands thoroughly after each part of this investigation. Note all safety alert symbols next to the steps in the Procedure and review the meanings of each symbol by referring to the symbol guide on page 10. If you wish students to perform the first investigation in Going Further, have them save test tubes 4 and 5. A microbiological filter will also be needed to perform the investigation.

Part A. Preparing a Bacteriophage Culture

A
Sterilizing the inoculating loop

B
Removing cotton plugs

C
Sterilizing the mouths of the test tubes

D
Transferring the culture

🔥 **1.** Obtain a culture of T-4 bacteriophage from your teacher. **CAUTION:** *Be very careful when working with microorganisms. Wash your hands thoroughly after each part of this investigation.*

🥽 **2.** Sterilize the inoculating loop by passing it 👁 through a Bunsen burner flame as shown in A of Figure 1. Allow the loop to remain in the flame until the entire length of the metal part has turned red. **CAUTION:** *When using a Bunsen burner, wear safety goggles and be sure that hair and loose clothing do not come into contact with the flame. Do not touch the end of the inoculating loop that is placed in the flame or allow it to come into contact with any flammable objects.*

3. While holding the sterile inoculating loop in one hand, pick up in the other hand the test tube containing the T-4 bacteriophage culture and one sterile test tube containing the nutrient broth.

4. Remove the cotton plugs from each test tube by grasping the plugs between the fingers of the hand holding the loop. This technique is shown in B of Figure 1. **Note:** *Transfer the cotton plugs from in between the last two fingers to between the second and third fingers as shown in D of Figure 1. Do not touch the parts of the cotton plugs that are placed inside the test tubes.*

5. Sterilize the mouths of the test tubes by quickly passing them through the flame two or three times as shown in C of Figure 1.

6. Carefully insert the inoculating loop into the test tube containing the T-4 bacteriophage culture and remove one loopful of culture. **Note:** *Allow the inoculating loop to cool before inserting it into the test tube.*

Figure 1

7. Transfer this loopful of T-4 bacteriophage culture to the test tube containing the nutrient broth.

8. Before replacing the cotton plugs on the two test tubes, sterilize the mouths of the test tubes. Also, resterilize the inoculating loop.

9. Mix the contents of the test tube containing the nutrient broth and bacteriophage culture by rotating the tube rapidly between your hands. With the glass-marking pencil, label this tube "Stock Phage Culture."

10. Place the remaining five tubes containing 1 mL each of nutrient broth in a test tube rack. With the glass-marking pencil, label them 1 through 5.

11. Transfer a loopful of culture from the stock phage culture to test tube 1 following steps 2 through 8.

12. Continue transferring loopfuls from test tube to test tube as shown in Figure 2. Stop when test tube 4 is inoculated. **Note:** *Do not inoculate test tube 5 with the bacteriophage culture.*

Figure 2

You may wish to have some or all of the groups use one nutrient agar plate for each of the five streaks.

Part B. Growing Bacteria and Bacteriophages on Agar

1. Obtain a nutrient agar plate and turn it upside down. Across the bottom of the plate, draw five lines with the glass-marking pencil. Number each line as shown in Figure 3. Turn the petri dish upright.

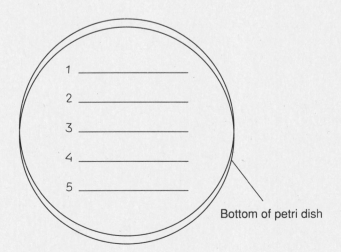

Figure 3

2. Obtain a culture of *E. coli*. Dip the sterile cotton swab into the culture of *E. coli*.

3. Raise the lid of the petri dish slightly and swab the entire surface of the agar plate with the cotton swab. Try to cover the surface of the agar plate as uniformly as possible

4. Using the sterile techniques described in steps 2 through 8 of Part A, remove a loopful of material from test tube 1 and·streak this on the surface of the nutrient agar plate following line 1. Replace the cotton plug.

5. Follow the same procedure for each of the remaining four test tubes, including test tube 5. Be sure to streak one loopful along the line that corresponds to the test tube number. **Note:** *Be sure to sterilize the loop after each streaking.*

6. After completing the streaking of the bacteriophage dilutions onto the nutrient agar plate, inoculate test tubes 1 through 5 with a loopful of *E. coli* culture. Be sure to follow the sterilization procedures for each inoculation. Mix the contents of each tube well by rapid rotation.

7. Incubate the plate and broth cultures in the incubator at 35° to 37°C.

8. Examine the plate and test tubes after 24 and 48 hours. In the appropriate place in Observations, sketch what you observe on the agar plate after 24 and 48 hours.

9. In the Data Table, record the results of your observations after 48 hours. In the first column, use a range of + to indicate minimum plaque formation to ++++ to indicate maximum plaque formation on the agar plate. In the second column, use a range of + for slightly cloudy to ++++ for maximum cloudiness in the test tubes.

10. Return the agar plate and test tubes to your teacher for proper disposal. Wash your hands thoroughly with soap and water.

Observations

After 24 hours   After 48 hours

Growth of Bacteria on Agar Plate

Data Table

Test Tube	Plaque formation (clearing on streaks)	Growth of *E. coli* (cloudiness in test tubes)
1		
2		
3	Answers will vary.	
4		
5		

Analysis and Conclusions

1. Why is it necessary to use aseptic techniques when culturing bacteria?

   Aseptic techniques prevent cultures of bacteria from becoming contaminated by other organisms.

2. What is happening to the bacteriophage culture as it is transferred from one test tube to the next? The bacteriophage culture becomes more diluted after each transfer.

3. In which streak is the growth of *E. coli* most abundant? Streak 5 should have the most abundant growth of *E. coli*.

4. In which streak are the plaques most evident? Answers may vary. Observable plaques may appear in streaks 3 and 4. These areas may not be apparent in the first two streaks because very small amounts of *E. coli* may survive.

5. **a.** In which tube was *E. coli* growing alone? *E. coli* was growing alone in test tube 5.

   b. Describe the appearance of the broth in this test tube. Explain this appearance.

   The broth should appear cloudy because no bacteriophages that would cause the *E. coli* cells to lyse are present.

6. a. In which test tube was the concentration of bacteriophages the greatest?

Test tube 1 contains the greatest concentration of bacteriophages.

b. Describe the appearance of the broth in this test tube. Explain this appearance.

The broth should appear clear because the bacteriophages have caused the *E. coli* cell to lyse.

Critical Thinking and Application

1. Why are viruses considered to be parasites? Viruses are considered to be parasites because they can carry out their life processes only inside of a host organism.

2. Could the viruses that exist today have been the first type of living thing? Explain your answer.

Because today's viruses require a host cell to reproduce, it is unlikely that viruses could have been the first type of living thing.

3. Viruses contain either DNA or RNA. How do you account for the fact that viruses need only one type of nucleic acid? In living cells, DNA carries the hereditary message, and RNA is involved in translating this message into proteins. A virus is not a living cell and needs only the hereditary message in order to infect and use cells and their nucleic acids to "translate" this message. Either DNA or RNA can be used to carry the hereditary information of the virus.

4. Viruses can sometimes induce the formation of tumors. Formulate a hypothesis about how viruses cause cells to grow out of control. Explain your answer. Viruses enter cells and inject their nucleic acid into cells. Under most conditions, this nucleic acid directs the formation of new viruses. However, it is feasible that this nucleic acid could program the cell to grow in an abnormal manner rather than to make new viruses and then burst apart. The reasoning behind this hypothesis is that nucleic acid contains the controlling information and causes changes to occur within cells.

Going Further

1. To demonstrate that viruses are filterable, obtain a microbiological filter from your teacher and filter the contents of test tube 4. Using the inoculating loop and aseptic techniques, inoculate test tube 5 with the filtered material and incubate the test tube at 35° to 37°C for 24 hours. What do you observe in test tube 5? What conclusions can you make?

2. Prepare a report on why agar is used in microbiological culturing. What properties of this medium make it suitable for the study of microorganisms?

You may want to refer students to pages 969–971 in the textbook for a discussion of nonspecific immune defenses.

Time required: 30 minutes plus an observation period after one week.

The Effect of Alcohol on the Growth of Microorganisms

Pre-Lab Discussion

The body's immune system sometimes cannot control an infection by itself. An *antimicrobial agent* is a chemical substance that kills or inhibits the growth of microorganisms. Such a substance may be either a synthetic chemical or a natural product. One type of antimicrobial agent is an *antiseptic*. An antiseptic is a chemical used to inhibit the growth of or kill microorganisms on living tissues. Antiseptics that are used on the skin may be swabbed on with sterile cotton. Soaps containing antiseptics leave a residue of the antiseptic on the skin after the soap is rinsed off, and this active residue may continue to kill microorganisms for an extended period of time.

In this investigation, you will observe how alcohol can be used as an antiseptic.

Problem

What is the effect of alcohol on the growth of microorganisms?

Materials *(per group)*

Dissolve 3 g beef extract, 5 g peptone, and 15 g agar in 1 L distilled water. Heat at low temperature until dissolved. Pour into petri dishes. Sterilize petri dishes in autoclave or pressure cooker for 15 minutes at 15 pounds pressure.

2 petri dishes containing sterile nutrient agar
Forceps soaking in alcohol
2 paper clips   The paper clips, thumbtacks, and pennies for this investigation should be used ones. If
2 thumbtacks   they are new, be sure to have students handle and touch them before the lab starts to be
2 pennies   sure that they have been in contact with common microorganisms.
Glass-marking pencil
Masking or clear tape
50-mL graduated cylinder
70% alcohol solution   Isopropyl alcohol is available from a drugstore.
100-mL beaker

Safety ⚗ 🧰 ▭

Put on a laboratory apron if one is available. Put on safety goggles. Handle all glassware carefully. Be careful when handling sharp instruments. Note all safety alert symbols next to the steps in the Procedure and review the meanings of each symbol by referring to the symbol guide on page 10.

Procedure

1. Set out the two petri dishes containing sterile nutrient agar, as well as the two thumbtacks, two pennies, and two paper clips. Each of the metal objects should be handled before beginning the procedure.

2. Use a glass-marking pencil to label the lids of the dishes. Label one dish "Control" and the other dish "Soaked in Alcohol." Also write the names of the group members and the date on the cover of each dish. **Note:** *Be sure to keep the dishes closed while labeling them.*

3. Use a graduated cylinder to pour 50 mL of 70% alcohol solution into a beaker.

4. Place one paper clip, one thumbtack, and one penny into the alcohol solution. Allow these objects to remain in the solution for 10 minutes.

5. Using a forceps that has been soaked in alcohol, place the other paper clip, other thumbtack, and other penny into the dish marked "Control." **Note:** *These objects should not be soaked in alcohol solution.* Immediately cover the dish and tape it closed.

6. Using the forceps, remove the paper clip, thumbtack, and penny from the beaker of alcohol solution. Place these objects into the dish marked "Soaked in Alcohol." Immediately cover the dish and tape it closed. See Figure 1.

Figure 1

7. Place the petri dishes in an undisturbed location indicated by your teacher for one week.

8. After one week, examine the contents of the two petri dishes. In the appropriate places in Observations, draw what you observe in each petri dish.

9. Follow your teacher's instructions for the proper disposal of all materials.

Observations

Control

Soaked in Alcohol

1. After one week what did you observe in the dish marked "Control"?

Most petri dishes will contain circular colonies of microorganisms growing around the objects in the dishes.

2. After one week, what did you observe in the dish marked "Soaked in Alcohol"?

Most petri dishes will have some circular colonies of microorganisms growing as well.

3. How did the growth of microorganisms in the two dishes compare?

Students should observe far more colonies of microorganisms in the dish marked "Control."

Analysis and Conclusions

1. What effect did the alcohol have on the growth of microorganisms?

The alcohol killed or inhibited the growth of most microorganisms.

2. Why did you use forceps, rather than your fingers, to place the objects in the petri dishes?

Fingers may have transferred microorganisms from the hand to the petri dish.

3. Why was it necessary to immediately close the petri dishes after you added the objects?

The petri dishes should stay closed to keep out any microorganisms from the air.

4. Why is it important that all starting pennies, thumbtacks, and paper clips have been touched?

Without starting microorganisms, they could not grow or be affected by the alcohol.

Critical Thinking and Application

1. Why do doctors soak their instruments in alcohol? The alcohol will kill certain microorganisms on the doctors' instruments that could cause infection in a patient.

2. Why should cuts on the skin be cleaned with an antiseptic and bandaged?

By cleaning cuts with an antiseptic and bandaging them, you kill and keep out most bacteria that can cause an infection.

3. A person who is burned over large areas of the body runs a high risk of developing a serious infection. Why is an infection likely to occur? The skin is the body's first line of defense against invading microorganisms. If the skin is damaged by a burn, it will be unable to fight an infection by acting as a barrier to microorganisms.

4. Suppose a person was born without an immune system. What are some of the precautions that would have to be taken so that the person could survive? The person would have to live in an environment that is totally free of any disease-causing organisms. The person may have to live in a type of "bubble" that contains air that is filtered. In addition, all surfaces would have to be disinfected and there would probably be no direct contact with other people.

Going Further

Repeat this investigation with other antiseptics such as hydrogen peroxide, mouthwashes, deodorants, and antiseptic soaps to determine their effectiveness in killing or inhibiting the growth of microorganisms.

90

> You may want to refer students to pages 993–995 in the textbook for a discussion of alcohol.
>
> Time required: 40 minutes.

The Effects of Alcohol on Human Reactions

Pre-Lab Discussion

Ethyl alcohol is a drug that is absorbed directly into the bloodstream from the stomach and small intestine. It takes only two minutes, and even less on an empty stomach, for the alcohol to reach the bloodstream. The blood carries the alcohol to various parts of the body. The liver is the major organ that metabolizes ethyl alcohol to carbon dioxide and water and releases energy.

Alcohol acts as a depressant on the central nervous system. High blood-alcohol concentrations tend to reduce the activity of bodily functions. The result is a numbing, or anesthetic, effect on the central nervous system. Alcohol affects the areas of the brain controlling judgment, memory, emotion, speech, vision, motor skills, muscular coordination, and balance. Heart, digestive, and respiratory rates slow down under the influence of alcohol.

In this investigation, you will simulate some of the effects of alcohol without really drinking any alcohol.

Problem

What are the effects of alcohol on a person's reactions?

Materials *(per group)*

Masking tape
Watch or clock with second hand
Pencil

Safety

Do not spin around in this investigation if you are under a doctor's care, have dizzy spells or heart problems, or are unable to participate in physical education classes.

Procedure
Part A. Walking the Line

1. Using masking tape, make a straight line about 3 meters long on the floor. One member of your group should walk from the beginning of this line to the end, putting the heel of one foot right against the toe of the other. A second member of the group should time how long it takes the person to walk from one end of the line to the other. A third group member should keep track of the number of times the walker accidentally misses the line.

2. To simulate the effect of drinking an excess amount of alcohol, the walker should spin around in place for 10 seconds. Be certain that the area is cleared of furniture and other obstacles. The other group members should stand nearby and act as spotters ready to catch the spinner if he or she starts to fall. **CAUTION:** *Do not spin if you are under a doctor's care, have dizzy spells or heart problems, or are unable to participate in physical education classes.*

3. As soon as the person finishes 10 seconds of spinning, lead him or her to the beginning of the line and have him or her repeat the walk described in step 1. Be sure to record the time and number of misses in Data Table 1.

4. Repeat steps 1 through 3 with each group member having an opportunity to be the walker. Record their results in Data Table 1.

Part B. Connecting the Dots

1. The object of this test is to draw a wavy line through the dots as shown in the sample in Observations. One of your group members will time you for 10 seconds while you connect as many dots as you can. At the end of 10 seconds, give yourself one point for each dot you cross and for each time you touch the top or bottom line without crossing over it. Record this information in Data Table 2.

2. Repeat the spinning procedure described in step 2 of Part A. Then repeat the dot test and see how many points you score this time. Record this information in Data Table 2.

3. Repeat steps 1 and 2 with each member of your group having an opportunity to connect the dots. Record their results in Data Table 2.

Part C. Using Statistics to Construct Graphs on Alcoholism

1. It is estimated that there are 14 million alcoholics in the United States. Of this number, 3.5 million are teenagers, 13 to 17 years old. Among teenage alcoholics, 6.25% are females.

2. On the circle graph in Observations, indicate the portion of the total population of alcoholics who are between the ages of 13 and 17, and male. Also indicate the number of female alcoholics between the ages of 13 and 17.

3. A recent survey of teenage drinking habits revealed the following:
   - 62% drank alcoholic beverages occasionally
   - 19% tried alcohol once
   - 18% never tried alcohol
   - 1% no comment

   Use the circle graph in Observations to graph these survey results.

Observations

Data Table 1

Name	Before Spinning		After Spinning	
	Time (sec)	Mistakes	Time (sec)	Mistakes
Answers will vary, but students should have longer times and more mistakes after spinning.				

Sample

Name _____ Class _____ Date _____

Data Table 2

Name	Score Before Spinning	Score After Spinning
Answers will vary, but students should have lower point scores after spinning.		

Alcoholics in the United States

Teenage Drinking Habits

Analysis and Conclusions

1. Based on your observations in this simulation of drinking alcohol, what effect does alcohol have on a person's reactions? Alcohol tends to impair motor skills, muscular coordination, and balance.

2. What is the effect of alcohol on the central nervous system? Alcohol acts as a depressant on the central nervous system.

3. According to the statistics given in Part C, what percentage of the total population of alcoholics are between the ages of 13 and 17? Of the total population of alcoholics, 25% are between the ages of 13 and 17.

Critical Thinking and Application

1. Why is alcohol technically classified as a legal drug? A drug is any substance that causes a change in body function, and alcohol does this. Alcohol depresses the central nervous system and reduces the activity of bodily functions. Although it is a drug, alcohol can be purchased at a store by anyone of legal age.

2. Alcohol is known to be a depressant. Why then does the consumption of alcohol sometimes result in a feeling of happiness? Alcohol affects the areas of the brain controlling emotion and judgment. The anesthetic, or numbing, effect of alcohol on the central nervous system can lead to a sense of well-being and happiness.

3. Explain why alcoholism is considered to be a disease. Alcoholism is considered to be a disease because it causes disturbances of body function and has characteristic symptoms.

4. Use the information in the accompanying chart to construct a line graph. Does the likelihood of having an accident increase proportionally with the amount of alcohol in the blood? The likelihood of having an accident increases exponentially, not proportionally, as the alcohol level in the blood increases.

% of Alcohol in Blood	Increased Likelihood of Having an Accident While Driving
0.00	1.0 x
0.02	1.5 x
0.04	2.0 x
0.06	2.5 x
0.08	4.0 x
0.10	6.0 x
0.12	10.0 x
0.14	19.0 x
0.16	30.0 x

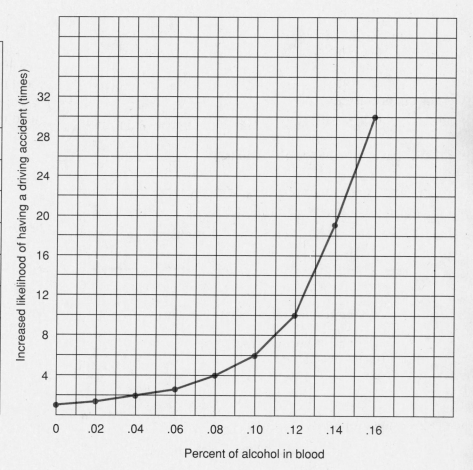

Percent of alcohol in blood

Going Further

1. Call your local chapter of Alcoholics Anonymous, Al-Anon, or Alateen and request information about the warning signs of alcoholism.
2. Using resources from within your community, prepare a panel discussion on topics related to drugs and their abuse that would interest students in your biology class. Invite outside experts from law enforcement groups, local and federal government agencies, and the medical profession to discuss these topics.

91

The Effects of Tobacco and Alcohol on Seed Germination

You may want to refer students to pages 993–997 in the textbook for a discussion of tobacco and alcohol.

Time required: 40 minutes and observation period of 2 days.

Pre-Lab Discussion

Ethyl alcohol, or ethanol, which is an ingredient in alcoholic beverages, is a drug absorbed directly into the bloodstream from the stomach and small intestine. A *drug* is any substance that causes change in body function. Alcohol acts as a depressant on the central nervous system. Depressants decrease the action of the central nervous system by reducing the ability of nerves to transmit impulses between the brain and the rest of the body.

Tobacco leaves contain substances that have been shown by scientists to be harmful to people and animals. The tar in tobacco has been linked to cancer. Tars and other substances in tobacco may also lead to heart and respiratory illnesses.

In this investigation, you will test the effect of alcohol and tobacco smoke on seed germination. A seed that is alive and healthy will germinate under proper conditions of moisture and temperature. But if a harmful substance is added to the seed's environment, it may change the number of seeds that will germinate.

Problem

How do tobacco and alcohol affect seed germination?

Materials *(per group)*

Cut a 30-cm length of glass tubing and a 20-cm length of glass tubing to fit a two-hole rubber stopper. Make a right angle bend in each, 10 cm from one end. Lubricate the pieces of glass tubing with glycerine and insert them into the rubber stopper. One aspirator can provide smoky water for several groups of students.

100-mL graduated cylinder	Filter paper
250-mL graduated cylinder	10 filterless cigarettes
250-mL Erlenmeyer flask	Matches
3 50-mL beakers	25 mL ethanol
Glass-marking pencil	150 mustard seeds
Faucet aspirator	Two-hole rubber stopper
Scissors	Glass tubing
Forceps	Narrow rubber tubing 5.5-cm length of 5-mm bore
Wide rubber tubing 8-cm length of 8-mm bore	Metric ruler
Aluminum foil	4 petri dishes and covers
Cotton	

Put on a laboratory apron if one is available. Put on safety goggles. Handle all glassware carefully. Be careful when using matches. Always use special caution when working with laboratory chemicals, as they may irritate the skin or cause staining of the skin or clothing. Never touch or taste any chemical unless instructed to do so. Keep alcohol away from any open flame. Be careful when handling sharp instruments. Note all safety alert symbols next to the steps in the Procedure and review the meanings of each symbol by referring to the symbol guide on page 10.

Procedure

🔥 1. Construct a smoking machine similar to the one shown in Figure 1.

Figure 1

2. Using a graduated cylinder, pour 150 mL of water into a 250-mL flask. Obtain from your teacher a two-hole rubber stopper with glass tubing already inserted. Place the stopper in the flask. Make sure the long glass tubing goes into the water. The short glass tubing, however, should not touch the water.

⬛ 3. With a gentle twisting motion, slide a 3-cm-long piece of narrow rubber tubing over the free end of the long glass tubing. Cut a 2-mm notch in each end of the 6-cm-long piece of wide rubber tubing. To construct your cigarette holder, slide the wide rubber tubing over the narrow rubber tubing.

4. Attach one end of a piece of narrow rubber tubing about 50 cm in length to the free end of the short glass tubing. Attach the other end to a faucet aspirator. When the water is turned on, it will produce a partial vacuum that will draw smoke from the cigarette through the water in the flask.

5. Insert a filterless cigarette into the cigarette holder. To catch falling ashes, put a petri dish under the cigarette.

6. Light the cigarette with a match. **CAUTION:** *Be careful when using matches.* Turn on the water. Smoke should bubble through the water. Increase the flow of faucet water through the aspirator if the smoke does not bubble freely through the water.

7. When the cigarette has burned almost to the holder, turn off the water. Using forceps, remove the cigarette, run water over it, and dispose of it in the petri dish with the ashes.

8. Repeat steps 5 through 7 until the smoke from 10 cigarettes has been bubbled through the water.

9. Place 50 mustard seeds in each of three 50-mL beakers.

10. Add 25 mL of water to one of the beakers. Label the beaker accordingly. Add 25 mL of ethanol to the second beaker and label it. **CAUTION:** *Keep alcohol away from an open flame.* To the last beaker add 25 mL of smoky water and label it. Cover the beakers with aluminum foil and set them aside for 24 hours.

11. After 24 hours, spread a thin layer of cotton across the bottom of each of three petri dishes. Place a piece of filter paper on top of the cotton. Pour the contents of each 50-mL beaker into a separate petri dish. Carefully spread the seeds out over the filter paper. Cover the petri dishes and label them accordingly. Set the petri dishes aside.

12. After another 24 hours, check the petri dishes for germinated seeds. Count the number of germinated seeds in each petri dish after one day. Record the results in the Data Table. Then set the petri dishes aside for another 24 hours. Count the number of germinated seeds in each petri dish after two days. Record this information in the Data Table.

Observations

Data Table

Substance	Number of Seeds Germinated	
	Day 1	Day 2
Water		
Alcohol	Answers will vary.	
Tobacco smoke		

1. How does the number of germinated seeds in ethanol compare to the number of germinated seeds in tap water? The germination rate for seeds soaked in alcohol should be lower than the germination rate for seeds soaked in tap water.

2. How does the number of germinated seeds in smoky water compare to the number of germinated seeds in tap water? The germination rate for seeds soaked in smoky water should be lower than the germination rate for seeds soaked in tap water.

Analysis and Conclusions

1. How does alcohol affect the central nervous system? _Alcohol acts as a depressant on the central_ _nervous system._

2. Based on your results, do you think alcohol is harmful to seeds? Explain your answer. _Yes. Students should find that most of the mustard seeds are unable to germinate after exposure to_ _alcohol._

3. To what human illnesses has tobacco been linked? _Tobacco has been linked to cancer, heart_ _disease, high blood pressure, respiratory illness, and stroke._

4. Based on your results, do you think tobacco is harmful to seeds? Explain your answer. _Yes. Students should find that most of the mustard seeds are unable to germinate after exposure to_ _tobacco._

Critical Thinking and Application

1. How might using filtered instead of unfiltered cigarettes change the results of this experiment? _The use of filtered cigarettes might allow more seeds to germinate than the use of unfiltered cigarettes._

2. Cigarette smoking causes a person's blood vessels to constrict (close up). What negative effects might this have on the body? _Constriction of the blood vessels will increase a person's blood_ _pressure. This increases the person's chance for having a heart attack or stroke._

3. Why should a person who has consumed alcohol not drive an automobile? _Alcohol is a depressant that slows reaction time and interferes with normal brain function. A driver under_ _the influence of alcohol is at a greater risk for an accident than a driver who has not consumed alcohol._

4. Cigarette smoke contains the toxic gas carbon monoxide, which has a 250 times higher ability to combine with the hemoglobin in red blood cells than atmospheric oxygen does. What effect would this have on the human body? When carbon monoxide combines with hemoglobin, the hemoglobin cannot absorb the needed oxygen. Therefore, the hemoglobin cannot carry oxygen throughout the body. The lack of oxygen can seriously damage or destroy the cells of the body, especially those of the brain and nervous system.

5. Caffeine is a substance found in coffee, tea, and chocolate that tends to increase a person's heart rate and breathing rate. Would you consider caffeine to be a drug? Explain your answer. Because it causes changes in body function, caffeine should be considered a drug.

Going Further

1. Using reference materials, research the medical and social problems created by drug abuse. Choose one drug, give its chemical name, and list its effects on the body. Also find out some of the social problems caused by the selling, buying, and use of this drug.

2. Write to organizations such as the American Lung Association, American Heart Association, and American Cancer Society for information about the hazards of smoking. Using this information, prepare charts for a bulletin board display.

The Oxygen Cycle

You may want to refer students to page 1025 in the textbook for a discussion of the oxygen cycle.

Time required: 30 minutes with 5 to 10 minutes of daily observation over a 7-day period.

Pre-Lab Discussion

Oxygen, which is needed by most living things for respiration, makes up about 21 percent of the atmosphere. It is also dissolved in water and is a part of water molecules themselves. The movement of oxygen through an ecosystem is called the *oxygen cycle*.

One phase of the oxygen cycle occurs during the process of photosynthesis. During photosynthesis, molecules of water are split, releasing oxygen into the atmosphere. Oxygen in the atmosphere is used by most organisms for respiration. One of the waste products of respiration is water. Water is released into the atmosphere and may later fall to the earth as precipitation. This water can be absorbed by plants, which break down the water and release oxygen, thus continuing the oxygen cycle.

In this investigation, you will examine the operation of the oxygen cycle in a closed environment.

Problem

How does the oxygen cycle work?

Materials *(per group)*

2 snails [1]
4 sprigs of *Elodea* [2]
Pond water
Masking tape
Bright light source
Bromthymol blue solution in dropper bottle [3]
4 culture tubes with tops [4]
Test tube rack

[1] Collect pond snails and *Elodea* in the spring and early summer from local ponds, streams, or canals, or order them from a biological supply house or local pet store. If the snails are kept in an aquarium with fish, they should be cleaned before use in this investigation. Snails may be kept for short periods of time in a jar or indefinitely in an aquarium with aquatic plants. Collect 2 L of pond water per class, or age the same amount of tap water for at least 24 hours.

[2] Be sure sprigs of *Elodea* are fresh and bright green. Use 10-cm pieces that include the growing tips.

[3] Dissolve 0.1 g bromthymol blue powder in 1 L distilled water. If solution appears green, add 4% sodium hydroxide solution to bromthymol blue drop by drop until color is blue. Bromthymol blue may also be purchased premixed from a biological supply house.

[4] Screw-top culture tubes (20 x 200 mm) with caps can be ordered from a biological supply house. You may also use large test tubes or small jars. The reaction takes less time in a small container.

Safety ⚗ 🥽 🔥 🧹

Put on a laboratory apron if one is available. Put on safety goggles. Handle all glassware carefully. Always use special caution when working with laboratory chemicals, as they may irritate the skin or cause staining of the skin or clothing. Never touch or taste any chemical unless instructed to do so. Follow your teacher's directions and all appropriate safety procedures when handling live animals. Note all safety alert symbols next to the steps in the Procedure and review the meanings of each symbol by referring to the symbol guide on page 10.

Procedure

1. Obtain four culture tubes with tops. Use the masking tape to prepare four labels as shown in Figure 1. Place one label on each culture tube.

Tube 1	Tube 2	Tube 3	Tube 4
2 sprigs *Elodea* and 1 snail	1 snail	2 sprigs *Elodea*	No organisms
Name	Name	Name	Name
Date	Date	Date	Date

Figure 1

2. Into tube 1 place two springs of *Elodea* and one snail. Into tube 2 place one snail. Into tube 3 place two sprigs of *Elodea*.

3. Fill all four tubes to the top with pond water. Add four drops of bromthymol blue solution to each tube. Seal each tube tightly. **CAUTION:** *Handle the bromthymol blue solution with care because it stains the skin and clothing.*

4. Set the tubes in a test tube rack and place them near a bright light.

5. After 24 hours, observe the tubes. Notice if the organisms are still alive. Note any color change in the water. Bromthymol blue solution is an indicator. In the presence of carbon dioxide, it changes color from blue to yellow. Record your observations in the Data Table.

6. Observe the tubes every day for seven days. Record your observations in the Data Table.

7. Empty all the tubes and dispose of the organisms according to your teacher's directions.

Observations

Data Table

Observations				
Day	Tube 1	Tube 2	Tube 3	Tube 4
1				
2				
3		Answers will vary.		
4				
5				
6				
7				

Analysis and Conclusions

1. What is the purpose of tube 4? Tube 4 acts as an experimental control.

_____

2. What changes occurred in the bromthymol blue solution in each tube?

Tube 1 The bromthymol blue solution may or may not change color.

Tube 2 The bromthymol blue solution will change to yellow, indicating the presence of carbon dioxide.

Tube 3 The bromthymol blue solution may or may not change color.

Tube 4 There should be no change in color.

3. At the end of seven days, what happened to the organism in tube 2? Why?

The snail in tube 2 should be dead. The snail died because of a lack of oxygen.

_____

_____

4. Why did the organisms in tube 1 remain alive? The *Elodea* gave off oxygen during photosynthesis.

The snail used the oxygen for respiration and gave off carbon dioxide. The *Elodea* used the carbon dioxide

during photosynthesis, thus completing the oxygen cycle.

_____

5. Explain why the plants alone in tube 3 remained alive. Plants produce oxygen during

photosynthesis. Oxygen is used during respiration. Carbon dioxide is given off during respiration and used

during photosynthesis. Plants are able to complete their own oxygen cycle.

_____

6. How does this investigation demonstrate the oxygen cycle? Answers will vary but should center

around plants producing oxygen that is used by animals. Animals, in turn, produce carbon dioxide that is

used by plants.

_____

_____

Critical Thinking and Application

1. What do you predict would happen if all of the tubes in the investigation were placed in the dark? Explain your prediction. The plants would die because they would be unable to undergo photosynthesis. After the plants died, the snails would also die due to lack of oxygen.

2. Explain the following statement: "Some of the oxygen you breathed yesterday might have been breathed by George Washington." Matter on Earth is constantly being recycled through living organisms and the nonliving environment. It is quite possible that some of the oxygen molecules breathed by Washington were also breathed in by the student.

3. Is it true that plants could exist on Earth without animals, but animals could not exist without plants? Explain your answer. Yes. Animals require both food and the oxygen produced by plants during photosynthesis. Plants complete their own oxygen cycle, using the wastes produced by one life process as ingredients for the next life process.

Going Further

Repeat this investigation with different organisms or different combinations of organisms in each tube. You may also want to alter the size of the culture tubes or other containers. Be sure that all containers remain tightly sealed throughout the observation period. Report your observations and conclusions to the class.

93

Adapting to the Cold

You may want to refer students to page 1011 in the textbook for a discussion of the tundra biome.

Time required: 40 minutes.

Pre-Lab Discussion

The *tundra* is a large terrestrial biome located in northern latitudes. This biome covers about 5.5 percent of the Earth's landmass. The climate of the tundra is very cold and dry. Winters are nine months long, and temperatures remain below freezing most of this time.

Picture yourself trudging through the tundra in –10°C weather, with the wind and wolves howling. A pretty chilling image, no doubt! Most people can avoid long exposure to such cold, but many tundra animals—the Arctic fox, polar bear, caribou, and moose, for example—spend winters entirely outdoors. Fortunately, they show adaptations to their cold biome.

In this investigation, you will discover two ways in which animals are protected from extreme temperatures in their biomes. You will also learn how to determine whether a material is a good insulator or a poor insulator of heat.

Problem

How do animals adapt to long-term exposure to cold?

Materials *(per group)*

3 250-mL containers with lids   8-oz yogurt cartons work well.
3 750–1000-mL containers with lids   24-oz cottage cheese cartons work well.
3 Celsius thermometers
100-mL graduated cylinder
Piece of foam rubber, 2.5 cm thick and approximately 21 cm x 28 cm
Scissors
Masking tape
Article of winter clothing such as a heavy sock, mitten, hat, or scarf
3 colored pencils
Hot tap water
Sand or soil
Natural materials such as leaves, dried grass, sawdust, or shredded paper

Safety ⚗ 🖐 🔥

Put on a laboratory apron if one is available. Handle all glassware carefully. Use extreme care when working with heated equipment or materials to avoid burns. Be careful when handling sharp instruments. Note all safety alert symbols next to the steps in the Procedure and review the meanings of each symbol by referring to the symbol guide on page 10.

Procedure

Part A. Homegrown Insulation

1. Do layers of natural insulation such as fur, feathers, or fat help animals stay warm? You will construct a model of three warmblooded animals to find out. A 250-mL container with lid will represent each of the three animals.

2. Number the containers 1, 2, and 3.

3. Measure the same amount of hot tap water into each container. **CAUTION:** *Be careful when handling hot water.* The water in each container should be the same temperature. If you want to standardize data, use 125 mL water at 40°C or 45°C.

4. Use the scissors to carefully punch a hold in each lid. **CAUTION:** *Be careful when using scissors.* The hole should be just large enough to insert a thermometer. Insert a thermometer into each lid. Place the lids on the containers.

5. Place animal container 1 in the foam jacket. Wrap animal container 2 in the winter clothing. Animal containers 1 and 2 represent two different kinds of winter coats. Leave animal container 3 as it is to represent neither fur nor fat. See Figure 1. Record the temperature of the "animals" every 5 minutes for 15 minutes in Data Table 1.   This investigation may be done in the classroom. On a cool day, results will be more dramatic if students work outdoors.

1   2   3

Figure 1

6. On Graph 1, plot the temperatures for each "animal." Use a different colored pencil for each "animal." Label the lines.

7. Clean the containers for use in Part B.

Part B. Finding Shelter in the Biome

1. If the outdoor temperature is −10°C, most animals need more protection than a coat of fur provides. Endothermic animals and some exothermic animals, such as snakes and salamanders, often live in underground burrows. Does the ground provide protection against the cold?

578

2. Set up three small containers as shown in Figure 2. They are now animals X, Y, and Z. All three go into shelters (the three 750–1000-mL containers). X is simply out of the wind, surrounded by air. Y finds a snug burrow in soil or sand. Z's home is lined with natural materials of your choice, such as leaves or wood chips.

Figure 2

3. Start with the same amount of hot water at the same temperature as you used in Part A. Record the temperature every 5 minutes for 15 minutes in Data Table 2.

4. On Graph 2, plot the temperatures for each "animal." Use a different colored pencil for each "animal." Label the lines.

Observations
Part A. Homegrown Insulation

Data Table 1

"Animal"	Temperature (°C)			
	0 min	5 min	10 min	15 min
1 Foam				
2 Winter clothing		Answers will vary.		
3 No coat				

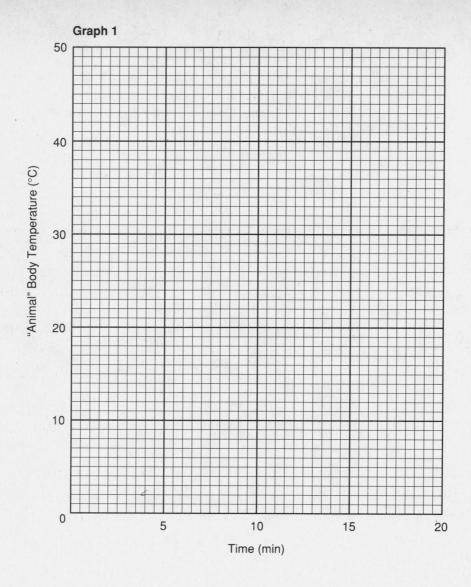

Graph 1

"Animal" Body Temperature (°C) vs. Time (min)

1. Which "animal" stayed warmest? Animal 1.

2. Which "animal" cooled fastest? Animal 3.

Part B. Finding Shelter in the Biome

Data Table 2

"Animal"	Temperature (°C)			
	0 min	5 min	10 min	15 min
X In air				
Y In soil		Answers will vary.		
Z In natural materials				

Graph 2

1. Which "animal" stayed warmest? Animal Y or Z, depending on the materials used.

2. Which "animal" cooled fastest? Animal X.

Analysis and Conclusions

1. What effect does a layer of insulation have on the temperature of an endothermic animal?

   A layer of insulation prevents the body temperature of the animal from dropping rapidly.

2. What is the best estimate of the temperature of "animal" X after 20 minutes?

   Students must extrapolate from Graph 2.

3. How does an underground burrow protect an animal from freezing?

An underground burrow provides insulation, which prevents heat loss.

Critical Thinking and Application

1. How does a heavy jacket keep a person warm? A heavy jacket provides insulation, which prevents the loss of body heat.

2. Eventually, the temperatures of all of the "animals" in this investigation return to room temperature. How do real animals continue to produce body heat?

Animals use food to produce heat energy for the body.

3. Two identical puppies are adopted by cousins. One puppy is taken to Alaska. The other goes to Florida. Two years later the cousins have a family reunion and bring their dogs. Both dogs have thick, furry coats. But the cousins are amazed to see that the dog from Alaska has soft, thick fur covering its abdomen whereas the dog from Florida does not. The dog from Florida has almost bare skin on its abdomen.

a. How does the fur covering the abdomen help the dog from Alaska?

The abdomen fur prevents the loss of body heat in cold Alaskan temperatures.

b. How does fur on the head, back, and legs help the dog from Florida? The dog from Alaska?

Hair on the head, back, and legs protects the dog from Florida against intense heat from the sun. For the dog from Alaska, the hair provides protection from the extreme cold.

c. How does the lack of fur on the underside help the dog from Florida?

Extra body heat can be given off when the dog lies in a cool spot. The underside is not usually exposed

to the sun.

4. In addition to fur, what other adaptive body feature might an animal have to protect itself from

the cold? Answers will vary but may include a thick layer of body fat, thick skin, feathers, footpads, and

hooves to allow for walking in the snow.

Going Further

Temperatures in the desert can easily climb to 50°C. Do fur and underground burrows protect animals from intense heat? Repeat the investigations. Put the "animals" above heating vents or in direct sunlight.

94

Counting a Population

You may want to refer students to pages 1033–1040 in the textbook for a discussion of populations.

Time required: 45 minutes.

Pre-Lab Discussion

A *population* is a group of individuals of the same species living in a given area. Biologists can use two different methods to determine the number of living things in a given area. The most accurate data would be obtained by counting each member of the population. However, in most situations this counting method is impractical and very time-consuming. A second method is to count a small sample of the population. The sample counted must be representative of the entire population. If the sample is not representative of the entire population, then the data collected are biased and therefore inaccurate. A random selection of areas in which to count organisms helps to eliminate bias. Every member of the population stands an equal chance of being counted.

In this investigation, you will demonstrate the technique of counting a random sample of population, from which you can estimate the size of an actual population.

Problem

How can the number of a population be estimated from a sample?

Materials *(per group)*

Plant and weed identification charts or books
3 sheets of notebook paper
Metric ruler
2-meter length of string
4 stakes or large nails
Forceps or garden gloves

This investigation can be used to count insect populations as well as plant populations.

Safety ◔ ▥

To avoid possible contact with poisonous or prickly plants, use forceps or wear gloves when collecting plant specimens. Use a field guide to identify dangerous plants. Be careful when handling sharp instruments. Note all safety alert symbols next to the steps in the Procedure and review the meanings of each symbol by referring to the symbol guide on page 10.

Procedure

1. Work with two partners.

2. On three separate sheets of notebook paper, make a copy of the chart shown in Figure 1. **Note:** *You will have three copies of the chart when you are finished.* Label the first chart "Sunlight," the second "Shade," and the third "Neglected."

(Location)	
Plant Type	Number

Figure 1

3. Select three different locations in the lawn around your school. One location should be in an area that receives constant sunlight. The second location should be in an area that is mostly shady. The third location should be a neglected area where weeds grow well.

4. At the sunny location, designate one person in the group to toss an object such as a pencil, a small rock, or a coin into the area. The person should close his or her eyes when tossing the object. Mark the spot where the object lands.

5. With the string and four stakes or nails, outline a 30 cm x 30 cm square around the marked spot. The marker should be in the center of the 30 cm x 30 cm square, as shown in Figure 2.

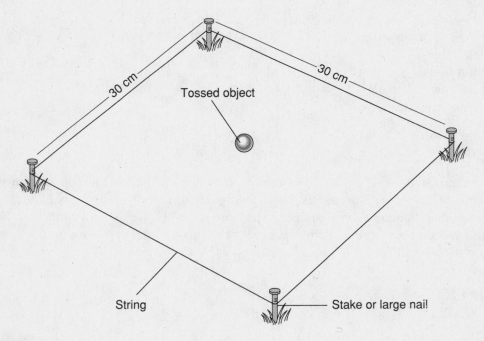

Figure 2

586

6. On the chart labeled "Sunlight," record the type and number of all plants in the square. If a plant cannot be identified, carefully remove a single leaf, flower, or individual plant for later identification. **CAUTION:** *Be able to identify poisonous or prickly plants. Use forceps or wear gloves when removing the plant specimens to avoid possible contact with poisonous or prickly plants.* Use plant identification books and charts in the classroom or library to identify unknown plants.

7. When you have finished counting population numbers and collecting specimens in the area, remove the stakes and string.

8. Repeat steps 4 through 7 for the shaded and neglected locations.

Observations

1. What was the total number of plants recorded at each location?

Sunlight _____

Shade _____ Answers will vary. _____

Neglected _____

2. What type of plant had the largest population number at each location?

Sunlight _____

Shade _____ Answers will vary. _____

Neglected _____

3. What type of plant had the smallest population number at each location?

Sunlight _____

Shade _____ Answers will vary. _____

Neglected _____

Analysis and Conclusions

1. Why was the person tossing the marker directed to close his or her eyes?

By closing his or her eyes, the person tossing the marker avoids influencing the throw.

_____

_____

_____

2. What characteristic or adaptation of the dominant plants enabled them to be so successful?

Answers will vary.

3. What environmental factors at each of the three locations might have limited the various plant populations? Answers will vary.

4. Would you expect the estimated total population number to be closer to the actual population number if an average of your classmates' results were taken? Explain your answer.

Yes. The larger the number of samples, the more accurate the final results.

5. Based on the results of this investigation, do you think that counting samples is an accurate method for counting a population? Explain your answer. Answers will vary. The method is accurate if a large enough sample is counted and if the sample accurately represents the whole population.

Critical Thinking and Application

1. How would you estimate the total population of any one type of plant in the entire school lawn? Measure the size of the entire lawn. Divide the area into equal-sized squares. Count the plants in 10 to 20 squares and calculate an average number. Multiply the average number by the total number of squares.

2. What considerations must be made when a marketing research team is polling a sample population for the sale of a new product? The sample of individuals polled must be large enough and must be representative of the whole population.

3. How might you count the number of individuals in a sample of a mobile population, such as mice on a prairie or fish in a pond? Biologists sometimes "trap" an area, count and tag all of the animals found there, and then release them. If the same area is "trapped" several times, the estimate of the total population will be fairly accurate.

4. List two factors that might cause the number of individuals in a population sample to change from month to month. Answers will vary, but might include seasonal temperature changes; seasonal moisture changes; the hatching of new eggs; the germination of new seeds; and the application of pesticides, insecticides, or fertilizers.

Going Further

1. Estimate the number of the following organisms in an area. Use the method of counting described in this investigation.

   a. tree seedlings in an area of dense shade versus an area with full sunlight

   b. earthworms in a garden

   c. insects in a field

2. Design an experiment to investigate the effect of the availability of space on populations. Plant seeds so that the density of the population varies, then compare their survival and growth rates.

95

Relationships in an Ecosystem

You may want to refer students to pages 1040–1042 in the textbook for a discussion of interactions within communities.

Time required:
Part A–30 minutes
Part B–30 minutes

Pre-Lab Discussion

An *ecosystem* consists of groups of organisms and their nonliving environment. Each ecosystem contains *biotic factors,* or living organisms, and *abiotic factors,* or physical (nonliving) components. Abiotic factors include soil, water, temperature, and light.

If you examine an outdoor ecosystem, you will find producers, consumers, and decomposers that form a variety of food webs. You may also find evidence of competition for food, space, and shelter; predator-prey relationships; and various types of symbiosis.

In this investigation, you will examine an outdoor ecosystem. In any outdoor activity, it is important that you disturb the environment as little as possible. When doing this investigation, remember that humans share this environment with wildlife.

Problem

What effect does protective coloration have on a predator-prey relationship? How many different interactions among organisms can you observe, directly or indirectly, in the environment around your school?

Materials *(per group)*

500 colored toothpicks (100 each of
5 different colors, including green)
Pencil and notepad
Toothpicks must be strewn about the area selected before class begins.

Safety

Handle toothpicks carefully when picking them up from the ground. As you observe the ecosystem around your school, do not pick up or touch any of the organisms you see. You will want to disturb organisms as little as possible to observe how they interact with other organisms in the environment. Note all safety alert symbols next to the steps in the Procedure and review the meanings of each symbol by referring to the symbol guide on page 10.

Procedure
Part A. Effects of Protective Coloration

1. Your teacher will scatter colored toothpicks over a grassy area. These toothpicks represent the food (prey) that you (predator) are hunting.

2. After the signal to begin is given, see how many prey you can capture in the allotted time.

3. Count the number of prey of each color that you captured. Include your results with the rest of the class. Record the class totals in the Data Table.

4. Repeat steps 2 and 3 and record the results for this trial in the Data Table.

Part B. Ecological Scavenger Hunt

1. In most scavenger hunts, you are asked to collect various items. However, in order to disrupt the wildlife in the area as little as possible, you will do your collecting with a pencil and notepad.

2. Search your assigned area for evidence that:

   a. Plants support all forms of animal life, either directly or indirectly.

   b. Humans and wildlife share environments.

   c. People have changed the environment.

   d. Wildlife exists in many different colors.

   e. Animals live in or have passed through this area.

   f. Humans and wildlife are subject to similar environmental problems.

   Record your observations.

3. What evidence can you find of the following?

   a. predator-prey relationships

   b. plant disease

   c. insect damage

   d. food webs

   e. symbiotic relationships

   Record your observations.

Observations
Part A. Effects of Protective Coloration

Data Table

Color of Toothpick	Trial 1	Trial 2
1.		
2.		
3.	Answers will vary.	
4.		
5.		
Total prey captured		

Part B. Ecological Scavenger Hunt

1. Summarize the observations you made in step 2 of Part B.

_____

_____

_____

Answers will vary.

_____

_____

_____

_____

_____

_____

2. Summarize the observations you made in step 3 of Part B.

_____

_____

_____

_____

Answers will vary.

_____

_____

_____

_____

_____

Analysis and Conclusions

1. What color prey were captured least often? Explain why this is so.

Answers will vary. Students should find that toothpicks whose color blends in best with the environment are

hardest to find.

2. What kinds of producers did you find in the area you studied? Answers will vary.

_____

_____

3. What kinds of consumers did you find in the area you studied? Answers will vary.

_____

_____

Critical Thinking and Application

1. List three animals that have protective coloration and can camouflage themselves in their environment. Answers will vary, but may include fish, deer, lizards, frogs, snakes, and insects.

_____

2. Do all ecosystems have consumers and producers? Explain your answer.

Most ecosystems will have consumers and producers. An ecosystem of producers can exist without

consumers, but an ecosystem of consumers cannot exist without producers.

_____

3. How might a change in season affect an ecosystem? A change in season produces changes in the

environment. Differences in temperature, rainfall, humidity, and so forth can cause changes in the types of

producers and consumers found in an ecosystem.

_____

4. How might the community around your school be affected if a new wing were added to your school building? Organisms that inhabit the soil, grass, trees, or other environments would die or be

forced to leave their habitats. Food sources for other animals within the community might also be destroyed.

_____

Going Further

1. Design variations for this predator-prey investigation. For example, you might shorten or lengthen the time allowed for searching, or assign each student one color of prey as the only kind he or she can capture. Study the results of each variation that you carry out. Draw conclusions showing the probable effect of each variation on a real-life situation.

2. Learn about local wild or native plant species that are used for food. See how many of these edible plants you can find. Prepare a wild edible plant book for your area.

96

You may want to refer students to pages 1009–1010 in the textbook for a discussion of ecological succession.

Time required: 30 minutes plus an observation period every two days for two weeks.

Ecological Succession

Pre-Lab Discussion

Over time, an ecosystem goes through a series of changes known as *ecological succession*. The changes happen within the structure of the community and usually are caused by the community itself. During ecological succession, organisms often change their environment in such a way as to make conditions less favorable for themselves and more favorable for other organisms.

Abiotic factors also play a role in ecological succession. Temperature, amounts of rainfall and light, geological features, and other abiotic factors may change. These changes may produce biotic changes. As ecological succession occurs, a stable *climax community* that is resistant to change is eventually established.

Most examples of ecological succession must be studied over a period of many years because it takes a long time for ecological succession to occur in the environment. However, a pond water culture can be used as a small-scale model of ecological succession that shows results in a relatively short period of time.

In this investigation, you will study ecological succession in a pond water culture.

Problem

How can a pond water culture be used to study a succession of populations in a community? *The pond water culture can be started with aquarium water or with water samples collected from a local pond, lake, stream, etc. A nutrient medium for the culture can be prepared by boiling hay, dried grass, or lettuce in aged tap water for 10 minutes. Allow the nutrient medium to cool and add it to the pond water culture.*

Materials *(per group)*

Pond water culture	3 glass slides
Large jar with lid	3 coverslips
Medicine dropper	Microscope
Aged tap water [1]	pH paper
Glass-marking pencil	

[1] Allow tap water to stand for 24 hours.

Safety ▲

Put on a laboratory apron if one is available. Handle all glassware carefully. Always handle the microscope with extreme care. You are responsible for its proper care and use. Use caution when handling glass slides as they can break easily and cut you. Note all safety alert symbols next to the steps in the Procedure and review the meanings of each symbol by referring to the symbol guide on page 10.

Procedure

▲ 1. Obtain a pond water sample from your teacher. Use the glass-marking pencil to put your group members' names on the outside of the jar. Carefully examine the culture. Observe the color, cloudiness, odor, and any layering of materials that may occur. Record the date and your observations in the Data Table.

2. Remove the lid from the culture jar and make three wet-mount slides of the pond water culture. Take the sample for each slide from a different part of the culture jar—top, middle, and bottom.

3. Examine each slide under a microscope, first under low power, then under high power. **CAUTION:** *When turning to the high-power objective, you should always look at the objective from the side of your microscope so that the objective does not hit or damage the slide.* Observe any organisms in the culture. Use the drawings in Figure 1 to identify the organisms you might observe in your pond water culture. In the appropriate place in the Data Table, record the type and approximate number of each organism you find on each slide.

Figure 1

4. Use pH paper to test the pH of the pond water culture in the jar. Record this information in the Data Table.

5. Repeat steps 1 through 4 every two days for a period of two weeks.

6. Use the graph provided in Observations to construct a line graph of the growth of any organism of your choice.

Observations

Data Table

Date	Appearance of Culture Water	pH of Culture Water	Species Present in Culture	Approximate Number of Individuals in Each Population
			Answers will vary.	

Graph

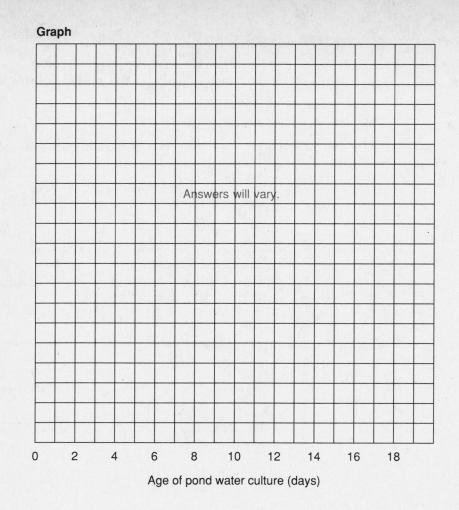

Approximate number of individuals in population

Answers will vary.

Age of pond water culture (days)

Analysis and Conclusions

1. Why should the pond water jar lid have holes punched in it? Without holes punched in the jar lid, the concentration of dissolved oxygen in the culture would drop, and many organisms would die.

2. What organisms were the first to become abundant in your pond water culture?
   Answers will vary, but bacteria are usually the first to appear in great numbers.

3. What population of organisms would you consider to be the climax community in the succession of the pond water culture? Explain your answer. Answers will vary.

4. What is the relationship between pH and the number of populations present in the pond water

culture? As the number and size of populations increase in a closed environment, waste materials

accumulate and the pH of the environment becomes more acidic.

_____

_____

5. Why might some populations have disappeared from the pond water culture?

Certain populations may have become a food source for other populations of organisms.

_____

_____

6. Describe any evidence of ecological succession you observed in your pond water culture.

Answers will vary.

_____

_____

_____

Critical Thinking and Application

1. A stable population suddenly experiences a tremendous growth in size. List two factors that

might be responsible for this growth. Answers will vary, but might include changes in environmental

conditions such as space, temperature, light, and moisture; changes in available food sources; and changes

in the populations of predator populations.

_____

_____

2. How is the competition between species related to the process of succession?

As the size of a population increases, competition for food and space increases. This competition results in

a decline in the size of the population and may lead to the succession of other populations of organisms.

_____

_____

3. Explain Figure 2 in terms of ecological succession. As one population increases in size, it makes more food available for another population, and so the first population declines in number and the second population increases. This process continues until a stable climax community develops.

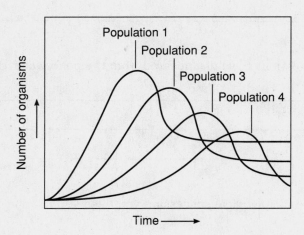

Figure 2

Going Further

1. Design an experiment to determine the effect of changes in the physical conditions (temperature, light, volume of container, etc.) on the ecological succession that takes place in the pond water culture.

2. Design an experiment to discover how the introduction of a foreign population into a pond water culture affects a normal succession.

3. Isolate a particular type of organism in your pond water culture. Set up an artificial environment with ideal conditions for the growth of the isolated species.

97

Investigating Air and Water Pollution

You may want to refer students to pages 1052–1063 in the textbook for a discussion of pollution.

Time required:
Part A–30 minutes
Part B–30 minutes

Pre-Lab Discussion

Although life on Earth depends on air and water, we are endangering these important resources by polluting them with harmful substances. The air we breathe contains the oxygen our cells need, but it also contains many other chemicals that can damage our bodies. Our atmosphere is polluted with smog, acid rain, carbon dioxide, and a variety of other chemicals that create problems for all organisms dependent on the atmosphere.

Despite the fact that the Earth's surface is 75 percent water, only a small fraction of that water can be used by living things. The pollution of our freshwater supply by chemicals, sewage, oil, and heated waste water interferes with many food chains. It also requires costly treatments to ensure the safety of our water supply.

In this investigation, you will conduct tests to determine the types of pollutants present in air and water samples taken from the area in which you live.

Problem

How can air and water pollution be detected?

Materials *(per group)*

4 glass slides
Petroleum jelly
Tongue depressors   Wooden craft sticks can also be used.
4 petri dishes
Glass-marking pencil
Microscope
Water samples A, B, and C   To 1 or 2 liters tap water (depending on class size), add the following:
3 stirring rods
pH test paper
3 test tubes with stoppers
3 medicine droppers

Sample A–soil, gravel, leaf matter, small amounts of motor oil, and detergent

Sample B–concentrated sulfuric acid until a pH of between 2 and 4 is reached

Sample C–sodium sulfite until an odor of rotten eggs is produced

Each group will need a small beaker of each sample.

Safety 🔬 📷 👁

Put on a laboratory apron if one is available. Put on safety goggles. Handle all glassware carefully. Always use special caution when working with laboratory chemicals, as they may irritate the skin or cause staining of the skin or clothing. Never touch or taste any chemical unless instructed to do so. Always handle the microscope with extreme care. You are responsible for its proper care and use. Use caution when handling glass slides as they can break easily and cut you. Note all safety alert symbols next to the steps in the Procedure and review the meanings of each symbol by referring to the symbol guide on page 10.

Procedure
Part A. Air Pollution

You might want to have students observe the types of particles emitted when an automobile starts. To collect these particles, tie a plastic bag around the cold exhaust pipe of your car. Start the car and then turn it off immediately. Have students examine the particles with a hand lens or a microscope.

🔬 1. Make four particle traps by using a tongue depressor to smear the center of four glass slides with petroleum jelly.

2. Place each particle trap in the bottom half of a petri dish. Cover each petri dish immediately.

3. Select one location on the school grounds for your particle traps. After obtaining your teacher's approval, place the four petri dishes containing the particle traps in the selected location. Make sure that the petri dishes are side by side.

4. Remove the lids of the petri dishes and expose the traps to the air for 20 minutes.

5. At the end of the exposure time, replace the lids. Use the glass-marking pencil to record the test location on the lid of each petri dish. Return to your classroom.

6. Carefully remove the particle trap from the first petri dish and place it on the stage of a microscope. Use the low-power objective to examine the slide. Count the number of trapped particles and record this number in Data Table 1.

7. Repeat step 6 for each of the remaining particle traps.

8. Calculate the average number of particles trapped at your selected location. Record this average in Data Table 1. To find the average number, add the number of particles counted on each trap and divide by 4.

9. Report your location and the average number of particles you trapped to the class. Using class data, complete Data Table 2.

10. Clean your laboratory equipment before proceeding with Part B of the investigation.

Part B. Water Pollution

🔬 📷 👁 1. Stir water sample A with a clean stirring rod.

2. Describe the appearance of the water in sample A. Record your observations in Data Table 3.

3. Using proper laboratory technique, determine if the water has an odor. Record your observations in Data Table 3.

4. To determine the pH of the water sample, use a clean medicine dropper to place a drop of the water sample on the pH test paper. Immediately compare the color with the chart on the pH paper container. Record the pH in Data Table 3.

5. Pour water from the sample into a test tube until it is half full. To check for the presence of detergents, place a stopper in the test tube and shake for 10 seconds. Foam on the top of the sample indicates the presence of detergents. Record your observations in Data Table 3.

6. Repeat steps 1 through 5 with water samples B and C.

Observations

Data Table 1

Particle Trap	Number of Particles
1	
2	Answers will vary.
3	
4	
Average	

Data Table 2

Particle Trap Location	Average Number of Trapped Particles
Answers will vary.	

Data Table 3

Test For:	Sample A	Sample B	Sample C
Appearance			
Odor		Answers will vary.	
pH			
Detergents			

Analysis and Conclusions

1. Why did you cover the particle traps between the time of preparation and the beginning of the exposure period? To prevent contamination before placement at the selected test location.

2. Which location showed the greatest air pollution? What do you think caused the pollution?
   Answers will vary.

3. Which location showed the least air pollution? Why? Answers will vary.

4. Why were four particle traps used at each location? Having several samples at each location provides the opportunity to average the data and increase their reliability.

5. If no particles were trapped at a given location, is it correct to assume that air at that location is not polluted? Explain your answer. No. Invisible gases and other chemicals would not be detected by a particle trap.

6. Why did you stir each water sample before conducting your tests?
   So that tests would be performed on a representative sample. So that any pollutants at the bottom of the sample would be dispersed.

7. Before completing the procedure, which water sample would you have predicted to be clean and safe for human use? Did this experiment change your evaluation of that sample? Explain your answer. Students will probably predict that sample B and/or C was the clearest. Answers will vary, but many students will conclude that clean-looking water may still contain dangerous pollutants even though there is no change in the water's appearance.

Critical Thinking and Application

1. In what type of weather would you expect air pollution to be the worst? Explain your answer.

   Warm, humid days with little air circulation, during temperature inversions.

   _____

   _____

2. How might pollutants be removed from water supplies? Answers will vary, but may include

   skimming oil from surface, filtering, settling, boiling, distilling, and adding chemicals.

   _____

3. What are some ways in which you can help reduce air and water pollution in your community?

   Answers will vary.

   _____

   _____

   _____

4. Explain how the statement "Think Globally, Act Locally" applies to the problems of air and

   water pollution. Answers will vary. Air and water pollution are global problems. If everyone works at the

   local level to reduce air and water pollution, global pollution problems can be lessened.

   _____

   _____

Going Further

Conduct a study of the pollution in your community. Use the air and water pollution tests from this investigation to determine air and water quality, and make a visual survey to evaluate land pollution. Report your findings on a map of the area. Be sure to identify the major landmarks; roadways; and residential, commercial, and industrial areas of your community on the map. Your map key should explain any colors or symbols used in reporting the data.

98

The Effects of Acid Rain on Seed Germination and Plant Growth

You may want to refer students to pages 1056–1057 in the textbook for a discussion of acid rain.

Time required:
Part A–20 minutes
Part B–20 minutes
5-minute observation period for 5 days

Pre-Lab Discussion

One serious result of air pollution is acid rain. Acid rain is the term used to describe any type of precipitation that has a pH below 6. Remember that the pH scale ranges from 1 to 14, with 7 being neutral. Substances with a pH from 1 to 6 are acidic; substances with a pH from 8 to 14 are alkaline (basic).

Acid rain forms when water vapor in the atmosphere combines with pollutants released by the burning of fossil fuels in industrial plants and in automobiles. When fossil fuels are burned, sulfur and nitrogen oxides are released. These pollutant gases combine with water vapor to form drops of sulfuric acid and nitric acid. Acid rain can damage buildings, plant and animal life, and soil. Dying forests and lifeless lakes in the northeastern United States, Canada, and Europe are being blamed on acid rain.

In this investigation, you will observe the effects of acid rain on seed germination and plant growth.

Problem

How does acid rain affect the germination of seeds and the growth of plants?

Materials *(per group)*

10 bean seeds   Soak the seeds overnight in the different rain solutions. Dry the seeds off
Empty beaker   before allowing students to handle.
Paper towels
Glass-marking pencil
Medicine dropper
Rain solutions   Prepare 5 different rain solutions. One solution should be distilled water; the remaining
Half a petri dish   solutions should range from very acidic to mildly acidic. Prepare the acid rain solutions by
Seedling plants[1]   adding 1–5 drops concentrated sulfuric acid to distilled water. You might want to use locally
Metric ruler   collected rainfall for one group solution.
Forceps   [1] Use beans or other fast-growing plants. You might want to obtain plants that are similar in
pH paper   size and age from a local nursery.

Put on a laboratory apron if one is available. Put on safety goggles. Handle all glassware carefully. Always use special caution when working with laboratory chemicals, as they may irritate the skin or cause staining of the skin or clothing. Never touch or taste any chemical unless instructed to do so. Note all safety alert symbols next to the steps in the Procedure and review the meanings of each symbol by referring to the symbol guide on page 10.

Procedure
Part A. The Effects of Acid Rain on the Germination of Seeds

1. From your teacher, obtain a beaker containing the rain solution you will be using during this investigation. Use pH paper to determine the pH of this rain solution. Record the pH in Data Table 1.

2. Loosely pack an empty beaker with paper towels.

3. Obtain 10 bean seeds that have been soaked in the rain solution assigned to you. Using forceps, place the bean seeds between the paper towels and the edge of the beaker so that you can easily observe the seeds each day. See Figure 1.

Medicine dropper

Paper towels

Bean seeds

Figure 1

4. Use the medicine dropper to moisten the paper towels with your assigned rain solution.

5. Cover the beaker with half of a petri dish and place the beaker in a well-lighted location.

6. Observe the seeds daily for signs of germination or other evidence of change. Record your observations in Data Table 1. You might want to refer students to pages 540–542 in the textbook for a review of seed germination.

7. Check the moisture in the paper towels each day. If necessary, moisten the paper towels with your assigned rain solution. Remind students to dampen, not drench, the paper towels so that their seeds will not become moldy.

8. Report your data to the class. As each group reports their data, complete Data Table 2.

Part B. The Effects of Acid Rain on Seedlings

1. Obtain a seedling plant from your teacher.

2. Label the plant with your name and the pH of your assigned rain solution.

3. Describe the appearance of your seedling plant in Data Table 3. Your description should include quantitative and qualitative data. Quantitative data might include the height and width of the plant and the number of leaves. Qualitative data might include the overall appearance, color, odor, and texture of the plant.

4. Place your plant in the sink or other area designated by your teacher. To simulate daily rainfall, sprinkle your plant's leaves and stem with 2 full medicine droppers of your rain solution. Be sure to moisten the soil each day with the rain solution.

5. Repeat step 4 every day for 5 days. Record you observations in Data Table 3.

Observations

Data Table 1

pH of Rain Solution _____

Day	Number of Germinating Seeds	Other Observed Changes
1		
2		
3		Answers will vary.
4		
5		

Data Table 2

Day	Number of Seeds Germinating				
	pH _____	pH _____	pH _____	pH _____	pH _____
1					
2					
3			Answers will vary.		
4					
5					

Data Table 3

pH of Rain Solution _____

Day	Appearance of Seedling Plant
1	
2	
3	will
4	
5	

Analysis and Conclusions

1. Would you classify the rain solution used by your group as acid rain? Why or why not?

   Answers will vary depending upon the solution each group used.

   _____

   _____

2. In which solution did the greatest number of seeds germinate? The least number of seeds germinate? Answers will vary, but more seeds will germinate in the pH range 5–7 than in the pH 2–4 range.

   _____

   _____

3. Which solution had the greatest effect on the seedling plant's growth and development? The least effect? Answers will vary.

   _____

   _____

4. Why is it necessary to observe the seeds and the seedling plant over a 5-day period?

   Bean seeds take 2–4 days to germinate. Without a minimum 5-day observation period, students would observe no change and might draw incorrect conclusions.

   _____

5. By adding an alkaline substance such as lime to soil, farmers can help neutralize the effects of acid rain on soil. Based on the results of this investigation, will adding lime to soil protect

crops from the effects of acid rain? Explain your answer. <u>No. More seeds might germinate, but the</u>

<u>seedlings would still be affected by acid rain.</u>

Critical Thinking and Application

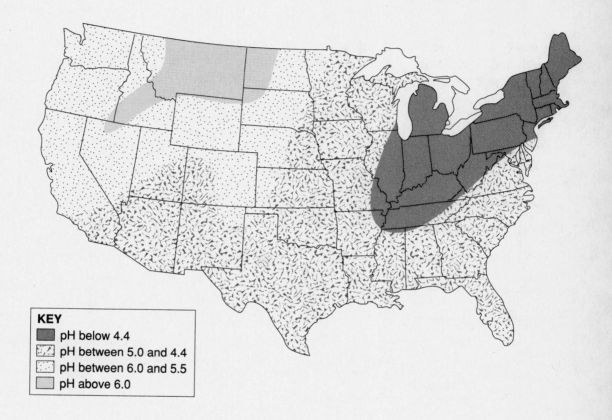

KEY
- ▓ pH below 4.4
- ▨ pH between 5.0 and 4.4
- ░ pH between 6.0 and 5.5
- ▒ pH above 6.0

Figure 2

Use the map in Figure 2 to answer questions 1 through 3. The map identifies the acidity of rainfall across the United States.

1. What is the pH of the rain in your area? Would it be considered acid rain?

Answers will vary.

_____

_____

2. What happens to the acidity of rain as you move from the east coast to the west coast?

It decreases.

3. How can you explain your answer to question 2? Answers will vary, but should include fewer people,

cars, large cities and industrial areas, and that prevailing winds blow west to east.

4. In the United States, most of our energy comes from burning fossil fuels. Because burning fossil fuels is the cause of acid rain, suggest alternative energy sources that could be used by industry and automobiles. Identify the advantages and disadvantages associated with each

type of energy source you listed. Answers will vary, but should include nuclear, solar, wind, tidal, and

geothermal energy.

5. If the United States government passed a law prohibiting the use of fossil fuels, predict the ecological and economic consequences that might ensue. Would these consequences be

positive or negative? Ecological—reduction of pollutants that cause acid rain; positive. Economic—more

expensive energy would lead to more costly products; negative.

Going Further

Design an experiment that would test the possible effects of different types of pollutants on seed germination and plant growth and development. Pollutants that you might use in your experiment include detergents, table salt, and motor oil.

Classifying Garbage

You may want to refer students to pages 1060–1063 in the textbook for a discussion of solid wastes.

Time required:

> 30 minutes on day 1
> 30-minute observation period after 7 days.

Pre-Lab Discussion

Throughout history, people have produced waste material, or garbage. And waste disposal has always been a problem that people have had to solve. Early civilizations had the option of moving to new locations when too much waste material accumulated near their homes. In addition, the garbage produced by early human societies was biodegradable; living organisms in the soil decomposed the waste material, thus solving the garbage problems.

Today, garbage is a major concern of our society. In addition to biodegradable materials, our garbage contains huge amounts of nonbiodegradable materials, which create more challenging waste disposal problems. And the problems of waste disposal increase with each passing year. Today, the average American produces 1000 kilograms of garbage annually. What happened to the 1000 kilograms you produced last year?

A common means of disposing of garbage is to add it to landfills. Landfills, however, are rapidly reaching capacity levels. In fact, many landfills are already full. Because of the mounting volume of garbage, new methods of disposal are needed. In planning for new methods, scientists must take into account the type of garbage, the effect of the garbage on the environment, and the cost of new technologies of disposal.

In this investigation, you will determine what types of garbage are biodegradable.

Problem

What types of garbage are most effectively disposed of in landfills?

Materials *(per group)*

Garbage
Garden soil
4 petri dishes
Scissors
Forceps
Newspaper
Medicine dropper
Water
Glass-marking pencil
Masking tape
Metric ruler
Trowel or scoop

The "garbage" should include pieces of food and food packaging. Foods that work well include meat, eggshell, bread, fruit, vegetables, and cereals. Packaging materials that should be available include paper, aluminum foil, cardboard, plastic wrap, and plastic foam cups.

Glass jars with lids could be substituted for petri dishes.

Put on a laboratory apron if one is available. Handle all glassware carefully. Be careful when handling sharp instruments. Note all safety alert symbols next to the steps in the Procedure and review the meanings of each symbol by referring to the symbol guide on page 10.

Procedure

🔥 1. With a glass-marking pencil, label the bottoms of the four petri dishes as follows: Dish 1, Dish 2, Dish 3, and Dish 4. Include your name and the date as well.

2. From the garbage provided by your teacher, use the forceps to select 4 different types of garbage. Be sure to select both food and nonfood items.

✂ 3. Use the scissors and forceps to cut or pull apart the samples so that they are approximately 2 square centimeters in size. You will need 3 small pieces of each item of garbage you select.

4. Use the forceps to place the 3 small pieces of each type of garbage into a labeled petri dish.

5. In the Data Table, record a brief description of the items of garbage in each petri dish. Indicate size, color, texture, odor, and other important features of each garbage sample.

6. Place the petri dish on newspaper and use the trowel or scoop to carefully fill each dish with garden soil. With the medicine dropper, add enough water to each dish to make the soil moist, but not soggy.

7. Place a cover on each dish and tape each dish closed with masking tape. Carefully turn each dish over so that the samples can be seen through the glass. Leave the dishes in a warm place.

8. In the appropriate place in the Data Table record your prediction of how each sample of garbage in each petri dish will look after one week.

9. Examine each dish after one week. Use the forceps to remove the samples of garbage. Record any changes in the size, color, texture, and odor of the samples.

10. Follow your teacher's instructions for the proper disposal of all materials.

Observations

Data Table

Dish	Type of Sample	Initial Description Date _____	Predicted Change	Final Description Date _____
1				
2		Answers will vary.		
3				
4				

1. Which sample(s) showed the greatest amount of change? Describe the kinds of changes that occurred. Answers will vary, but fruit, bread, vegetable, and meat products will decompose—get soft, change color, develop strong odors.

_____

_____

2. Which sample(s) showed the least amount of change? Describe the kinds of changes that occurred. Answers will vary, but aluminum foil and plastics do not change.

_____

_____

Analysis and Conclusions

1. Based on the results of this investigation, identify the samples you studied as biodegradable or nonbiodegradable. Answers will vary depending on garbage samples.

_____

_____

2. Which materials might be recycled? Answers will vary, but might include paper, plastics, glass, and aluminum products.

_____

_____

3. What substances in the petri dishes caused the decay of the materials that showed evidence of change? Bacteria and molds found in the soil.

_____

_____

Critical Thinking and Application

1. What types of waste material should be disposed of in landfills? Biodegradable products that can be broken down by organisms in the soil.

_____

_____

2. Many communities are charging additional fees if people do not separate their garbage into recyclable and nonrecyclable bundles. What are the environmental benefits of this policy?

Reduces the amount of nonbiodegradable garbage for disposal, saves landfill space, and reduces the

demand on natural resources.

3. How can you reduce the amount of trash you produce each day? Answers will vary.

Going Further

Design an experiment to determine the amount of garbage you produce in a day. Use your daily figure to calculate the amount of garbage you produce in a year. You may use a calculator or a computer for your computations. Prepare a graph or chart that illustrates the different types of materials found in the garbage you produce.